FOOD MICROBIOLOGY

FOURTH EDITION

William C. Frazier

Professor Emeritus of Bacteriology
University of Wisconsin—Madison

Dennis C. Westhoff

Chairman, Department of Animal Sciences
University of Maryland

McGRAW-HILL BOOK COMPANY

New York St. Louis San Francisco Auckland Bogotá Caracas
Colorado Springs Hamburg Lisbon London Madrid Mexico
Milan Montreal New Delhi Oklahoma City Panama Paris
San Juan São Paulo Singapore Sydney Tokyo Toronto

FOOD MICROBIOLOGY
INTERNATIONAL EDITION 1988

Exclusive rights by McGraw-Hill Book Co. – Singapore
for manufacture and export. This book cannot be re-
exported from the country to which it is consigned by
McGraw-Hill.

67890BJE954

This book was set in Times Roman by the
College Composition Unit in cooperation with
Ruttle, Shaw & Wetherill, Inc.
The editor was Elizabeth Dollinger;
the cover designer was John Hite;
the production supervisor was Friederich W. Schulte.
New drawings were done by Accurate Art.

Library of Congress Cataloging-in-Publication Data

Frazier, William C. (William Carroll)
  Food microbiology.
  Includes index.
  1. Food—Microbiology.   2. Food—Preservation.
I. Westhoff, D.C. (Dennis C.)   II. Title.
QR115.F7   1988   576'.163   87-15264
ISBN 0-07-021921-4

When ordering this title use ISBN 0-07-100436-X

Printed in Singapore

ABOUT THE AUTHORS

WILLIAM C. FRAZIER is Professor Emeritus of Bacteriology at the University of Wisconsin—Madison. He held a teaching position at the University from 1919 until completing his doctorate in agricultural bacteriology in 1924. He then served as a microbiologist for the U.S. Department of Agriculture until 1934, when he returned to Madison as a professor of agricultural bacteriology. He was responsible for developing a new academic program in food bacteriology and was appointed department chairman in 1943. He retired from the University of Wisconsin at Madison in 1966. Dr. Frazier was responsible for the development of this text, now in its fourth edition. He served as secretary-treasurer of the American Society of Microbiology (1943–45) and was elected an honorary member of the society in 1970. He has authored numerous scientific publications and several books including *Fundamentals of Dairy Science* and *Microbiology, General and Applied.*

DENNIS C. WESTHOFF is Professor of Food Science and chairman of the Department of Animal Sciences at the University of Maryland. He has lectured extensively on the subject of food microbiology in South America, the Middle East, and the United States, and teaches both undergraduate and graduate level courses on the subject at the University of Maryland. Additionally, Dr. Westhoff has served as a consultant to private industry and the U.S. Food and Drug Administration. He has authored numerous journals, review articles, and publications, including a book entitled *All About Yogurt,* geared to the consumer. Another work, in progress, describes the history of the development of the original pasteurization time/temperature combinations.

CONTENTS

PREFACE TO THE FOURTH EDITION

The first edition of this book was published in 1958. At that time, W. C. Frazier suggested that the purpose of *Food Microbiology* was to condense into a volume of modest size the basics of food microbiology, together with illustrations of these principles, in such a form that the book could serve as a college textbook or as an aid to workers in fields related to the food industry. Furthermore, each of the main subjects treated in this book is worthy of a separate volume, but limitations of space do not permit the inclusion of all the material that specialists, in their enthusiasm for their fields, might wish to see. W. C. Frazier tried to avoid giving undue attention to any single phase of food microbiology, and he included a limited amount of food technology so that the reader had a basic understanding of the processing of some foods.

The second edition was printed in 1967 and contained considerably more information that had become available on the microbial content of foods and on their preservation and spoilage. Several changes were made at that time in the arrangement of the material.

Revision of the second edition began in 1976, and the third edition was published in 1978. Since that time, thousands of papers have been published in the area of food microbiology, and new techniques in food processing have evolved. Promising methods, such as the irradiation of foods, were not permitted when the third edition was published, and the chapter on irradiation was deleted from that edition. Now there has been renewed interest in the irradiation process, and Chapter 10, "Irradiation of Foods," has been rewritten and reincorporated into the text.

Food Microbiology has been on a long revision cycle: 1957, 1968, 1978 and 1988, and therefore, what is added or changed must stand the test of time. Adding "contemporary" references must be done carefully to ensure that the book is not dated by current opinions, particularly in controversial areas. An example is the current concern regarding *Listeria monocytogenes* and the adequacy of milk pasteurization. As the text was being revised, a limited number of reports on the heat resistance of *L. monocytogenes* was available. Obviously, not all the questions regarding its heat resistance nor the adequacy of the minimum times and temperatures established for pasteurization had been answered.

Bergey's Manual of Determinative Bacteriology (8th edition) was published just prior to the release of the third edition of *Food Microbiology*. Many of the bacterial names familiar to the food microbiologist had been renamed or declared invalid species. An appendix was included in the third edition of *Food Microbiology* which described the current status of the names of these organisms. Names that were no longer accepted were marked with an asterisk in the text and were discussed in the appendix. We have continued this practice in the fourth edition. Recently, *Bergey's Manual of Systematic Bacteriology,* Volumes 1 and 2 have been published. Again, there have been changes in nomenclature and changes in taxonomy. We continue to cite the organisms as they originally appear in the literature. The asterisks are used to help food microbiologists make the transition to the new names.

We regret that we are unable to give acknowledgment and thanks to all the people whose reports have been the basis for many of the facts and tables presented in this edition. We have attempted to use and refer to major papers or review articles, which can be a source of additional references in a given area.

Several individuals were asked to make comments on the book prior to this revision, and others reviewed and commented on individual chapters or sections following revision. We express our thanks to the following individuals for their time, criticisms, and suggestions: Alan Kempton, Thomas J. Montville, Barbara Dill, and Richard Kinsley, Jr.

William C. Frazier

Dennis C. Westhoff

PREFACE TO THE THIRD EDITION

Since publication of the second edition much new information on the microbiology of foods has become available. New techniques in food processing eliminate some microbiological problems and create new ones. Methods once thought promising have been abandoned, e.g., the irradiation of foods with gamma rays, no longer permitted in the United States.

In response to suggestions, changes have been made in the arrangement of some of the information presented. For example, the characteristics of foods which affect their microbiology have been moved to the first chapter. In the light of information available since the previous edition, the chapters on foodborne diseases have been expanded.

Because the latest edition of *Bergey's Manual of Determinative Bacteriology* has made changes in the nomenclature of many of the bacteria familiar to food microbiologists and invalidated the names of others, an appendix has been included which briefly describes the current status of the names of these organisms. Names that are no longer accepted are marked with an asterisk in the text and are discussed in the appendix.

We regret that we are unable to give acknowledgment and thanks to all the people whose reports have been the basis for many of the facts presented. We have attempted to use and refer to major papers or review articles, which can be a source of additional references.

We wish to express our thanks for criticism and advice from those who have made suggestions for revision of the second edition: Dr. E. H. Marth of the University of Wisconsin, Dr. H. W. Walker of Iowa State University, Dr. D. Y. C. Fung of Pennsylvania State University, and Dr. R. H. Vaughn of the University of California. We also are grateful for suggestions and materials from Dr. F. L. Bryan of the Center for Disease Control, Dr. D. E. Bigbee of the University of Maryland, Dr. D. A. Kautter of the Food and Drug Administration, Dr. R. W. Johnston of the United States Department of Agriculture,

Carolina State University, and S. Doores and F. Feldstein of the University of Maryland.

William C. Frazier

Dennis C. Westhoff

FOOD
MICROBIOLOGY

PART ONE

FOOD AND MICROORGANISMS

An understanding of the interactions between microorganisms and foods can be appreciated only if we realize that the food, by its composition, dictates the resulting flora. Understanding a food's chemistry is a necessary prerequisite to understanding its microbiology. Chapter 1 outlines the important parameters of foods that affect their microbiology. Chapter 2 discusses the major groupings of food-borne microorganisms. The contamination of foods with microorganisms (Chapter 3) is discussed only briefly in this first section because this subject will be considered repeatedly in following sections of the text. Similarly, Chapter 4 outlines general principles of spoilage, with additional discussions on specific commodities to follow in later sections.

FOOD AS A SUBSTRATE
FOR MICROORGANISMS

The interactions between microorganisms, plants, and animals are natural and constant. The ecological role of microorganisms and their importance in all the geochemical cycles in nature is well documented. Since the human food supply consists basically of plants and animals or products derived from them, it is understandable that our food supply can contain microorganisms in interaction with the food.

In most cases microorganisms use our food supply as a source of nutrients for their own growth. This, of course, can result in deterioration of the food. By increasing their numbers, utilizing nutrients, producing enzymatic changes, and contributing off-flavors by means of breakdown of a product or synthesis of new compounds they can "spoil" a food. This is a normal consequence of the action of microorganisms, since one of their functions in nature is to convert reduced forms of carbon, nitrogen, and sulfur in dead plants and animals to the oxidized forms required by plants, which in turn are consumed by animals. So by simply "doing their thing" in nature they frequently can render our food supply unfit for consumption. To prevent this we minimize the contact between microorganisms and our foods (prevent contamination) and also eliminate microorganisms from our foods, or at least adjust conditions of storage to prevent their growth (preservation).

When the microorganisms involved are pathogenic, their association with our food supply is critical from a public health point of view. Many of our foods will support the growth of pathogenic microorganisms or at least serve as a vector of them. Here again, we attempt to prevent their entrance and growth in our foods or eliminate them by processing.

3

Interactions between microorganisms and our foods are sometimes beneficial, as exemplified by the many cultured products consumed and enjoyed.

What are the governing factors in these interactions? Why is this interaction
beneficial at some times and not at others? Why do some foods support the
growth of microorganisms more readily than others? Why are some foods very
stable in regard to microbial deterioration? Food is the substrate, and so the
characteristics of a food are an important consideration. The type of microorganisms present and the environmental conditions also are important. However, the food or substrate dictates what can or cannot grow. By understanding
the characteristics of the food or substrate one can make predictions about the
microbial flora that may develop.

A knowledge of the factors that favor or inhibit the growth of microorganisms
is essential to an understanding of the principles of food spoilage and preservation. The chief compositional factors of a food that influence microbial activity are
hydrogen-ion concentration, moisture, oxidation-reduction (O-R) potential, nutrients, and the presence of inhibitory substances or barriers.

HYDROGEN-ION CONCENTRATION (pH)

Every microorganism has a minimal, a maximal, and an optimal pH for growth.
Microbial cells are significantly affected by the pH of food because they apparently have no mechanism for adjusting their internal pH. In general, yeasts
and molds are more acid-tolerant than bacteria. The inherent pH of foods varies, although most foods are neutral or acidic. Foods with low pH values (below 4.5) usually are not readily spoiled by bacteria and are more susceptible to
spoilage by yeasts and molds. A food with an inherently low pH would therefore tend to be more stable microbiologically than a neutral food. The excellent keeping quality of the following foods is related to their restrictive pH:
fruits, soft drinks, fermented milks, sauerkraut, and pickles. Some foods have
a low pH because of inherent acidity; others, e.g., the fermented products, have
a low pH because of developed acidity from the accumulation of lactic acid
during fermentation.

Molds can grow over a wider range of pH values than can most yeasts
and bacteria, and many molds grow at acidities too great for yeasts and bacteria. Most fermentative yeasts are favored by a pH of about 4.0 to 4.5, as
in fruit juices, and film yeasts grow well on acid foods such as sauerkraut
and pickles. On the other hand, most yeasts do not grow well in alkaline
substrates and must be adapted to such media. Most bacteria are favored
by a pH near neutrality, although some, such as the acid formers, are favored by moderate acidity, and others, e.g., the actively proteolytic bacteria, can grow in media with a high (alkaline) pH, as found in the white of a
stored egg.

The buffers in a food, i.e., the compounds that resist changes in pH, are important not only for their buffering capacity but also for their ability to be espe-

cially effective within a certain pH range. Buffers permit an acid (or alkaline) fermentation to go on longer with a greater yield of products and organisms than would otherwise be possible. Vegetable juices have low buffering power, permitting an appreciable decrease in pH with the production of only small amounts of acid by the lactic acid bacteria during the early part of sauerkraut and pickle fermentations. This enables the lactics to suppress the undesirable pectin-hydrolyzing and proteolytic competing organisms. Low buffering power makes for a more rapidly appearing succession of microorganisms during a fermentation than does high buffering power. Milk, on the other hand, is fairly high in protein (a good buffer) and therefore permits considerable growth and acid production by lactic acid bacteria in the manufacture of fermented milks before growth of the starter culture is finally suppressed.

The pH of a product can be readily determined with a pH meter, but this value alone may not be sufficient for predicting microbial responses. It is also desirable, for example, to know the acid responsible for a given pH, because some acids, particularly the organic acids, are more inhibitory than others. The inhibitory properties of many of the organic acids, including acetic, benzoic, citric, lactic, proprionic, and sorbic acids, make them widely used as acidulants or preservatives in foods. Also, changes in titratable acidity are not always evident from pH measurements.

Not only are the rates of growth of microorganisms affected by pH, so are the rates of survival during storage, heating, drying, and other forms of processing. Also, the initial pH may be suitable, but because of competitive flora or growth of the organism itself, the pH may become unfavorable. Conversely, the initial pH may be restrictive, but the growth of a limited number of microorganisms may alter the pH to a range that is more favorable for the growth of many other microorganisms.

MOISTURE REQUIREMENT: THE CONCEPT OF WATER ACTIVITY

Microorganisms have an absolute demand for water, for without water no growth can occur. As might be expected, the exact amount of water needed for growth of microorganisms varies. This water requirement is best expressed in terms of available water or water activity a_w, the vapor pressure of the solution (of solutes in water in most foods) divided by the vapor pressure of the solvent (usually water). The a_w for pure water would be 1.00, and for a 1.0 m solution of the ideal solute the a_w would be 0.9823. The a_w ($\times$ 100) would be in equilibrium with the relative humidity (RH) of the atmosphere about the food. In other words, $a_w \times 100$ = equilibrium relative humidity (ERH) (%), or $\frac{ERH}{100} = a_w$. A relative humidity about a food corresponding to an a_w lower than that of the food would tend to dry the surface of the food; conversely, if the relative humidity were higher than that corresponding to the a_w, the latter would be increased at the surface of the food. The a_w for many groups of foods is summarized in Table 1-1.

TABLE 1-1
PRINCIPAL GROUPS OF FOODS AND THEIR a_w

a_w Values	Food
0.98 and above	Fresh meat and fish
	Fresh fruits and vegetables
	Milk and most beverages
	Canned vegetables in brine
	Canned fruits in light syrup
0.93–0.98	Evaporated milk
	Tomato paste
	Processed cheese
	Bread
	Canned cured meats
	Fermented sausage (not dried)
	Canned fruits in heavy syrup
	Gouda cheese
0.85–0.93	Dry or fermented sausage
	Dried beef
	Raw ham
	Aged cheddar cheese
	Sweetened condensed milk
0.60–0.85	Dried fruit
	Flour
	Cereals
	Jams and jellies
	Nuts
	Some aged cheeses
	Intermediate-moisture foods
Below 0.60	Chocolate
	Confectionery
	Honey
	Biscuits
	Crackers
	Potato chips
	Dried eggs, milk, and vegetables

Source: Adapted from Christian, 1980.

Water is made unavailable in various ways:

1 Solutes and ions tie up water in solution. Therefore, an increase in the concentration of dissolved substances such as sugars and salts is in effect a drying of the material. Not only is water tied up by solutes, but water tends to leave the microbial cells by osmosis if there is a higher concentration of solute outside the cells than inside.

2 Hydrophilic colloids (gels) make water unavailable. As little as 3 to 4 percent agar in a medium may prevent bacterial growth by leaving too little available moisture.

3 Water of crystallization or hydration is usually unavailable to microorganisms. Water itself, when crystallized as ice, no longer can be used by microbial cells. The a_w of water-ice mixtures (vapor pressure of ice divided by vapor pressure of water) decreases with a decrease in temperature below 0 C. The a_w values of pure water are 1.00 at 0 C, 0.953 at −5 C, 0.907 at −10 C, 0.846 at −15 C, 0.823 at −20 C, and so on. In a food, as more ice is formed, the concentration of solutes in the unfrozen water is increased, lowering its a_w.

The reduction of a_w by a solute depends primarily on the total concentration of dissolved molecules and ions, each of which is surrounded by water molecules held more or less firmly. The solution then has a lower freezing point and a lower vapor pressure than does pure water. The organisms must compete with these particles for water molecules. The decrease in vapor pressure for an ideal solvent follows Raoult's law: The vapor pressure of the solution relative to that of the pure solvent is equal to the mole fraction of the solvent; that is, $p/p_0 = n_2/n_1 + n_2$, where p and p_0 are the vapor pressures of the solution and solvent and n_1 *and* n_2 are the number of moles of solute and solvent, respectively. Although a_w varies with temperature, the variations are only slight within the range of temperatures permitting microbial growth. However, as the concentration of solutes increases, a variation in temperature becomes more important in regard to a_w because of an increasing effect on ionization.

Each microorganism has a maximal, optimal, and minimal a_w for growth. This range depends upon factors discussed subsequently. As the a_w is reduced below the optimal level, there is a lengthening of the lag phase of growth, a decrease in the rate of growth, and a decrease in the amount of cell substance synthesized—changes that vary with the organism and with the solute employed to reduce a_w.

Factors that may affect a_w requirements of microorganisms include the following.

1 The kind of solute employed to reduce the a_w. For many organisms, especially molds, the lowest a_w for growth is practically independent of the kind of solute used. Other organisms, however, have lower limiting a_w values with some solutes than with others. Potassium chloride, for example, usually is less toxic than sodium chloride, and it in turn is less inhibitory than sodium sulfate.

2 *The nutritive value of the culture medium.* In general, the better the medium for growth, the lower the limiting a_w

3 *Temperature.* Most organisms have the greatest tolerance to low a_w at about optimal temperatures.

4 *Oxygen supply.* Growth of aerobes takes place at a lower a_w in the presence of air than in its absence, and the reverse is true of anaerobes.

5 *pH.* Most organisms are more tolerant of low a_w at pH values near neutrality than in acid or alkaline media.

6 *Inhibitors.* The presence of inhibitors narrows the range of a_w for growth of microorganisms.

Methods for the control of a_w are (1) equilibration with controlling soluti-- (2) determination of the water-sorption isotherm for the food (Iglesia Chirife, 1976), and (3) addition of solutes.

Methods for measuring or establishing a_w values of foods include freezing-point determinations, manometric techniques, and electrical devices. Freezing-point determinations are feasible only on liquid foods with high a_w values. The measurement is based on the Clausius-Clapeyron equation for dilute solutions (Strong et al., 1970). A manometric technique for directly measuring the vapor pressure in the vapor space surrounding a food is considered very accurate. This technique and the device are described in detail by Labuza (1974). Various electrical devices for measuring a_w indirectly have been employed. The most common use sensors which measure relative humidity in the vapor space surrounding a food based on electrical resistance. One such device is shown in Figure 1-1. The probes vary in their sensitivity to relative humidity ranges and must be selected on the basis of expected results. The food is placed in a jar, and equilibration of the water in the food and vapor space is usually obtained in one to several hours. As the current is passed through the salt-coated filament of the probe, the resistance is determined and a readout is shown on the dial. Calibration charts are used to convert readout values to a_w or percent relative humidity.

A collaborative study conducted on a comparison of a_w methodology (Labuza et al., 1976) showed manometric vapor-pressure determinations to be the most accurate.

Most bacteria grow well in a medium with a water activity a_w approaching 1.00 (at 0.995 to 0.998, for example); i.e., they grow best in low concentrations of sugar or salt, although there are notable exceptions that will be mentioned later. Culture media for most bacteria contain not more than 1 percent sugar and 0.85 percent sodium chloride ("physiological salt solution"); as little as 3

FIGURE 1-1
An apparatus for determining a_w values in food. Various sensors (foreground) for ranges of water activity values are equilibrated with the food in the sealed jars. (*American Instrument Company, Silver Spring, Md.*)

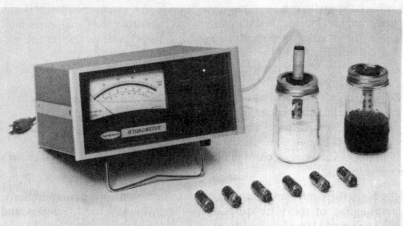

to 4 percent sugar and 1 to 2 percent salt may inhibit some bacteria. The optimal a_w and the lower limit for growth vary with the bacterium as well as with food, temperature, pH, and the presence of oxygen, carbon dioxide, and inhibitors; they are lower for bacteria able to grow in high concentrations of sugar or salt. Examples of reported lower limits of a_w for growth of some food bacteria are 0.97 for *Pseudomonas,* 0.96 for *Escherichia coli,* 0.95 for *Bacillus subtilis,* 0.945 for *Enterobacter aerogenes,* 0.86 for *Staphylococcus aureus,* and 0.93 for *Clostridium botulinum.* Other bacteria will grow with the a_w below 0.90. These figures would be different under other conditions of growth than those used in obtaining the values. Some optimal a_w figures reported for food bacteria are 0.99 to 0.995 for *Staph. aureus* and *Salmonella* spp., 0.995 for *E. coli,* and 0.982 for *Streptococcus faecalis.*

Molds differ considerably in optimal a_w and range of a_w for germination of the asexual spores. The range for spore germination is greater at temperatures near the optimum for germination and in a better culture medium. The minimal a_w for spore germination has been found to be as low as 0.62 for some molds and as high as 0.93 for others (e.g., *Mucor, Rhizopus,* and *Botrytis*). Each mold also has an optimal a_w and range of a_w for growth. Examples of optimal a_w are 0.98 for an *Aspergillus* sp., 0.99 to 0.98 for a *Rhizopus* sp., and 0.99 for a *Penicillium* sp. The a_w would have to be below 0.62 to stop all chances for mold growth, although an a_w below 0.70 inhibits most molds causing food spoilage and an a_w below 0.94 inhibits molds such as *Rhizopus* and below 0.85 inhibits *Aspergillus* spp. The reduction of the a_w below the optimum for a mold delays spore germination and reduces the rate of growth and therefore can be an important factor in food preservation. Many of the molds can grow in media with an a_w approaching 1.00 (pure water).

A consideration of the moisture requirements of microorganisms leads to some general conclusions:

1 Each organism has its own characteristic optimal a_w and its own range a_w for growth for a given set of environmental conditions. Factors affecting the moisture requirements of organisms are (a) the nutritive properties of the substrate, (b) its pH, (c) its content of inhibitory substances, (d) availability of free oxygen, and (e) temperature. The range of a_w permitting growth is narrowed if any of these environmental factors is not optimal and is narrowed still more if two or more conditions are not favorable.

2 An unfavorable a_w will result not only in a reduction in the rate of growth but also in a lowered maximal yield of cells.

3 The more unfavorable the a_w of the substrate, the greater the delay (lag) in initiation of growth or germination of spores. This often is as important in food preservation as is reduction in the rate of growth of the organism.

4 In general, bacteria require more moisture than yeasts, and yeasts more than molds, as shown in Table 1-2, which shows lower limits of a_w for bacteria, yeasts, and molds. There are notable exceptions to this generalization, however, as some molds have a higher minimal a_w for growth (and spore germination) than do many yeasts and some bacteria.

TABLE 1-2
LOWEST a_w VALUES PERMITTING GROWTH
OF SPOILAGE ORGANISMS

Group of microorganisms	Minimal a_w value
Many bacteria	0.91
Many yeasts	0.88
Many molds	0.80
Halophilic bacteria	0.75
Xerophilic fungi	0.65
Osmophilic yeasts	0.60

Source: After Mossel and Ingrams, 1955.

5 Microorganisms that can grow in high concentrations of solutes, e.g., sugar and salt, obviously have a low minimal a_w. Halophilic bacteria require minimal concentrations of dissolved sodium chloride for growth. Osmophilic yeasts grow best in high concentrations of sugar. (See Chapter 2.)

OXIDATION-REDUCTION POTENTIAL

The oxygen tension or partial pressure of oxygen about a food and the O-R potential, or reducing and oxidizing power of the food itself, influence the type of organisms which will grow and hence the changes produced in the food. The O-R potential of the food is determined by (1) the characteristic O-R potential of the original food, (2) the poising capacity, i.e., the resistance to change in potential, of the food, (3) the oxygen tension of the atmosphere about the food, and (4) the access which the atmosphere has to the food. Air has a high oxygen tension, but the head space in an "evacuated" can of food would have a low oxygen tension.

From the standpoint of ability to use free oxygen, microorganisms have been classified as **aerobic** when they require free oxygen, **anaerobic** when they grow best in the absence of free oxygen, and **facultative** when they grow well either aerobically or anaerobically. Molds are aerobic, most yeasts grow best aerobically, and bacteria of different kinds may be aerobic, anaerobic, or facultative. From the standpoint of O-R potential, a high (oxidizing) potential favors aerobes but will permit the growth of facultative organisms, and a low (reducing) potential favors anaerobic or facultative organisms. However, some organisms that are considered aerobic can grow (but not well) at surprisingly low O-R potentials. Growth of an organism may alter the O-R potential of a food enough to restrain other organisms. Anaerobes, for example, may lower the O-R potential to a level inhibitory to aerobes.

The O-R potential of a system is usually written Eh and measured and expressed in terms of millivolts (mV). A highly oxidized substrate would have a positive Eh, and a reduced substrate a negative Eh. Aerobic microorganisms including bacilli, micrococci, pseudomonads, and acinetobacters require positive Eh values or positive mV O-R potentials. Conversely, anaerobes including clostridia and bacteriodes require negative Eh values or negative mV O-R potentials.

Most fresh plant and animal foods have a low and well-poised O-R potential in their interior: the plants because of reducing substances such as ascorbic acid and reducing sugars and animal tissues because of—SH (sulfhydryl) and other reducing groups. As long as the plant or animal cells respire and remain active, they tend to poise the O-R system at a low level, resisting the effect of oxygen diffusing from the outside. Therefore, a piece of fresh meat or a fresh whole fruit would have aerobic conditions only at and near the surface. The meat could support aerobic growth of slime-forming or souring bacteria at the surface at the same time that anaerobic putrefaction was proceeding in the interior. This situation may be altered by processing procedures. Heating may reduce the poising power of the food by means of destruction or alteration of reducing and oxidizing substances and also allow more rapid diffusion of oxygen inward, either because of the destruction of poising substances or because of changes in the physical structure of the food. Processing also may remove oxidizing or reducing substances; thus clear fruit juices have lost reducing substances by their removal during extraction and filtration and therefore have become more favorable to the growth of yeasts than was the original juice containing the pulp.

In the presence of limited amounts of oxygen the same aerobic or facultative organisms may produce incompletely oxidized products, such as organic acids, from carbohydrates, when with plenty of oxygen available complete oxidation to carbon dioxide and water might result. Protein decomposition under anaerobic conditions may result in putrefaction, whereas under aerobic conditions the products are likely to be less obnoxious.

NUTRIENT CONTENT

The kinds and proportions of *nutrients* in the food are all-important in determining what organism is most likely to grow. Consideration must be given to (1) foods for energy, (2) foods for growth, and (3) accessory food substances, or vitamins, which may be necessary for energy or growth.

Foods for Energy

The carbohydrates, especially the sugars, are most commonly used as an energy source, but other carbon compounds may serve, e.g., esters, alcohols, peptides, amino acids, and organic acids and their salts. Complex carbohydrates, e.g., cellulose, can be utilized by comparatively few organisms, and starch can be hydrolyzed by only a limited number of organisms. Microorganisms differ even in their ability to use some of the simpler soluble sugars. Many organisms cannot use the disaccharide lactose (milk sugar) and therefore do not grow well in milk. Maltose is not attacked by some yeasts. Bacteria often are identified and classified on the basis of their ability or inability to utilize various sugars and alcohols. Most organisms, if they utilize sugars at all, can use glucose.

The ability of microorganisms to hydrolyze pectin, which is characteristic of some kinds of bacteria and many molds, is important, of course, in the softening or rotting of fruits and vegetables or fermented products from them.

A limited number of kinds of microorganisms can obtain their energy from fats but do so only if a more readily usable energy food, such as sugar, is absent. First, the fat must be hydrolyzed with the aid of lipase to glycerol and fatty acids, which then can serve as an energy source for the hydrolyzing organism or other organisms. In general, aerobic microorganisms are more commonly involved in the decomposition of fats than are anaerobic ones, and the lipolytic organisms usually are also proteolytic. Direct oxidation of fats containing unsaturated fatty acids usually is chemical.

Hydrolysis products of proteins, peptides, and amino acids, for example, serve as an energy source for many proteolytic organisms when a better energy source is lacking and as foods for energy for other organisms that are not proteolytic. Meats, for example, may be low in carbohydrate and therefore decomposed by proteolytic species, e.g., *Pseudomonas* spp., with successive growth of weakly proteolytic or nonproteolytic species that can utilize the products of protein hydrolysis. Organisms differ in their ability to use individual amino acids for energy. This is because it is the number of molecules (or moles) of sugar which affects a_w, and a percentage is usually expressed as weight per unit volume.

Not only is the kind of energy food important but also its concentration in solution and hence its osmotic effect and the amount of available moisture. For a given percentage of sugar in solution, the osmotic pressure will vary with the weight of the sugar molecule. Therefore, a 10% solution of glucose has about twice the osmotic pressure of a 10% solution of sucrose or maltose; i.e., it ties up twice as much moisture. In general, molds can grow in the highest concentrations of sugars and yeasts in fairly high concentrations, but most bacteria grow best in fairly low concentrations. There are, of course, notable exceptions to this generalization: Osmophilic yeasts grow in as high concentrations of sugar as molds, and some bacteria can grow in fairly high concentrations of sugar.

Of course, an adequate supply of foods for growth will favor utilization of the foods for energy. More carbohydrate will be used if a good nitrogen food is present in sufficient quantity than will be the case if the nitrogen is poor in kind or amount. Organisms requiring special accessory growth substances might be prevented from growing if one or more of these "vitamins" were lacking, and thus the whole course of decomposition might be altered.

Foods for Growth

Microorganisms differ in their ability to use various nitrogenous compounds as a source of nitrogen for growth. Many organisms are unable to hydrolyze proteins and hence cannot get nitrogen from them without help from a proteolytic organism. One protein may be a better source of nitrogenous food than another because of different products formed during hydrolysis, especially peptides and amino acids. Peptides, amino acids, urea, ammonia, and other simpler nitrogenous compounds may be available to some organisms but not to others or may be usable under some environmental conditions but not under others. Some of the lactic acid bacteria grow best with polypeptides as nitrogen foods, cannot attack casein, and do not grow well with only a limited number of kinds of amino acids present. The presence of fermentable carbohydrate in a substrate usually results in an acid fermentation and suppression of proteolytic bacteria and hence in what is called a "sparing" action on the nitrogen compounds. Also, the production of obnoxious nitrogenous products is prevented or inhibited.

Many kinds of molds are proteolytic, but comparatively few genera and species of bacteria and very few yeasts are actively proteolytic. In general, proteolytic bacteria grow best at pH values near neutrality and are inhibited by acidity, although there are exceptions, such as proteolysis by the acid-proteolytic bacteria that hydrolyze protein while producing acid.

Carbon for growth may come partly from carbon dioxide, but more often it comes from organic compounds.

The minerals required by microorganisms are nearly always present at the low levels required, but occasionally an essential mineral may be tied up so that it is unavailable, lacking, or present in insufficient amounts. An example is milk, which contains insufficient iron for pigmentation of the spores of *Penicillium roqueforti*. Bacteria causing septicemia usually have the ability to bind some of the iron in blood. Only strains which can compete for transferrin iron are able to grow well in human blood.

Accessory Food Substances, or Vitamins

Some microorganisms are unable to manufacture some or all of the vitamins needed and must have them furnished. Most natural plant and animal foodstuffs contain an array of these vitamins, but some may be low in amount or lacking. Thus meats are high in B vitamins and fruits are low, but fruits are high in ascorbic acid. Egg white contains biotin but also contains avidin, which ties up biotin, making it unavailable to microorganisms and eliminating as possible spoilage organisms those which must have biotin supplied. The processing of foods often reduces the vitamin content. Thiamine, pantothenic acid, the folic acid group, and ascorbic acid (in air) are heat-labile, and drying causes a loss in vitamins such as thiamine and ascorbic acid. Even storage of foods for long periods, especially if the storage temperature is elevated, may result in a decrease in the level of some of the accessory growth factors.

Each kind of bacterium (or other microorganism) has a definite range of food requirements. For some species the range is wide, and growth takes place in a variety of substrates, as is true for coliform bacteria; but for others, e.g., many of the pathogens, the range is narrow and the organisms can grow in only a limited number of kinds of substrates. Thus, bacteria differ in the foods that they can utilize for energy: Some can use a variety of carbohydrates, e.g., the coliform bacteria and *Clostridium* spp., and others only one or two, while some can use other carbon compounds such as organic acids and their salts, alcohols, and esters (*Pseudomonas* spp.). Some can hydrolyze complex carbohydrates, although others cannot. Likewise, the nitrogen requirements of bacteria such as *Pseudomonas* spp. may be satisfied by simple compounds such as ammonia or nitrates; or more complex compounds such as amino acids, peptides, or proteins may be utilized or even required, as is true for the lactics. Bacteria also vary in their need for vitamins or accessory growth factors; some (*Staph. aureus*) synthesize part and others (*Pseudomonas* or *E. coli*) all of the factors needed, and still others must have them all furnished (the lactics and many pathogens). It should be emphasized that in general, the better the medium for an organism, the wider the ranges of temperature, pH, and a_w over which growth can take place.

INHIBITORY SUBSTANCES AND BIOLOGICAL STRUCTURE

Inhibitory substances, originally present in the food, added purposely or accidentally, or developed there by growth of microorganisms or by processing methods, may prevent growth of all microorganisms or, more often, may deter certain specific kinds. Examples of inhibitors naturally present are the lactenins and anticoliform factor in freshly drawn milk, lysozyme in egg white, and benzoic acid in cranberries. A microorganism growing in a food may produce one or more substances inhibitory to other organisms, products such as acids, alcohols, peroxides, and even antibiotics. Propionic acid produced by the propionibacteria in Swiss cheese is inhibitory to molds; alcohol formed in quantity by wine yeasts inhibits competitors; and nisin produced by certain strains of *Streptococcus lactis* may be useful in inhibiting lactate-fermenting, gas-forming clostridia in curing cheese and undesirable in slowing down some of the essential lactic acid streptococci during the manufacturing process. There also is the possibility of the destruction of inhibitory compounds in foods by microorganisms. Certain molds and bacteria are able to destroy some of the phenol compounds that are added to meat or fish by smoking or benzoic acid added to foods; sulfur dioxide is destroyed by yeasts resistant to it; and lactobacilli can inactivate nisin. Heating foods may result in the formation of inhibitory substances: Heating lipids may hasten autoxidation and make them inhibitory, and browning concentrated sugar sirups may result in the production of furfural and hydroxymethyl furfural, which are inhibitory to fermenting organisms. Long storage at warm temperatures may produce similar results.

The effect of the *biological structure* of food on the protection of foods against spoilage has been noted. The inner parts of whole, healthy tissues of living plants and animals are either sterile or low in microbial content. Therefore, unless opportunity has been given for their penetration, spoilage organisms within may be few or lacking. Often there is a protective covering about the food, e.g., the shell on eggs, the skin on poultry, the shell on nuts, and the rind or skin on fruits and vegetables, or we may have surrounded the food with an artificial coating, e.g., plastic or wax. This physical protection of the food not only may help its preservation but also may determine the kind, rate, and course of spoilage. Layers of fat over meat may protect that part of the flesh, or scales may protect the outer part of the fish. On the other hand, an increase in exposed surface brought about by peeling, skinning, chopping, or comminution may serve not only to distribute spoilage organisms but also to release juices containing food materials for the invaders. The disintegration of tissues by freezing may accomplish a similar result.

In meat the growth of spoilage bacteria takes place mostly in the fluid between the small meat fibers, and it is only after rigor mortis that much of this food material is released from the fibers to become available to spoilage organisms.

COMBINED EFFECTS OF FACTORS AFFECTING GROWTH

Each of the compositional factors of foods—a_w, pH, O-R potential, and nutrient content—can significantly affect the resulting microbial flora. Many of these factors interact, and therefore one must be concerned with the total ecology of the food. For example, a microorganism growing near its optimal pH will be more tolerant to changes in a_w than will one growing close to its minimal or maximal pH. Therefore, a combined inhibitory effect of an unfavorable pH and a_w can be noted. To prevent or retard growth, several of these factors can be manipulated rather than adjusting one to an inhibitory level.

Factors affecting the germination of spores of *Clostridium botulinum* have indicated interactions or combined effects involving a_w, pH, temperature, O-R potential, and sodium chloride and sodium nitrate concentrations. The difficulty of collecting numerous data points over a wide range of variables may result in the need to construct mathematical models to predict a suitable preservation system. Techniques for describing the effect of two factors affecting growth (pH and a_w) plus temperature have been used to predict the level of a possible hazard resulting from the growth of *Staph. aureus* and *Salmonella typhimurium* (Broughall and Brown, 1984).

BIBLIOGRAPHY

Brock, T. D. 1970. Biology of microorganisms. Prentice-Hall, Inc., Englewood Cliffs, N.J.

Broughall, J. M., and C. Brown. 1984. Hazard analysis applied to microbial growth in foods: development and application of three-dimensional models to predict bacterial growth. Food Micro. 1:13–22.

Brown, M. H., and O. Emberger. 1980. Oxidation-reduction potential. *In* J. H. Silliker (ed.), Microbial ecology of foods, Vol. I, chap. 6. Academic Press, Inc., New York.

Christian, J. H. B. 1980. Reduced water activity. *In* J. H. Silliker (ed.), Microbial ecology of foods, Vol. I, chap. 4. Academic Press, Inc., New York.

Corlett, D. A. Jr., and M. H. Brown. 1980. pH and acidity. *In* J. H. Silliker (ed.), Microbial ecology of foods, Vol. I, chap. 5. Academic Press, Inc., New York.

Dawson, P. S. S. (ed.). 1974. Benchmark papers in microbiology. Volume VIII. Microbial growth. Dowden, Hutchinson and Ross, Inc., Stroudsburg, Pa.

Heidelbaugh, N. D., and M. Karel. 1975. Intermediate moisture food technology. *In* S. A. Goldblith (ed.), Freeze drying and advanced food technology, chap. 38. Academic Press, Inc., New York.

Iglesias, H. A., and J. Chirife. 1976. A model for describing the water sorption behavior of foods. J. Food Sci. 41:984–992.

Jay, J. M. 1978. Modern food microbiology. Van Nostrand Reinhold Company, New York.

Labuza, T. P. 1974. Sorption phenomena in foods: theoretical and practical aspects. *In* C. Rha (ed.), Theory, determination and control of physical properties of food materials, chap. 10. D. Reidel Publishing Co., Dordrecht, Holland.

Labuza, T. P., K. Acott, S. R. Tatini, and R. Y. Lee. 1976. Water activity determination: a collaborative study of different methods. J. Food Sci. 41:910–917.

Loncin, M. 1975. Basic principles of moisture equilibria. *In* S. A. Goldblith (ed.), Freeze drying and advanced food technology, chap 37. Academic Press, Inc., New York.

Marth, E. H. 1966. Antibiotics in foods: naturally occurring, developed and added. Residue Rev. 12:65–161.

Mossel, D. A. A., and M. Ingram. 1955. The physiology of the microbial spoilage of foods. J. Appl. Bacteriol. 18:233–268.

Scott, W. J. 1957. Water relations of food spoilage microorganisms. Adv. Food Res. 7:83–127.

Stanier, R. Y., E. A. Adelberg, and J. Ingraham. 1976. The microbial world. Prentice-Hall, Inc., Englewood Cliffs, N.J.

Strong, D. H., E. Foster, and C. Duncan. 1970. Influence of A_w on the growth of Clostridium perfringens. Appl. Microbiol. 19:980–984.

Troller, J. A. 1972. The water relations of food-borne bacterial pathogens: a review. J. Milk Food Technol. 36:276–288.

Troller, J. A., and J. H. B. Christian. 1978. Water activity and food. Academic Press, Inc., New York.

MICROORGANISMS IMPORTANT IN FOOD MICROBIOLOGY

Food microbiologists must become acquainted with the microorganisms important in foods, at least to an extent that will enable them to identify the main types in order to make use of what is known about their characteristics and compare results with those of other workers. The first section of this chapter briefly outlines the identification and classification of food molds, because these organisms are not studied much in the usual beginning course in microbiology. There is some discussion of the classification of yeasts, but no attempt has been made to cover determinative bacteriology, a subject to which the student usually receives an adequate introduction in a first course in microbiology.

MOLDS

Mold growth on foods, with its fuzzy or cottony appearance, sometimes colored, is familiar to everyone, and usually food with a moldy or "mildewed" food is considered unfit to eat. While it is true that molds are involved in the spoilage of many kinds of foods, special molds are useful in the manufacture of certain foods or ingredients of foods. Thus, some kinds of cheese are mold-ripened, e.g., blue, Roquefort, Camembert, Brie, Gammelost, etc., and molds are used in making Oriental foods, e.g., soy sauce, miso, sonti, and others discussed later. Molds have been grown as food or feed and are employed to produce products used in foods, such as amylase for breadmaking or citric acid used in soft drinks. Some molds do produce various toxic metabolites (mycotoxins), which are discussed in Chapter 25.

GENERAL CHARACTERISTICS OF MOLDS

The term "mold" is a common one applied to certain multicellular, filamentous fungi whose growth on foods usually is readily recognized by its fuzzy or cottony appearance. The main part of the growth commonly appears white but may be colored or dark or smoky. Colored spores are typical of mature mold of some kinds and give color to part or all of the growth. The thallus, or vegetative body, is characteristic of thallophytes, which lack true roots, stems, and leaves.

Morphological Characteristics

The morphology, i.e., the form and structure, of molds, as judged by their macroscopic and microscopic appearance, is used in their identification and classification.

Hyphae and Mycelium   The mold thallus consists of a mass of branching, intertwined filaments called **hyphae** (singular **hypha**), and the whole mass of these hyphae is known as the **mycelium.** The hyphae may be **submerged,** or growing within the food, or **aerial,** or growing into the air above the food. Hyphae also may be classed as **vegetative,** or growing, and hence involved chiefly in the nutrition of the mold, or **fertile,** involved in the production of reproductive parts. In most molds the fertile hyphae are aerial, but in some molds they may be submerged. The hyphae of some molds are full and smooth, but the hyphae of others are characteristically thin and ragged. A few kinds of molds produce **sclerotia** (singular **sclerotium),** which are tightly packed masses of modified hyphae, often thick-walled, within the mycelium. These sclerotia are considerably more resistant to heat and other adverse conditions than is the rest of the mycelium, and for this reason they may be important in some processed food products.

Microscopic examination of mold hyphae reveals characteristics useful in the identification of genera. Molds are divided into two groups: **septate,** i.e., with cross walls dividing the hypha into cells; and **noncoenocytic, septate** with the hyphae apparently consisting of cylinders without cross walls. The nonseptate hyphae have nuclei scattered throughout their length and are considered multicellular. The hyphae of most molds are clear, but some are dark or smoky. Hyphae may appear uncolored and transparent on microscopic examination but colored when large masses of hyphae are viewed macroscopically.

Septate hyphae increase in length by means of division of the tip cell (apical growth) or of cells within the hypha (intercalary growth), the type of growth being characteristic of the kind of mold. Division of the nuclei distributed throughout nonseptate hyphae is accompanied by an increase in the length of filaments.

Special mycelial structures or parts aid in the identification of molds. Examples are the rhizoids, or "holdfasts," of *Rhizopus* and *Absidia,* the foot cell in *Aspergillus,* and the dichotomous, or Y-shaped, branching in *Geotrichum,* which are all described subsequently.

Reproductive Parts or Structures   Molds can grow from a transplanted piece of mycelium. Reproduction of molds is chiefly by means of asexual spores. Some molds also form sexual spores. Such molds are termed "perfect" and are classified as either *Oomycetes* or *Zygomycetes* if nonseptate, or *Ascomycetes* or *Basidiomycetes* if septate, in contrast to "imperfect" molds, the *Fungi Imperfecti* (typically septate), which have only asexual spores.

Asexual Spores   The asexual spores of molds are produced in large numbers and are small, light, and resistant to drying. They are readily spread through the air to alight and start new mold thallus where conditions are favorable. The three principal types of asexual spores are (1) **conidia** (singular **conidium**) (Figure 2-1), (2) **arthrospores**, or **oidia** (singular **oidium**) (Figure 2-2), and (3) **sporangiospores** (Figure 2-3). Conidia are cut off, or bud, from special fertile hyphae called **conidiophores** and usually are in the open, i.e., not enclosed in any container, in contrast to the sporangiospores, which are in a **sporangium** (plural **sporangia**), or sac, at the tip of a fertile hypha, the **sporangiophore**. Arthrospores are formed by fragmentation of a hypha, so that the cells of the hypha become arthrospores. Examples of these three kinds of spores will be given in the discussion of important genera of molds. A fourth kind of asexual spore, the **chlamydospore,** is formed by many species of molds when a cell here and there in the mycelium stores up reserve food, swells, and forms a thicker wall than

FIGURE 2-1
Diagram of a simple conidial head of *Aspergillus.*

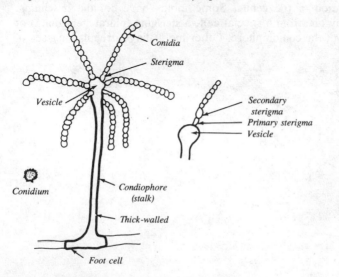

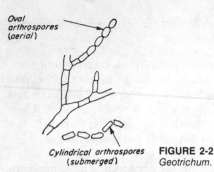

Oval arthrospores (aerial)

Cylindrical arthrospores (submerged)

FIGURE 2-2
Geotrichum.

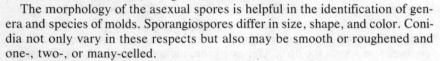

that of surrounding cells. This chlamydospore, or resting cell, can withstand unfavorable conditions better than ordinary mold mycelium can and later, under favorable conditions, can grow into a new mold.

The morphology of the asexual spores is helpful in the identification of genera and species of molds. Sporangiospores differ in size, shape, and color. Conidia not only vary in these respects but also may be smooth or roughened and one-, two-, or many-celled.

Also helpful in the identification of molds is the appearance of the fertile hyphae and the asexual spores on them. If sporangiospores are formed, points to be noted are whether the sporangiophores are simple or branched, the type of branching, and the size, shape, color, and location of the sporangia. The swollen tip of the sporangiophore, the **columella**, which usually projects into the sporangium, assumes shapes typical of species of mold. Conidia may be borne singly on conidiophores or in spore heads of differing arrangement and complexity. A glance at the general appearance of a spore head often is sufficient for identification of the genus. Some molds have conidia in chains, squeezed off one by one from a special cell, a **sterigma** (plural **sterigmata**) or **phialide**, at the tip of the conidiophore. Other molds have irregular masses of

FIGURE 2-3
Rhizopus.

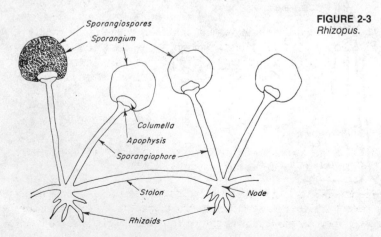

Sporangiospores

Sporangium

Columella

Apophysis

Sporangiophore

Stolon

Node

Rhizoids

conidia, which cut off from the tip of the conidiophore without evident sterigmata. These masses of conidia may be loosely or tightly packed or even
enslimed. The conidia of some molds bud from the conidiophore and continue
to multiply by budding; they appear yeastlike.

Sexual Spores The molds which can produce sexual spores are classified on
the basis of the manner of formation of these spores and the type produced.
The nonseptate molds (*Phycomycetes*) that produce **oospores** are termed *Oomycetes*. These molds are mostly aquatic; however, included in this group are several important plant pathogens, i.e., the "downy mildews" which cause late
blight of potatoes and buckeye rot of tomatoes. The oospores are formed by
the union of a small male gamete and a large female gamete. The *Zygomycetes*
form **zygospores** by the union of the tips of two hyphae which often appear similar and which may come from the same mycelium or from different mycelia.
Both oospores and zygospores are covered by a tough wall and can survive
drying for long periods. The *Ascomycetes* (septate) form sexual spores known
as **ascospores**, which are formed after the union of two cells from the same mycelium or from two separate mycelia. The ascospores, resulting from cell division after conjugation, are in an **ascus**, or sac, with usually eight spores per
ascus. The asci may be single or may be grouped within a covering called an
ascocarp, formed by branching and intertwining adjacent hyphae. The *Basidiomycetes,* which include most mushrooms, plant rusts, smuts, etc., form a
fourth type of sexual spore, the basidiospore.

Cultural Characteristics

The gross appearance of a mold growing on a food often is sufficient to indicate its class or order. Some molds are loose and fluffy; others are compact.
Some look velvety on the upper surface, some dry and powdery, and others
wet or gelatinous. Some molds are restricted in size, while others seem limited
only by the food or container. Definite zones of growth in the thallus distinguish some molds, e.g., *Aspergillus niger*. Pigments in the mycelium—red, purple, yellow, brown, gray, black, etc—are characteristic, as are the pigments of
masses of asexual spores; green, blue-green, yellow, orange, pink, lavender,
brown, gray, black, etc. The appearance of the reverse side of a mold on an
agar plate may be striking, like the opalescent blue-black or greenish-black color
of the underside of *Cladosporium*.

Physiological Characteristics

The physiological characteristics of molds will be reviewed only briefly here
and will be discussed in more detail subsequently.

Moisture Requirements In general most molds require less available moisture than do most yeasts and bacteria. An approximate limiting total moisture
content of a given food for mold growth can be estimated, and therefore it has

been claimed that below 14 to 15 percent total moisture in flour or some dried fruits will prevent or greatly delay mold growth.

Temperature Requirements Most molds would be considered mesophilic i.e., able to grow well at ordinary temperatures. The optimal temperature for most molds is around 25 to 30 C, but some grow well at 35 to 37 C or above, e.g., *Aspergillus* spp., and some at still higher temperatures. A number of molds are **psychrotrophic**; i.e., they grow fairly well at temperatures of refrigeration, and some can grow slowly at temperatures below freezing. Growth has been reported at as low as −5 to −10 C. A few are **thermophilic**; i.e., they have a high optimal temperature.

Oxygen and pH Requirements Molds are aerobic; i.e., they require oxygen for growth; this is true at least for the molds growing on foods. Most molds can grow over a wide range of hydrogen-ion concentration (pH 2 to 8.5), but the majority are favored by an acid pH.

Food Requirements Molds in general can utilize many kinds of foods, ranging from simple to complex. Most of the common molds possess a variety of hydrolytic enzymes, and some are grown for their amylases, pectinases, proteinases, and lipases.

Inhibitors Compounds inhibitory to other organisms are produced by some molds, such as penicillin from *Penicillium chrysogenum* and clavacin from *Aspergillus clavatus*. Certain chemical compounds are **mycostatic**, inhibiting the growth of molds (sorbic acid, propionates, and acetates are examples), or are specifically **fungicidal**, killing molds.

Initiation of growth of molds is slow compared to that of bacteria or yeasts, so that when conditions are favorable for all these organisms, molds usually lose out in the competition. After mold growth is under way, however, it may be very rapid.

CLASSIFICATION AND IDENTIFICATION OF MOLDS

Molds are plants of the kingdom Myceteae. They have no roots, stems, or leaves and are devoid of chlorophyll. They belong to the *Eumycetes,* or true fungi, and are subdivided further to subdivisions, classes, orders, families, and genera.

The following criteria are used chiefly for differentiation and identification of molds:

1 Hyphae septate or nonseptate
2 Mycelium clear or dark (smoky)
3 Mycelium colored of colorless
4 Whether sexual spores are produced and the type: oospores, zygospores, or ascospores
5 Type of asexual spores: sporangiospores, conidia, or arthrospores (oidia)

6 Characteristics of the spore head
  a Sporangia: size, color, shape, and location
  b Spore heads bearing conidia: single conidia, chains, budding conidia, or masses; shape and arrangement of sterigmata or phialides; gumming together of conidia
7 Appearance of sporangiophores or conidiophores: simple or branched, and if branched the type of branching; size and shape of columella at tip of sporangiophore; whether conidiophores are single or in bundles
8 Microscopic appearance of the asexual spores, especially of conidia: shape, size, color; smooth or rough; one-, two-, or many-celled
9 Presence of special structures (or spores): stolons, rhizoids, foot cells, apophysis, chlamydospores, sclerotia, etc.

An excellent introduction to the food-borne fungi has been prepared by Samson et al. (1984). Included in the text are illustrations of numerous food-borne molds, actual photomicrographs of molds, photographs of molds on agar surfaces, and a key to identification.

Molds of Industrial Importance

Several molds of industrial importance are outlined by genus, with typical morphological structures presented in the accompanying figures.

Mucor   Mucor (Figures 2-4 and 2-5) are involved in the spoilage of some foods and the manufacture of others. A widely distributed species is *M. racemosus*. *M. rouxii* is used in the "Amylo" process for the saccharification of starch, and mucors help ripen some cheeses (e.g., Gammelost) and are used in making certain Oriental foods.

Zygorrhynchus   These soil molds are similar to *Mucor* except that the zygospore suspensors are markedly unequal in size (Figure 2-6).

Rhizopus   Rhizopus stolonifer, the so-called bread mold, is very common and is involved in the spoilage of many foods: berries, fruits, vegetables, bread, etc. (Figures 2-7 and 2-3).

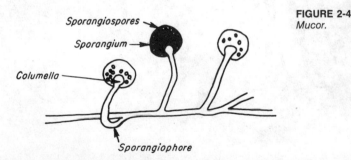

FIGURE 2-4
Mucor.

Sporangiospores
Sporangium
Columella
Sporangiophore

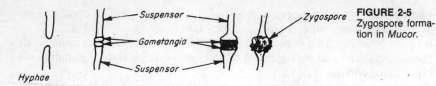

FIGURE 2-5
Zygospore formation in *Mucor*.

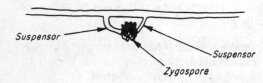

FIGURE 2-6
Zygospore formation in *Zygorrhynchus*.

FIGURE 2-7
Photomicrograph of *Rhizopus nigricans*. Note rhizoids and sporangiophores arising from node, and sporangia at ends of sporangiophores (X200). (*Courtesy of Harper & Row, Publishers, Incorporated. From W. B. Sarles et al., Microbiology: General and Applied, 2d ed. Copyright © 1956, New York.*)

Absidia Similar to *Rhizopus*, except that sporangia are small and pear-shaped (Figure 2-8).

Thamnidium *Thamnidium elegans* is found on meat in chilling storage, causing "whiskers" on the meat (Figure 2-9).

Aspergillus (Figures 2-1 and 2-10) The aspergilli are very widespread. Many are involved in the spoilage of foods, and some are useful in the preparation of certain foods. Raper and Fennell (1965) list eighteen groups of aspergilli and

FIGURE 2-8
Diagram of *Absidia*, showing locations of sporangiophores and rhizoids.

FIGURE 2-9
Thamnidium.

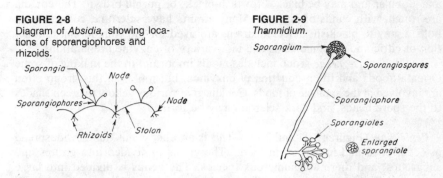

FIGURE 2-10
Photomicrograph of *Aspergillus niger,* showing fruiting heads bearing chains of conidia (X200). (*Courtesy of Harper and Row, Publishers, Incorporated. From W. B. Sarles et al., Microbiology: General and Applied, 2d ed. Copyright © 1956, New York.*)

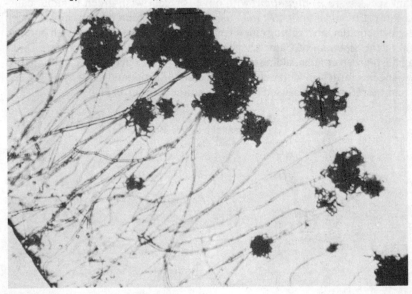

recognize 132 species, but only a few will be mentioned here. The *A. glaucus* group, with *A. repens* as an important species, is often involved in food spoilage. The molds grow well in high concentrations of sugar and salt and hence in many foods of low moisture content. Conidia of this group are some shade of green, and ascospores are in asci within yellow to reddish perithecia. Some authors include these molds in the *Ascomycetes* and the genus *Eurotium,* a name reserved for members having a perfect (sexual) stage.

The *A. niger* group, with *A. niger* as a leading species, is widespread and may be important in foods. The spore-bearing heads are large, tightly packed, and globular and may be black, brownish-black, or purple-brown. The conidia are rough, with bands of pigment. Many strains have sclerotia, colored from buff to gray to blackish. Selected strains are used for the commercial production of citric and gluconic acids and in a variety of enzyme preparations.

The *A. flavus-oryzae* group includes molds important in the making of some Oriental foods and the production of enzymes, but molds in this group often are involved in the spoilage of foods. Conidia give various yellow to green shades to the spore heads, and dark sclerotia may be formed.

Penicillium (Figures 2-11 and 2-12)   This is another genus that is widespread in occurrence and important in foods. The genus is divided into groups and subgroups, and there are numerous species. The genus is divided into large groups on the basis of the branching of the spore-bearing heads, or penicilli (little brushes). These heads, or verticillata, are a whorl or cluster of three, or more elements: sterigmata, metulae (subbranches), and branches (Figure 2-12). *P. expansum,* the blue-green-spored mold, causes soft rots of fruits. Other important species are *P. digitatum,* with olive- or yellowish-green conidia, causing a soft rot of citrus fruits; *P. italicum,* called the "blue contact mold," with blue-green conidia, also rotting citrus fruit; *P. camemberti,* with grayish conidia, useful in the ripening of Camembert cheese; and *P. roqueforti* (Figure 2-13), with bluish-green conidia, aiding in the ripening of blue cheeses, e.g., Roquefort. A few species form asci with ascospores in cleistothecia, and a few exhibit sclerotia and therefore have caused trouble in canned acid foods.

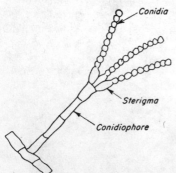

Conidia
Sterigma
Conidiophore

FIGURE 2-11
Diagram of a simple *Penicillium.*

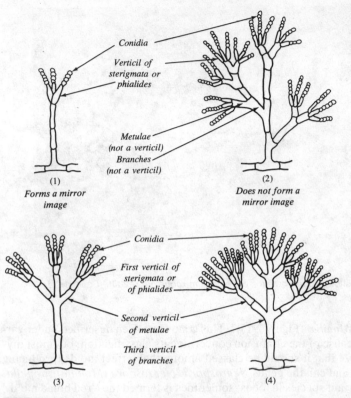

FIGURE 2-12
Diagram showing different types of *Penicillium* molds: (1) monoverticillata symmetrica, (2) monoverticillata asymmetrica, (3) biverticillata symmetrica, and (4) polyverticillata symmertrica.

Trichothecium The common species, *T. roseum* (Figure 2-14), is a pink mold which grows on wood, paper, fruits such as apples and peaches, and vegetables such as cucumbers and cantaloupes. This mold is easily recognized by the clusters of two-celled conidia at the ends of short, erect conidiophores. Conidia have a nipplelike projection at the point of attachment, and the smaller of the two cells of each conidium is at this end.

Geotrichum (Oospora or Oidium) This genus is included with the yeastlike fungi by some writers and with the molds by others. Species may be white, yellowish, orange, or red, with the growth appearing first as a firm, feltlike mass that later becomes soft and creamy. *Geotrichum candidum (Oospora lactis),* often called the "dairy mold," gives white to cream-colored growth. The hyphae are septate and in common species are dichotomously branched. The asexual spores are arthrospores (oidia), which may appear rectangular if from submerged hyphae and oval if from aerial hyphae.

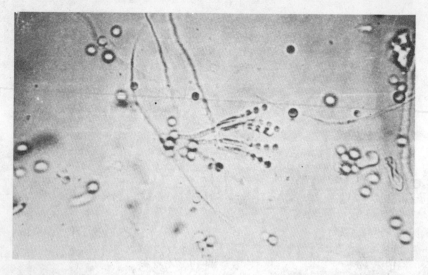

FIGURE 2-13
Photomicrograph showing fruiting heads of *Penicillium roqueforti* (X200). (*Courtesy of K. B. Raper.*)

Neurospora (Monilia) (Figure 2-15) This genus has been described under various names because of the confusion concerning its classification, but most mycologists believe that it should be classed among the perfect molds (producing sexual spores) and call the genus *Neurospora*. *Neurospora (Monilia) sitophila,* the most important species in foods, sometimes is termed the "red bread mold" because its pink, loose-textured growth often occurs on bread. It also grows on sugarcane bagasse and on various foods. The perfect, or ascosporogenous, stage seldom is seen.

FIGURE 2-14
Trichothecium.

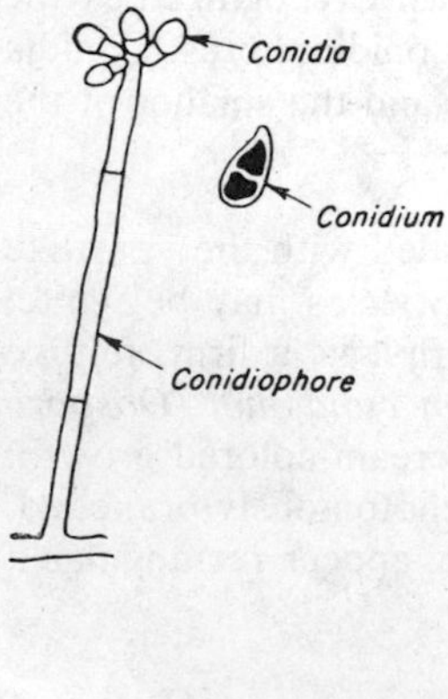

Conidia

Conidium

Conidiophore

FIGURE 2-15
Neurospora (Monilia).

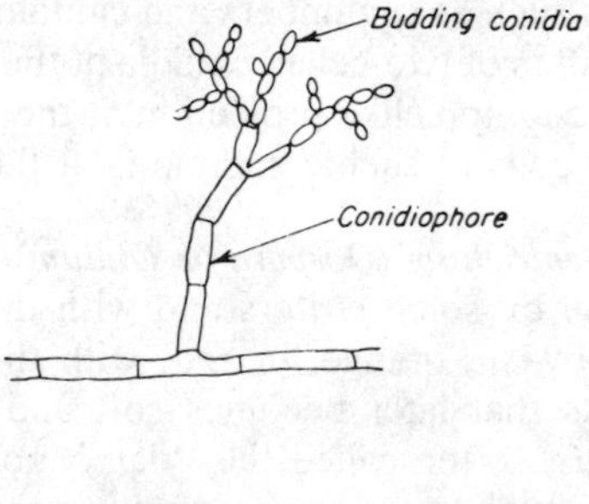

Budding conidia

Conidiophore

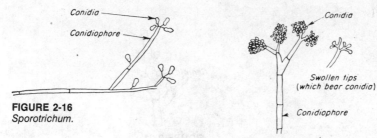

FIGURE 2-16
Sporotrichum.

FIGURE 2-17
Botrytis cinerea.

Sporotrichum Among the saprophytic species is *S. carnis* (Figure 2-16), found growing on chilled meats, where it causes "white spot."

Botrytis One species important in foods is *B. cinerea* (Figure 2-17). It causes a disease of grapes but may grow saprophytically on many foods.

Cephalosporium (Figure 2-18) *C. acremonium* is a common species.

Trichoderma *T. viride* (Figure 2-19) is a common species. The mature mold plant is bright green because the balls of green conidia are glued together, and tufts of white hyphae (sterile) stick up well above the conidiophores.

Scopulariopsis *S. brevicaulis* (Figure 2-20) is a common species. This genus may be confused with *Penicillium,* for both have brushlike penicilli and chains of spores cut off from the sterigmata, but the conidia of *Scopulariopsis* are never green. Conidiophores may be branched or unbranched in *Scopulariopsis,* and simple or complex, and the branching usually is irregular. The spore-bearing heads may vary from complex, branching systems with penicilli to single sterigmata arising from short branches of aerial hyphae. The spores are distinctive in microscopic appearance and are not green but commonly yellowish-brown; they are lemon-

FIGURE 2-18
Cephalosporium.

FIGURE 2-19
Trichoderma.

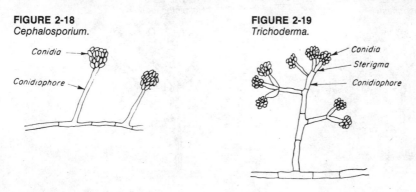

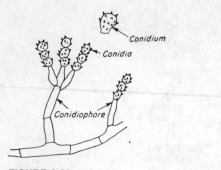

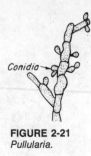

FIGURE 2-21
Pullularia.

FIGURE 2-20
Scopulariopsis.

shaped, thick-walled, spiny, and pointed at one end, with a thick ring at the opposite end. Colonies are brownish and cottony.

Pullularia (Figure 2-21)   Ovate, hyaline conidia (blastospores or buds from preexisting cells) borne as lateral buds on all parts of the mycelium. Colonies are pale and slimy and yeastlike when young, becoming mycelial and dark and leathery in age. *P. pullulans* is a common species.

Cladosporium   C. *herbarum* (Figure 2-22) is a leading species. These dark molds cause "black spot" on a number of foods, on cellar walls, etc. Colonies of C. *herbarum* are restricted in growth and are thick, velvety, and olive- to gray-green; the reverse side of the plant is a striking opalescent blue-black to greenish-black.

Helminthosporium (Figure 2-23)   Species of this genus are for the most part plant pathogens but may grow saprophytically on vegetable materials.

FIGURE 2-22
Cladosporium.

FIGURE 2-23
Helminthosporium.

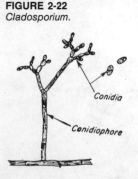

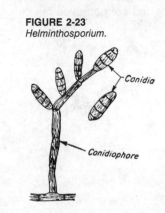

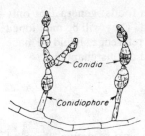

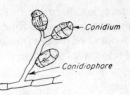

FIGURE 2-25
Stemphylium.

FIGURE 2-24
Alternaria.

Alternaria   Molds of this genus are common causes of the spoilage of foods. *A. citri* (rotting citrus fruits), *A. tenuis,* and *A. brassicae* are common species. The mass of mycelium usually is dirty gray-green, but hyphae often look nearly colorless under the microscope. The brown, many-celled conidia (Figure 2-24) are in a chain on the conidiophore.

Stemphylium (Figure 2-25)   This, too, is a common genus. The conidia are dark and multicellular but have fewer cross walls than those of *Alternaria* and are rounded at both ends.

Fusarium   Molds of this genus often grow on foods. The species are very difficult to identify, and the appearance of growth is variable (Figure 2-26).

Endomyces   Yeastlike fungi, forming mycelium and arthrospores. Some species rot fruits.

Monascus   Colonies of *M. purpureus* are thin and spreading and reddish or purple in color. Found on dairy products and on Chinese red rice (ang-khak).

Sclerotinia   Some species cause rots of vegetables and fruits, where they are present in the conidial stage. The lemon-shaped conidia are in chains, with a "plug" separating conidia.

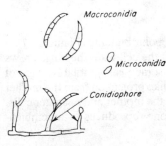

FIGURE 2-26
Fusarium.

In the preceding discussion of molds important in foods, genera that only occasionally grow on specific foods have been omitted. They will be mentioned with those foods. For the descriptions of these genera, reference should be made to text and reference books on fungi listed at the end of this chapter.

YEASTS AND YEASTLIKE FUNGI

Like mold, the term "yeast" is commonly used but hard to define. As used here it refers to those fungi which are generally not filamentous but unicellular and ovoid or spheroid and which reproduce by budding or fission.

Yeasts may be useful or harmful in foods. Yeast fermentations are involved in the manufacture of foods such as bread, beer, wines, vinegar, and surface-ripened cheese, and yeasts are grown for enzymes and for food. Yeasts are undesirable when they cause spoilage of sauerkraut, fruit juices, sirups, molasses, honey, jellies, meats, wine, beer, and other foods.

GENERAL CHARACTERISTICS OF YEASTS

Yeasts are classified chiefly on their morphological characteristics, although their physiological ones are more important to the food microbiologist.

Morphological Characteristics

The morphological characteristics of yeasts are determined by microscopic examination.

Form and Structure   The form of yeasts may be spherical to ovoid, lemon-shaped, pear-shaped, cylindrical (Figure 2-27), triangular, or even elongated into a false or true mycelium. They also differ in size. Visible parts of the structure are the cell wall, cytoplasm, water vacuoles, fat globules, and granules,which may be metachromatic, albuminous, or starchy. Special staining is necessary to demonstrate the nucleus.

Reproduction

Most yeasts reproduce asexually by multilateral or polar budding (Figure 2-27), a process in which some of the protoplasm bulges out the cell wall; the bulge grows in size and finally walls off as a new yeast cell. In some yeasts, notably some of the film yeasts, the bud appears to grow from a tubelike projection from the mother cell. Replicated nuclear material is divided between the mother and daughter cells. A few species of yeasts reproduce by fission, and one reproduces by a combination of fission and budding.

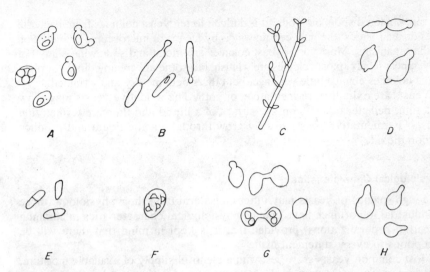

FIGURE 2-27
Yeasts of different shapes: (A) *Saccharomyces cerevisiae,* with budding cells and one ascus with four ascospores, (B) *Candida* yeast, with elongated cells, (C) *Candida,* showing pseudomycelium, (D) apiculate (lemon-shaped) yeast, (E) *Schizosaccharomyces,* mutliplying by fission, (F) *Hansenula,* with ascospores shaped like derby hats, (G) *Zygosaccharomyces,* showing conjugation with ascus and four ascospores, (H) flask-shaped yeasts.

Sexual reproduction of "true" yeasts (*Ascomycotina*) results in the production of ascospores, the yeast cell serving as the ascus. The formation of ascospores follows conjugation of two cells in most species of true yeasts, but some may produce ascospores without conjugation, followed by conjugation of ascospores or small daughter cells. The usual number of spores per ascus and the appearance of the ascospores are characteristic of the kind of yeast. The ascospores may differ in color, in smoothness or roughness of their walls, and in their shape (round, oval, reniform, bean- or sickle-shaped, Saturn- or hat-shaped, hemispherical, angular, fusiform, or needle-shaped).

"False" yeasts, which produce no ascospores or other sexual spores, belong to the *Fungi Imperfecti*. Cells of some yeasts become chlamydospores by formation of a thick wall about the cell, for example, *Candida, Rhodotorula,* and *Cryptococcus*.

Cultural Characteristics

For the most part, the appearance of massed yeast growth is not useful in the identification of yeasts, although growth as a film on the surface of liquid media suggests an oxidative or film yeast, and production of a carotenoid pigment indicates the genus *Rhodotorula*. However, the appearance of the growth is important when it causes colored spots on foods. It is difficult to tell yeast colonies from bacterial ones on agar plates; the only certain way is by means of microscopic examination of the organisms. Most young yeast colonies are moist and somewhat slimy but may appear mealy; most colonies are whitish, but some are cream-colored or pink. Some colonies change little with age, but others become dry and wrinkled.

Yeasts are oxidative, fermentative, or both. The oxidative yeasts may grow as a film, pellicle, or scum on the surface of a liquid and then are termed *film yeasts*. Fermentative yeasts usually grow throughout the liquid and produce carbon dioxide.

Physiological Characteristics

Although species of yeasts may differ considerably in their physiology, those of industrial importance have enough physiological characteristics in common to permit generalizations, provided that it is kept in mind that there will be exceptions to every statement made.

Most common yeasts grow best with a plentiful supply of available moisture. But since many yeasts grow in the presence of greater concentrations of solutes (such as sugar or salt) than most bacteria, it can be concluded that these yeasts require less moisture than the majority of bacteria. Most yeasts require more moisture than molds, however. On the basis of water activity or a_w (see Chapter 1), yeasts may be classified as ordinary if they do not grow in high concentrations of solutes, i.e., in a low a_w, and as osmophilic if they do. Lower limits of a_w for ordinary yeasts tested thus far range from 0.88 to 0.94. Specific examples of minimal a_w are 0.94 for a beer yeast, 0.90 for a yeast from condensed milk, and 0.905 for a bakers' yeast. By contrast, osmophilic yeasts have been found growing slowly in media with an a_w as low as 0.62 to 0.65 in sirups, although some osmophilic yeasts are stopped at about 0.78 in both salt brine and sugar sirup. Each yeast has its own characteristic optimal a_w and range of a_w for growth for a given combination of environmental conditions. These a_w values will vary with the nutritive properties of the substrate, pH, temperature, availability of oxygen, and presence or absence of inhibitory substances.

The range of temperature for growth of most yeasts is, in general, similar to that for molds, with the optimum around 25 to 30 C and the maximum about 35 to 47 C. Some kinds can grow at 0 C or less. The growth of most yeasts is favored by an acid reaction in the vicinity of pH 4 to 4.5, and they will not grow well in an alkaline medium unless adapted to it. Yeasts grow best under aerobic conditions, but the fermentative types can grow anaerobically, although slowly.

In general, sugars are the best source of energy for yeasts, although oxidative yeasts, e.g., the film yeasts, oxidize organic acids and alcohol. Carbon dioxide produced by bread yeasts accomplishes the leavening of bread, and alcohol made by the fermentative yeasts is the main product in the manufacture of wines, beer, industrial alcohol, and other products. The yeasts also aid in the production of flavors or "bouquet" in wines.

Nitrogenous foods utilized vary from simple compounds such as ammonia and urea to amino acids and polypeptides. In addition, yeasts require accessory growth factors.

Yeasts may change in their physiological characteristics, especially the true, or ascospore-forming, yeasts, which have a sexual method of reproduction. These yeasts can be bred for certain characteristics or may mutate to new forms. Most yeasts can be adapted to conditions which previously would not support good growth. Illustrative of different characteristics within a species is the large number of strains of *Saccharomyces cerevisiae* suited to different uses, e.g., bread strains, beer strains, wine strains, and high-alcohol-producing strains or varieties.

CLASSIFICATION AND IDENTIFICATION OF YEASTS

The true yeasts are in the subdivision *Ascomycotina,* and the false, or asporogenous, yeasts are in the subdivision *Fungi Imperfecti* or *Deuteromycotina.* Additional information on the classification and identification of yeasts can be found in Barnett et al. (1983).

Certain yeasts are actually represented in two different genera based on whether they reproduce sexually. Several examples, with equivalent names, are listed in Table 2-1.

The principal bases for the identification and classification of genera of yeasts are as follows:

1 Whether ascospores are formed.
2 If they are spore-forming:
  a The method of production of ascospores:
    (1) Produced without conjugation of yeast cells (parthenogenetically). Spore formation may be followed by (a) conjugation of ascospores or (b) conjugation of small daughter cells.

TABLE 2-1
EQUIVALENT NAMES OF SOME YEASTS

Diploid perfect (sexual) stage	Haploid imperfect (asexual) stage
Kluyveromyces marxianus (syn. *K. fragilis* and *Saccharomyces fragilis*)	*Candida kefyr* (syn. *C. pseudotropicalis*)
Kluyveromyces marxianus var. *lactis* (syn. *Saccharomyces lactis*)	*Candida sphaerica* (syn. *Torulopsis candida*)
Debaryomyces hansenii	*Candida famata* (syn. *Torulopsis candida*)
Pichia burtonii	*Candida variabilis* (syn. *Candida fibrae*)

Source: based on Lodder, 1984.

    (2) Produced after isogamic conjugation (conjugating cells appear similar).

    (3) Produced by heterogamic conjugation (conjugating cells differ in appearance).

  b Appearance of ascospores: shape, size, and color. Most spores are spheroidal or ovoid, but some have odd shapes, e.g., most species of *Hansenula*, which look like derby hats (Figure 2-27 F).

  c The usual number of ascospores per ascus: one, two, four, or eight.

3 Appearance of vegetative cells: shape, size, color, inclusions.

4 Method of asexual reproduction:

  a Budding.

  b Fission.

  c Combined budding and fission.

  d Arthrospores (oidia).

5 Production of a mycelium, pseudomycelium, or no mycelium.

6 Growth as a film over surface of a liquid (film yeasts) or growth throughout medium.

7 Color of macroscopic growth.

8 Physiological characteristics (used primarily to differentiate species or strains within a species):

  a Nitrogen and carbon sources.

  b Vitamin requirements.

  c Oxidative or fermentative: film yeasts are oxidative; other yeasts may be fermentative or fermentative and oxidative.

  d Lipolysis, urease activity, acid production, or formation of starchlike compounds.

YEASTS OF INDUSTRIAL IMPORTANCE

Most yeasts used industrially are in the genus *Saccharomyces*. The term "wild yeast" is applied to any yeast other than the one being used or encouraged. Thus a yeast employed in one process could be a wild yeast in another. Most of the troublesome wild yeasts are asporogenous, or false, yeasts.

    Genus *Schizosaccharomyces* These yeasts, which reproduce asexually by fission and form four or eight ascospores per ascus after isogamic conjugation, have been found in tropical fruits, molasses, soil, honey, and elsewhere. A common species is *S. pombe*.

    Genus *Saccharomyces* Cells of these yeasts may be round, ovate, or elongated and may form a pseudomycelium. Reproduction is by multipolar budding or by ascospore formation, which may follow conjugation or may develop from diploid cells when these represent the vegetative stage. The ascospores, one to four per ascus, are usually round or ovate. The leading species, *S. cerevisiae*, is employed in many food industries, with special strains used for the leavening of bread, as top yeasts for ale, for wines, and for the production of alcohol, glycerol, and invertase. Top yeasts are very active fermenters and grow rapidly at 20 C. The clumping of the cells and the rapid evolution of CO_2 sweep the cells to the surface, hence the term top yeast. Bottom yeast do not clump, grow more slowly, and are best fermenters at lower temperatures (10 to 15 C). The absence of clumping and the slower growth and evolution of CO_2 permit the yeast to settle to the bottom, hence the term bottom yeast. These characteristics of brewers' yeast are observations and do not explain why some yeast clump, or flocculate. A detailed discussion on the theories regarding the flocculation of brewers' yeasts can be found in Rose and Harrison (1970).

S. cerevisiae var. *ellipsoideus* is a high-alcohol-yielding variety used to produce industrial alcohol, wines, and distilled liquors. *S. uvarum*, a bottom yeast, is used in making beer. *S. fragilis* and *S. lactis*, because of their ability to ferment lactose, may be important in milk or milk products. *S. rouxii* and *S. mellis* are osmophilic.

According to Lodder (1984), many of the *Saccharomyces* have been reclassified. For example, *S. uvarum* is now considered a variant of *S. cerevisiae*, *S. fragilis* is now *Kluyveromyces marxianus*, and *S. lactis* is now *K. marxianus* var. *lactis*. *S. rouxii*, *S. mellis*, and *S. nussbaumeri* are now *Zygosaccharomyces rouxii*. *Debaryomyces kloeckeri* is now *D. hansenii*.

Genus *Kluyveromyces*. These yeasts reproduce by multilateral budding, and ascopores are liberated upon maturity. See *S. fragilis* and *S. lactis* in the previous section.

Genus *Zygosaccharomyces* Some workers (Ludder, 1984) consider this a subgenus of *Saccharomyces*. These yeasts are notable for their ability to grow in high concentrations of sugar (hence they are termed **osmophilic**) and are involved in the spoilage of honey, sirups, and molasses and in the fermentation of soy sauce and some wines. *Z. nussbaumeri* grows in honey.

Genus *Pichia* These oval to cylindrical yeasts may form pseudomycelia. Ascospores are round or hat-shaped, and there are one to four per ascus. A pellicle is formed on liquids; e.g., *P. membranaefaciens* grows a pellicle on beers or wines.

Genus *Hansenula* These yeasts resemble *Pichia* in appearance but are usually more fermentative, although some species form pellicles. Ascospores are hat- or Saturn-shaped.

Genus *Debaryomyces* These round or oval yeasts form pellicles on meat brines. Ascospores have a warty surface. *D. kloeckeri* grows on cheese and sausage.

Genus *Hanseniaspora* These lemon-shaped (apiculate) yeasts grow in fruit juices. *Nadsonia* yeasts are large and lemon-shaped.

False Yeasts (*Fungi Imperfecti*)

Genus *Torulopsis* These round to oval fermentative yeasts with multilateral budding cause trouble in breweries and spoil various foods. *T. sphaerica* ferments lactose and may spoil milk products. Other species can spoil sweetened condensed milk, fruit-juice concentrates, and acid foods.

Genus *Candida* These yeasts form pseudohyphae or true hyphae, with abundant budding cells or blastospores, and may form chlamydospores. Many form films and can spoil foods high in acid and salt. *C. utilis* is grown for food and feed. *C. krusei* has been grown with dairy starter cultures to maintain the activity and increase the longevity of the lactic acid bacteria. Lipolytic *C. lipolytica* can spoil butter and oleomargarine.

Genus *Brettanomyces* These ogive- or arch-shaped yeasts produce high amounts of acid and are involved in the late fermentation of Belgian lambic beer and English beers. They also are found in French wines. *B. bruxellansis* and *B. lambicus* are typical species.

Genus *Kloeckera* These are imperfect apiculate or lemon-shaped yeasts. *K. apiculata* is common on fruits and flowers and in the soil.

Genus *Trichosporon* These yeasts bud and form arthrospores. They grow best at low temperatures and are found in breweries and on chilled beef. *T. pullulans* is a common species.

Genus *Rhodotorula* These red, pink, or yellow yeasts may cause discolorations on foods, e.g., colored spots on meats or pink areas in sauerkraut.

Groups of Yeasts

Film yeasts, in the genera *Pichia, Hansenula, Debaryomyces, Candida,* and *Trichosporon,* grow on the surface of acid products such as sauerkraut and pickles, oxidize the organic acids, and enable less acid-tolerant organisms to continue the spoilage. *Hansenula* and *Pichia* tolerate high levels of alcohol and may oxidize it in alcoholic beverages. *Pichia* species are encouraged to grow on Jerez and Arbois wine, to which they are supposed to impart distinctive flavors and esters. *Debaryomyces* is very salt tolerant and can grow on cheese brines with as much as 24 percent salt. The film yeasts produce little or no alcohol from sugars.

Apiculate or *lemon-shaped yeasts,* in *Saccharomycodes, Hanseniaspora, Nadsonia,* and *Kloeckera,* are considered objectionable in wine fermentations because they give off-flavors, low yields of alcohol, and highly volatile acid.

Osmophilic yeasts (Saccharomyces rouxii and *S. mellis)* grow well in an environment of high osmotic pressure, i.e., in high concentrations of sugars, salts, or other solutes, causing spoilage of dry fruits, concentrated fruit juices, honey, maple sirup, and other high-sugar solutions.

Salt-tolerant yeasts grow in curing brines, salted meats and fish, soy sauce, miso paste, and tamari sauce. The most salt-tolerant of the film yeasts are species of *Debaryomyces,* which grow on curing brines and on meats and cucumbers in them, as does *Saccharomyces rouxii,* which can grow as a film on brine. Yeasts in various other genera (*Torulopsis, Brettanomyces,* and others) also grow in brines. Yeasts grow in soy sauce with its high content of salt (about 18 percent). *Saccharomyces rouxii* is considered of great importance in the production of alcohol and flavor, but species of *Torulopsis, Pichia, Candida,* and *Trichosporon* also may grow. Film-forming *S. rouxii* and *Pichia* are sometimes involved in the spoilage of soy sauce. Similar yeasts are involved in miso production, but kinds will vary as the salt concentration is varied between 7 and 20 percent.

BACTERIA

Although determinative bacteriology (classification and identification of bacteria) is beyond the scope of this book and should be reviewed in other textbooks, some of the morphological, cultural, and physiological characteristics of bacteria will be mentioned briefly because of their relationship to the preservation or spoilage of foods.

MORPHOLOGICAL CHARACTERISTICS IMPORTANT IN FOOD BACTERIOLOGY

One of the first steps in the identification of bacteria in a food is microscopic examination to ascertain the shape, size, aggregation, structure, and staining reactions of the bacteria present. The following characteristics may be of special significance.

Encapsulation

The presence of capsules (Figure 2-28) or slime may account for sliminess or ropiness of a food. In addition, capsules serve to increase the resistance of bacteria to adverse conditions, such as heat or chemicals. To the organism they may serve as a source of reserved nutrients. Most capsules are polysaccharides of dextrin, dextran, or levan.

Formation of Endospores

Bacteria of the genera *Bacillus, Clostridium, Desulfotomaculum, Sporolactobacillus* (rods), and *Sporosarcina* (cocci) share the ability to form endospores

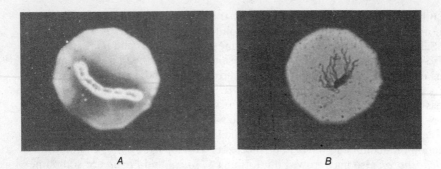

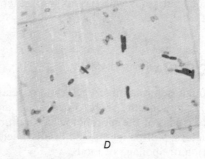

FIGURE 2-28
Bacterial structures: (A) capsules, (B) flagella, (C) granules in *Lactobacillus bulgaricus**, (D) spores of *Bacillus subtilis*. (*Courtesy of P. R. Elliker.*)

(Figure 2-29). Of primary interest to the food microbiologist are the spore-forming species of the genera *Bacillus* (aerobic and some facultative anaerobic) and *Clostridium* (anaerobic). Endospores are formed at an intracellular site, are very refractile, and are resistant to heat, ultraviolet light, and desiccation. Lysis of the vegetative cell releases the free endospore, which may remain dormant with no detectable metabolism for years. The complete cycle of vegetative cell through sporulation to the free spore, possible extended dormancy, and then germination of the spore and outgrowth back to the vegetative cell is extremely complex.

Sporulation usually appears in the late logarithmic phase of growth, possibly because of nutrient depletion or product accumulation. During this transition of vegetative cell to spore, the spore becomes refractile, there is a massive uptake of Ca^{2+} ions, and synthesis of dipicolinic acid (DPA) occurs, a compound absent from vegetative cells. The acquisition of heat resistance by the forming spore is closely correlated to the formation of DPA and the Ca^{2+} uptake.

Germination is favored, in general, by conditions that are favorable to growth of the vegetative cells, but it may take place under conditions that do not permit such growth, e.g., at low temperatures. It is triggered by mixtures of amino acids, by Mg^{2+} and Mn^{2+} ions, by glucose, by dipicolinic acid plus Ca^{2+} ions, and by heat shocking or heat activation, which activates dormant enzymes. The optimal temperature and time for heat shocking depends on the kind of spore, the heat treatment being greater for spores of thermophiles, for example, than for those of mesophiles. Germination is inhibited by sorbic acid at an acid pH, by some divalent cations, by starch, and by oleic and linoleic acids.

"Dormancy" of spores has been defined as delayed germination (and outgrowth) under conditions apparently favorable for it. The spores fail to germinate, however, probably because of unfavorable conditions such as inhibitors in the environment or lack of essential nutrients, e.g., amino acids. Some spores may germinate but fail to grow out, and some may have been damaged by heat, radiation, or other agents, so that they need a more complex or specialized medium for growth than their ancestors did. Delayed germination of spores from a few days to many months has been reported, e.g., dormancy from a few days to 3 or 4 months with spores of *Bacillus megaterium* and for 15 days to 72 months with spores of *Clostridium botulinum*.

Formation of Cell Aggregates

It is characteristic of some bacteria to form long chains and of others to clump under certain conditions. It is more difficult to kill all bacteria in intertwined chains or sizable clumps than to destroy separate cells.

CULTURAL CHARACTERISTICS IMPORTANT IN FOOD BACTERIOLOGY

Bacterial growth in and on foods often is extensive enough to make the food unattractive in appearance or otherwise objectionable. Pigmented bacteria cause

FIGURE 2-29
Photomicrograph showing terminal endospores in a rod. The spores are clear in the left-hand field and stained in the right-hand field (X1300). (*Courtesy of J. Nowak.*)

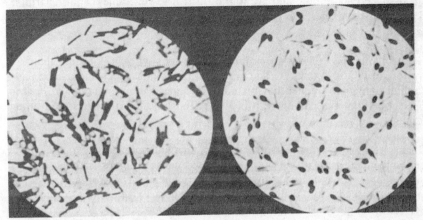

discolorations on the surfaces of foods; films may cover the surfaces of liquids; growth may make surfaces slimy; or growth throughout the liquids may result in undesirable cloudiness or sediment.

PHYSIOLOGICAL CHARACTERISTICS IMPORTANT IN FOOD BACTERIOLOGY

The bacteriologist is concerned with the growth and activity of bacteria (and other microorganisms) in foods and with the accompanying chemical changes. These changes include hydrolysis of complex carbohydrates to simple ones; hydrolysis of proteins to polypeptides, amino acids, and ammonia or amines; and hydrolysis of fats to glycerol and fatty acids. O-R reactions, which are utilized by the bacteria to obtain energy from foods (carbohydrates, other carbon compounds, simple nitrogen-carbon compounds, etc.), yield such products as organic acids, alcohols, aldehydes, ketones, and gases. A knowledge of the factors that favor or inhibit the growth and activity of bacteria is essential to an understanding of the principles of food preservation and spoilage. These changes will be discussed in more detail in subsequent chapters.

GENERA OF BACTERIA IMPORTANT IN FOOD BACTERIOLOGY

The following discussion emphasizes the characteristics of genera of bacteria that make them important in foods and pays less attention to the characteristics used in their classification and identification. The classification given in Bergey's Manual of Systematic Bacteriology, vols. I and II, 1984 and 1986, will be followed. Names that are no longer accepted for one reason or another are marked with an asterisk and discussed in the Appendix.

Genus *Acetobacter*   These bacteria oxidize ethyl alcohol to acetic acid. They are rod-shaped and motile and are found on fruits, vegetables, souring fruits, and alcoholic beverages. They are a definite spoilage problem in alcoholic beverages.

Genus *Aeromonas*   These are gram-negative rods with an optimum temperature for growth of 22 to 28 C. They are facultative anaerobes and can be psychrophilic. They are frequently isolated from aquatic environments. *A. hydrophila* can be a human pathogen; it is also pathogenic to fish, frogs, and other mammals.

Genus *Alcaligenes*   As the name suggests, an alkaline reaction usually is produced in the medium of growth. *A. viscolactis** causes ropiness in milk, and *A. metalcaligenes** gives a slimy growth on cottage cheese. These organisms come from manure, feeds, soil, water, and dust. This genus also contains organisms which were formerly classified in the genus *Achromobacter*.

Genus *Alteromonas*   Several former species of *Pseudomonas* are now classified as *Alteromonas*. They are marine organisms that are potentially important in seafoods.

Genus *Arthrobacter*   A predominant soil organism, it is inert in most foods. However, some species can grow at 5 C and would be considered psychrotrophs.

Genus *Bacillus*   The endospores of species of this aerobic to facultative genus usually do not swell the rods in which they are formed. Different species may be mesophilic or thermophilic, actively proteolytic, moderately proteolytic, or nonproteolytic, gas-forming or not, and lipolytic or not. In general the spores of the mesophiles, e.g., *B. subtilis,* are less heat-resistant than spores of the thermophiles. Spores of the obligate thermophiles, e.g., *B. stearothermophilus,* are more resistant than those of facultative thermophiles, e.g., *B. coagulans*. The actively proteolytic species usually may also sweet-curdle milk; *B. cereus* is such a species. The two chief acid- and gas-forming species, *B. polymyxa* and *B. macerans,* sometimes are termed "aerobacilli." Many of the mesophiles can form acid from glucose or other sugar but usually form only a small amount that often is neutralized by ammonia produced from the nitrogenous food. The thermophilic flat sour bacteria that spoil canned vegetables can produce considerable amounts of lactic acid from sugar, and such a culture, e.g., *B. coagulans,* may be employed for the manufacture of lactic acid. The soil is an important source of *Bacillus* species.

Several strains, as recognized by their American Type Culture Collection (ATCC) number, are important as test organisms in sterility testing. *Bacillus pumilus* (ATCC 27142) is recommended for determining the suitability of gamma radiation sterilization. *B. stearothermophilus* (ATCC 7953) is recommended for testing procedures involving steam sterilization. *B. subtilis* (ATCC 6633) is also used for steam sterilization procedures and as the test organism for penicillin detected in milk. *B. subtilis* var. *niger* (ATCC 9372) is recommended for ethylene oxide sterilization testing.

Genus *Brevibacterium*   *B. linens* is related to *Arthrobacter globiformis* and may be synonymous. *B. linens* may be important in the surface smear of certain cheeses, e.g., brick or Limburger, where the culture produces an orange-red pigmentation and helps ripening.

Genus *Brochotrix*   These are gram-positive rods which can form long filamentouslike chains that may fold into knotted masses. The optimum temperature for growth is 20 to 25 C, but growth can occur over a temperature range of 0 to 45 C depending on the strain. Growth can occur between pH 5.0 and 9.0 (optimum pH, 7.0) and in the presence of 6.5 to 10.0% NaCl. The organisms will not survive heating at 63 C for 5 min. *D* values at 63 C have been calculated to be 0.1 min. They can spoil a wide variety of meats and meat products when they are stored aerobically or vacuum packed and held refrigerated. *B. thermosphacta* is the only species listed.

Genus *Campylobacter* These bacteria were originally classified in the genus *Vibrio*. They are oxidase-positive, catalase-positive, gram-negative, curved, and S-shaped or spiral shaped. They prefer reduced oxygen tension. Several strains of *C. fetus* subsp. *jejuni* have been associated with gastroenteritis in humans (Chapter 24).

Genus *Clostridium* The endospores of species of this genus of anaerobic to microaerophilic bacteria usually swell the end or middle of the rods in which they are formed. All species are catalase-negative. Many species actively ferment carbohydrates with the production of acids (usually including butyric) and gases (usually carbon dioxide and hydrogen). Different species may be mesophilic or thermophilic and proteolytic or nonproteolytic. *C. thermosaccharolyticum* is an example of a saccharolytic obligate thermophile; this organism causes gaseous spoilage of canned vegetables. Putrefaction of foods often is caused by mesophilic, proteolytic species, such as *C. lentoputrescens** and *C. putrefaciens*. The violent disruption of the curd in milk by *C. perfringens* or similar species results in a "stormy fermentation" of milk, and the lactate-fermenting *C. butyricum* is a cause of late gas in cured cheese. The soil is the primary source of *Clostridium* spp., although they also may come from bad silage, feeds, and manure.

Genus *Corynebacterium* The diphtheria organism, *C. diptheriae,* may be transported by foods. *C. bovis,* with the slender, barred, or clubbed rods characteristic of the genus, is commensal on the cow's udder, can be found in aseptically drawn milk, and may be a cause of bovine mastitis.

Genus *Desulfotomaculum* A gram-negative rod which swells when an endospore forms. They are common inhabitants of the soil, fresh water, and the rumen. Sulfur compounds can serve as the terminal electron acceptor in respiration and thereby be reduced to hydrogen sulfide. *C. nigrificans,* which is responsible for sulfide stinker spoilage in canned foods, is now called *D. nigrificans.*

Genus *Enterobacter* Some were formerly classified as *Aerobacter*. They are widely distributed in nature; a member of the coliform group.

Genus *Erwinia* The species of this genus are plant pathogens that cause necrosis, galls, wilts, or soft rots in plants and therefore damage the plants and vegetable and fruit products from them. *E. carotovora* is associated with the market disease called "bacterial soft rot." *E. carotovora* subsp. *carotovora* causes rotting in a large number of plants. *E. carotovora* subsp. *atroseptica* produces a black rot in potatoes. *E. carotovora* subsp. *betavasculorum** causes soft rot in sugar beets.

Genus *Escherichia*   Found in feces, a predominant gram-negative rod isolated from the intestinal tract of warm-blooded animals and widely distributed in nature. One of the "coliform group," the genus is divided into many biotypes and serotypes, some of which can be pathogenic to humans (Chapter 24).

Genus *Flavobacterium*   The yellow- to orange-pigmented species of this genus may cause discolorations on the surface of meats and be involved in the spoilage of shellfish, poultry, eggs, butter, and milk. Some of the organisms are psychrotrophic and have been found growing on thawing vegetables. Some of the *Flavobacterium* species have been classified in the genus *Halobacterium*.

Genus *Gluconobacter*   (Formerly *Acetomonas*). Species can oxidize ethanol to acetic acid. *G. oxydans* causes ropiness in beer following viscous growth in beer or wort.

Genus *Halobacterium*   Bacteria of this genus, e.g., *H. salinarium,* are obligate halophiles and are usually chromogenic. They may grow and cause discolorations on foods high in salt, such as salted fish. Many bacteria formerly classified as *Flavobacterium* are now included in this genus.

Genus *Klebsiella*   Many are capsulated. Commonly associated with the respiratory and intestinal tracts of humans. *K. pneumoniae* is the causative organism for a bacterial pneumonia in humans.

Family *Lactobacillaceae*

Genus *Lactobacillus*   The lactobacilli are rods, usually long and slender, that form chains in most species (Figure 2-30). They are microaerophilic, (some strict anaerobes are known), are catalase-negative and gram-positive, and ferment sugars to yield lactic acid as the main product. They ferment sugar chiefly to lactic acid if they are homofermentative, with small amounts of acetic acid, carbon dioxide, and trace products; if they are heterofermentative, they produce appreciable amounts of volatile products, including alcohol, in addition to lactic acid. The homofermentative lactobacilli with optimal temperatures of 37 C or above include *L. bulgaricus**, *L. helveticus, L. lactis**, *L. acidophilus, L. thermophilus**, and *L. delbrueckii. L. fermentum* is the chief example of a heterofermentative lactobacillus growing well at higher temperatures. The homofermentative lactobacilli with lower optimal temperatures include *L. casei, L. plantarum,* and *L. leichmannii*;* heterofermentative species are *L. brevis, L. buchneri, L. pastorianus**, *L. hilgardii,* and *L. trichodes**. All the above species except *L. delbrueckii, L. leichmannii, L. hilgardii, L. trichodes**, and some strains of *L. brevis* ferment lactose with the production of lactic acid and therefore may be of importance in the dairy industries. Chief sources of the lactobacilli are plant surfaces, manure, and dairy products.

Characteristics that make the lactobacilli important in foods are (1) their ability to ferment sugars with the production of considerable amounts of lactic acid, mak-

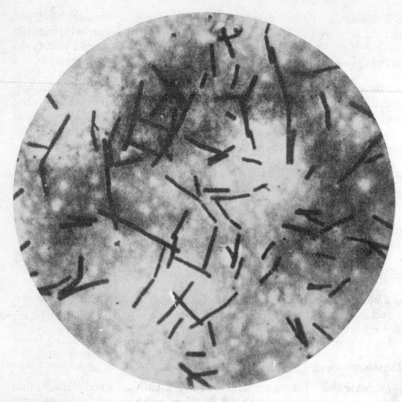

FIGURE 2-30
Photomicrograph of *Lactobacillus bulgaricus** (X1000).

ing it possible to use them in the production of fermented plant and dairy products or the manufacture of industrial lactic acid but resulting in the deterioration of some products, e.g., wine or beer, (2) production of gas and other volatile products by heteroferentative species, sometimes with damage to the quality of food, as with *L. fermentum* growing in Swiss cheese or *L. hilgardii* or *L. trichodes** in wines, (3) their inability to synthesize most of the vitamins they require, making them unable to grow well in foods poor in vitamins but useful in assays for the vitamin content of foods, and (4) the heat resistance, or thermoduric properties, of most of the high-temperature lactobacilli, enabling them to survive pasteurization or other heating processes, such as that given the curd in the manufacture of Swiss and similar cheeses.

Species of *Lactobacillus* different from the ones already mentioned have been found growing in refrigerated meats, but only a few names for these lactobacilli have been suggested, e.g., *L. viridescens* for one causing greening of sausage and *L. salinmandus** for one growing in sausage. These lactobacilli are exceptional because of their ability to grow at low temperatures.

Genus *Leuconostoc* This genus, called *Betacoccus* by Orla-Jensen, contains the heterofermentative lactic streptococci, which ferment sugar to lactic acid plus considerable amounts of acetic acid, ethyl alcohol, and carbon dioxide. The ability of *L. dextranicum** and *L. cremoris** to ferment citric acid of milk and produce the desirable flavoring substance diacetyl (the more reduced acetoin and 2,3-butanediol also are produced) and to stimulate the lactic streptococci has led to their inclusion in the so-called "lactic starter" for buttermilk, butter, and cheese.

Some of the characteristics of *Leuconostoc* species that make them important in foods are (1) production of diacetyl and other flavoring products; (2) tolerance of salt concentrations, e.g., in sauerkraut and dill-pickle fermentations, permitting *L. mesenteroides* to carry on the first part of the lactic fermentation, (3) ability to initiate fermentation in vegetable products more rapidly than other lactics or other competing bacteria and to produce enough acid to inhibit nonlactics, (4) tolerance of high sugar concentrations (up to 55 to 60 percent for *L. mesenteroides*), permitting the organism to grow in sirups, liquid cake and ice-cream mixes, etc., (5) production of considerable amounts of carbon dioxide gas from sugars, leading to undesirable "openness" in some cheeses, spoilage of foods high in sugars (sirups, mixes, etc.), and leavening in some breads, (6) heavy slime production in media containing sucrose. This is a desirable characteristic for the production of dextran but a hazard in materials high in sucrose, as in the production of sucrose from sugarcane or beets.

The habitat of this genus is the surface of plants.

Genus *Listeria* These bacteria are gram-positive, non-spore-forming rods with tumbling motility. *L. monocytogenes* can cause food-borne disease outbreaks (Chapter 24)

Genus *Microbacterium* Bacteria of this genus are important because of their resistance to adverse conditions and their use in production of vitamins. They are small, nonmotile, gram-positive, asporogenous, catalase-positive, aerobic, homofermentative, lactic acid–producing rods, which sometimes produce palisade arrangements. *M. lacticum* is the species usually encountered. Microbacteria are very resistant to heat for non-spore-forming bacteria, surviving pasteurization of milk readily and even temperatures of 80 to 85 C for 10 min. They therefore are among the thermodurics that give high counts in pasteurized dairy products, such as market milk and dry milk. Their range of temperature for growth is 15 to 35 C, and their optimum is about 30 C. Therefore, in plating for these organisms, incubation of plates should be at below 35 C, preferably at about 30 C.

Genus *Micrococcus** The micrococci* are spherical cells arranged in irregular masses, clusters, tetrads, or packets. Most of the species prominent in foods are gram-positive, aerobic, and catalase-positive. They have an optimal temperature around 25 to 30 C and grow well on ordinary laboratory culture media. Otherwise, it is difficult to generalize about their characteristics, which may differ considerably from species to species. The following characteristics make various groups of micrococci important in foods: (1) Some species can utilize ammonium salts or other simple nitrogenous compounds as a sole source of nitrogen, (2) most species can ferment sugars with the production of moderate amounts of acid, (3) some are acid-proteolytic (*M. freudenreichii**), (4) some are very salt tolerant and hence able to grow at relatively low levels of available moisture; these grow in meat-curing brines, brine tanks, etc., (5) many are thermoduric, i.e., survive the pasteurization treatment given market milk (*M. varians*), (6) some are pigmented and discolor the surfaces of foods on which they grow; *M. luteus* is yellow, for example, and *M. roseus* is pink, and (7) some of the micrococci can grow fairly well at temperatures around 10 C or below.

Micrococci* are widespread in nature but have been isolated most often from dust and water. They often are found on inadequately cleaned and sanitized food utensils and equipment.

Genus *Mycobacterium* The tubercle bacilli that cause tuberculosis, *M. tuberculosis,* has been spread by foods, especially raw milk from infected cows.

Genus *Pediococcus* The cocci occur singly, in pairs or short chains, or in tetrads (division in two planes) and are gram-positive, catalase-negative, and microaerophilic. They are homofermentative, fermenting sugars to yield 0.5 to 0.9 percent acid, mostly lactic, and they grow fairly well in salt brines up to 5.5 percent and poorly in concentrations of salt up to about 10 percent. Their range of temperatures for growth is from about 7 to 45 C, but 25 to 32 C is best. The characteristics that make the organism important in foods have been mentioned: salt tolerance, acid production, and temperature range, especially the ability to grow at cool temperatures. Pediococci have been found growing during the fermentation of brined vegetables and have been found responsible for the spoilage of alcoholic beverages, e.g., beer, where their production of diacetyl is undesirable. *P. damnosus* can spoil beer. *P. cerevisiae** has been used as starter culture in fermented sausages.

Genus *Photobacterium* The genus includes coccobacilli and occasional rods which can be luminescent. They are not widespread; however, *P. phosphoreum* has been known to cause phosphorescence of meats and fish.

Genus *Propionibacterium* Members of this genus may be found in foods. These bacteria are small, nonmotile, gram-positive, asporogenous, catalase-positive, and anaerobic to aerotolerant rods that often are coccoid and sometimes in chains. They ferment lactic acid, carbohydrates, and polyalcohols to propionic and acetic acids and carbon dioxide. In Swiss cheese certain species (e.g., *Propionibacterium freudenreichii*) ferment the lactates to produce the gas that helps form the holes, or eyes, and also contribute to the flavor. Pigmented propionibacteria can cause color defects in cheese.

Genus *Proteus* Bacteria of this genus have been involved in the spoilage of meats, seafood, and eggs. The presence of these bacteria in large numbers in unrefrigerated foods has made them suspect as a cause of food poisoning (Chapter 24).

Genus *Pseudomonas* A number of species of *Pseudomonas* can cause food spoilage. These bacteria are gram-negative, usually motile, asporogenous rods.

Characteristics of some of the *Pseudomonas* species that make them important in foods are (1) their ability to utilize a large variety of noncarbohydrate carbon compounds for energy and their inability to use most carbohydrates, (2) their ability to produce a variety of products that affect flavor deleteriously, (3) their ability to use simple nitrogenous foods, (4) their ability to synthesize their own growth factors or vitamins, (5) the proteolytic and lipolytic activity of some species, (6) their aerobic tendencies, enabling them to grow rapidly and produce oxidized products and slime at the surfaces of foods, where heavy contamination is most likely, (7) their ability to grow well at low (refrigeration) temperatures, (8) pigment production by some species, e.g., the greenish fluorescence by pyoverdin of *Pseudomonas fluorescens* and white, cream-colored, reddish, brown, or even black (*P. nigrifaciens**) colors of other species, and (9) their resistance to many disinfectants and sanitizers used in the food industry.

On the other hand, the pseudomonads are limited by a fairly high a_w (0.97 to 0.98), are readily killed by heat, grow poorly if oxygen is not readily available, are not especially resistant to drying, and grow poorly or not at all above 43 C.

Genus *Salmonella* Species of these enteric pathogens may grow in foods and cause food infections (Chapter 24); usually they are only transported by foods.

Genus *Serratia* Many species produce a pink or magenta pigment and may cause red discolorations on the surface of foods. *S. marcescens* is the most common species.

Genus *Shigella* Species of *Shigella,* causing bacillary dysenteries, may be transported by foods (Chapter 24).

Genus *Sporolactobacillus* *Lactobacillus inulinus* has been classified as *S. inulinus* because of its ability to form endospores. It does resemble *Lactobacillus* in many characteristics.

Genus *Sporosarcina* A gram-positive coccus that forms endospores. *S. ureae* and *S. halophila* are the two species listed.

Genus *Staphylococcus* The gram-positive staphylococci grow singly, in pairs, in tetrads, or in irregular, grapelike clusters. The most important species, *S. aureus,* usually gives yellow to orange growth, although it may be white on occasion. The species requires an organic source of nitrogen and is facultative in oxygen requirements. Many of the beta-hemolytic, coagulase-positive strains are pathogenic, and some produce an enterotoxin which causes food poisoning (Chapter 24).

Genus *Streptococcus* The cocci in this genus are characteristically in pairs, in short chains, or in long chains, depending on the species and the conditions of growth, and all are homofermentative. The streptococci may be classified serologically by a precipitin reaction into Lancefield groups with capital-letter designations (A, B, C, D, etc.), but ordinarily the streptococci important in foods are divided into four groups: the pyogenic, viridans, lactic, and enterococcus groups.

The pyogenic (pus-producing) group includes species of pathogenic streptococci, of which *S. agalactiae,* a cause of mastitis in cows, and *S. pyogenes,* a cause of human septic sore throat, scarlet fever, and other diseases, are representatives that have been found in raw milk. The pyogenic streptococci cannot grow at 10 or 45 C.

The viridans groups includes *S. thermophilus,* a coccus important in cheeses made by cooking the curd at high temperatures and in certain fermented milks such as yogurt, and *S. bovis,* which comes from cow manure and saliva and like *S. thermophilus* is thermoduric and therefore counted in the plating of pasteurized milk. These species can grow at 45 C but not at 10 C.

The lactic group contains the important dairy bacteria, *S. lactis* (Figure 2-31) and *S. cremoris*,* which can grow at 10 C but not at 45 C. These bacteria are used as starters for cheese, cultured buttermilk, and some types of butter, along with *Leuconostoc* spp., and *S. lactis* often is concerned in the souring of raw milk. These

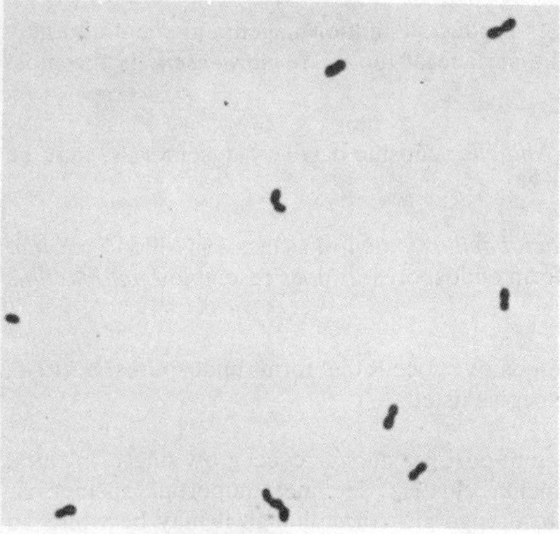

FIGURE 2-31
Photomicrograph of *Streptococcus lactis** (X1000).

lactic bacteria tolerate no more than 2 to 4 percent salt and therefore are not concerned in the lactic fermentation of brined vegetables. Some sources of the lactics are green plants, feeds, silage, and utensils.

The enterococcus group consists of *S. faecalis* and *S. faecium*, and some related subspecies. *S. faecalis* and *S. faecium* resemble each other but can be distinguished by physiological tests. *S. faecalis* is usually the more heat-resistant and comes more from human sources, whereas *S. faecium* has been reported to be more from plant sources. *S. faecalis* subsp. *liquefaciens** is an acid-proteolytic variety of *S. faecalis,* and *S. faecalis* subsp. *zymogenes** is a beta-hemolytic variety. *S. faecalis* and *S. faecium* are commonly found in raw foods. Bacteria of this group can grow at both 10 and 45 C. The enterococci have several characteristics in common that make them unusual streptococci: (1) They are thermoduric, readily surviving the pasteurization treatment of milk or even more heating, (2) they tolerate 6.5 percent and more of salt, (3) they can grow at the alkaline pH of 9.6, and (4) they can grow over a wide range of temperatures, some multiplying at as low as 5 to 8 C and most of them at as high as 48 to 50 C. *S. faecalis* also has been found growing on bacon. As indicated by the name, the enterococci originate in the intestinal tracts of human beings and animals and are sometimes used as indicator organisms of fecal contamination of foods and, more often, as a measure of plant sanitation. They also can survive in dairy products and may contaminate utensils and equipment.

The enterococci most frequently isolated from foods are *S. faecalis* and *S. faecium;* however, all of the Lancefield group D streptococci can be considered enterococci. The group D streptococci include *S. faecalis, S. faecalis* subsp. *liquefaciens*, S. faecalis* subsp. *zymogenes*, S. faecium, S. faecium* subsp. *durans*, S. bovis, S. equinus,* and *S. avium.*

The term "fecal streptococci" is often used in the food industry to describe those enterococci which are used as indicator organisms (see page 56).

Genus *Streptomyces* Members of this genus can cause undesirable flavors and appearance when growing on foods; musty or earthy odors and tastes from these organisms may be absorbed by nearby foods when growth of the streptomyces is near at hand. These aerobic higher bacteria grow to form a much-branched mycelium and bear conidia in chains.

Genus *Vibrio* Bacteria in this genus are widely distributed in fresh and salt water, in soil, and in the alimentary canal of humans and animals. Some are moderately halophilic. Some species are pathogenic to humans (Chapter 24).

Genus *Yersinia* Can be found in the soil. *Y. pestis* is the causative organism of plague in humans and in rats and other rodents. Some strains of *Y. enterocolitica* are also pathogenic and have been reported to be causative agents of food-borne disease outbreaks (Chapter 24). Formerly classified as *Pasteurella,* they are now in the family *Enterobacteriaceae* because of their close taxonomical relationship to *Salmonella.*

GROUPS OF BACTERIA IMPORTANT IN FOOD BACTERIOLOGY

Bacteria important in foods often are grouped on the basis of one common characteristic without regard for their systematic classification. It is obvious that some bacterial species might be included in two or more of these artificial groups. Examples of the commonly employed groupings will be presented.

Lactic Acid–Forming Bacteria, or Lactics

The most important characteristic of the lactic acid bacteria is their ability to ferment sugars to lactic acid. This may be desirable in making products such as sauerkraut and cheese but undesirable in terms of spoilage of wines. Because they form acid rapidly and commonly in considerable amounts, they usually eliminate for the time being much of the competition from other microorganisms.

The major genera include *Leuconostoc, Lactobacillus, Streptococcus,* and *Pediococcus.*

Acetic Acid–Forming Bacteria, or Acetics

Most of acetic acid bacteria now belong to one of two genera, *Acetobacter* and *Gluconobacter*. Both oxidize ethyl alcohol to acetic acid, but *Acetobacter* is capable of oxidizing acetic acid further to carbon dioxide. Characteristics that make the acetic acid bacteria important are (1) their ability to oxidize ethanol to acetic acid, making them useful in vinegar manufacture and harmful in alcoholic beverages, (2) their strong oxidizing power, which may result in the oxidation of the desired product, acetic acid, by undesirable species or by desirable species under unfavorable conditions; this oxidizing power may be useful, as in the oxidation of D-sorbitol to L-sorbose in the preparation of ascorbic acid by synthetic methods, and (3) excessive sliminess of some species, e.g., *Acetobacter aceti subsp. suboxydans*,* that clog vinegar generators.

Butyric Acid–Forming Bacteria, or Butyrics

Most bacteria of this group are spore-forming anaerobes of the genus *Clostridium*.

Propionic Acid–Forming Bacteria, or Propionics

Most bacteria of this group are in the genus *Propionibacterium,* although propionic cocci have been reported.

Proteolytic Bacteria

This is a heterogeneous group of actively proteolytic bacteria which produce extracellular proteinases, so termed because the enzymes diffuse outside the cells. All bacteria have proteinases inside the cell, but only a limited number of kinds have extracellular proteinases. The proteolytic bacteria may be divided into those which are aerobic or facultative and may be spore-forming or not and those which are anaerobic and spore-forming. *Bacillus cereus* is an aerobic, spore-forming, proteolytic bacterium, *Pseudomonas fluorescens* is non-spore-forming and aerobic to facultative, and *Clostridium sporogenes* is spore-forming and anaerobic. Many of the species of *Clostridium, Bacillus, Pseudomonas,* and *Proteus* are proteolytic. Some bacteria, termed "acid-proteolytic," carry on an acid fermentation and proteolysis simultaneously. *Streptococcus faecalis* var. *liquefaciens** and *Micrococcus caseolyticus** are acid-proteolytic. Some bacteria are putrefactive; i.e., they decompose proteins anaerobically to produce foul-smelling compounds such as hydrogen sulfide, mercaptans, amines, indole, and fatty acids. Most proteolytic species of *Clostridium* are putrefactive, as are some species of *Proteus, Pseudomonas,* and other genera of nonsporeformers. Putrefaction of split products of proteins also can take place. Some *Pseudomonas* species are known to produce proteinase that can survive ultrahigh heat treatments.

Lipolytic Bacteria

This is a heterogeneous group of bacteria which produce lipases enzymes which catalyze the hydrolysis of fats to fatty acids and glycerol. Many of the aerobic, actively proteolytic bacteria also are lipolytic. *Pseudomonas fluorescens,* for example, is strongly lipolytic. *Pseudomonas, Alcaligenes, Staphylococcus, Serratia,* and *Micrococcus* are genera that contain lipolytic species. Many of the microbial lipases are resistant to processing techniques. The absence of viable lipolytic bacteria from a spoiled food should not be considered as proof that the product is free of microbial lipases.

Saccharolytic Bacteria

These bacteria hydrolyze disaccharides or polysaccharides to simpler sugars. A limited number of kinds of bacteria are amylolytic, i.e., possess amylase to bring about the hydrolysis of starch outside the cell. *Bacillus subtilis* and *Clostridium butyricum* are amylolytic. Few kinds of bacteria can hydrolyze cellulose. Species of *Clostridium* sometimes are classified as proteolytic ones that may or may not attack sugars or saccharolytic ones that attack sugars but not proteins. *C. lentoputrescens** is proteolytic but ordinarily does not ferment carbohydrates, whereas *C. butyricum* is nonproteolytic but ferments sugars.

Pectinolytic Bacteria

Pectins are complex carbohydrates that are responsible for cell-wall rigidity in vegetables and fruits. Pectic substances derived from citrus fruits can be used in commercial products as gelling agents. A variety of pectolytic enzymes called pectinase may be responsible for softening of plant tissues or loss of gelling power or body in various foods. Species of *Erwinia, Bacillus, Clostridium, Achromobacter, Aeromonas, Arthrobacter,* and *Flavobacterium* as well as species of molds may be pectinolytic.

Thermophilic Bacteria, or Thermophiles

These bacteria, with an optimal temperature at least above 45 C but usually 55 C or above, are important in foods held at high temperatures. Thermophilic flat sour spoilage of low-acid canned foods is caused by *B. stearothermophilus.* Gaseous thermophilic spoilage of canned foods is a result of growth by *C. thermosaccharolyticum.*

Thermoduric Bacteria

Thermoduric bacteria are usually defined as those which can survive a heat treatment such as pasteurization. *Bacillus* species, micrococci*, and enterococci can survive pasteurization of liquid eggs. Bacteria in the genera *Clostridium, Bacillus, Micrococcus, Streptococcus, Lactobacillus,* and *Microbacterium* are frequently encountered in foods. Occasionally molds such as *Byssochlamys fulva* and even *Aspergillus* and *Penicillium* are thermoduric. Some thermoduric bacteria, such as *Bacillus* and enteroccocci, can also be psychrotrophic (see the following section). In milk, where higher pasteurization and longer refrigeration times are significant, these heat-resistant, or thermoduric, psychrotrophs often can be found.

Psychrotrophic Bacteria, or Psychrotrophs

These bacteria are able to grow at commercial refrigeration temperatures. Unlike psychrophiles, psychrotrophs do not have their optimal temperature for growth at refrigeration temperatures; rather, their optimum is usually between 25 C and 30 C. Most of the bacteria responsible for the loss of quality in nonsterile refrigerated foods, excluding seafoods, are psychrotrophs. Psychrotrophic bacteria are found chiefly in the genera *Pseudomonas, Flavobacterium, Achromobacter,* and *Alcaligenes,* although *Micrococcus, Lactobacillus, Enterobacter, Arthrobacter,* and other genera may contain psychrotrophic species. Additionally, various yeasts and molds are able to grow at refrigeration temperatures.

Halophilic Bacteria, or Halophiles

Truly halophilic bacteria require certain minimal concentrations of dissolved sodium chloride for growth. Those bacteria, including *Pseudomonas, Moraxella, Flavobacterium, Acinetobacter,* and *Vibrio* species, which grow best in media with 0.5 to 3.0 percent salt, are considered slightly halophilic. These microorganisms are isolated from many species of fish and shellfish. Bacteria which are isolated from foods such as salted fish, brined meats, and some salted vegetables and which grow best in media with 3.0 to 15 percent salt are referred to as moderate halophiles. Such bacteria are found in the genera *Bacillus, Micrococcus, Vibrio, Acinetobacter,* and *Moraxella.* Occasionally in heavily brined foods, 15 to 30 percent salt, extreme halophiles such as *Halobacterium* and *Halococcus* species can be isolated. Frequently, they are also pigmented pink or red. Other bacteria are salt-tolerant; i.e., halotolerant bacteria can grow with or without salt. Usually they are capable of growing in foods containing 5.0 percent salt or more; they include some *Bacillus, Micrococcus, Corynebacterium, Streptococcus,* and *Clostridium* species. Other halophilic or halotolerant bacteria important in foods are found in the genera *Sarcina, Pseudomonas, Pediococcus,* and *Alcaligenes.*

Osmophilic or Saccharophilic Bacteria

The most frequently encountered osmophilic microorganisms in foods are various species of yeasts. Osmophilic bacteria are those which grow in high concentrations of sugar; however, most bacteria called osmophiles are merely sugar-tolerant, e.g., species of *Leuconostoc.*

Pigmented Bacteria

Colors produced by pigmented bacteria growing on or in foods range through the visible spectrum and also include black and white. Examples will be numerous in a subsequent discussion of spoilage of foods. All species in some genera are pigmented, as in *Flavobacterium* (yellow to orange) and *Serratia* (red). Pigmented species are found in many genera; many species of *Micrococcus* are pigmented, for example. Also, pigmented varieties occur within some species, e.g., the rust-colored *Lactobacillus plantarum* that discolors cheese. *Halobacterium* species are pigmented pink, red, or red to orange. *Halococcus* species are pigmented red or red to orange.

Slime- or Rope-Forming Bacteria

Examples of these bacteria already have been given: *Alcaligenes viscolactis*, Enterobacter aerogenes,* and *Klebsiella oxytoca,* causing ropiness of milk, and *Leuconostoc* spp., producing slime in sucrose solutions and slimy surface growth of various bacteria occurring on foods. Some of the species of *Streptococcus* and *Lactobacillus* have varieties that make milk slimy or ropy. A micrococcus makes curing solutions for meats ropy. Strains of *Lactobacillus plantarum* and other lactobacilli may cause ropiness in various fruit, vegetable, and grain products, e.g., in cider, sauerkraut, and beer. Some *Bacillus* species are responsible for ropiness in bread.

Gas-Forming Bacteria

Many kinds of bacteria produce such small amounts of gas and yield it so slowly that it ordinarily is not detected. This sometimes is true of the hetero-fermentative lactics, although under other conditions gas evolution is evident. Among the genera that contain gas-forming bacteria are *Leuconostoc, Lactobacillus* (heterofermentative), *Propionibacterium, Escherichia, Enterobacter, Proteus, Bacillus* (the aerobacilli), and *Clostridium*. Bacteria of the first three genera produce only carbon dioxide, and those of the other genera yield both carbon dioxide and hydrogen.

Coliform and Fecal Coliform Group

Coliforms are short rods that are defined as aerobic and facultative anaerobic, Gram-negative, non-spore-forming bacteria which ferment lactose with gas formation. The leading species of coliform bacteria are *Escherichia coli* and *Enterobacter aerogenes;* however, as many as twenty species may conform to these criteria, including species of other *Enterobacteriaceae* and even *Aeromonas* species. The fecal coliform group includes coliforms capable of growth at an elevated temperature (44.5 or 45 C). The original purpose of the elevated incubation tests was to differentiate coliforms of fecal origin from those of nonfecal origin. The designation "fecal coliform" or "coliform" is not taxonomically valid; rather, the terms refer to groups of bacteria that can grow under specific test conditions.

Procedures for coliform counts, fecal coliform counts, and even *E. coli* counts on foods are widely used and accepted as indicators. The use of "indicator" microorganisms began with the use of *E. coli* testing in water as a substitute for the testing of *Salmonella typhi*. The concept is based on Shardingen's suggestion in 1892 that members of the species we now call *E. coli* be used as an index or indicator of fecal pollution since they can be recovered with less difficulty than *Salmonella* species. Other indicator groups or tests suggested or used include the fecal streptococci or enterococci, the *Enterobacteriaceae,* staphylococci (suggesting the possible presence of *S. aureus* enterotoxin or handling abuse), and the presence of *Geotrichum candidum*, the machinery mold, as an indicator of plant sanitation and contaminated equipment.

Some of the characteristics that make the coliform bacteria important in food spoilage are (1) their ability to grow well in a variety of substrates and to utilize a number of carbohydrates and some other organic compounds as food for energy and a number of fairly simple nitrogenous compounds as a source of nitrogen, (2) their ability to synthesize most of the necessary vitamins, (3) the ability of the group to grow well over a fairly wide range of temperatures, from below 10 C to about 46 C, (4) their ability to produce considerable amounts of acid and gas from sugars, (5) their ability to cause off-flavors, often described as "unclean" or "barny", and (6) the ability of *E. aerogenes* to cause sliminess or ropiness of foods.

BIBLIOGRAPHY

Ainsworth, G. C., F. K. Sparrow, and A. L. Sussman (eds.). 1973. The fungi: An advanced treatise. Volume IVB, A taxonomic review with keys: *Basidiomycetes* and lower fungi. Academic Press, Inc., New York.

Barnett, H. L. 1955. Illustrated genera of imperfect fungi. Burgess Publishing Company, Minneapolis.

Barnett, J. A., and R. J. Pankhurst. 1974. A new key to the yeasts. North-Holland Publishing Co., Amersterdam.

Barnett, J. A., R. W. Payne, D. Yarrow. 1983. Yeast characteristics and identification. Cambridge University Press, Cambridge.

Bessey, E. A. 1950. Morphology and taxonomy of fungi. McGraw-Hill Book Company, New York.

Beuchat, L. R. 1978. Food and beverage mycology. AVI Publishing Company, Inc., Westport, Conn.

Buchanan, R. E., and N. E. Gibbons. 1974. Bergey's manual of determinative bacteriology. 8th ed. The Williams & Wilkins Company, Baltimore.

Burnett, J. H. 1968. Fundamentals of mycology. St. Martin's Press, New York.

Carr, J. G., C. V. Cutting, and G. C. Whiting (eds.). 1975. Lactic acid bacteria in beverages and food. Academic Press, Inc., New York.

Cheung, B. A., and D. C. Westhoff. 1983. Isolation and identification of ropy bacteria from raw milk. J. Dairy Sci. 66:825–834.

Cook, A. H. (ed.). 1958. The chemistry and biology of yeasts. Academic Press, Inc., New York.

Foster, J. W. 1949. Chemical activities of fungi. Academic Press, Inc., New York.

Funder, S. 1968. Practical mycology. 3rd rev. ed. Haffner Press, New York.

Gerhardt, P., R. N. Costilow, and H. L. Sadoff (eds.). 1975. Spores. Volume VI. American Society for Microbiology, Ann Arbor, Mich.

Gilman, J. C. 1945. A manual of soil fungi. Iowa State College Press, Ames.

Hankin, L., and G. H. Lacy. 1984. Pectinolytic microorganisms. *In* M. L. Speck (ed.), Compendium of methods for the microbiological examination of foods. 2d ed., chap. 15. American Public Health Association, Washington, D.C.

Krieg, N. R., and J. G. Holt. 1984. Bergey's manual of systematic bacteriology, vol. 1. The Williams & Wilkins Company, Baltimore.

Lodder, J. 1984. General classification of the yeasts. *In* J. Lodder (ed.), The yeasts. 3d ed. North-Holland Publishing Co., Amsterdam.

Mehlman, I. J. 1984. Coliforms, fecal coliforms, *Escherichia coli* and enteropathogenic *E. coli*. *In* M. L. Speck (ed.), Compendium of methods for the microbiological examination of foods. 2d ed., chap. 25. American Public Health Association, Washington, D.C.

Mrak, E. M., and H. J. Phaff. 1948. Yeasts. Annu. Rev. Microbiol. 2:1–46.

Nelson, F. E., and K. M. Sorrells. 1984. Thermoduric microorganisms. *In* M. L. Speck (ed.), compendium of methods for the microbiological examination of foods. 2d ed., chap. 10. American Public Health Association, Washington, D.C.

Onishi, H. 1963. Osmophilic yeasts. Adv. Food Res. 12:53–94.

Pelczar, M. L., and R. D. Reid. 1972. Microbiology. McGraw-Hill Book Company, New York.

Raper, K. B., and D. I. Fennell. 1965. The genus *Aspergillus*. The Williams & Wilkins Company, Baltimore.

Raper, K. B., and C. Thom. 1949. A manual of the penicillia. The Williams & Wilkins Company, Baltimore.

Rose, A. H., and J. S. Harrison. 1970. The yeasts. Volume III. Yeast technology. Academic Press, Inc., New York.

Rose, A. H., and J. S. Harrison. 1971. The yeasts. Volume II. Physiology and biochemistry of yeasts. Academic Press, Inc., New York.

Sampson, R. A., E. S. Hoehstra, and C. A. N. van Oorschot. 1984. Introduction to food-borne fungi. Centraalbureau voor Schimmelcultures, Netherlands.

Scott, W. J. 1957. Water relations of food spoilage microorganisms. Adv. Food Res. 7:83–127.

Smith, J. E., and D. R. Berry (eds.). 1975. Industrial mycology. Volume I. The filamentous fungi. John Wiley & Sons, Inc., New York.

Sneath, P. H. A., N. S. Mair, M. E. Sharpe, and J. G. Holt (eds.). 1986. Bergey's manual of systematic bacteriology, vol. 2. The Williams & Wilkins Company, Baltimore.

Stanier, R. Y., E. A. Adelberg, and J. Ingraham. 1976. The microbial world. 4th ed. Prentice-Hall, Inc., Englewood Cliffs, N.J.

Thatcher, F. S., and D. S. Clark (eds.). 1968. Microorganisms in foods. Volume I. Their significance and methods of enumeration. University of Toronto Press, Toronto.

Toshinobu, A. 1968. Acetic acid bacteria: classification and biochemical activities. University Park Press, Baltimore.

CONTAMINATION OF FOODS

Growing plants carry a typical flora of microorganisms on their surfaces and may become contaminated from outside sources. Animals likewise have a typical surface flora plus an intestinal one, give off organisms in excretions and secretions, and also become contaminated from outside sources. Plants and animals with parasitic disease, of course, carry the pathogen causing the disease. The inner, healthy tissues of plants and animals, however, have been reported to contain few living microorganisms or none. Microorganisms from various natural sources are indicated in Table 3-1.

FROM GREEN PLANTS AND FRUITS

The natural surface flora of plants varies with the plant but usually includes species of *Pseudomonas, Alcaligenes, Flavobacterium,* and *Micrococcus* and coliforms and lactic acid bacteria. Lactic acid bacteria include *Lactobacillus brevis* and *plantarum, Leuconostoc mesenteroides* and *dextranicum,* and *Streptococcus faecium* and *faecalis. Bacillus* species, yeasts, and molds also may be present. The numbers of bacteria will depend on the plant and its environment and may range from a few hundred or thousand per square centimeter of surface to millions. The surface of a well-washed tomato, for example, may show 400 to 700 microorganisms per square centimeter, while an unwashed tomato would have several thousand. Outer tissue of unwashed cabbage might contain 1 million to 2 million microorganisms per gram, but washed and trimmed cabbage might contain 200,000 to 500,000. The inner tissue of the cabbage, where the surface of the leaves would harbor primarily the natural flora, contains fewer kinds and lower numbers, ranging from a few hundred to 150,000 per gram. Exposed surfaces of plants become contaminated from soil, water, sewage, air, and animals, so that microorganisms from these sources are added to the natural flora. Whenever conditions for growth of natural flora and contaminants

TABLE 3-1
SOURCES OF BACTERIAL CONTAMINATION

	Humans				Animals				Water			
	Skin	Intestine	Feces	Other	Skin	Intestine	Feces	Other	Salt	Fresh	Soil	Foods
Acetobacter												+
Acinetobacter	+	+	+	+						+	+	+
Aeromonas			+	+		+	+			+	+	+
Alcaligenes		+				+			+	+	+	+
Alteromonas					+				+			+
Arthrobacter											+	
Bacillus		+				+			+	+	+	+
Brevibacterium		+			+				+		+	+
Brochotrix					+		+				+	
Campylobacter	+	+	+		+	+	+			+	+	+
Clostridium	+					+			+	+	+	
Corynebacterium	+		+	+	+			+				+
Desulfotomaculum						+			+	+	+	+
Enterobacter		+	+				+	+	+	+	+	+
Erwinia			+				+					+
Escherichia		+				+						
Flavobacterium		+						+	+	+	+	
Gluconobacter											+	+
Halobacterium									+			
Klebsiella		+				+					+	
Lactobacillus	+	+	+		+	+	+					+
Leuconostoc												+
Listeria	+	+	+		+	+	+				+	+
Microbacterium											+	
Micrococcus	+				+					+	+	
Moraxella	+		+				+					+
Pediococcus										+		+
Photobacterium							+	+				
Propionibacterium	+	+	+	+	+	+	+	+			+	
Proteus		+				+					+	
Pseudomonas			+						+	+	+	
Salmonella	+	+			+	+			+			
Serratia										+	+	+
Shigella	+					+						
Staphylococcus	+		+	+	+							+
Streptococcus	+	+	+	+	+	+		+				+
Vibrio	+					+			+	+		
Yersinia	+	+	+		+		+					+

are present, increases in numbers of special kinds of microorganisms take place, especially following harvesting, as will be discussed subsequenty. Some fruits have been found to contain viable microorganisms in their interior. Normal, healthy tomatoes have been shown to contain *Pseudomonas*, coliforms, *Achromobacter**, *Micrococcus,* and *Corynebacterium,* and yeasts have been found inside undamaged fruits. Organisms also have been found in healthy root and tuber vegetables.

FROM ANIMALS

Sources of microorganisms from animals include the surface flora, the flora of the respiratory tract, and the flora of the gastrointestinal tract. The natural surface flora of meat animals usually is not as important as the contaminating microorganisms from their intestinal or respiratory tracts. However, hides, hooves, and hair contain not only large numbers of microorganisms from soil, manure, feed, and water but also important kinds of spoilage organisms. Feathers and feet of poultry carry heavy contamination from similar sources. The skin of many meat animals may contain micrococci, staphylococci and beta-hemolytic streptococci. Staphylococci on the skin or from the respiratory tract may find their way onto the carcass and then to the final raw product. The feces and fecal-contaminated products of animals can contain many enteric organisms, including *Salmonella*. Salmonellosis in animals can result in contamination of animal products or by-products and thus contaminate foods derived from them with *Salmonella*.

Pig or beef carcasses may be contaminated with salmonellae. Because of further processing and handling, very few of these organisms result in human salmonellosis. Actually, meat from slaughtered animals is not frequently associated with human salmonellosis. Statistics in recent years have incriminated eggs and egg products much more frequently. Salmonellosis associated with eggs has been reduced because of the pasteurization of egg products.

Many infectious disease agents of animals can be transmitted to people via foods, but this represents only one of several transmission routes. Many of these diseases have been reduced or eliminated by improvement in animal husbandry, but a listing of agents of animal disease causing infections from foods would include *Brucella, Mycobacterium tuberculosis, Coxiella, Listeria, Campylobacter,* beta-hemolytic streptococci, *Salmonella,* enteropathogenic *Escherichia coli,* parasites, and viruses.

Animals, from the lowest to the highest forms, contribute their wastes and finally their bodies to the soil and water and to plants growing there. Little attention has been paid to the direct contamination of food plants from this source, except insofar as coliform bacteria or enterococci may be added. Insects and birds cause mechanical damage to fruits and vegetables, introduce microorganisms, and open the way for microbial spoilage.

FROM SEWAGE

When untreated domestic sewage is used to fertilize plant crops, there is a like-lihood that raw plant foods will be contaminated with human pathogens, espe-cially those causing gastrointestinal diseases. The use of "night soil" as a fer-tilizer still persists in some parts of the world but is rare in the United States. In addition to the pathogens, coliform bacteria, anaerobes, enterococci, other intestinal bacteria, and viruses can contaminate the foods from this source. Nat-ural waters contaminated with sewage contribute their microorganisms to shell-fish, fish, and other seafood.

Treated sewage going onto soil or into water also contributes microorgan-isms, although it should contain smaller numbers and fewer pathogens than does raw sewage.

FROM SOIL

The soil contains the greatest variety of microorganisms of any source of con-tamination. Whenever microbiologists search for new kinds of microorganisms or new strains for special purposes, they usually turn first to the soil. Not only numerous kinds of microorganisms but also large total numbers are present in fertile soils, ready to contaminate the surfaces of plants growing on or in them and the surfaces of animals roaming over the land. Soil dust is whipped up by air currents, and soil particles are carried by running water to get into or onto foods. The soil is an important source of heat-resistant spore-forming bacteria. No attempt will be made to list the microorganisms important in food micro-biology that could come from the soil, but it can be stated with certainty that nearly every important microorganism can come from soil. Especially impor-tant are various molds and yeasts and species of the bacterial genera *Bacillus, Clostridium, Enterobacter, Escherichia, Micrococcus, Alcaligenes, Flavo-bacterium, Chromobacterium, Pseudomonas, Proteus, Streptococcus, Leuco-nostoc,* and *Acetobacter* as well as some of the higher bacteria such as the actino-mycetes and the iron bacteria.

Modern methods of food handling usually involve washing the surfaces of foods and hence the removal of much of the soil from those surfaces, and care is taken to avoid contamination by soil dust.

FROM WATER

Natural waters contain not only their natural flora but also microorganisms from soil and possibly from animals or sewage. **Surface** waters in streams or pools and **stored** waters in lakes and large ponds vary considerably in their microbial content, from many thousands per milliliter after a rainstorm to the compar-atively low numbers that result from self-purification of quiet lakes and ponds or of running water. **Ground** waters from springs or wells have passed through layers of rock and soil to a definite level; hence most of the bacteria, as well as the greater part of other suspended material, have been removed. Bacterial numbers in these waters may range from a few to several hundred bacteria per milliliter

The kinds of bacteria in natural waters are chiefly species of *Pseudomonas, Chromobacterium, Proteus, Micrococcus, Bacillus, Streptococcus* (enterococci), *Enterobacter,* and *Escherichia.* Bacteria of the last three genera probably are contaminants rather than part of the natural flora. These bacteria in the water surrounding fish and other sea life establish themselves on the surfaces and in the intestinal tracts of the sea fauna.

The food microbiologist is interested in two aspects of water bacteriology: (1) public health aspects and (2) economic aspects. From the public health point of view the water used about foods should be absolutely safe to drink, i.e., free from pathogens. Tests for indicator bacteria can be confirmed and completed by methods described in American Public Health Association (1985). *Escherichia coli,* which is considered more often of intestinal origin, can be distinguished from *Enterobacter aerogenes,* which is found on plant surfaces and in soils more often than in intestinal contents. Some control laboratories run total plate counts and coliform tests on the water at regular intervals and chlorinate more heavily at the first sign that something may be wrong. Many nonfermenting bacteria such as *Pseudomonas* species actually grow in water lines and are not detected by traditional coliform analysis; therefore, total plate counts are important. Chlorination of drinking water is practiced when there is any doubt about the sanitary quality of the water, the amount of chlorine finally present ranging from 0.025 to 2 or more parts of available chlorine per million parts of water, depending on the composition of the water and the amount of contamination.

From the economic point of view, a water with agreeable chemical and bacteriological characteristics is desired for use in connection with the food being handled or processed. The water should have an acceptable taste, odor, color, clarity, chemical composition, and bacterial content and should be available in sufficient volume at a desired temperature; it also should be uniform in composition. Desirable chemical composition is affected by hardness and alkalinity as well as by the content of organic matter, iron, manganese, and fluorine.

As has been stated, the water used about foods should meet the bacteriological standards for drinking water and should be acceptable from the sanitary viewpoint as well as the economic viewpoint. Usually, however, water is more important from the standpoint of the kinds of microorganisms it may introduce into or onto foods than from the standpoint of the total numbers. Contamination may come from water used as an ingredient, for washing foods, for cooling heated foods, and for manufactured ice for preserving foods. For each food product there will be certain microorganisms to be feared especially. The gas-forming coliform bacteria may enter milk from cooling-tank water and cause trouble in cheese made from the milk. Anaerobic gas formers may enter foods from soil-laden water. Cannery cooling water often contains coliform and other spoilage bacteria that enter canned foods during cooling through minute defects in the seams or seals of the cans. This water commonly is chlorinated, but there have been reports that a chlorine-resistant flora can build up in time. Bacteria causing ropiness of milk, e.g., *Alcaligenes viscolactis** and *Enterobacter aerogenes,* usually come from water, as do slime-forming species of *Achromobacter,** *Alcaligenes,* and *Pseudomonas,* which cause trouble in cottage cheese. The bacterium causing the surface taint of butter, *Pseudomonas putrefaciens,** comes primarily from water. The iron bacteria, whose sheaths contain ferric hydroxide, may gum up an entire water supply and are difficult to eliminate. The bacterial flora of crushed ice to be applied to fish or other food consists mostly of *Corynebacterium, Alcaligenes, Flavobacterium, Pseudomonas,* and *cocci.*

It is evident from the preceding discussion that it is important to select a location with a good water supply when establishing a plant for handling or processing foods, and it often is necessary to treat the water to render it of satisfactory chemical and bacteriological quality. Water supplies should be protected against sewage pollution. They may be purified by sedimentation in reservoirs or lakes, by filtration through sand or finer filters, or by chlorination, ultraviolet irradiation, or boiling. Only partial purification is likely to result from sedimentation. Efficient filtration greatly reduces the microbial content, but filters sometimes can be a source of contamination of the water with undesirable bacteria. Thus the filters for water for soft drinks have sometimes been found to add large numbers of coliform bacteria. Treatment of water with ultraviolet rays has been used on water for soft drinks.

FROM AIR

Contamination of foods from the air may be important for sanitary as well as economic reasons. Disease organisms, especially those causing respiratory infections, may be spread among employees by air, or the food product may become contaminated. Total numbers of microorganisms in a food may be increased from the air, especially if the air is being used for aeration of the product, as in growing bread yeast, although the numbers of organisms introduced by sedimentation from air usually are negligible. Spoilage organisms may come from air, as may those interfering with food fermentations. Mold spores from air may give trouble in cheese, meat, sweetened condensed milk, and sliced bread and bacon.

Sources of Microorganisms in Air

Air does not contain a natural flora of microorganisms, for all that are present have come there by accident and usually are on suspended solid materials or in moisture droplets. Microorganisms get into air on dust or lint; dry soil; spray from streams, lakes, or oceans; droplets of moisture from coughing, sneezing, or talking; and growths of sporulating molds on walls, ceilings, floors, foods, and ingredients. Thus the air around a plant manufacturing yeast usually is high in yeasts, and the air of a dairy plant may contain bacteriophages or at least the starter bacteria being used there.

Kinds of Microorganisms in Air

The microorganisms in air have no opportunity for growth but merely persist there, and the kinds that are most resistant to desiccation will live the longest. Mold spores, because of their small size, resistance to drying, and large numbers per mold plant, are usually present in air. Many mold spores do not water-wet readily and therefore are less likely to sediment from humid air than are particles that wet readily. It is possible for any kind of bacterium to be suspended in air, especially on dust particles or in moisture droplets, but some kinds are more commonly found than others in undisturbed air. Cocci usually are more numerous than rod-shaped bacteria, and bacterial spores are relatively uncommon in dust-free air. Yeasts, especially asporogenous chromogenic ones, are found in most samples of air. Of course, whenever dusts or sprays of various materials are carried up into the air, the microorganisms characteristic of those suspended materials will be present: soil organisms from soil and dust, water organisms from water spray, plant organisms from feed or fodder dust, etc.

Numbers of Microorganisms in Air

The numbers of microorganisms in air at any given time depend on such factors as the amount of movement, sunshine, humidity, location, and the amount of suspended dust or spray. Numbers vary from less than one per cubic foot at a mountaintop to thousands in very dusty air. Individual microorganisms and those on suspended dust or in droplets settle out in quiet air; conversely, moving air brings organisms up into it. Therefore, numbers of microorganisms in air are increased by air currents caused by movements of people, by ventilation, and by breezes. Direct rays from the sun kill microorganisms suspended in air and hence reduce numbers. Dry air usually contains more organisms than does similar air in a moist condition. Rain or snow removes organisms from the air, so that a hard, steady rainfall may practically free the air of organisms.

According to a review of airborne contamination of foods by Heldman (1974), various surveys have indicated that (1) the microbial populations of different processing plants are similar, (2) populations vary tremendously in numbers from one part of a given plant to another, (3) populations in a plant are related to air quality outside the plant, and (4) population levels are related to the level of activity of workers.

Treatment of Air

It has been pointed out that numbers of microorganisms in air may be reduced under natural conditions by sedimentation, sunshine, and washing by rain or snow. Removal of microorganisms from air by artificial means may involve these principles or those of filtration, chemical treatment, heat, or electrostatic precipitation. The most frequently used of these methods is filtration through fibers of various sorts, e.g., cotton, fiber glass, etc., or activated carbon. The fibers are replaced periodically or sterilized with heat or a gas. Washing by means of a water spray or by bubbling air through water is not efficient and seldom is used by itself. Chemical treatments of air are finding increasing use. Passage of air through tunnels lined with ultraviolet lamps or installation of these lamps in a room or over an area where contamination from air is feared is used in some places. Electrostatic precipitation of dust particles and microorganisms from air also has been accomplished successfully. Heat treatment of air at very high temperatures has been successful but expensive.

After the microorganisms have been removed from air, precautions must be taken to prevent their reentrance. Positive pressure in rooms keeps outside air away. Filters in ventilating or air-conditioning systems prevent the spread of organisms from one part of a plant to another, and ultraviolet-irradiated air locks at doors reduce the numbers of organisms carried in by workers.

DURING HANDLING AND PROCESSING

The contamination of foods from the natural sources just discussed may take place before the food is harvested or gathered or during handling and processing of the food. Additional contamination may come from equipment coming in contact with foods, from packaging materials, and from personnel. The processor attempts to clean and "sanitize" equipment to reduce such contamination and to employ packaging materials that will minimize

TABLE 3-2
NUMBER OF WORKERS ENGAGED IN DIFFERENT
OCCUPATIONS AND POSITIVE CULTURES OF COAGULASE-
NEGATIVE AND COAGULASE-POSITIVE STAPHYLOCOCCI,
FECAL COLIFORMS, AND ENTEROCOCCI OBTAINED FROM
THEIR HANDS

Occupation	Numbers of workers examined	Workers with positive cultures	
		No.	%
Nonfood employment	200	87	43.5
Mechanized food industry	127	68	53.5
Catering service	207	151	72.9
Bakeries	27	26	96.3
Ripened cheese industry	124	114	91.9
Meat industry	129	125	96.9

Source: Seligmann and Rosenbluth (1975).

contamination. The term "sanitize" is used here rather than "sterilize" because although an attempt is made to sterilize the equipment, i.e., free it of all living organisms, sterility is seldom attained. Contamination during handling and processing of individual kinds of foods will be discussed in later chapters on those foods.

Personnel in food processing plants can contaminate foods during handling and processing. Various workers suggest that human beings shed from 10^3 to 10^4 viable organisms per minute. The numbers and types of organisms shed are closely related to the subjects' working environment.

Since the role of the food handler in food-borne disease outbreaks has been clearly demonstrated, from a public health aspect this source of contamination has received considerable attention. Table 3-2 demonstrates the potential contamination of foods from the hands of various workers.

BIBLIOGRAPHY

Alexander, M. 1961. Introduction to soil microbiology. John Wiley & Sons, Inc., New York.

American Public Health Association. 1985. Standard methods for the examination of water and wastewater. 16th ed., New York.

Avens, J. S., and B. F. Miller. 1970. Quantifying bacteria on poultry carcass skin. Poultry Sci. 49:1309–1315.

Baldock, J. D. 1975. Microbiological monitoring of the food plant: methods to assess bacterial contamination on surfaces. J. Milk Food Technol. 37:361–368.

Bryan, F. L. 1977. Disease transmitted by foods contaminated by waste water. J. Food Prot. 40:45–56.

Cannon, R. Y. 1966. Populations and types of microorganisms in the air of fluid milk plants. J. Dairy Sci. 49:704–709.

Collins, V. G. 1964. The fresh water environment and its significance in industry. J. Appl. Bacteriol. 27:143–150.

Gainey, P. L., and T. H. Lord. 1952. Microbiology of water and sewage. Prentice-Hall, Inc., Englewood Cliffs, N.J.

Green, K. M., and D. O. Cliver. 1975. Removal of virus from septic tank effluent. *In* Proceedings of national home sewage disposal symposium. American Society of Agricultural Engineers. St. Joseph, Mich.

Gregory, P. H. 1961. The microbiology of the atmosphere. Interscience Publishers (Division of John Wiley & Sons, Inc.), New York.

Heldman, D. R. 1974. Factors influencing air-borne contamination of foods: a review. J. Food Sci. 39:962–969.

International Commission on Microbiological Specifications for Foods. 1980. Microbial ecology of foods. Volume 1. Factors affecting life and death of microorganisms. Academic Press, New York.

Kitchell, A. G., G. C. Ingram, and W. R. Hudson. 1973. Microbiological sampling in abattoirs. *In* R. G. Board and D. W. Lovelock (eds.), Sampling: Microbiological monitoring of environments. Academic Press, Inc., London.

Kotula, A. W., and J. A. Kinner. 1964. Air-borne microorganisms in broiler processing plants. Appl. Microbiol. 12:179–185.

Larkin, E. P. 1973. The public health significance of viral infections of food animals. *In* B. C. Hobbs and J. H. B. Christian (eds.), The microbiological safety of foods. Academic Press, Inc., London.

Moulton, F. R. (ed.). 1942. Aerobiology. American Association for the Advancement of Science, Washington, D.C.

Mundt, J. O. 1961. Occurrence of enterococci: bud, blossom, and soil studies. Appl. Microbiol. 9:541–544.

Patterson, J. T. 1971. Microbiological assessment of surfaces. Food Technol. 6:63–72.

Samish, Z., R. Etinger-Tulczynska, and M. Bick. 1963. The microflora within the tissue of fruits and vegetables. J. Food Sci. 28:259–266.

Seligmann, R., and S. Rosenbluth. 1975. Comparison of bacterial flora on hands of personnel engaged in non-food and in food industries: a study of transient and resident bacteria. J. Milk Food Technol. 38:673–677.

Sinell, H. J. 1973. Food infection communicated from animal to man. *In* B. C. Hobbs and J. H. B. Christian (eds.), The microbiological safety of foods. Academic Press, Inc., London.

Sproul, O. T. 1973. Quality of recycled water: fate of infectious agents. J. Inst. Can. Sci. Technol. Aliment. 6:91–104.

Sunga, F. C. A., D. R. Heldman, and T. I. Hendrick. 1966. Characteristics of air-borne microorganism populations in packaging areas of a dairy plant. Mich. Agr. Exp. Stn. Q. Bull. 49.

Treanor, A. I. 1978. Water problems in the food industry. Chem. Ind. 11:431–437.

Troller, J. A. 1983. Sanitation in food processing. Academic Press, Inc., New York.

GENERAL PRINCIPLES UNDERLYING SPOILAGE: CHEMICAL CHANGES CAUSED BY MICROORGANISMS

FITNESS OR UNFITNESS OF FOOD FOR CONSUMPTION

When is a food fit to eat? According to Thom and Hunter (1924), "A product is fit for food if a discriminating consumer, knowing the story of its production and seeing the material itself, will eat it, and, conversely the same product is spoiled when such an examiner refuses it as food." According to this definition, the fitness of the food will depend on the person judging it, for what one person will eat another will not. Some of the British, for example, like their game meat "high," with a strong flavor developed by hanging, or aging, the meat, while most Americans would call this meat spoiled. The buried fish, titmuck, eaten by the Eskimos is a malodorous, semiliquid product that most of us would consider inedible. Starving people might eat food they would not consume under normal conditions.

Despite differences between individuals in their judgment of fitness of food, they would agree on certain criteria for assurance of fitness:

1 *The desired stage of development or maturity.* Fruits should be at a certain but differing stage of ripeness; sweet corn should be young enough to be tender and milky; poultry preferably is from birds that are fairly young.

2 *Freedom from pollution at any stage in production or handling.* Vegetables should not be consumed raw if they had been fertilized with sewage; oysters from waters contaminated with sewage should be rejected; food handled by dirty or diseased workers should be spurned; food contaminated by flies or rodents should be suspect.

3 *Freedom from objectionable change resulting from microbial attack or action of enzymes of the food.* Sometimes it is difficult to draw a line between spoilage by microorganisms and harmless growth, or the same type of change may be considered undesirable in one food and desirable in another. Thus the homemaker says that sour milk has spoiled, but the cultured buttermilk made by a lactic acid fermentation is good. Putrefaction in meat means definite spoilage, but putrefactive changes in Limburger cheese are normal to the ripening process. Some changes termed spoilage may be only changes in appearance or physical characteristics, as in wilted lettuce or flabby carrots, although the product probably has undergone no microbial spoilage and there has been little loss in nutritive value. Yet each one of us has his or her own idea about whether a food is spoiled and usually can come to a decision about its edibility without much difficulty.

CAUSES OF SPOILAGE

Decay or decomposition of an undesirable nature usually is implied when the term "spoiled" is applied to food, while food unfit to eat for sanitary reasons usually is not called spoiled. Spoilage may be due to one or more of the following:

1 Growth and activity of microorganisms (or higher forms occasionally). Often a succession of organisms is involved.

2 Insects.

3 Action of the enzymes of the plant or animal food.

4 Purely chemical reactions, i.e., those not catalyzed by enzymes of the tissues or of microorganisms.

5 Physical changes, such as those caused by freezing, burning, drying, pressure, etc.

The discussion to follow will be devoted chiefly to spoilage caused by microorganisms.

CLASSIFICATION OF FOODS BY EASE OF SPOILAGE

On the basis of ease of spoilage, foods can be placed in three groups:

1 *Stable or nonperishable foods.* These foods, which do not spoil unless handled carelessly, include such products as sugar, flour, and dry beans.

2 *Semiperishable foods.* If these foods are properly handled and stored, they will remain unspoiled for a fairly long period, e.g., potatoes, some varieties of apples, waxed rutabagas, and nutmeats.

3 *Perishable foods.* This group includes most important daily foods that spoil readily unless special preservative methods are used. Meats, fish, poultry, most fruits and vegetables, eggs, and milk belong in this classification.

Most foods fall into one of these three groups, but some are near enough to the borderline to be difficult to place.

FACTORS AFFECTING KINDS AND NUMBERS OF MICROORGANISMS IN FOOD

The kind of spoilage of foods by microorganisms and enzymes will depend on the *kinds* and *numbers* of these agents present and on the environment about them. Most raw foods contain a variety of bacteria, yeasts, and molds and may contain plant or animal enzymes as the case may be. Because of the particular environmental conditions, only a small proportion of the kinds of microorganisms present will be able to grow rapidly and cause spoilage—usually a single kind of organism but sometimes two or three types—and these may not have been predominant in the original food. If spoilage by the first organism or organisms is allowed to proceed, one or more other kinds of organisms are likely to produce secondary spoilage, or a further succession of organisms and changes may be involved.

The kinds and numbers of microorganisms that will be present on or in food will be influenced by the kind and extent of contamination, previous opportunities for the growth of certain kinds, and pretreatments which the food has received.

Contamination may increase numbers of microorganisms in the food and may even introduce new kinds. Thus wash water may incorporate surface-taint bacteria in butter; plant equipment may add spoilage organisms to foods during processing; washing machines may add them to eggs; and dirty boats may add them to fish. The increased "bioburden" of microorganisms, especially those which cause spoilage, makes preservation more difficult; i.e., spoilage is more likely and more rapid and perhaps takes a different form from that which would have appeared without the contamination.

Growth of microorganisms in or on the food obviously will increase numbers or the bioburden of microorganisms and presumably in most foods will bring about the greatest increase in the organisms most likely to be involved in spoilage. The heavier bioburden will add to the difficulty of preventing spoilage of the food and may influence the kind of spoilage to be anticipated.

Pretreatments of foods may remove or destroy some kinds of microorganisms, add organisms, or change the proportions of those present or inactivate part or all of the food enzymes and thus limit the number of spoilage agents and hence the possible types of spoilage. Washing, for example, may remove organisms from the surface or may add some from the wash water. If washing is by means of an antiseptic or germicidal solution, numbers of organisms may be greatly reduced and some kinds may be eliminated. Treatment with rays, ozone, sulfur dioxide, or germicidal vapors will reduce numbers and be selective of kinds. High temperatures will kill more and more organisms and leave fewer and fewer kinds as the heat treatment is increased. Storage under various conditions may either increase or decrease kinds and numbers. Any of these methods, as well as other treatments not mentioned, will influence the numbers, kinds, proportions, and health of the microorganisms.

FACTORS AFFECTING THE GROWTH OF MICROORGANISMS IN FOOD

Associative Growth

Associations of microorganisms with each other are involved in spoilage or fermentations of most kinds of food. Competition between the different kinds of bacteria, yeasts, and molds in a food ordinarily determines which one will outgrow the others and cause its characteristic type of spoilage. If conditions are favorable for all, bacteria usually grow faster than yeasts, and yeasts faster than molds. Therefore, yeasts outgrow bacteria only when they are predominant in the first place or when conditions are such as to slow the bacteria. Molds can predominate only when conditions are better for them than for yeasts or bacteria. The different kinds of bacteria present compete among themselves, with one kind usually outstripping the others. Likewise, if yeasts are favored, one kind usually will outgrow others; and among the molds one kind will find conditions more favorable than will other kinds. Microorganisms are not always antagonistic, or **antibiotic**, to each other, however, and may sometimes be **symbiotic**, i.e., mutually helpful, or they may grow simultaneously without seeming to aid or hinder each other. Two kinds of microorganisms may be **synergistic**; i.e., when growing together they may be able to bring about changes, such as fermentations, that neither could produce alone. *Pseudomonas syncyanea** growing alone in milk produces only a light-brownish tinge, and *Streptococcus lactis* causes no color change in milk; however, when the two organisms grow together, a bright blue color develops, resulting from a pH effect on the brown pigment produced by *P. syncyanea*.

A most important effect of a microorganism on another is the **metabiotic** one, which occurs when one organism makes conditions favorable for growth of the second. Both organisms may be growing at the same time, but more commonly one succeeds the other. Most natural fermentations or decompositions of raw foods illustrate metabiosis. Raw milk at room temperature normally first supports an acid fermentation by *Streptococcus lactis* and coliform bacteria until the bacteria are inhibited by the acid they have produced. Next the acid-tolerant lactobacilli increase the acidity further until they are stopped. Then film yeasts and molds grow over the top, finally reducing the acidity so that proteolytic bacteria can become active. Metabiosis in sauerkraut fermentation is discussed in Chapter 22. The normal succession of organisms is first, miscellaneous bacteria, chiefly coliform; second, *Leuconostoc mesenteroides;* third, *Lactobacillus plantarum;* and last, *Lactobacillus brevis*.

Effect of Environmental Conditions

The environment determines which of the different kinds of microorganisms present in a food will outgrow the others and cause its characteristic type of change or spoilage. The factors that make up this environment are interrelated and in combination determine the organisms that will grow and the effects to be produced. Chief among these factors are the physical and chemical properties of the food, the availability of oxygen, and the temperature.

Physical State and Structure of the Food   The physical state of the food, its colloidal nature, and whether it has been frozen, heated, moistened, or dried, together with its biological structure, may have an important influence on whether a food will spoil and the type of spoilage.

The *water* in food, its location, and its availability constitute one of the most important factors influencing microbial growth. Water may be considered both as a chemical compound necessary for growth and as part of the physical structure of the food.

The moisture requirements of molds, yeasts, and bacteria have been discussed in Chapter 1. It has been emphasized that all microorganisms require moisture for growth and that all grow best in the presence of a plentiful supply. This moisture must be *available* to the organisms, i.e., not tied up in any way, such as by solutes or by a hydrophilic colloid such as agar. Solutes such as salt and sugar dissolved in the water cause an osmotic pressure that tends to draw water from the cells if the concentration of dissolved materials is greater outside the cells than inside. It should be recalled that when the relative humidity of the air about the food corresponds to the available moisture or the water activity a_w of the food, the food and air about it will be in equilibrium in regard to moisture.

A dry food such as bread is most likely to be spoiled by molds; sirups and honey, with their fairly high sugar content and hence lowered a_w favor the growth of osmophilic yeasts; and moist, neutral foods such as milk, meats, fish, and eggs ordinarily are spoiled by bacteria. However, environmental factors other than moisture should be kept in mind in predicting the type of microorganism apt to cause spoilage. Grape juice, for example, may favor yeasts because of its fairly high sugar content and low pH but will support the growth of bacteria if incubation temperatures are too high or too low for fermentative yeasts. Refrigerated foods may mold in the presence of air but undergo bacterial spoilage in its absence. Honey, although its sugar content is too high for most yeasts but not for some of the molds, rarely is spoiled by molds because of fungistatic substances present.

An a_w as low as 0.70 makes unlikely any spoilage by microorganisms of a food held at room temperature. This is approximately the level of available moisture in dry milk at 8 percent total moisture, dried whole egg at 10 to 11 percent, flour at 13 to 15 percent, nonfat dry milk at 15 percent, dehydrated fat-free meat at 15 percent, seeds of leguminous crops at 15 percent, dehydrated vegetables at 14 to 20 percent, dehydrated fruits at 18 to 25 percent, and starch at 18 percent (Mossel and Ingram, 1955).

It is possible for microorganisms growing in food to change the level of available moisture by release of metabolic water or by changing the substrate so as to free water. In the production of ropiness in bread, for example, it is supposed that *Bacillus subtilis* causes the release of moisture as a result of the decomposition of starch and in this way makes conditions more favorable for its own growth. Destruction of moisture-holding tissues, as in fruits by molds, may make water available to yeasts or bacteria.

Freezing not only prevents microbial growth if the temperature is sufficiently low but also is likely to damage tissues, so that juices released on thawing favor microbial growth. Freezing also increases the concentration of solutes in the unfrozen portion as the temperature is lowered, slowing and finally stopping the growth of organisms able to grow at temperatures below 0 C. Freezing also effects the removal of water from hydrophilic colloids that is not wholly reabsorbed on thawing.

Heat processing may change not only the chemical composition of the food but also its structure by softening tissues; releasing or tying up moisture; destroying or forming colloidal suspensions, gels, or emulsions; and changing the penetrability of the food to moisture and oxygen. Protein may become denatured and therefore more available to some organisms than it was in the native state. Starch or protein may become gelated, releasing moisture and becoming more easily decomposed. For the reasons indicated, cooked food usually is more easily decomposed than is the original fresh food.

Changes in the colloidal constituents of foods may be caused by agencies other than the freezing or heating processes, e.g., by sound waves, but the results are similar. Emulsions of fat and water are more likely to spoil, and the spoilage will spread more rapidly when water is the continuous phase and fat the discontinuous one, as in French dressing, compared with butter, where the reverse is true.

The effect of the *biological structure* of food on the protection of foods against spoilage has been discussed in Chapter 1.

Chemical Properties of the Food   The chemical composition of a food determines how satisfactory it will be as a culture medium for microorganisms. Each organism has its own characteristic ability to utilize certain substances as a source of energy, a carbon source, and/or a source of nitrogen.

Properties of a food dictating the numbers and type of organisms that will grow in and possibly spoil a food have been discussed in Chapter 1 and include (1) pH, or hydrogen-ion concentration, (2) nutrient content, (3) moisture availability, (4) O-R potential, and (5) possible presence of inhibitory substances.

Temperature   Any nonsterile food is likely to spoil in time if it is moist enough and unfrozen. There is likelihood of spoilage at any temperature between −5 and 70 C. Since microorganisms differ so widely in their optimal, minimal, and maximal temperatures for growth, it is obvious that the temperature at which a food is held will have a great influence on the kind, rate, and amount of microbially induced change that will take place. Even a small change in temperature may favor an entirely different kind of organism and result in a different type of spoilage. Molds and yeasts, for the most part, do not grow well above 35 to 37 C and therefore would not be important in foods held at high temperatures. On the other hand, molds and yeasts grow well at ordinary room temperatures, and many of them grow fairly well at low temperatures, some even at freezing or slightly below. Although most bacteria grow best at ordinary temperatures, some (thermophiles) grow well at high temperatures and others (psychrophiles and psychrotrophs) at chilling temperatures. Therefore, molds often grow on refrigerated foods, and thermophilic bacteria grow in the hot pea blanchers. Raw milk held at different temperatures supports the initial growth of different bacteria. At temperatures near freezing, cold-tolerant bacteria, e.g., species of *Pseudomonas* and *Alcaligenes,* are favored; at room temperatures *Streptococcus lactis* and coliform bacteria usually predominate; at 40 to 45 C thermoduric species, e.g., *S. thermophilus* and *S. faecalis,* grow first; and at 55 to 60 C thermophilic bacteria such as *Lactobacillus thermophilus** will grow.

It should be kept in mind that the temperature at which a raw food is stored may affect its self-decomposition and therefore its susceptibility to microbial spoilage. As noted in Chapter 12, wrong storage temperatures for fruits weaken them and may make them more likely to spoil.

Temperatures commonly used in handling and storing foods, especially in the market and in the home, are very different in different countries. In this country, refrigeration of most perishable foods is the rule and keeping such foods at atmospheric temperatures for very long is the exception, but the reverse is true in many foreign lands. Therefore, the most commonly occurring type of spoilage of a food may be entirely different in different countries. In the United States, concern with spoilage of most perishable foods mostly concerns changes at chilling temperatures, and psychrotrophic strains of *Pseudomonas, Flavobacterium, Alcaligenes,* and other genera and certain yeasts and molds would be important. Where foods are not refrigerated customarily, the prevailing atmospheric temperatures of the area would be significant, and differences during the seasons of the year would have to be considered. During seasons or at times when the climate is temperate, ordinary mesophilic bacteria, yeasts, and molds would assume importance. During hot weather, 26.7 to 43 C and above, organisms favored by these temperatures would be important, such as coliform bacteria and species of *Bacillus, Clostridium, Streptococcus, Lactobacillus,* and other genera. Tropical temperatures would be unfavorable to most yeasts and molds. Under exceptional conditions, foods, especially canned varieties, sometimes are held at temperatures favoring thermophiles, as was often true during World War II, when canned foods were stored under tarpaulins in the tropics.

The combination of all of the factors just discussed and the kinds, numbers, and proportions of microorganisms present and their environment as controlled by physical and chemical properties of the food, oxygen tension and oxidation-reduction potential, and temperature will determine the kinds of microorganisms most likely to grow in a food and hence the changes to be produced. All these factors should be considered in making predictions regarding the stability of shelf life. Table 4-1 summarizes frequently employed processing modifications and their effect on the resulting keeping quality and on the microbial flora of major foods.

Examples will be cited throughout the chapters to follow on the spoilage of specific foods. Sometimes a change in only one of the factors mentioned will be enough to limit the change to be expected, but more often several factors exert a combined effect. Thus a combination of low moisture, refrigerator temperature, high acidity, and high sugar would make mold growth more likely than growth of yeasts or bacteria. But increasing the moisture content and the temperature would change conditions to favor yeasts, and decreasing the acidity and sugar content would encourage bacteria.

CHEMICAL CHANGES CAUSED BY MICROORGANISMS

Because of the great variety of organic compounds in foods and the numerous kinds of microorganisms that can decompose them, many different chemical changes are possible and many kinds of products can result. The following discussion is concerned only with the important types of decomposition of main constituents of foods and the chief products produced.

Changes in Nitrogenous Organic Compounds

Most of the nitrogen in foods is in the form of proteins which must be hydrolyzed by enzymes of the microorganisms or of the food to polypeptides, simpler peptides, or amino acids before they can serve as nitrogenous food for most organisms. Proteinases catalyze the hydrolysis of proteins to peptides, which may give a bitter taste to foods. Peptidases catalyze the hydrolysis of polypeptides to simpler peptides and finally to amino acids. The latter give flavors, desirable or undesirable, to some foods; e.g., amino acids contribute to the flavor of ripened cheeses.

For the most part these hydrolyses do not result in particularly objectionable products. Anaerobic decomposition of proteins, peptides, or amino acids, however, may result in the production of obnoxious odors and is then called **putrefaction**. It results in foul-smelling, sulfur-containing products, such as hydrogen, methyl, and ethyl sulfides and mercaptans, plus ammonia, amines (e.g., histamine, tyramine, piperidine, putrescine, and cadaverine), indole, skatole, and fatty acids.

When microorganisms act on amino acids, they may deaminate them, decarboxylate them, or both, resulting in the products listed in Table 4-2. *Escherichia coli,* for example, produces glyoxylic acid, acetic acid, and ammonia from glycine; *Pseudomonas* also produces methylamine and carbon dioxide; and clostridia give acetic acid, ammonia, and methane. From alanine these three organisms produce (1) an α-keto acid, ammonia, and carbon dioxide, (2) acetic acid, ammonia, and carbon dioxide, and (3) propionic acid, acetic acid, ammonia, and carbon dioxide, respectively. From serine, *E. coli* produces

TABLE 4-1
CLASSIFICATION OF THE MAJOR FOODS IN ORDER OF INCREASING MICROBIOLOGICAL KEEPING QUALITY

Class	"Processing" including heat treatment, compositional modification, and packing	Stability characteristic		Examples	Predominant microbial flora at retail
		Temp., C	Time of spoilage-free storage		
1	None of functional nature	<10	10–40 hr	Fresh meat, milk, fish, poultry, eggs, vegetables	Psychrotrophic, nonfermentative gram-negative rods
2	Pasteurization, followed by hermetic packing	<10	3 days to 2 weeks	Dairy products, sliced cured meat products	Sporing rods and Lancefield group D streptococci
3	Reduction of water activity to ca. 0.95, pH reduction and addition of preservatives, in combination with hermetic packing	<10	A few weeks	"Gaffelbitter" and similar semipreserved fish products	Lactobacilli, streptococci, yeasts and molds
4	Reduction of water activity to ca. 0.85, pH/a_w/lactic acid combinations of equivalent microbistatic effect, pasteurization	25	Many weeks	Condensed milk, mayonnaise, margarine, smoked sausage	Yeasts, molds
5	Reduction of water activity to ca. 0.80, sometimes in combination with pH reduction	25	Unlimited, i.e., until chemical reactions interfere	Shelf-stable products such as salami, stockfish, sauces	Molds
6	Reduction of water activity, to <0.60	35	Unlimited	Dehydrated foods	Bacilli, group D streptococci, mold spores
7	Appertization	35	Unlimited	Canned cured meat products and fruits	An occasional spore, i.e., counts of <10^2/g
8	Sterilization	Any	Unlimited	Canned milk, soups, meat, vegetables, and fish	None

Source: Mossel (1983).

77

TABLE 4-2
PRODUCTS FROM THE MICROBIAL DECOMPOSITION OF AMINO ACIDS

Chemical process	Products
Oxidative deamination	Keto acid + NH_3
Hydrolytic deamination	Hydroxy acid + NH_3
Reductive deamination	Saturated fatty acid + NH_3
Desaturation deamination (at α and β positions)	Unsaturated fatty acid + NH_3
Mutual O-R between pairs of amino acids	Keto acid + fatty acid + NH_3
Decarboxylation	Amine + GO_2
Hydrolytic deamination + decarboxylation	Primary alcohol + NH_3 + CO_2
Reductive deamination + decarboxylation	Hydrocarbon + NH_3 + CO_2
Oxidative deamination + decarboxylation	Fatty acid + NH_3 + CO_2

pyruvic acid and ammonia, and species of *Clostridium* give propionic acid, formic acid, and ammonia. As stated previously, the sulfur in sulfur-bearing amino acids may be reduced to foul-smelling sulfides or mercaptans. *Desulfotomaculum nigrificans* (formerly *C. nigrificans*), an obligate anaerobe, can reduce sulfate to sulfide and produces hydrogen sulfide from cystine.

Other nitrogenous compounds decomposed include (1) amides, imides, and urea, from which ammonia is the principal product, (2) guanidine and creatine, which yield urea and ammonia, and (3) amines, purines, and pyrimidines, which may yield ammonia, carbon dioxide, and organic acids (chiefly lactic or acetic).

Changes in Nonnitrogenous Organic Compounds

The main nonnitrogenous foods for microorganisms, mostly used to obtain energy but possibly serving as sources of carbon, include carbohydrates, organic acids, aldehydes and ketones, alcohols, glycosides, cyclic compounds, and lipids.

Carbohydrates Carbohydrates, if available, usually are preferred by microorganisms to other energy-yielding foods. Complex di-, tri-, or polysaccharides usually are hydrolyzed to simple sugars before utilization. A monosaccharide, such as glucose, aerobically would be oxidized to carbon dioxide and water and anaerobically would undergo decomposition involving any of six main types of fermentation: (1) an alcoholic fermentation, as by yeasts, with ethanol and carbon dioxide as the principal products, (2) a simple lactic fermentation, as by homofermentative lactic acid bacteria, with lactic acid as the main product, (3) a mixed lactic fermentation, as by heterofermentative lactic acid bacteria, with lactic and acetic acids, ethanol, glycerol, and carbon dioxide as the chief products, (4) the coliform type of fermentation, as by coliform bacteria, with lactic, acetic, and formic acids, ethanol, carbon dioxide, hydrogen, and perhaps acetoin and butanediol as likely products, (5) the propionic fermentation, by propionibacteria, producing propionic, acetic, and succinic acids and carbon dioxide, or (6) the butyric-butyl-isopropyl fermentations, by anaerobic bacteria, yielding butyric and acetic acids, carbon dioxide, hydrogen, and in some instances acetone, butylene glycol, butanol, and 2-propanol. A variety of other products are possible from sugars when different microorganisms are active, including higher fatty acids, other organic acids, aldehydes, and ketones.

Organic Acids   Many of the organic acids usually occurring in foods as salts are oxidized by organisms to carbonates, causing the medium to become more alkaline. Aerobically the organic acids may be oxidized completely to carbon dioxide and water, as is done by film yeasts. Acids may be oxidized to other, simpler acids or to other products similar to those from sugars. Saturated fatty acids or lower ketonic derivatives are degraded to acetic acid, two carbons at a time, aided by coenzyme A. Unsaturated or hydroxy fatty acids may be degraded partially in a similar manner but must be converted to a saturated acid (or ketonic derivative) for complete beta oxidation.

Other Compounds   Alcohols usually are oxidized to the corresponding organic acid, e.g., ethanol to acetic acid. Glycerol may be dissimilated to products similar to those from glucose. Glycosides, after hydrolysis to release the sugar, will have the sugar dissimilated characteristically. Acetaldehyde may be oxidized to acetic acid or reduced to ethanol. Cyclic compounds are not readily attacked.

Lipids   Fats are hydrolyzed by microbial lipase to glycerol and fatty acids, which are then dissimilated as outlined previously. Microorganisms may be involved in the oxidation of fats, but autooxidation is more common (see Chapter 19). Phospholipids may be degraded to their constituent phosphate, glycerol, fatty acids, and nitrogenous base, e.g., choline. Lipoproteins are made up of proteins, cholesterol esters, and phospholipids.

Pectic Substances   Protopectin, the water-insoluble parent pectic substance in plants, is converted to pectin, a water-soluble polymer of galacturonic acid which contains methyl ester linkages and varying degrees of neutralization by various cations. It gels with sugar and acid. Pectinesterase causes hydrolysis of the methyl ester linkage of pectin to yield pectic acid and methanol. Polygalacturonases destroy the linkage between galacturonic acid units of pectin or pectic acid to yield smaller chains and ultimately free D-galacturonic acid, which may be degraded to simple sugars.

BIBLIOGRAPHY

Allen, L. A. 1964. The biochemistry of industrial micro-organisms. Chem. Ind. May 23, pp. 877–880.

Barker, H. A. 1956. Bacterial fermentations. John Wiley & Sons, Inc., New York.

Dainty, R. H. 1971. The control and evaluation of spoilage. J. Food Technol. 6:209–224.

Desrosier, N. W. 1963. The technology of food preservation. Rev. ed. AVI Publishing Co., Inc., Westport, Conn.

Diendoerfer, F. H., R. I. Mateles, and A. H. Humphrey. 1963. 1961 fermentation process review. Appl. Microbiol. 11:272–303.

Goresline, H. E. 1955. Food spoilage and deterioration. *In* F. C. Blanck (ed.), Handbook of food and agriculture, chap. 13. Reinhold Publishing Corporation, New York.

Gunsalus, I. C., and R. Y. Stanier (eds.). 1961. The bacteria. Volume 2. Metabolism. Academic Press, Inc., New York.

Guthrie, R. K. (ed.). 1972. Food sanitation. AVI Publishing Co., Inc., Westport, Conn.

Halvorson, H. O. 1951. Food spoilage and food poisoning. *In* M. B. Jacobs (ed.), The chemistry and technology of food and food products, chap. 11. 2d ed. Interscience Publishers (Division of John Wiley & Sons, Inc.), New York.

Halvorson, H. O. 1953. Principles of food microbiology. J. Milk Food Technol. 16:73–76.

Hankin, L., and G. R. Stephens. 1972. What tests usefully predict keeping quality of perishable foods? J. Milk Food Technol. 35:574–576.

Jay, J. M. 1986. Modern food microbiology. 3d. ed. Van Nostrand Reinhold Company, New York.

Margalith, P., and Y. Schwartz. 1970. Flavor and microorganisms. Adv. Appl. Microbiol. 36–83.

Miller, B. M., and W. Litsky. 1976. Industrial microbiology. McGraw-Hill Book Company, New York.

Molin, N., and A. Erichsen. 1964. Microbial inhibitors in food. Almquist and Wiksell, Stockholm.

Mossel, D. A. A. 1983. Essentials and perspectives of microbail ecology of foods. *In* T. A. Roberts and F. A. Skinner (eds.), Food microbiology: advances and prospects. Academic Press, Inc., New York.

Mossel, D. A. A., and M. Ingram. 1955. The physiology of the microbial spoilage of foods. J. Appl. Bacteriol. 18:233–268.

Rainbow, C., and A. H. Rose (eds.). 1963. Biochemistry of industrial microorganisms. Academic Press, Inc., New York.

Schultz, H. W. (ed.). 1960. Food enzymes. AVI Publishing Co., Inc., Westport, Conn.

Scott, W. J. 1957. Water relations of food spoilage microorganisms. Adv. Food Res. 7:83–127.

Speck, R. V. 1981. Thermophilic organisms in food spoilage: sulfide spoilage anaerobes. J. Food Prot. 44:149–153.

Spencer, R. 1971. Microbial spoilage of foods. II. A review, 1969–1970. Br. Manuf. Ind. Res. Ass. Sci. Tech. Sur. 66, Surrey, England.

Thatcher, F. S., and D. S. Clark (eds.). 1968. Microorganisms in foods: their significance and methods of enumeration. University of Toronto Press, Toronto.

Thom, C., and A. C. Hunter. 1924. Hygienic fundamentals of food handling. The Williams & Wilkins Company, Baltimore.

Weiser, H. H., G. J. Mountney, and W. A. Gould. 1971. Practical food microbiology and technology. 2d ed. AVI Publishing Co., Inc., Westport, Conn.

TWO

PRINCIPLES OF FOOD PRESERVATION

In this section we outline the principles, especially those of a microbiological nature, involved in the various methods of food preservation.

As a result of improved methods of preservation and transportation, our diet has become more varied and better balanced, perishable foods have been made available year-round instead of only seasonally, the preparation of meals has been made easier, and foods in general are being produced in a cleaner and more sanitary manner than before. In addition, these improved methods of preservation and transportation have made it possible for countries with excesses in certain commodities to help needy countries by providing food supplements of high quality.

TWO

PRINCIPLES OF FOOD PRESERVATION

GENERAL PRINCIPLES OF FOOD PRESERVATION: ASEPSIS, REMOVAL, ANAEROBIC CONDITIONS

Foods for human consumption can be divided into eight main groups, four of plant and four of animal origin, and several lesser groups. The eight main classes of foods are as follows:

Foods from plants	Foods from animals
Cereals and cereal products	Meats and meat products
Sugar and sugar products	Poultry and eggs
Vegetables and vegetable products	Fish and other seafood
Fruits and fruit products	Milk and milk products

To the list of foods of plant origin could be added spices and other flavoring materials, nutmeats, and fungi grown for food (yeasts, molds, mushrooms, etc.). Sodium chloride is a mineral food, a flavoring material, an essential nutrient, and a chemical preservative. Some foods may be fortified with minerals, e.g., iron and calcium compounds added to flour. Some of the coloring and flavoring materials used in foods are synthetic. Vitamins usually are present in foods but may be added or consumed separately after chemical synthesis or production by microorganisms.

Most kinds of food are readily decomposed by microorganisms unless special methods are used for their preservation.

METHODS OF FOOD PRESERVATION

The chief methods of food preservation are as follows:

1 Asepsis, or keeping out microorganisms.

2 Removal of microorganisms.

3 Maintenance of anaerobic conditions, e.g., in a sealed, evacuated container.

4 Use of high temperatures.

5 Use of low temperatures.

6 Drying; this includes the tying up of water by solutes, hydrophilic colloids, etc.

7 Use of chemical preservatives, either developed by microorganisms or added.

8 Irradiation.

9 Mechanical destruction of microorganisms, e.g., by grinding, high pressures, etc. (not used industrially).

10 Combinations of two or more of the above methods. Only rarely is a single method effective, and usually several are combined. For example, canned foods are preserved by heat-processing them in an evacuated, sealed can. When preservative methods are combined, the required intensity of each usually is reduced to less than that for preservation by one agency alone. When benzoate or sorbate is added to fruit juices, less heat is required for sterilization of these products. If salt, sugar, and vinegar are all added to catsup, pickles, or relishes, each can be used at a lower concentration than if only one were added. Foods previously irradiated with gamma rays or treated with antibiotic tylosin require less heat for their sterilization than foods not so treated. Numerous other examples will be found in subsequent chapters.

PRINCIPLES OF FOOD PRESERVATION

In accomplishing the preservation of foods by the various methods, the following principles are involved:

1 Prevention or delay of microbial decomposition
   a By keeping out microorganisms (asepsis)
   b By removal of microorganisms, e.g., by filtration
   c By hindering the growth and activity of microorganisms, e.g., by low temperatures, drying, anaerobic conditions, or chemicals
   d By killing the microorganisms, e.g., by heat or radiation

2 Prevention or delay of self-decomposition of the food
   a By destruction or inactivation of food enzymes, e.g., by blanching
   b By prevention or delay of purely chemical reactions, e.g., prevention of oxidation by means of an antioxidant

3 Prevention of damage because of insects, animals, mechanical causes, etc., a subject beyond the scope of this text

The methods used to control the activities of microorganisms usually are effective against enzymatic activity in the food or chemical reactions. Methods such as drying and the use of low temperatures, however, permit autodecomposition to continue unless special precautions are taken. For example, most vegetables are blanched (heated) to inactivate their enzymes before being frozen.

Delay of Microbial Decomposition

Many common methods of food preservation depend not on the destruction or removal of microorganisms but on delay in the initiation of growth and hindrance to growth once it has begun.

A summary of the major preservation factors and their mode of action and achievement is presented in Table 5-1.

Growth Curve of Microbial Cultures   Whenever microorganisms are added to a food and conditions are favorable, the organisms will begin to multiply and will pass through a succession of phases. When counts of organisms are made periodically and the results are plotted with logarithms of numbers of organisms per milliliter as ordinates and time units as abscissas, a **growth curve** is obtained, as shown in Figure 5-1. This curve ordinarily is divided into phases

FIGURE 5-1
Growth curve. A to B, lag phase; B to C, phase of positive acceleration; C to D, logarithmic or exponential phase; D to E, phase of negative acceleration; E to F, maximal stationary phase; F to G, accelerated death phase; G to H, death phase; and H to I, survival phase.

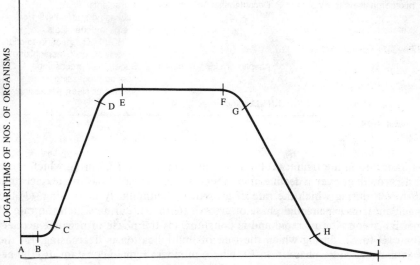

TABLE 5-1
CLASSIFICATION OF PRESERVATION FACTORS

Mode of action	Preservation factor	Mode of achievement
Inactivation of microorganisms	Heat	Pasteurization
		Sterilization
	Radiation	Radicidation
		Radurization
		Radappertization
Inhibition or slowing of growth of microorganisms	Cool	Chill
		Freeze
	Restrict water (reduce water activity)	Dry
		Add salt
		Add sugar
		Add glycerol
		Add other solutes or use combinations of the above
	Restrict oxygen	Vacuum pack
		Nitrogen pack
	Increase carbon dioxide	CO_2 pack
	Acidify	Add acids
		Lactic fermentation
		Acetic fermentation
	Alcohol	Fermentation
		Fortification
	Add preservatives	Inorganic (e.g., sulphite, nitrite)
		Organic (e.g., sorbate, benzoate, parabens, etc.)
		Antibiotics (e.g., nisin)
		Smoke
Restriction of access of microorganisms to product	Microstructure control	Emulsions (w/o)
	Decontamination	Ingredients
		Packaging materials, e.g., by chemicals (HCl, H_2O_2) heat, irradiation (ionizing or X; nonionizing)
	Aseptic or clean handling	Superclean processing
		Aseptic processing
		Aseptic or clean packaging
	Packaging	

Source: Gould et al. (1983).

as indicated in the figure: (1) the initial **lag phase** (*A* to *B*), during which there is no growth or even a decline in numbers, (2) the phase of **positive acceleration** (*B* to *C*), during which the rate of growth is continuously increasing, (3) the **logarithmic** or **exponential phase** of growth (*C* to *D*), during which the rate of multiplication is most rapid and is constant, (4) the phase of **negative acceleration** (*D* to *E*), during which the rate of multiplication is decreasing, (5) the **maximal stationary phase** (*E* to *F*), where numbers remain constant, (6) the ac-

celerated death phase (*F* to *G*), (7) the **death phase** or phase of decline (*G* to *H*), during which numbers decrease at a faster rate than new cells are formed, and (8) the **survival phase** (*H* to *I*), during which no cell division occurs but remaining cells survive on endogenous nutrients. With many bacteria (or other microorganisms) the numbers do not decrease at a fixed rate to zero, as indicated by the unbroken line in the figure, but taper off very gradually as low numbers are approached, as shown by the broken line, and a few viable cells remain for some time.

Applications to Food Preservation   Especially important in food preservation (i.e., prevention of spoilage) is the lengthening, as much as possible, of the lag phase and the phase of positive acceleration. This can be accomplished in different ways:

1 *By introducing as few spoilage organisms as possible,* i.e., by reducing the amount of contamination; the fewer organisms present, the longer the lag phase.

2 *By avoiding the addition of actively growing organisms* (from the logarithmic phase of growth). Such organisms might be growing on unclean containers, equipment, or utensils that come in contact with foods.

3 *By one or more unfavorable environmental conditions:* unfavorable food, moisture, temperature, pH, or O-R potential, or presence of inhibitors. The more unfavorable the conditions, the longer the delay of the initiation of growth.

4 *By actual damage to organisms by processing methods such as heating or irradiation.* Thus, for example, bacteria or their spores subjected to sublethal heat treatments have been found to require a better culture medium for growth than do the unheated organisms. Often a combination of methods for delaying the initiation of growth is enough to give a food the desired storage life.

From the growth curve, the generation time of the organisms, i.e., the time that elapses between the formation of a daughter cell and its division into two new cells, can be calculated. The generation time will be shortest during the logarithmic phase of growth, and its length will vary with the environmental conditions during growth, e.g., the type of food, its pH, temperature, O-R potential, available moisture, and presence of inhibitors. The generation time shortens as conditions become more favorable and lengthens as they become less favorable. Any change in the environment that will extend the generation time will more than proportionally lengthen the keeping time of the food. A drop in temperature, for example, will lengthen the generation time and hence the keeping time. If we start with a single cell, and if it divides every 30 min, there will be about 1 million cells in 10 hr but only about 1,000 cells if the generation time is 60 min and only 32 cells if it is 120 min. This emphasizes the importance of avoiding contamination of food with microorganisms that are in the logarithmic phase of growth, for when their generation time is the shortest, the lag phase will be brief or nonexistent and multiplication will proceed at its most rapid rate.

Prevention of Microbial Decomposition

Microbial decomposition of foods will be prevented if all spoilage organisms are killed (or removed) and recontamination is prevented. Merely stopping the multiplication of microorganisms, however, does not necessarily prevent decomposition, for viable organisms or their enzymes may continue to be active. As will be pointed out in later chapters, killing microorganisms by most agencies is easier when smaller initial numbers are present than with larger numbers; this reemphasizes the importance of contamination. Especially important is the introduction or building up of microorganisms resistant to the lethal agent being employed, for example, heat-resistant bacterial spores when foods are to be heat-processed. Vegetative cells of organisms in their logarithmic phase of growth are least resistant to lethal agencies, and they are more resistant in their late lag or maximal stationary phase of growth.

ASEPSIS

In nature there are numerous examples of asepsis, or keeping out microorganisms, as a preservative factor. The inner tissues of healthy plants and animals usually are free from microorganisms, and if any microorganisms are present, they are unlikely to initiate spoilage. If there is a protective covering about the food, microbial decomposition is delayed or prevented. Examples of such coverings are the shells of nuts, the skins of fruits and vegetables, the husks of ear corn, the shells of eggs, and the skin, membranes, or fat on meat or fish. It is only when the protective covering has been damaged or decomposition has spread from the outer surface that the inner tissues are subject to decomposition by microorganisms.

In the food industries an increasing amount of attention is being given to the prevention of the contamination of foods, from the raw material to the finished product. The food technologist is concerned with the "bioburden" of microorganisms on or in a food and considers both kinds and numbers of organisms present. The *kinds* are important in that they may include spoilage organisms, those desirable in a food fermentation, or even pathogenic microorganisms. The *numbers* of microorganisms are important because the more spoilage organisms there are, the more likely food spoilage will be, the more difficult will be the preservation of food, and the more likely will be the presence of pathogens. The bioburden may be the result of contamination, growth of organisms, or both. The quality of many kinds of foods is judged partly by the numbers of microorganisms present. Following are some examples of the importance of aseptic methods in food industries.

Packaging of foods is a widely used application of asepsis. The covering may range from a loose carton or wrapping, which prevents primarily contamination during handling, to the hermetically sealed container of canned foods, which, if tight, protects the processed contents from contamination by microorganisms.

In the dairy industry, contamination with microorganisms is avoided as much as is practicable in the production and handling of market milk and milk for other purposes, and the quality of the milk is judged by its bacterial content.

In the canning industry the bioburden, or load, of microorganisms determines the heat process necessary for the preservation of a food, especially if the contamination introduces heat-resistant spoilage organisms, such as spore-forming thermophiles that may come from equipment; and the sealed can prevents recontamination after the heat treatment.

In the meat-packing industry sanitary methods of slaughter, handling, and processing reduce the load and thus improve the keeping quality of the meat or meat products.

In industries involving controlled food fermentation, e.g., in cheese making, the fewer the competing organisms in the fermenting material, the more likely the success of the fermentation.

REMOVAL OF MICROORGANISMS

For the most part the removal of microorganisms is not very effective in food preservation, but under special conditions it may be helpful. Removal may be accomplished by means of filtration, centrifugation (sedimentation or clarification), washing, or trimming.

Filtration is the only successful method for the complete removal of organisms, and its use is limited to clear liquids. The liquid is filtered through a previously sterilized "bacteriaproof" filter made of sintered glass, diatomaceous earth, unglazed porcelain, membrane pads, or similar material, and the liquid is forced through by positive or negative pressure. This method has been used successfully with fruit juices, beer, soft drinks, wine, and water.

Centrifugation, or sedimentation, generally is not very effective, in that some but not all of the microorganisms are removed. Sedimentation is used in the treatment of drinking water but is insufficient by itself. When centrifugation (clarification) is applied to milk, the main purpose is not to remove bacteria but to take out other suspended materials, although centrifugation at high speeds removes most of the spores.

Washing raw foods can be helpful in their preservation but may be harmful under some conditions. Washing cabbage heads or cucumbers before their fermentation into sauerkraut and pickles, respectively, removes most of the soil microorganisms on the surface and in this way increases the proportion of desirable lactic acid bacteria in the total flora. Washing fresh fruits and vegetables removes soil organisms that may be resistant to the heat process during the canning of these foods. Obviously the removal of organisms and of food for them from equipment coming into contact with foods, followed by a germicidal treatment of the apparatus, is an essential and effective procedure during the handling of all kinds of foods. Washing foods may be dangerous if the water adds spoilage organisms or increases the moisture so that growth of spoilage organisms is encouraged.

Trimming away spoiled portions of a food or discarding spoiled samples is important from the standpoint of food laws and may be helpful in food preservation. Although large numbers of spoilage organisms are removed in this way, heavy contamination of the remaining food may take place. Trimming the outer leaves of cabbage heads is recommended for the manufacture of sauerkraut.

MAINTENANCE OF ANAEROBIC CONDITIONS

A preservative factor in sealed, packaged foods may be the anaerobic conditions in the container. A complete fill, evacuation of the unfilled space (the head space in a can), or replacement of the air by carbon dioxide or by an inert gas such as nitrogen will bring about anaerobic conditions. Spores of some of the aerobic spore-formers are especially resistant to heat and may survive in canned food but be unable to germinate or grow in the absence of oxygen. Production of carbon dioxide during fermentation and accumulation at the surface will serve to make conditions anaerobic there and prevent the growth of aerobes.

BIBLIOGRAPHY

Aschehoug, V., and R. Vesterhus. 1941. The microbiology of food perservation. Zentralbl. Bakteriol. Parasitenkd., II Abt. 104:169–185.

Bate-Smith, E. C., and T. N. Norris (eds.). 1952. A symposium on quality and preservation of foods. Cambridge University Press, London.

Desrosier, N. W. 1970. The technology of food preservation. 3d ed. AVI Publishing Co., Inc., Westport, Conn.

Farrel, J., and A. Rose. 1967. Temperature effects on microorganisms. Annu. Rev. Microbiol. 21:101–120.

Fellers, C. R. 1955. Food preservation. In F. C. Balnck (ed.), Handbook of food and agriculture, chap. 11. Reinhold Publishing Corporation, New York.

Gould, G. W., M. H. Brown, and B. C. Fletcher. 1983. Mechanisms of action of food preservation procedures. In T. A. Roberts and F. A. Shinner (eds.), Food microbiology: advances and prospects. Academic Press, Inc., New York.

Jay, J. M. 1986. Modern food microbiology. 3d ed. Van Nostrand Reinhold Company, New York.

Lechtman, S. C., and O. Fanning (eds.). 1957. The future of food preservation. Midwest Research Institute, Kansas City.

Nickerson, J. T., and A. T. Sinskey. 1972. Microbiology of foods and food processing. American Elsevier Publishing Company, New York.

Pike, M. 1964. Food science and technology. John Murray (Publishers), Ltd., London.

Stumbo, C. R. 1976. Thermobacteriology in food processing. Academic Press, Inc., New York.

PRESERVATION BY USE OF HIGH TEMPERATURES

The killing of microorganisms by heat is supposed to be caused by the denaturation of the proteins and especially by the inactivation of enzymes required for metabolism. The heat treatment necessary to kill organisms or their spores varies with the kind of organism, its state, and the environment during heating. Depending on the heat treatment employed, only some of the vegetative cells, most or all of the cells, part of the bacterial spores, or all of them may be killed. The heat treatment selected will depend on the kinds of organisms to be killed, other preservative methods to be employed, and the effect of heat on the food.

FACTORS AFFECTING HEAT RESISTANCE (THERMAL DEATH TIME)

Cells and spores of microorganisms differ widely in their resistance to high temperatures. Some of these differences are the result of factors that can be controlled, but others are characteristic of the organisms and cannot always be explained. There are differences in heat resistance within a population of cells or spores, as illustrated by the frequency distribution curve in Figure 6-1. A small number of cells have low resistance (points A to B); most of the cells have a medium resistance (points B to C); and a small number have high resistance (points C to D). Conditions of growth may favor one or the other of these groups, and, by selection, cultures that are more or less heat-resistant than usual can be produced.

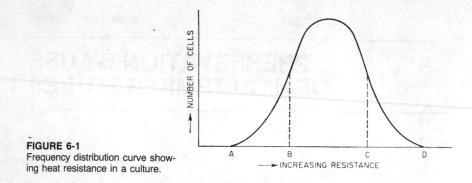

FIGURE 6-1
Frequency distribution curve showing heat resistance in a culture.

Certain factors are known to affect the heat resistance of cells or spores and must be kept in mind when microorganisms are compared and when heat treatments for the destruction of an organism are considered. The chief known factors are as follows:

1 *The temperature-time relationship.* The time for killing cells or spores under a given set of conditions decreases as the temperature is increased. This is illustrated in Table 6-1 by the results of Bigelow and Esty (1920) with 115,000 spores of flat sour bacteria per milliliter in corn juice at pH 6.1
2 *Initial concentration of spores (or cells).* The more spores or cells present, the greater the heat treatment necessary to kill all of them. Bigelow and Esty heated spores of a thermophile from spoiled canned food in corn juice at pH 6.0 at 120 C, with the results shown in Table 6-2.
3 *Previous history of the vegetative cells or spores.* The conditions under which the cells have been grown and spores have been produced and their treatment thereafter will influence their resistance to heat.

TABLE 6-1
EFFECT OF TEMPERATURE OF HEATING ON TIME
NEEDED TO KILL SPORES OF FLAT SOUR BACTERIA

Temperature, C	Thermal death time, or time to destroy all spores, min
100	1,200
105	600
110	190
115	70
120	19
125	7
130	3
135	1

Source: Bigelow and Esty (1920).

TABLE 6-2
EFFECT OF INITIAL NUMBERS OF SPORES ON TIME REQUIRED
TO KILL THEM

Initial concentration of spores, number/ml	Thermal death time, or time required to kill all spores, min at 120 C
50,000	14
5,000	10
500	9
50	8

Source: Bigelow and Esty (1920).

a *Culture medium.* The medium in which growth takes place is especially important. The effect of the nutrients in the medium, their kind, and the amount vary with the organism, but in general the better the medium for growth, the more resistant the cells or spores. The presence of an adequate supply of accessory growth factors usually favors the production of heat-resistant cells or spores. This probably is why vegetable infusions and liver extract increase heat resistance. According to Curran (1935), spores formed and aged in soil or oats are more resistant than those in broth or agar. Carbohydrates, amino acids, and organic acid radicals have an effect, but it is difficult to predict. A small amount of glucose in a medium may lead to increased heat resistance, but more sugar may result in the formation of enough acid to cause decreased heat resistance. Some salts seem to have an effect; phosphate and magnesium ions, for instance, are said to decrease the heat resistance of bacterial spores produced in a medium containing them. Prolonged exposure to metabolic products reduces the heat resistance of cells and spores.

b *Temperature of incubation.* The temperature of growth of cells and the temperature of sporulation influences their heat resistance. In general, resistance increases as the incubation temperature is raised toward the optimum for the organism and for many organisms increases further as the temperature approaches the maximum for growth. *Escherichia coli,* for example, is considerably more heat-resistant when grown at 38.5 C, which is near its optimal temperature, than at 28 C. Spores of *Bacillus subtilis,* grown at different temperatures in 1 percent peptone water, were heated with the results shown in Table 6-3.

c *Phase of growth or age.* The heat resistance of vegetative cells varies with the stage of growth and of spores with their age. Bacterial cells show their greatest resistance during the late lag phase but almost as great resistance during their maximum stationary phase, followed by a decline in resistance (see Chapter 5). The cells are least resistant during their phase of logarithmic growth. Very young (immature) spores are less resistant than are mature ones. Some spores increase in resistance during the first weeks of storage but later begin to decrease in resistance.

TABLE 6-3
EFFECT OF TEMPERATURE
OF FORMATION OF
SPORES OF *BACILLUS
SUBTILIS* ON THEIR HEAT
RESISTANCE

Temperature of incubation, C	Time to kill at 100 C, min
21–23	11
37 (optimum)	16
41	18

Source: Williams (1929).

TABLE 6-4
EFFECT OF pH ON HEAT
RESISTANCE OF SPORES
OF *BACILLUS SUBTILIS*

pH	Time of survival, min
4.4	2
5.6	7
6.8	11
7.6	11
8.4	9

Source: Williams (1929).

d *Desiccation.* Dried spores of some bacteria are harder to kill by heat than are those kept moist, but this apparently does not hold for all bacterial spores.

4 *Composition of the substrate in which cells or spores are heated.* The material in which the spores or cells are heated is so important that it must be stated if a thermal death time is to have meaning.

a *Moisture.* Moist heat is a much more effective killing agent than dry heat, and as a corollary dry materials require more heat for sterilization than moist ones. In the bacteriological laboratory about 15 to 30 min at 121 C in the moist heat of an autoclave will effect sterilization of ordinary materials, but 3 to 4 hr at 160 to 180 C is necessary when the dry heat of an oven is employed. Spores of *Bacillus subtilis* are killed in less than 10 min in steam at 120 C, but in anhydrous glycerol 170 C for 30 min is required.

b *Hydrogen-ion concentration* (pH). In general, cells or spores are most heat-resistant in a substrate that is at or near neutrality. An increase in acidity or alkalinity hastens killing by heat, but a change toward the acid side is more effective than a corresponding increase in alkalinity. Spores of *B. subtilis* heated at 100 C in 1:15 *m* phosphate solutions, adjusted to various pH values, gave the results shown in Table 6-4. Other examples will be given in the discussion of the heat processing of canned foods.

Cameron (1940) divided canned foods into the **acid food**, the pH values of which are below 4.5, and the **low-acid foods**, with a pH above 4.5. Acid foods include the common fruits and certain vegetable products, and the low-acid foods are those such as meat, seafood, milk, and most of the common vegetables. A further subdivision was suggested by Cameron (1940).

(1) Low-acid foods, with a pH above 5.3, including such foods as peas, corn, lima beans, meats, fish, poultry, and milk (although Cameron included only vegetables and fruits in his original grouping).

(2) Medium-acid foods, with a pH between 5.3 and 4.5, including such foods as spinach, asparagus, beets, and pumpkin.

(3) **Acid foods**, with a pH between 4.5 and 3.7, including such foods as tomatoes, pears, and pineapple.

(4) **High-acid foods,** with a pH of 3.7 and below, including such foods as berries and sauerkraut.

The effect of the pH of the substrate is complicated by the fact that heating at high temperature causes a decrease in the pH of low- or medium-acid foods; and the higher the original pH, the greater the drop in pH caused by heating. Foods with an original pH of less than 5.5 to 5.8 change little in acidity as a result of heating.

c *Other constituents of the substrate.* The only salt present in appreciable amounts in most foods is sodium chloride, which in low concentrations has a protective effect on some spores.

Sugar seems to protect some organisms or spores but not others. The optimal concentration for protection varies with the organism: it is high for some osmophilic organisms and low for others, high for spores and low for non osmophilic cells. The protective effect of sugar may be related to a resulting decrease in a_w. A reduced a_w does result in an increase in observed heat resistance.

Solutes differ in their effect on bacteria. Glucose, for example, protects *Escherichia coli* and *Pseudomonas fluorescens* against heat better than sodium chloride at a_w levels near the minimum for growth. On the other hand, glucose affords practically no protection or is even harmful to *Staphylococcus aureus,* whereas sodium chloride is very protective.

Since the concentration of solutes may affect the heat process necessary for sterilization, canners sometimes further classify foods as high-soluble-solids foods, such as sirups and concentrates, and low-soluble-solids foods, such as fruits, vegetables, and meats.

Colloidal materials, especially proteins and fats, are protective against heat. This is well illustrated in Table 6-5 by the data of Brown and Peiser (1916) who used *thermal death points.*

TABLE 6-5
EFFECT OF PROTECTIVE SUBSTANCES ON HEAT
RESISTANCE OF BACTERIA

Substance	Temperature, C		
	S. lactis	E. coli	L. bulgaricus
Cream	69–71	73	95
Whole milk	63–65	69	91
Skim milk	59–63	65	89
Whey	57–61	63	83
Broth	55–57	61	

It will be observed that as the content of protective substances (proteins and fat) decreased in the media, the temperature needed to kill the organism in 10 minutes decreased.
Source: Brown and Peiser (1916).

Antiseptic or germicidal substances in the substrate aid heat in the destruction of organisms. Thus hydrogen peroxide plus heat is used to reduce the bacterial content of sugar and is the basis of a process for milk.

HEAT RESISTANCE OF MICROORGANISMS AND THEIR SPORES

The heat resistance of microorganisms usually is expressed in terms of their **thermal death time**, which is defined as the time it takes at a certain temperature to kill a stated number of organisms (or spores) under specified conditions. This sometimes is referred to as the **absolute thermal death time** to distinguish it from the **majority thermal death time** for killing most of the cells or spores present and the **thermal death rate**, expressed as the rate of killing. **Thermal death point**, now used little, is the temperature necessary to kill all the organisms in 10 min.

The reports of different workers on the comparative heat resistance of various kinds of yeasts, molds, and bacteria and their spores do not entirely agree because of differences between the cultures used and the conditions during heating. Therefore, only generalizations will be made, with the results of some workers cited as examples.

Heat Resistance of Yeasts and Yeast Spores

The resistance of yeasts and their spores to moist heat varies with the species and even the strain and, of course, with the substrate in which they are heated. In general the ascospores of yeasts need only 5 to 10 C more heat for their destruction than the vegetative cells from which they are formed. Most ascospores are killed by 60 C for 10 to 15 min; a few are more resistant, but none can survive even a brief heating at 100 C. Vegetative yeasts usually are killed by 50 to 58 C for 10 to 15 min. Both yeasts and their spores are killed by the pasteurization treatments given milk (62.8 C for 30 min or 71.7 C for 15 sec), and yeasts are readily killed in the baking of bread, where the temperature of the interior reaches about 97 C.

Heat Resistance of Molds and Mold Spores

Most molds and their spores are killed by moist heat at 60 C in 5 to 10 min, but some species are considerably more heat-resistant. The asexual spores are more resistant than ordinary mycelium and require a temperature 5 to 10 C higher for their destruction in a given time. Many species of *Aspergillus* and some of *Penicillium* and *Mucor* are more resistant to heat than are other molds; a very heat resistant mold on fruits is *Byssochlamys fulva* (Paecillomyces), with resistant ascospores. The pasteurizing treatments given milk usually kill all molds and their spores, although spores of some aspergilli, not commonly found in milk, could survive such a heat process.

Sclerotia are especially difficult to kill by heat. Some can survive a heat treatment of 90 to 100 C for a brief period and have been known to cause spoilage in canned fruits. It was found that 1,000 min at 82.2 C or 300 min at 85 C was necessary to destroy sclerotia from a species of *Penicillium*.

Mold spores are fairly resistant to dry heat. Data from various workers indicate that dry heat at 120 C for as long as 30 min will not kill some of the more resistant spores.

Heat Resistance of Bacteria and Bacterial Spores

The heat resistance of vegetative cells of bacteria varies widely with the species, from some of the delicate pathogens that are easily killed to thermophiles that may require several minutes at 80 to 90 C. A few general statements can be made about the heat resistance of vegetative cells of bacteria: (1) cocci usually are more resistant than rods, although there are many notable exceptions, (2) the higher the optimal and maximal temperatures for growth, the greater the resistance to heat is likely to be, (3) bacteria that clump considerably or form capsules are more difficult to kill than those which do not, (4) cells high in lipid content are harder to kill than are other cells.

A few examples of thermal death times of bacterial cells are shown in Table 6-6.

It should be kept in mind that these thermal death times (and those to be given later for spores) are for various concentrations of cells (or spores), heated in different substrates, and might be higher or lower under other conditions.

The heat resistance of bacterial spores varies greatly with the species of bacterium and the conditions during sporulation. Resistance at 100 C may vary from less than 1 min to over 20 hr. In general, spores from bacteria with high optimal and maximal temperatures for growth are more heat-resistant than those from bacteria growing best at lower temperatures. Or a sporeformer growing with another of higher heat resistance may have increased resistance, e.g.,

TABLE 6-6
THERMAL DEATH TIMES OF BACTERIAL CELLS

Bacterium	Time, min	Temperature, C
Neisseria gonorrhoeae	2–3	50
Salmonella typhi	4.3	60
Staphylococcus aureus	18.8	60
Escherichia coli	20–30	57.3
Streptococcus thermophilus	15	70–75
Lactobacillus bulgaricus*	30	71

TABLE 6-7
THERMAL DEATH TIMES OF BACTERIAL SPORES

Spores of	Time to kill at 100 C, min
Bacillus anthracis	1.7
Bacillus subtilis	15–20
Clostridium botulinum	100–330
Clostridium calidotolerans*	520
Flat sour bacteria	Over 1,030

Clostridium perfringens growing with *C. sporogenes*. Examples of thermal death times of bacterial spores are given in Table 6-7.

Heat Resistance of Enzymes

Although most food and microbial enzymes are destroyed at 79.4 C, some may withstand higher temperatures, especially if high-temperature–short-time heating is employed.

One of the goals of a thermal process (Witter, 1983) is to inactivate enzymes that can cause product deterioration during storage. Generally, thermal processes designed to inactivate microorganisms will also inactivate enzymes of concern. There are, however, notable exceptions. For example, some hydrolases (proteinases and lipases) will retain a substantial level of activity after an ultrahigh-temperature process. The residual activity of these enzymes may spoil the processed product during long-term storage. Another enzyme, bovine phosphatase, is actually used as a "monitor" in the pasteurization of milk. Detection of the bovine enzyme in processed milk usually indicates that the milk was not properly pasteurized. False positives are possible if high levels of microbial phosphatase are present.

DETERMINATION OF HEAT RESISTANCE
(THERMAL DEATH TIME)

A complete description of all the procedures and apparatus used in the determination of the heat resistance of bacterial spores is beyond the scope of this text. For a discussion of methods used in suspending and heating spores and the various apparatus employed see Nickerson and Sinskey (1972). Also, a very complete discussion of all aspects of thermal resistance determinations can be found in the National Canners Association Manual (1968).

The simple glass-tube method of Esty and Meyer (1922) for the determination of thermal death time will be outlined, and only brief mention will be made of the more involved methods used by canning laboratories. In the tube method a quantity of standardized spore (or cell) suspension in a buffer solution or a food liquor is sealed in small glass tubes, which are heated in a bath thermostatically controlled at a selected temperature. Tubes are removed periodically, cooled immediately, and either incubated directly or subcultured into anappropriate medium for incubation to test for the growth of survivors. A brief outline of the method follows.

Preparation of the Spore (or Cell) Suspension

Several bacteria are used as "test organisms," depending on the process employed (Table 6-8). The organisms to be tested are grown in a culture medium, at a temperature and for a period of time that will produce resistant spores (or cells). They are washed off from solid media or centrifuged from liquid media, usually are washed, and are made into a suspension. Care must be taken to break up or remove clumps, or the results will be irregular. This is accomplished by shaking with glass beads or sand or by filtration through cotton, gauze, filter paper, etc. Sometimes spore suspensions are reincubated for 24 hr to complete sporulation. Spore suspensions then are pasteurized to kill the vegetative cells which might have a protective effect. Next the number of spores (or cells) per unit volume of suspension is determined by a cultural or direct counting method. This stock suspension is diluted in the heating medium to the desired concentration of spores or cells for the test and distributed in 1-ml portions in glass vials, which are sealed and refrigerated. The medium in which the cells or spores are to be heated may be a buffered phosphate solution or food or food liquor. The volume of suspension of organisms added should be small (1 to 2·percent) to avoid changing the composition of the heating substrate. A concentration of approximately 1 million (1×10^6) cells or spores per milliliter or gram is recommended.

Heating to Determine the Thermal Death Time

The heating of the vials is done in an agitated and thermostatically controlled bath of oil for higher temperatures or water for temperatures below 100 C. Tubes

TABLE 6-8
BACTERIA USED AS TEST ORGANISMS

Bacteria used	Processing or test purpose
Clostridium sporogenes (P.A. 3679)	Inoculated pack studies
Bacillus subtilis var. niger* (syn. B. globigii, ATCC 9372)	Hot air and ethylene oxide studies
Bacillus pumilus (ATCC 27142)	Cobalt or gamma radiation sterilization
Bacillus stearothermophilus (ATCC 7953)	Steam sterilization
Bacillus subtilis (ATCC 6633)	Steam sterilization

are heated at one temperature for varying intervals of time. The following precautions are taken:

1 The vials are brought to a definite temperature before introduction into the bath, usually at 0 C, obtained in a bath of ice water. An arbitrary preheating time, for example, 30 sec, is allowed before timing begins. Vials of resistant spores sometimes are preheated to 100 C in boiling water before being introduced into the bath.

2 When an oil bath is used, vials are wiped dry before their introduction and are carefully sealed, for water will cause foaming of the oil.

3 If many iced vials are introduced at the same time, an allowance is made for the cooling effect on the bath.

4 The multiple-tube method should be used if accuracy is desired. At least five replicate vials should be used in exploratory runs, and twenty-five to thirty when tubes are being removed at short intervals. The fewer the number of replicates, the more likely the occurrence of "skips," i.e., killing after a certain period, followed by survival after a longer heating period.

5 Cooling should be prompt and rapid and usually is done in ice water.

Test for Viability (Survival)

If the substrate in which the heating is done is a good culture medium for the organism and if the organism can grow anaerobically, the vials can be incubated to test for the growth of survivors. Otherwise, the contents of the vial are subcultured into a good culture medium, which is incubated under optimal conditions for the organism. If the number of survivors is desired, a quantitative count is made by the agar plate or another cultural method. The composition of the medium used to test for survival is very important, since the spores or cells that have been exposed to drastic heat treatments may be more exacting in their nutritive requirements than the spores or cells before heating.

Instead of vials, the American Can Company laboratories use special flat cans that can be evacuated, sealed, and then heated and cooled in small steam sterilizers. Workers in the laboratories of the National Food Processors Association use a unit with valves which allows the withdrawal of samples periodically under aseptic conditions. This technique is useful in the determination of thermal death rates. Several of these procedures have been illustrated by Lopez (1981).

THERMAL DEATH TIME (TDT) CURVES

One method for obtaining data and plotting TDT curves is referred to as the **growth–no-growth method**. An example of data that might be obtained by this procedure using a series of six tubes or vials at each time interval is presented in Table 6-9. At a heating temperature of 110 C for 110 min none of six tubes contained survivors, but there were survivors following 80 min of heating. Thus

TABLE 6-9
THERMAL DEATH TIME DATA

Temperature	Corrected heating time, min	Number of samples	
		Heated	Positive
110 C (230 F)	25	6	6
	40	6	6
	60	6	6
	80	6	5
	110	6	0
	140	6	0
115.6 C (240 F)	10	6	6
	14	6	6
	18	6	6
	22	6	2
	28	6	0
	36	6	0
121 C (250 F)	3	6	6
	4	6	6
	5.5	6	2
	7.5	6	0
	10	6	0
	13	6	0

Source: Condensed from National Canners Association (1968). Data on PA 3679 in strained peas.

for these specific conditions (number of spores, heating menstruum, etc.) the thermal death time at 110 C is greater than 80 min but less than or equal to 110 min.

If the TDT values from Table 6-9 are plotted on semilogarithmic paper, the curve in Figure 6-2 results. Temperature is plotted as arithmetic values, and time in minutes as logarithms or on a logarithmic scale. In this example a single line (line A) is drawn above all the survivor points and below all the destruction points. Alternatively, all the survivor points are connected with a line and all the destruction points are connected with a line. Then the average of the slope of these two lines is drawn as a single line.

The classical endpoint method of Bigelow and Esty (1920) is quite similar except that in this approach survival is attained in only one of several tubes when heated at each temperature. For example, in their original work a spore population of 6×10^9 per tube was used, and heating continued until only one tube out of ten contained one or more survivors. For practical purposes, this represents a population of 6×10^{10} being reduced to perhaps 1. The time required can arbitrarily be used as the TDT. The TDTs can be plotted as above, and a TDT curve can be obtained.

A third approach to constructing a TDT curve is first to obtain death rate curves or survivor curves at several temperatures. For example, if during heating of a spore population, counts of survivors are made at various time inter-

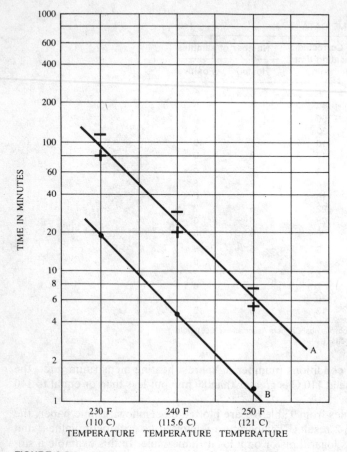

FIGURE 6-2
TDT curve from data in Table 6-9.

vals, a survivor curve can be drawn. As represented in Figure 6-3, the number of survivors is plotted on the logarithmic scale and time is plotted on the arithmetic scale. The line is the death rate curve. The symbol D is used for the decimal reduction time, i.e., that time of heating at a temperature to cause a 90 percent reduction in the count of viable spores (or cells). This is the time for the survivor curve to traverse one logarithmic cycle. In the hypothetical curves of Figure 6-3, D equals 10 min. For a given spore suspension a TDT curve can be constructed if the D values at several temperatures are known. Thus, one plots D values (minutes) on the logarithmic scale of semilogarithmic paper and degrees Fahrenheit on the arithmetic scale. A line drawn through these points would represent a TDT curve. Actually, this line should be referred to as a "phantom" TDT curve since it has the slope but not the exact position when

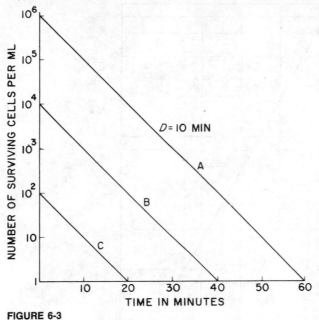

FIGURE 6-3
Hypothetical survivor curves.

compared with points plotted from complete destruction times for a particular concentration of spores. Line *B* in Figure 6-2 is drawn from *D* values of the data obtained from the experiment used to plot line *A*.

Whether an endpoint method or a growth-no-growth method is used or *D* values, TDTs are plotted to give a TDT curve like that in Figure 6-4 for flat sour spores from the data in Table 6-1. The straight line indicates that the order of death by heat is logarithmic, in other words, that the death rate is constant. From the straight line obtained or an extension of it, TDTs for temperatures and times not listed can be estimated. The slope of the line is termed the *z* value and is the interval in temperature, in degrees Fahrenheit, required for the line to pass through one logarithmic cycle on the semilogarithmic paper. In other words, *z* represents the degrees Fahrenheit required to reduce the TDT tenfold. The *z* value can also be expressed in degrees Celsius but should be stated as *z* C. *F* is the time in minutes required to destroy the organism in a specified medium at 250 F (121.1 C). The uncorrected *z* value from Figure 6-4 is 19, and the *F* value[1] is 16.4 min. These values will vary with the heat resistance and concentration of the test organism and with the medium in which it is heated. From the *z* and *F* values, process times can be calculated.

[1] The symbol F_0 is used to express the *F* value when *z* equals 18; the *z* values for many of the more resistant spore-forming bacteria, and hence those important in canning, often approximate 18, and therefore this value often is used when food processing times are to be calculated.

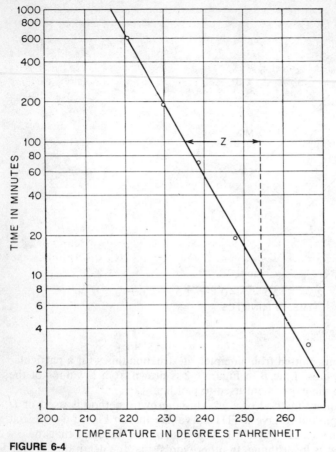

FIGURE 6-4
TDT curve for spores of flat sour bacteria; 115,000 spore per milliliter in corn at pH 6.1 ($z = 19$).

12D CONCEPT

The "classical" values or TDT runs with spores of *C. botulinum* are those of Esty and Meyer (1922). The total number of spores used in their experiments was 6.0×10^{10}, which they reduced to 0.1 spore during heating at 250 F (121 C). Although their TDTs were based on complete destruction of this population, the value 12*D* or 12-logarithmic-cycle reduction is customarily assumed from their TDT curve. A TDT at 250 F of 2.78 min was obtained from Esty and Meyer's curve. Townsend et al. (1938) recalculated the data, considering lag times, and arrived at an *F* value of 2.45 min at 250 F for *Clostridium botulinum* type A. The slope of this TDT curve is based on a *z* value of 18 F (actually 17.6 F); therefore, *F* values at other temperatures can be obtained from the line.

As a safety measure, the canning industry has recommended a 12D heat treatment for *C. botulinum* spores in low-acid foods, i.e., enough heat or process lethality to reduce 10^{12} spores to one spore per milliliter. In reality, starting populations would never approach 1×10^{12} spores per milliliter or gram; therefore, 12D reflects processing to extreme fractions of a spore or one spore surviving in one can among an extremely large number of cans processed (Figure 6-5). Stumbo (1964) presented an illustration of the 12D concept as follows: assuming that D has a value of 0.21 min for *C. botulinum* at 250 F and that each can of food contains one spore, a process at 250 F for 2.52 min would reduce *C. botulinum* spores to one spore in 10^{12} cans. This can be shown mathematically as follows:

$$F_0 = D_{250}(\log a - \log b)$$
$$= 0.21 \,(\log 1 - \log 10^{-12})$$
$$= 0.21 \times 12 = 2.52$$

When it is considered that processes employed commercially usually exceed this F_0 value (treatments of $F_0 = 6.0$ to 8.0 are not unusual) to eliminate the

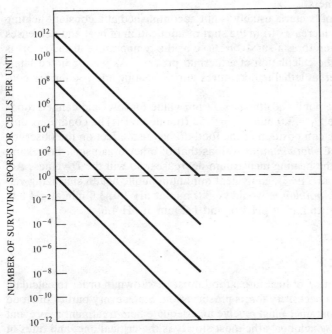

FIGURE 6-5
Extrapolation of hypothetical survivor curves illustrating a 12D or 12-log-cycle reduction.

more heat-resistant thermophilic sporeformers, an additional safety margin is realized. The 12D concept is therefore somewhat arbitrary but universally used. The understanding of D values and length of time to reduce a given population when a given D value is known or assumed can be further clarified by consulting Figure 6-3.

As shown, the larger the initial number of cells or spores, the longer it will take to reduce the numbers to one per milliliter. With the D value of 10 min, as in the figure, this would require 60 min if the initial number of spores was 1 million per milliliter and only 20 min with 100 spores. After 80 min theoretically there would be 0.01 spore per milliliter, or 1 spore per 100 ml of heating medium. The concept of processing to result in fractions of a spore per unit or one spore in a total of many units is also illustrated in Figure 6-5. Survivor curves are not always the straight lines indicated in the figure. Convex curves have been attributed to the clumping of cells or spores or to the ability of injured cells to repair a certain amount of damage.

It has been assumed that concave curves are the result of unequal resistance among cells or spores. There may be a shoulder at the start of the curve, indicating slower inactivation of cells or spores, or there may be a tailing off when numbers have been reduced greatly, indicating a few cells or spores more resistant than the others.

Actually death of bacteria usually is not accomplished at a constant heating temperature, for it increases from the start of application of heat and decreases during cooling. Therefore, a survivor curve at the temperature of the retort is not sufficient for the calculation of a thermal process. As will be noted later, lethal rates at different lethal temperatures during heating and cooling are considered.

A minimum safe public health sterilization value for low-acid canned foods is considered to be $F_0 = 3.0$ min ($F_0 = 2.52$ rounded off). The conditions during heating and the composition of the food do have an effect on the observed heat resistance of *C. botulinum* as well as that of other organisms. For example, as the pH of the heating menstruum decreases, so will the D values. According to Pflug et al. (1985), equivalent minimum public health sterilizing values at 250 F for *C. botulinum* would be 3.0 min at pH 7.0, 3.0 min at pH 6.0, 2.3 min at pH 5.5, 1.6 min at pH 5.0, and 1.2 min at pH 4.6.

HEAT PENETRATION

The rate of penetration of heat into a food must be known in order to calculate the thermal process necessary for its preservation. Since every part of the food in a can or other container must receive an adequate heat treatment to prevent spoilage, that part which heats the most slowly is the critical one, and rates of change in the temperature of that part—usually near the center of containers of foods heating by conduction and farther down when heating is by convection—are measured.

Heat penetration from an external source to the center of the can may take place by conduction, where heat passes from molecule to molecule; by convection, where heat is transferred by movement of liquids or gases; or, as is usually the case, by a combination of conduction and convection. Conduction is slow in foods and rapid in metals. The rate of heat transfer by convection depends on the opportunity for currents in the liquid and the rate of flow of these currents.

When both conduction and convection are involved in the heating of foods, they may function simultaneously or successively. When solid particles of food are suspended in a liquid, the particles heat by conduction and the liquid heats by convection. Some foods change in consistency during heating, and a broken heating curve results. This is true of sugar sirups, brine-packed whole-grain corn, and certain thick soups and tomato juices.

The factors that determine the time required to bring the center of the container of food up to the sterilizing temperature are as follows:

1 *The material of which the container is made.* Glass has a slower rate of heat penetration than a metal can.
2 *The size and shape of the container.* The larger a can is, the longer it will take to reach a given temperature at the center because the distance to the center of the larger can is greater and it has less surface per volume or weight. Hence, larger cans are heated longer proportionally but not to as high a temperature at the center. Of course, the shape of the can determines the radius; a long, slim cylindrical can will heat faster than will the same volume in a compact cylindrical form.
3 *Initial temperature of the food.* Actually the temperature of the food in a can when it goes into the retort (steam sterilizer) makes practically no difference in the time required for the center of the can to reach the retort temperature, for a food at a low initial temperature heats faster than the same food at a higher initial temperature. However, the food with the higher starting temperature is in the lethal range for the microorganisms for a longer time, and its average temperature during heating is higher than the food in the can with a lower initial temperature. A high initial temperature is important in processing canned foods that heat slowly, such as cream-style corn, pumpkin, and meat.
4 *Retort temperature.* Replicate cans of food placed in retorts of different temperatures reach the respective temperatures at practically the same time; however, fastest heating would take place in the hottest retort, and the food would reach lethal temperatures most rapidly.
5 *Consistency of can contents and size and shape of pieces.* All of these are important in their effect on heat penetration. The size and kind of pieces of food and what happens to them during cooking warrant their division into three classes.
   a *Pieces that retain their identity,* i.e., do not cook apart. Examples are peas, plums, beets, asparagus, and whole-grain corn. If the pieces are small and in brine, as with peas, heating is almost as in water. If the pieces are large,

heating is delayed, because the heat must penetrate to the center of the pieces before the liquor can reach the retort temperature. Large beets or large stalks of asparagus heat more slowly than small ones.

b *Pieces that cook apart and become mushy or viscous.* These heat slowly, because heat penetration becomes mostly by conduction rather than convection. This takes place in cream-style corn, squash, pumpkin, and sweet potatoes.

c *Pieces that layer.* Asparagus layers vertically; hence, convection currents travel mostly up and down. Spinach layers horizontally, producing a "baffle-board effect," which interferes with convection currents. Layering is greatly affected by the degree of fill of the can.

Consistency of the can contents is affected by some of the sauces added. Tomato sauce on baked beans slows down heat penetration more than plain sauce does. Starch interferes increasingly as the concentration is raised toward 6 percent, but further increases in starch have little additional effect. Sodium chloride never is added in high enough concentrations to have an appreciable effect on rates of heating. The rate of heat penetration decreases with increasing concentrations of sugar, but this effect is counteracted somewhat by the marked decrease in the viscosity of sugar solutions, even heavy ones, with increase in temperature.

6 *Rotation and agitation.* Rotation or agitation of the container of food during heat processing will hasten heat penetration if the food is at all fluid, but it also may cause undesirable physical changes in some foods. It makes comparatively little difference in the process time of foods that allow free convection currents and have very small particles, such as peas. On the other hand, agitation is very helpful with foods that layer, such as spinach, tomatoes, and peach halves. With older equipment it is not practical to roll cans faster than 10 to 12 rpm, but newer methods of end-over-end rotation permit higher speeds. Rotation is used successfully with canned evaporated milk, and shaking is used with foods in the form of pastes or purees. A process for brined, whole-kernel corn employs heating in a continuous cooker of high-boiling liquid with the can contents mixed by being on the periphery of a rotating reel or by rotation on rollers.

The *cooling* operation involves the same principles of heat transfer as the heating process. Rapid, artificial cooling is recommended because it can be well controlled. Cooling that is too slow may cause overcooking of the food and may permit the growth of thermophiles.

DETERMINATION OF THERMAL PROCESSES

The following data are needed for the calculation of thermal processes for a canned food: (1) the TDT curve for the most heat-resistant organism likely to be present in the food; in low-acid foods this usually would be for the spores of a thermophile, e.g., the flat sour organism, and (2) the heat penetration and cooling curves for the food in the size and type of container to be used. One of three methods is used to determine the heat process: (1) the graphical method, (2) the formula method, or (3) the nomogram method.

By each of these methods **equivalent processes** can be calculated, i.e., heat processes that effect the same killing of microorganisms in the food.

The principle is similar for all three of the methods for the calculation of thermal processes, but since the graphical method is the simplest to explain, it will be outlined and the others will be only briefly mentioned.

General Method for Calculation of Process Time

To calculate the time in minutes t necessary to destroy a certain number of test organisms (or spores) in a given container of a food by heating at the temperature T, knowing the values for z and F, the following equations are employed (t/F = time to destroy organism at temperature T if $F = 1$; F/t = lethal rate at T):

$$\frac{\log t - \log F}{\log 10 \ (= 1)} = \frac{250 - T}{z}$$

Then

$$\log \frac{t}{F} = \frac{250 - T}{z} \quad \text{and} \quad \frac{t}{F} = \text{antilog} \ \frac{250 - T}{z}$$

or

$$t = F \ \text{antilog} \ \frac{250 - T}{z}$$

The Graphical Method

Briefly, the graphical method, as described by Bigelow et al. (1920), is as follows:

1 The TDT curve for the most resistant spoilage organism likely to be encountered is determined in the food being canned. TDTs from this curve are converted to **lethal rates** for the various heating temperatures. The lethal rate for a temperature is the reciprocal of the TDT; thus, if it takes 400 min at 210 F to kill all the spores in a food, the lethal rate is $1/400 = 0.0025$.

2 The heat-penetration (and cooling) curve for the food and can size involved is determined.

3 Lethal rates for the different temperatures at the center of the can during the length of the heating and cooling process are plotted on the heat-penetration (and cooling) curve, as is illustrated in Figure 6-6. In this figure lethal rates are 0.01 unit per side of a square, and the times are 10 min per side of a square. An

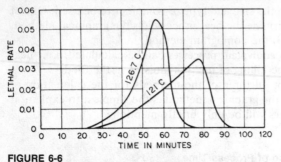

FIGURE 6-6
Equivalent lethality curves with retort at 126.7 C and 121 C.
Corn in no. 2 cans; 50,000 spores per milliliter.

area equal to ten squares under the lethality curve is unity, which means that destruction of all of the spores (or cells) has been accomplished. If this area is less than ten squares, the process is inadequate; if more than ten squares, it is greater than needed. The area beneath the curve is measured by means of a planimeter. In Figure 6-6 the heat treatment for 56 min at 126.7 C was found to be adequate, and for 78 min at 121 C.

The Formula Method

The formula method applies data from the TDT and heat-penetration curves to an equation, by means of which the thermal process is calculated mathematically. For details of this method see Ball and Olson (1957).

The Nomogram Method

The nomogram method is the most rapid one for the estimation of thermal process times. It involves the application of the data on TDTs and heat penetration to a graphic representation of these numerical relations and has an advantage over the previously described methods in that the "coming-up time" of the steam pressure sterilizers is considered. The original article by Olson and Stevens (1939) should be consulted for a description of this method.

Regardless of the method used for the calculation of thermal process times, they are verified by actual tests on canned food. An experimental pack is inoculated with a known concentration of spores of the resistant spoilage organism. These cans and uninoculated controls are processed for several time intervals near that calculated for the temperature chosen, are incubated to test for spoilage, and are subcultured to test for sterility. Usually a margin of safety is allowed beyond the minimal treatment for killing the spores being tested when recommendations are made concerning a thermal process time. It should be kept in mind that the processes recommended will be successful only for the concentration of spores used and might not take care of gross contamination beyond that level.

HEAT TREATMENTS EMPLOYED IN PROCESSING FOODS

The temperature and time used in heat-processing a food will depend on what effect heat has on the food and what other preservative methods are to be employed. Some foods, such as milk and peas, can be heated to only a limited extent without undesirable changes in appearance or loss in palatability, whereas others, like corn or pumpkin, can undergo a more rigorous heat treatment without marked change. The greater the heat treatment, the more organisms will be killed, up to the heating that will produce sterility of the product. If not all the organisms are killed, either the heating must destroy all potential spoilage organisms or the food must be handled thereafter so as to delay or prevent the growth of surviving spoilage organisms. In canning, an attempt is made to kill all organisms that could spoil the food during later handling; in pasteurization, most of the spoilage organisms are killed but others survive and must be inhibited by low temperatures or some other preservative method if spoilage is to be prevented. The various degrees of heating used on foods might be classified as (1) pasteurization, (2) heating at about 100 C, and (3) heating above 100 C.

Pasteurization

Pasteurization is a heat treatment that kills part but not all of the microorganisms present and usually involves the application of temperatures below 100 C. The heating may be by means of steam, hot water, dry heat, or electric currents, and the products are cooled promptly after the heat treatment. Pasteurization is used (1) when more rigorous heat treatments might harm the quality of the product, as with market milk, (2) when one aim is to kill pathogens, as with market milk, (3) when the main spoilage organisms are not very heat resistant, such as the yeasts in fruit juices, (4) when any surviving spoilage organisms will be taken care of by additional preservative methods to be employed, as in the chilling of market milk, and (5) when competing organisms are to be killed, allowing a desired fermentation, usually by added starter organisms, as in cheese making.

Preservative methods used to supplement pasteurization include (1) refrigeration, e.g., of milk, (2) keeping out microorganisms, usually by packaging the product in a sealed container, (3) maintenance of anaerobic conditions, as in evacuated, sealed containers, (4) addition of high concentrations of sugar, as in sweetened condensed milk, and (5) presence or addition of chemical preservatives, e.g., the organic acids on pickles.

Times and temperatures used in the pasteurizing process depend on the method employed and the product treated. The high-temperature–short-time (HTST) method employs a comparatively high temperature for a short time, whereas the low-temperature–long-time, or holding (LTH), method uses a lower temperature for a longer time. Some examples follow of pasteurizing treatments given various types of foods. The minimal heat treatment of market milk is at 62.8 C for 30 min in the holding method; at 71.7 C for at least 15 sec in the HTST method; and at 137.8 C for at least 2 sec in the ultrapasteurized method. One basis for the selection of this treatment is the thermal resistance of the rickettsia responsible for Q fever, *Coxiella burnetti,* an organism that may be transmitted by milk. The heat treatment often is greater when milk is to be used for other purposes, but it sometimes is slighted in cheese making, in which event the cheese should be aged, as is raw-milk cheese. Ice cream mix is pasteurized at various temperatures for different times, usually receiving a greater heat treatment than market milk. For example, ice cream mix may be heated at 71.1 C for 30 min or at 82.2 C for 16 to 20 sec. Grape wines may be pasteurized for 1 min at 82 to 85 C in bulk, whereas fruit wines sometimes are heated to 62.8 C or over and bottled hot. Beer may be pasteurized at 60 C or above, the time varying with the temperature. Dried fruits usually are pasteurized in the package at 65.6 to 85 C for 30 to 90 min, the treatment varying with the kind of fruit and the size of the package. The pasteurizing treatment given fruit juices depends on their acidity and whether they are in bulk or in the bottle or can. Recommended for bottled grape juice is 76.7 C for 30 min or flash treatment in bulk at 80 to 85 C, and for apple juice 60 C if bottled and 85 to 87.8 C for 30 to 60 sec in bulk. The average heat treatment for carbonated juices would be 65.6 C for 30 min. When vinegar is pasteurized in the bottle in a water bath, all the vinegar is brought to at least 65.6 C. If flash-pasteurized, the vinegar is heated so as to be at 65.6 to 71.1 C when the bottle is closed. When pasteurized in bulk, the vinegar is held at 60 to 65.6 C for 30 min.

Heating at about 100 C

Formerly, home canners processed all foods for varying lengths of time at 100 C or less. This treatment was sufficient to kill everything but bacterial spores in the food and often was sufficient to preserve even low- and medium-acid foods. Now, however, most home canners use pressure cookers for the less acid foods. Many acid foods can be processed successfully at 100 C or less, for example, sauerkraut and highly acid fruits. A temperature of approximately 100 C is obtained by boiling a liquid food, by immersion of the container of food in boiling water, or by exposure to flowing steam. Some very acid foods, e.g., sauerkraut, may be preheated to a temperature somewhat below 100 C, packaged hot, and not further heat-processed. Blanching fresh vegetables before freezing or drying involves heating briefly at about 100 C.

During **baking**, the internal temperature of bread, cake, or other bakery products approaches but never reaches 100 C as long as moisture is present, although the oven is much hotter. The temperature of unsealed canned goods heated in the oven cannot exceed the boiling temperature of the liquid present. As will be indicated subsequently, bacterial spores that survive the baking of bread (maximal temperature about 97 C) may cause ropiness. **Simmering** is incipient or gentle boiling, with the temperature about 100 C.

In **roasting** meat the internal temperature reaches only about 60 C in rare beef, up to 80 C in well-done beef, and 85 C in a pork roast. **Frying** gets the outside of the food very hot, but the center ordinarily does not reach 100 C. **Cooking** is an indefinite term with little meaning. In the food industry, however, the term "cook" implies a specific time and temperature for a thermal process. **Warming up** a food may mean anything from a small increase in temperature up to heating to 100 C.

Heating above 100 C

Temperatures above 100 C usually are obtained by means of steam under pressure in steam-pressure sterilizers or retorts. The temperature in the retorts increases with rising steam pressures. Thus with no pressure the temperature at sea level is 100 C; with 5 lb of pressure, 109 C; with 10 lb, 115.5 C; and with 15 lb, 121.5 C. When liquid foods are to be sterilized before their introduction into sterile cans, high steam pressures are used to apply a high temperature for a few seconds.

Milk can be heated to temperatures up to 150 C by use of steam injection or steam infusion followed by "flash evaporation" of the condensed steam and rapid cooling. Processes such as this for milk have been referred to as ultrahigh-temperature, or UHT, processes. With sufficient holding times on the order of several seconds, the process would "sterilize" the milk.

Heat treatments used in the processing of canned foods will be discussed further in the following section.

Canning

Canning is defined as the preservation of foods in sealed containers and usually implies heat treatment as the principal factor in the prevention of spoilage. Most canning is in "tin cans," which are made of tin-coated steel, or in glass containers, but increasing use is being made of containers that are partially or wholly of aluminum, of plastics as pouches or solid containers, or of a composite of materials. Therefore, the word "canning" is a general term and is often replaced by "hermetically sealed containers."

Spallanzani in 1765 preserved food by heating it in a sealed container. Other workers, as well, had employed heat processes in attempts to prevent the spoilage of food, but it remained for a Frenchman, Nicolas Appert, who has been called the "father of canning," to experiment on the heating of foods in sealed containers and to publish directions for preservation by canning. His work, mostly in the years 1795 to 1810, was prompted by the offer of a prize by the French government for a published method for preserving foods for the armed forces. Appert won the 12,000 francs in 1809 for a treatise that was published a year later under the name The Book for All Households; or the Art of Preserving Animal and Vegetable Substances for Many Years. Appert gave exact directions for the preservation of a wide variety of foods in cork-stoppered, wide-mouthed glass bottles, which he heated for hours in boiling water. Nothing was known at the time about the relationship of microorganisms to the spoilage of foods, yet Appert worked out methods that were good enough to be followed for years after by home and commercial canners, who referred to the process as "Appertization".

Succeeding improvements in the canning process have been chiefly in methods of heat processing, in the construction of the container, and in the calculation of the heat processes required. From the time of Appert until 1850, canners heat-processed food much as he did, although there was much secrecy about actual times used. About 1850 European workers began using baths of oil, salt brine, or calcium chloride solution to obtain temperatures above 100 C, and in 1860 Solomon introduced the use of the calcium chloride bath in this country, reducing process times from 5 to 6 hr to $\frac{1}{2}$ hr and aiding in the canning of food during the American Civil War. Experiments on the use of steam under pressure for heat processing were conducted by Appert and his descendants, but the method was dangerous because of the lack of safety devices. Schriver, a Philadelphia canner, is credited with the development of the closed and controlled retort in this country and received a patent for it in 1874. Equipment for the rotation or agitation of containers during processing has been developed within the past quarter century and applied to various foods. High-temperature–short-time methods of heating, such as the Martin process, have received increased attention.

Appert's original container, the cork-stoppered, wide-mouthed glass jar, was used in much of the early canning. The tin canister, abbreviated by Americans to "tin can," was patented by Peter Durand in England in 1810 and has been used increasingly since that time. The first cans were crudely made by hand with soldered seams and small openings in the tops. It took an expert to make 60 to 70 cans per day; modern machines can turn out 300 to 400 per minute. The modern sanitary, or open-top, can, with its double-crimped top and crimped side seam, was developed during the last few years of the nineteenth century; since then there have been improvements in gaskets and sealing compounds.

Most modern cans are made of steel plate coated with tin. The trend is toward a thinner and more even coating of tin. **Enamels** are coated onto flat sheets of plate before the manufacture of cans to prevent or slow discoloration or corrosion. Sanitary, or standard, enamel is used for cans for highly colored fruits and berries or for beets to prevent the fading of color caused by tin plate. C enamel contains zinc oxide, so that the white ZnS is formed instead of the dark FeS when low-acid, sulfur-bearing foods such as corn are canned, and darkening of the interior of the can is thus avoided. This enamel is not usable for meat, for the fat would loosen and flake the enamel. Special enamels are employed for certain products, e.g., milk, meats, wine and beer, soups and entrees, and some fruit juices.

Glass containers are used for the canning of many foods and have been greatly improved since the days of Appert.

Aluminum containers are available but do not as yet withstand strong mechanical stresses and therefore are used mostly for products that do not require high vacuums or high-temperature processing, e.g., beer, frozen fruits, frozen juice concentrates, and cheese. Ends of fiber or metal containers sometimes are made of aluminum, as is the easy-opening device on beer cans; and some foods, e.g., for astronauts, are placed in collapsible aluminum tubes.

Flexible pouches or bags, made of plastic or of plastic laminated with foil, are being employed mostly for packaging frozen, dried, or unprocessed foods. They are also used for foods that can be packaged hot, although steam-pressure sterilization of foods in pouches has been accomplished. Pressurized canned foods will be discussed subsequently.

The Canning Procedure

The general procedures in the canning of food will be mentioned only briefly here. A reference on food technology or canning such as Lopez (1981) should be consulted for technical details. Raw food for canning should be freshly harvested, properly prepared, inspected, graded if desired, and thoroughly washed before introduction into the can. Many vegetable foods are **blanched** or scalded briefly by hot water or steam before packaging. The blanching washes the food further, "sets" the color, softens the tissues to aid packing, helps form the vacuum, and kills some microorganisms. A brine, consisting of salt solution or salt plus sugar, is added to some canned vegetables; and sugar sirups may be added to fruits. The container is evacuated before sealing, usually by heating the head space, or unfilled part of the container, but often by mechanical means.

The Heat Process

Methods for the calculation of heat processes for canned foods have been discussed earlier in this chapter. The canner aims for complete sterilization of most foods but does not always attain it. Instead of killing all microorganisms in the food, the canner may kill all that could spoil the food under normal conditions of storage and may leave some that are unable to grow, making the can of food "commercially sterile," "practically sterile," or "bacterially inactive."

The heat processes necessary for the preservation of canned foods depend on the factors that influence the heat resistance of the most resistant spoilage organism and those which affect heat penetration. The Research Laboratory of the National Food Processors Association publishes bulletins that recommend minimal heat processes for various foods in different sizes of glass or metal containers. (Low-acid foods are treated in Bull. 26-L.)

With higher retort temperatures the times would be shorter, and the processes would vary with the varieties of food canned, the sauces used, the can size and shape, the initial temperature of the food, and other factors. The process time for food consisting of a mixture of discrete particles and a finely divided component in water or brine can be shortened by means of the "Strata-Cook" process. The components, e.g., creamed, whole-grain corn and brine, are stratified in the container and kept separated during heating. This method takes advantage of the fact that small differences in the water content of a food heating by conduction do not have much effect on the rate of heat penetration and that a thin layer of such food will heat faster than a thicker one. Starch that does not coagulate also aids in heat penetration. Table 6-10 shows that foods with loose liquor require less heat than solidly packed ones. Acid foods require less heat than those nearer neutrality. Some very acid foods, such as sauerkraut, may be packed hot and require no further heating. Some foods, e.g., globe artichokes, that can be damaged by high temperatures are acidified and then processed at lower temperatures.

The heating ordinarily is done in retorts, with or without steam pressure as the food demands. HTST heat processes, now used for some fluid foods, require special equipment for sterilizing the food in bulk, sterilizing the containers and lids, and filling and sealing the sterile containers under aseptic conditions. The Dole process is an example of the HCF, or heat-cool-fill, method. In the Martin HTST Sterile Canning System, mixed liquid and solid pieces are heated directly by contact with high-temperature steam before aseptic canning. When a particular heat-resistant spoilage organism is feared, an HTST treatment may be given a liquid food before canning, followed by a milder heat treatment of the food in the can. Thus tomato juice may be presterilized at 121 to 132 C to kill spores of *Bacillus coagulans* before canning, and then the sealed

TABLE 6-10
PROCESS TIMES RECOMMENDED FOR SOME VEGETABLES
IN CAN SIZE 307 × 409

Food	Temperature, C		Minutes at retort temperature
	Minimum initial	Retort	
Asparagus spears (tips down, in brine)	48.9	115.6	26
Beans, lima (in brine)	48.9	115.6	36
Beans in heavy sauce	60.0	115.6	115
Corn, cream style	60.0	115.6	105
Corn, whole kernel (in brine)	60.0	115.6	46
Potatoes, sweet, solid pack	65.6	115.6	100
Pumpkin	60.0	115.6	86

Source: Condensed from National Canners Association Research Laboratory Bulletin 26-L, 1976.

cans of juice are given a milder heating. In the SC, or sterilizing and closing, process, sterilization of the food is accomplished before the can is sealed. In the PFC, or pressure-filler-cooker, method, the food is sterilized by high-pressure steam and filled into the can; then the can is sealed and the heat processing is continued as long as necessary before cooling. In dehydrocanning, e.g., of apple slices, the food is dried to about half its original weight before canning.

Other ways of heating cans are by means of a direct gas flame, by steam injection, by heating in a fluidized bed of granular solids, and by the hydrostatic sterilizer, which consists of a vertical tank with conveyors that carry cans down through a water leg, up into live steam, and then up and out through a second water leg. In the "Flash 18" method, canning is done in a high-pressure (18-psi) chamber. The product is given an HTST treatment to bring it to processing temperature, and the cans are filled, closed, and partially cooled in the chamber.

Heat is also being combined with other preservative agencies, e.g., antibiotics, irradiation, or chemicals, e.g., hydrogen peroxide. To date, most of this work has been experimental.

Pressurized Packaged Foods

Pressurized packaged liquids or pastes, called aerosols, are packed under pressure of a propellant gas, usually carbon dioxide, nitrogen, or nitrous oxide, so as to dispense the food as a foam, spray, or liquid. Many foods are now being so packaged, e.g., whipped cream and other toppings, beverage concentrates, salad dressings, condiments, oils, jellies, and flavoring substances. The pressurized foods are subject to microbial spoilage unless adequate preservative methods are employed. Acid foods may be heated, canned, and then gassed, but the gassing process may contaminate the food. Aseptic canning is a possibility for low- and medium-acid foods. Process requirements for pasteurized foods, e.g., whipped cream and other toppings, are similar with or without gas pressure. The gas used as a propellant may have an influence on the kinds of organisms likely to grow. Nitrogen, for example, would not inhibit aerobes if a little oxygen were present, but carbon dioxide would be inhibitory under the same condition. Carbon dioxide under pressure inhibits many microorganisms, including aerobic bacteria and molds, but does not inhibit lactic acid bacteria, *Bacillus coagulans, Streptococcus faecalis,* or yeasts. Nitrous oxide represses some fungi.

The Cooling Process

Following the application of heat, the containers of food are cooled as rapidly as is practicable. The cans may be cooled in the retort or in tanks by immersion in cold water or by a spray of water. Glass containers and large cans are cooled more gradually to avoid undue strain or even breakage. This tempering process involves the use of warm water (or spray), the temperature of which is lowered as cooling progresses. Final cooling of containers usually is by means of air currents.

The leakage of cooling water through imperfections in the container or its seal and the resultant spoilage will be discussed later (Chapter 19).

Canning in the Home

For many years home canners have used processes similar to those of Appert, with the temperature of heating not exceeding 100 C. This has been accomplished by one of three methods: (1) a bath of boiling water, in which the containers were immersed, (2) a steamer, in which the containers were exposed to flowing steam, or (3) oven heat. When jars are heated in the oven, the temperature cannot exceed the boiling point of the food unless the containers are sealed and pressure develops, and this results in the risk of explosion of the jars. These processes are sufficient for acid foods such as fruits but are not considered adequate for low-acid foods such as peas, corn, and meats. Modern methods of home canning use the pressure cooker for the heat processing of low-acid foods according to directions that are available in state and federal bulletins on home canning.

In the **cold-pack** method of home canning, the food is not heated before being placed into the jar or other container, in contrast to the **hot-pack** method, where the food is precooked, is hot when transferred to the container, and is immediately heat-processed. It is obvious that the cold-packed food will require more of a heat treatment in the container than will hot-packed food. The cold-pack method is not recommended for vegetables and meats.

BIBLIOGRAPHY

American Can Company. 1947. The canned food reference manual. 3d ed. American Can Company, New York.

Anonymous. 1964. HTST and aseptic techniques gain. Food Eng. 36(11):79.

Anonymous. 1973. Thermally processed low-acid foods packaged in hermetically sealed containers. Fed. Regist. 38(16):2398–2410.

Ball, C. O., and F. C. W. Olson. 1957. Sterilization in food technology. McGraw-Hill Book Company, New York.

Bean, P. G. 1983. Developments in heat treatment processes for shelf-stable products. *In* T. A. Roberts and F. A. Skinner (ed.), Food microbiology: advances and prospects. Academic Press, Inc., New York.

Bigelow, W. D., and J. R. Esty. 1920. Thermal death point in relation to time of typical thermophilic organisms. J. Infect. Dis. 27:602–610.

Bigelow, W. D., G. S. Bohart, A. C. Richardson, and C. O. Ball. 1920. Heat penetration in processing canned foods. Natl. Canners Assoc. Bull. no. 162.

Brighton, K. W., D. W. Riester, and O. G. Braun. 1963. Technical problems presented by new containers and materials. Food Technol. 17(9):22–31.

Cameron, E. J. 1940. Report on canned vegetables. J.A.O.A.C. 23:607–608.

Curran, H. R. 1935. The influence of some environmental factors upon the thermal resistance of bacterial spores. J. Infect. Dis. 56:196–202.

Esty, J. R., and K. F. Meyer. 1922. The heat resistance of spores of *Clostridium botulinum* and allied anaerobes. J. Infect. Dis. 31:650–658.

Food Engineering Staff. 1962. Advances in processing methods. Food Eng. 34(2):37–52.

Gelber, P. 1963. Numerous refinements in aseptic processing. Food Process. 24(4):61–66.

Goldblith, S. A., M. A. Joslyn, and J. T. R. Nickerson (eds.). 1961. An introduction to the thermal processing of foods. AVI Publishing Co., Inc., Westport, Conn. (This volume contains most of the classic papers on canning referred to in this chapter. Therefore, these papers are not listed separately here.

Halvorson, H. O. 1959. Symposium on initiation of bacterial growth. IV. Dormancy, germination, and outgrowth. Bacteriol. Rev. 23:267–272.

Hansen, N. H., and H. Riemann. 1963. Factors affecting the heat resistance of nonsporing organisms. J. Appl. Bacteriol. 26:314–333.

Hays, G. L., and D. W. Riester. 1958. Microbiological aspects of pressure packaged foods. Soap Chem. Spec. 34(9):113, 115–119, 121.

Herson, A. C., and E. D. Hulland. 1964. Canned foods: an introduction to their microbiology. Chemical Publishing Company, Inc., New York.

Lechowich, R. V., and Z. J. Ordal. 1962. The influence of the sporulation medium on heat resistance, chemical composition, and termination of *Bacillus megaterium* spores. Can. J. Microbiol. 8:287–295.

Levinson, H. S., and M. T. Hyatt. 1964. Effect of sporulation medium on heat resistance, chemical composition, and germination of *Bacillus megaterium* spores. J. Bacteriol. 87:876–886.

Lopez, A. 1981. A complete course in canning: basic information on canning. Canning Trade, Inc., Baltimore.

Lopez, A. 1981. A complete course in canning: processing procedures for canned food products. Canning Trade, Inc., Baltimore.

Mayer, P. C., K. Robe, and J. B. Klis. 1961. "Canning" without cans. Food Process. 22(11):36–39.

Nair, J. H. 1964. Hydrostatic sterilizers. Food Eng. 35(12):37–42.

National Canners Association. 1968. Laboratory manual for food canners and processors. 3d ed. AVI Publishing Co., Inc., Westport, Conn.

National Canners Association. 1976. Processes for low-acid canned foods in metal containers. 11th ed. Natl. Canners Ass. Bull. 26-L.

Nickerson, J. T., and A. J. Sinskey. 1972. Microbiology of foods and food processing. American Elsevier Publishing Co., New York.

Olson, J. C., and P. M. Nottingham. 1980. Temperature. *In* J. H. Silliker (ed.), Microbial ecology of foods. Volume 1. Factors affecting life and death of microorganisms. Academic Press, Inc., New York.

Olson, F. C. W., and H. P. Stevens. 1939. Nomograms for graphic calculation of thermal processes for non-acid canned foods exhibiting straight-line semilogarithmic heating curves. Food Res. 4:1–20.

Perkins, W. E., D. H. Ashton, and G. M. Evancho. 1975. Influence of the z value of *Clostridium botulinum* on the accuracy of process calculations. J. Food Sci. 40:1189–1192.

Pflug, I. J. 1960. Thermal resistance of microorganisms to dry heat: design of apparatus, operational problems and preliminary results. Food Technol. 14:483–487.

Pflug, I. J., J. H. Bock, and F. E. Long. 1963. Sterilization of food in flexible packages. Food Technol. 17:1167–1172.

Pflug, I. J., J. E. Odlang, and R. Christensen. 1985. Computing minimum public health sterilizing value for food with pH values from 4.6 to 6.0. J. Food Prot. 48:848–850.

Pigott, G. M. 1963. Fluidized-bed heat processing of canned foods. Food Process. 24(11):79–82.

Sachsel, G. F. 1963. Fluidized-bed cooking. Food Process. 24(11)77–78.

Schott, D. 1964. Latest developments in the sterilization of canned foods. Food Can. 24(1):28–29.

Stumbo, C. R. 1964. Heat processing. Food Technol. 18:1373–1375.

Stumbo, C. R. 1972. Thermobacteriology in food processing. 2d ed. Academic Press, Inc., New York.

Townsend, C. T., J. R. Esty, and J. C. Baselt, 1938. Heat resistance studies on spores of putrefactive anaerobes in relation to determination of safe processes for canned foods. Food Res. 3:323–330.

Walters, A. H. 1964. Microbial resistance. Food Eng. 36(11):57.

Williams, O. B. 1929. The heat resistance of bacterial spores. J. Infect. Dis. 44:421–465.

Witter, L. D. 1983. Elevated temperature preservation. *In* A. H. Rose (ed.), Food microbiology. Academic Press, Inc., New York.

Xezones, H., and I. J. Hutchings. 1965. Thermal resistance of *Clostridium botulinum* (62A) spores as affected by fundamental food constituents. I. Effect of pH. Food Technol. 19:1003–1005.

Ziemba, J. V. 1964. "Flash 18" sequel to aseptic canning. Food Eng. 36(3):122–126.

PRESERVATION BY USE OF LOW TEMPERATURES

Low temperatures are used to retard chemical reactions and action of food enzymes and to slow down or stop the growth and activity of microorganisms in food. The lower the temperature, the slower will be chemical reactions, enzyme action, and microbial growth; a low enough temperature will prevent the growth of any microorganism.

Any raw plant or animal food may be assumed to contain a variety of bacteria, yeasts, and molds which need only conditions for growth to bring about undesirable changes in the food. Each microorganism present has an optimal, or best, temperature for growth and a minimal temperature below which it cannot multiply. As the temperature drops from this optimal temperature toward the minimal, the rate of growth of the organism decreases and is slowest at the minimal temperature. Cooler temperatures will prevent growth, but slow metabolic activity may continue. Therefore, the cooling of a food from ordinary temperatures has a different effect on the various organisms present. A drop of 10° may stop the growth of some organisms and slow the growth of others but to an extent that would vary with the kind of organism. A further decrease of 10° in temperature would stop the growth of more organisms and make still slower the growth of the others. Low-temperature storage can therefore act as a significant environmental factor influencing the type of spoilage flora to predominate, as illustrated in Table 7-1.

The growth and metabolic reactions of microorganisms depend on enzymes, and the rate of enzyme reactions is directly affected by temperature. The most

TABLE 7-1
TYPES OF BACTERIA CAUSING SPOILAGE
OF CHICKEN MEAT

	Spoilage flora at each temperature, %		
	1C	**10C**	**15C**
Pseudomonas	90	37	15
Acinetobacter	7	26	34
Enterobacteriaceae	3	15	27
Streptococcus		6	8
Aeromonas		4	6
Others		12	10

Source: Tompkin (1973).

TABLE 7-2
GROWTH RATE OF *PSEUDOMONAS FRAGI* AT VARIOUS TEMPERATURES

Temperature, C	Average exponential generation time, min
0	667
2.5	462
5.0	300
7.5	207
10.0	158
20.0	65

Source: Nickerson and Sinskey (1972).

important aspect of this temperature effect is reflected in a decrease in the rate of growth of a microorganism when the temperature is lowered, as can be seen in Table 7-2.

GROWTH OF MICROORGANISMS AT LOW TEMPERATURES

In general, freezing prevents the growth of most foodborne microorganisms and refrigeration temperatures slow growth rates. Commercial refrigeration temperatures, i.e., lower than 5 to 7.2 C, effectively retard the growth of many foodborne pathogens. One notable exception is *Clostridium botulinum* type E, which has a minimum temperature for growth of about 3.3 C (Table 7-3). *Yersinia*

TABLE 7-3
LOW TEMPERATURE GROWTH OF SOME FOODBORNE
BACTERIAL PATHOGENS.

Organism	Minimum temperature for growth, C	Reference
Aeromonas hydrophila	1–5	Eddy (1960)
Bacillus cereus	7	Chung et al. (1976)
Campylobacter jejuni	27	Kreig (1984)
Clostridium botulinum (E)	3.3	Schmidt et al. (1961)
Clostridium perfringens	20 (most strains)	
	6 (rarely)	Kreig (1984)
Escherichia coli	4	Olsvik and Kapperud (1982)
Listeria monocytogenes	3	Gray and Killinger (1966)
Plesiomonas shigelloides	8	Kreig (1984)
Salmonella	5.2	Matches and Liston (1968)
Staphylococcus aureus	10	Genigeorgis et al. (1969)
Vibrio parahaemolyticus	5	Beuchat (1975)
Yersinia enterocolitica	1–7	Hanna et al. (1977)

enterocolitica can survive and grow at temperatures as low as 0 to 3 C (Stern and Pierson, 1979). An earlier reference suggested a minimum temperature of 1 to 7 C (Table 7-3). Although concern has been expressed about the low temperature growth limits of *Salmonella* (Table 7-3), Mossel et al. (1981) examined the growth potential of numerous strains and found that only one strain, *S. panama* R IV 1917, could grow at 4 C. Other bacterial foodborne pathogens have a minimum temperature for growth below 7.2 C, and refrigeration therefore may not be depended on to prevent significant growth indefinitely.

A few examples, reported by various workers, of low-temperature growth of microorganisms are of interest. Of the molds, *Cladosporium* and *Sporotrichum* have been found growing on foods at −6.7 C and *Penicillium* and *Monilia* at −4 C. Growth by one yeast has taken place at −34 C, and two others grew at −18 C (Michener and Elliott, 1964). Bacteria have been reported growing at temperatures as low as −5 C on meats, −10 C on cured meats, −11 C on fish, −12.2 C on vegetables (peas), and −10 C in ice cream; yeast at −5 C on meats and −17.8 C on oysters; and molds at −7.8 C on meats and vegetables and −6.7 C on berries.

TEMPERATURES EMPLOYED IN LOW-TEMPERATURE STORAGE

Many of the terms used in connection with low-temperature storage are applied rather loosely; e.g., the term "cold storage" may refer to the use of temperatures above or below freezing, although the application of mechanical refrigeration is implied. More often it is considered to be storage above 0 C. The term "frozen storage" is more obvious; the product is stored in a frozen state, but the exact temperature would depend on the product. Most commercial storage freezers are at or below −18 C.

Common, or Cellar, Storage

The temperature in common, or cellar, storage usually is not much below that of the outside air and seldom is lower than 15 C. Root crops, potatoes, cabbage, celery, apples, and similar foods can be stored for limited periods. The deterioration of such fruits and vegetables by their own enzymes and by microorganisms is not prevented but is slower than at atmospheric temperatures. Too low a humidity in the storage cellar results in losses of moisture from the stored food, and too high a humidity favors spoilage by microorganisms. In locations where no refrigeration is available common storage of all foods is the rule.

Chilling, or "Cold Storage"

Chilling storage is at temperatures not far above freezing and usually involves cooling by ice or by mechanical refrigeration. It may be used as the main preservative method for foods or for temporary preservation until some other preservative process is applied. Most perishable foods, including eggs, dairy products, meats, seafood, vegetables, and fruits, may be held in chilling storage for a limited time with little change from their original condition. Enzymatic and microbial changes in the foods are not prevented but are slowed considerably.

Factors to be considered in connection with chilling storage include the temperature of chilling, the relative humidity, air velocity and composition of the atmosphere in the storeroom, and the possible use of ultraviolet rays or other radiations.

Temperature   The lower the temperature of storage, the greater the cost. Therefore, although most foods will keep best at a temperature just above their freezing point, they are not necessarily stored at this low temperature. Instead, the chilling temperature is selected on the basis of the kind of food and the time and conditions of storage. Certain foods have an optimal storage temperature or range of temperatures well above the freezing point and may be damaged by lower temperatures. A well-known example is the banana, which should not be kept in the refrigerator; it keeps best at about 13.3 to 16.7 C. Some varieties of apples undergo "low-temperature breakdown" at temperatures near freezing, and sweet potatoes keep best at 10 to 12.8 C.

The temperature of a refrigerator is mechanically controlled but varies in different parts, usually between 0 and 10 C.

Relative Humidity   The optimal relative humidity of the atmosphere in chilling storage varies with the food stored and with environmental factors such as temperature, composition of the atmosphere, and ray treatments. Too low a relative humidity results in loss of moisture and hence of weight, the wilting and softening of vegetables, and the shrinkage of fruits. Too high a relative humidity favors the growth of spoilage microorganisms. The highest humidity, near saturation, is required for most bacterial growth on the surface of foods; less moisture is needed by yeasts, about 90 to 92 percent, and still less by molds, which can grow in a relative humidity of 85 to 90 percent. Changes in humidity, as well as in temperature, during storage may cause "sweating," or precipitation of moisture, on the food. A moist surface favors microbial spoilage, e.g., slime on the moist surface of sausage.

Examples of how the optimal relative humidity and the temperature for chilling storage vary with the food stored are given in Table 7-4.

Ventilation   Ventilation or control of air velocities of the storage room is important in maintaining a uniform relative humidity throughout the room, removing odors, and preventing the development of stale odors and flavors. The rate of air circulation affects the rate of drying of foods. If adequate ventilation is not provided, food in local areas of high humidity may undergo microbial decomposition.

Composition of Storage Atmosphere   The amounts and proportions of gases in the storage atmosphere influence preservation by chilling. Usually no attempt is made to control the composition of the atmosphere, although stored plant

TABLE 7-4
OPTIMAL RELATIVE HUMIDITIES AND STORAGE
TEMPERATURES FOR RAW FOODS

Product	Temp., C	RH, %
Apricots	−0.5–0	85–90
Bananas	11.7–15.6	85–90
Beans (snap), peppers	7.2	85–90
Cabbage, lettuce, carrots	0	90–95
Lemons	12.8–14.4	85–90
Melons (cantaloupe)	4.4–10	80–85
Nuts	0–2.2	65–70
Onions	0	70–75
Tomatoes (ripe)	4.4–10	85–90

Source: From USDA Handb. 66.

foods continue to respire, using oxygen and giving off carbon dioxide. In recent years, however, increased attention has been given to "gas storage" of foods, where the composition of the atmosphere has been controlled by the introduction of carbon dioxide, ozone (experimentally) or other gas or the removal of carbon dioxide. Gas storage (see page 206) ordinarily is combined with chilling storage. It has been found that in the presence of optimal concentrations of carbon dioxide or ozone, (1) a food will remain unspoiled for a longer period, (2) a higher relative humidity can be maintained without harm to the keeping quality of certain foods, or (3) a higher storage temperature can be used without shortening the keeping time of the food than is possible with ordinary chilling storage. It is especially advantageous to be able to maintain a high relative humidity without added risk of microbial spoilage, because many foods keep their original qualities better if they lose little moisture.

The optimal concentration of carbon dioxide in the atmosphere varies with the food stored, from the approximately 2.5 percent reported to be best for eggs and 10 percent for chilled beef up to the 100 percent for bacon. For some foods, e.g., apples, the concentration of oxygen as well as that of carbon dioxide is significant, and a definite ratio of these gases is sought. Respiring plant cells may evolve too much carbon dioxide into the storage room for some foods, and then part of it must be removed.

Irradiation   The combination of ultraviolet irradiation with chilling storage helps preserve some foods and may permit the use of a higher humidity or storage temperature than is practicable with chilling alone. Ultraviolet lamps have been installed in rooms for the storage of meat and cheese.

Freezing or "Frozen Storage"

The storage of foods in the frozen condition has been an important preservative method for centuries where outdoor freezing temperatures were available. With the development of mechanical refrigeration and the quick-freezing processes, the frozen food industry has expanded rapidly. Even in the home, the freezing of foods has become extensive, now that home deep freezers are readily available. Under the usual conditions of storage of frozen foods, microbial growth is prevented entirely and the action of food enzymes is greatly retarded. The lower the storage temperature, the slower will be any chemical or enzymatic reactions, but most of them will continue slowly at any temperature now used in storage. Therefore, it is a common practice to inactivate enzymes of vegetables by scalding or blanching before freezing when practicable.

Selection and Preparation of Foods for Freezing   The quality of the food to be frozen is of prime importance, for the frozen food can be no better than the food was before it was frozen. Fruits and vegetables are selected on the basis of their suitability for freezing and their maturity and are washed, trimmed, cut, or otherwise pretreated as desired. Most vegetables are scalded or blanched, and fruits may be packed in a sirup. Meats and seafood are selected for quality and are handled so as to minimize enzymatic and microbial changes. Most foods are packaged before freezing, but some foods in small pieces, e.g., strawberries, may be frozen before packaging.

The scalding or blanching of vegetables ordinarily is done with hot water or steam, the extent of the treatment varying with the food. This brief heat treatment is supposed to accomplish the following: (1) inactivation of most of the plant enzymes which otherwise might cause toughness, change in color, mustiness, loss in flavor, softening, and loss in nutritive value, (2) reduction (as high as 99 percent) in the numbers of microorganisms on the food, (3) enhancement of the green color of vegetables such as peas, broccoli, and spinach, (4) wilting of leafy vegetables such as spinach, making them pack better, and (5) displacement of air entrapped in the tissues.

Freezing of Foods   The rate of freezing of foods depends on a number of factors, such as the method employed, the temperature, circulation of air or refrigerant, size and shape of package, and kind of food. **Sharp freezing** usually refers to freezing in air with only natural air circulation or at best with electric fans. The temperature is usually −23.3 C or lower but may vary from −15 to −29 C, and freezing may take from 3 to 72 hr. This sometimes is termed **slow freezing** to contrast it to **quick freezing,** in which the food is frozen in a relatively short time. Quick freezing is variously defined but in general implies a freezing time of 30 min or less and usually the freezing of small packages or units of food. Quick freezing is accomplished by one of three general methods: (1) direct immersion of the food or the packaged food in a refrigerant, as in the freezing of fish in brine or of berries in special sirups, (2) indirect contact with the refrigerant, where the food or package is in contact with the passage through which the refrigerant at −17.8 to −45.6 C flows, or (3) air-blast freezing, where frigid air at −17.8 to −34.4 C is blown across the materials being frozen.

A method for the overseas shipment of frozen, packaged foods involves nitrogen freezing of the cartoned foods in a special aluminum case and ordinary storage on the ship. The original low temperature and the insulation guarantee that the food will remain in the frozen condition for the desired period. Certain fruits and vegetables, fish, shrimp, and mushrooms now are being frozen by means of liquid nitrogen. For **dehydrofreezing,** fruits and vegetables have about half their moisture removed before freezing.

The advantages claimed for quick freezing over slow freezing are that (1) smaller ice crystals are formed, hence there is less mechanical destruction of intact cells of the food, (2) there is a shorter period of solidification and therefore less time for diffusion of soluble materials and separation of ice, (3) there is more prompt prevention of microbial growth, and (4) there is more rapid slowing of enzyme action. Quick-frozen foods, therefore, are supposed to thaw to a condition more like that of the original food than slow-frozen foods. This seems to be true for some foods, e.g., vegetables, but not necessarily for all foods. Research on fish, for example, has indicated little advantage for quick freezing over slow freezing.

Changes during Preparation for Freezing   The rate and kind of deterioration of foods before freezing will depend on the condition of the food at harvesting or slaughter and the methods of handling thereafter. The temperatures at which the food is held and other environmental conditions will determine the kinds of microorganisms to grow and the changes to be produced. The condition of the food at the time of freezing will determine the potential quality of the frozen food.

Changes during Freezing   The quick-freezing process rapidly slows chemical and enzymatic reactions in the foods and stops microbial growth. A similar effect is produced by sharp or slow freezing, but with less rapidity. The physical effects of freezing are of great importance. There is an expansion in volume of the frozen food, and ice crystals form and grow in size. These crystals usually are larger with slow freezing, and more ice accumulates between tissue cells than with quick freezing and may crush cells. Water is drawn from the cells to form such ice, with a resultant increase in the concentration of solutes in the unfrozen liquor, which in this way has a constantly dropping freezing point until a stable condition is reached. It is claimed that the ice crystals rupture tissue cells or even microorganisms, but some workers minimize the importance of such an effect. The increased concentration of solutes in the cells hastens the salting out, dehydration, and denaturation of proteins and causes irreversible changes in colloidal systems, such as the syneresis of hydrophilic colloids. Furthermore, it is thought to be responsible for killing microorganisms.

Changes during Storage   During storage of the food in the frozen condition chemical and enzymatic reactions proceed slowly. Meat, poultry, and fish proteins may become irreversibly dehydrated, the red myoglobin of meat may be oxidized—especially at surfaces—to brown metmyoglobin, and fats of meat and fish may become oxidized and hydrolyzed. The unfrozen, concentrated solution of sugars, salts, etc., may ooze from packages of fruits or concentrates during storage as a viscous material called the **metacryotic liquid.** Fluctuation in the storage temperature results in growth in the size of ice crystals and in physical damage to the food. Desiccation of the food is likely to take place at its surface during storage. When ice crystals evaporate from an area at the surface, a defect called **freezer burn** is produced on fruits, vegetables, meat, poultry, and fish. The spot usually appears dry, grainy, and brownish; in this area the chemical changes mentioned above take place, and the tissues become dry and tough.

At freezing temperatures vegetative cells of microorganisms that are unable to multiply will, in time, die. There is a slow but continuous decrease in numbers of viable microorganisms as storage continues, with some species dying more rapidly than others but with representatives of most species surviving for months or even years.

Changes during Thawing Most of the changes that seem to appear during thawing are the result of freezing and storage but do not become evident earlier. When the ice crystals melt, the liquid either is absorbed back into the tissue cells or leaks out from the food. Slow, well-controlled thawing usually results in better return of moisture to the cells than does rapid thawing and results in a food more like the original food that was frozen. The pink or reddish liquid that comes from meat on thawing is called **drip,** or **bleeding,** and the liquid oozing from fruits or vegetables on thawing is termed **leakage.** The wilting or flabbiness of vegetables and the mushiness of fruits on thawing are chiefly the result of physical damage during freezing. During thawing the rate of action of enzymes in the food will increase, but the time for action will be comparatively short if the food is utilized promptly.

If thawing is reasonably rapid and the food is used promptly, there should be little trouble with growth of microorganisms because the temperatures will be too low for any appreciable amount of growth. Only when the thawing is very slow or when the thawed food is allowed to stand at room temperature is there opportunity for any considerable amount of growth and activity of microorganisms. The kinds of organisms growing depend on the temperature of thawing and the time the food was allowed to stand after thawing.

Disposal of Thawed Foods Sometimes power failures lead to partial or complete thawing of foods in freezers. Thawed fruits may be refrozen. Flesh foods and vegetables may be refrozen if the packages still contain some ice. Refrozen foods will contain large ice crystals and may show leakage of liquid (syneresis) and mushiness. If thawed, flesh foods can be used if their temperature is below 3.3 C. In case of doubt, the food should be discarded.

Precooked Frozen Foods Precooked frozen foods include such a variety of types of foods and food products that they can be most conveniently discussed together. Most such foods are meat, fish, or poultry products, e.g., soups, creamed products, stews, pies, fried fish or poultry, chow mein, barbecued meat, meat loaf, and chicken à la king. Some bakery products, fruits, and vegetables may be cooked and then frozen, however. The precooking process usually is enough to kill any pathogens in the raw material and greatly reduce the total number of microorganisms present. Most samples of precooked frozen foods examined by various workers suggest that such items can be prepared commercially with total counts of less than 50,000 per gram. The cooking process would not destroy any preformed staphylococcus toxin in the food. Enterococci survive freezing and persist longer during storage than do coliform bacteria and therefore are recommended as "indicator bacteria" for possible fecal contamination.

It is especially important to prevent contamination of the food after the precooking, for any pathogenic or spoilage organism then introduced would find competition from other organisms greatly reduced and the cooked food probably a better culture medium than the original raw material if opportunity for growth were given. Therefore it also is important that cooling and freezing be done promptly after cooking so as to give no opportunity for such growth.

If these precooked frozen foods are kept at warm temperatures too long after thawing, there may be growth and toxin production by food-poisoning organisms, although no such occurrence has ever been reported. The final cooking or "warming up" of these products in the home or restaurant is not always enough of a heat treatment to greatly reduce numbers of organisms present or guarantee that any pathogens present will be killed or toxins destroyed.

EFFECT OF SUBFREEZING AND FREEZING TEMPERATURES ON MICROORGANISMS

It is difficult to discuss the consequences of freezing on microorganisms because of the numerous variables and observed effects. An obvious problem with such observations is that it is impossible to study effects of freezing on cells without observing effects of cooling (decrease to 0 C) and effects of thawing. Marth (1973) has summarized the freezing of microorganisms as involving (1) cooling of the cells to 0 C, (2) further cooling with extra- and possibly intracellular ice-crystal formation, (3) concentration of extra- and intracellular solutes, (4) storage of cells in a frozen state, and (5) thawing of the cells and substrate.

Freezing usually results in a considerable reduction in the number of viable organisms in a food. This observed decrease in recoverable numbers can be the result of lethal or sublethal effects.

Lethal Effects

Many cells are killed by freezing, but this is not a sterilization procedure. One of the most widely used techniques for the *preservation* of cultures is by freezing and frozen storage, usually in liquid nitrogen. Lethal effects are thought to be the result of denaturation or flocculation of essential cell proteins or enzymes possibly as a result of the increased concentration of solutes in the un-frozen water or perhaps in part because of physical damage by ice crystals. Rapid cooling of cells from an optimal temperature to 0 C can also result in death. This observation is referred to as **cold shock** and is thought to be related to alterations of lipids in the membrane with damage to the permeability of the cell or to the release of repair enzyme inhibitors, e.g., a ribonuclease inhibitor.

Sublethal Effects

During normal microbiological enumeration on frozen foods a reduction in numbers may not always represent true death of the population. Actually, some of the cells may be in an injured or damaged state which prevents their recovery for enumeration. Cells in this state have been referred to as freeze-injured, frost-injured, or metabolically injured. Freezing of microorganisms in a food may therefore result in cryoinjury. Since these cells can be recovered if repair time is permitted or additional nutritional factors are added to the enumeration media, they are not really dead.

The attention given to cryoinjury of microorganisms in frozen foods is related to a concern over the significance of bacteriological standards on such items, the adequacy of enumeration procedures, the pathogenicity of injured pathogens, and interpretation of viable numbers of microorganisms in frozen foods.

Response of Microorganisms to Freezing

The following variables or factors occur during freezing and perhaps dictate why some microorganisms die, some are injured, and some are not damaged.

1 *The kind of microorganism and its state.* Resistance to freezing varies with the kind of microorganism, its phase of growth, and whether it is a vegetative cell or a spore. Christophersen (1973) has classified microorganisms on the basis of sensitivity to freezing as (*a*) susceptible, (*b*) moderately resistant, and (*c*) insensitive organisms. The vegetative cells of yeast and mold and many gram-negative bacteria would be in the first group. Gram-positive organisms including staphylococci and enterococci would be in the second group. The third group would be predominantly sporeformers, since the spores of bacilli and clostridia are very resistant to freezing. Bacteria in the logarithmic phase of growth would be more easily killed than those in other phases.

2 *The freezing rate.* There appears to be a critical range of temperatures (see below) which result in lethal effects; therefore, faster freezing rates would tend to be less destructive since the critical range would be passed through faster.

3 *The freezing temperature.* High freezing temperatures are more lethal. More organisms are inactivated at −4 to −10 C than at −15 to −30 C.

4 *The time of frozen storage*. The initial killing rate during freezing is rapid, but it is followed by a gradual reduction of microorganisms and is referred to as **storage death**. The number of viable organisms decreases with lengthened time of storage. Storage of frozen foods in the critical range of temperatures would result in a more rapid reduction than at higher or lower freezing temperatures.

5 *The kind of food*. The composition of the food influences the rate of death of organisms during freezing and storage. Sugar, salt, proteins, colloids, fat, and other substances may be protective, whereas high moisture and low pH may hasten killing.

6 *Influence of defrosting*. The response of microorganisms to the rate of defrosting varies. Rapid warming has been found to be harmful to some bacteria.

7 *Alternate freezing and thawing*. Alternate freezing and thawing is reported to hasten the killing of microorganisms but apparently does not always do so.

8 *Possible events during freezing of the cell*. As the temperature is lowered, more and more water freezes. The remaining or unfrozen free water at each temperature therefore becomes more and more concentrated with solutes (salts, proteins, nucleic acids, etc.). This can change the pH of cellular matter, concentrate electrolytes, alter colloidal states, denature proteins, and increase viscosity. Ice crystals can form outside the cell ("extracellular ice") and draw water out of the cell with a resulting dehydration or concentration effect. Intracellular crystals may form and grow or crystallize right through the cell, resulting in altered permeability or "holes" in the membrane and cell wall. Intracellular ice is thought to be more harmful to cells than are extracellular ice crystals.

BIBLIOGRAPHY

American Society of Refrigeration Engineers. 1951. The refrigeration data book, New York.

Anonymous. 1961*a*. Relative stabilities of frozen foods. Food Process. 22(1):41–43.

Anonymous. 1961*b*. Super cold for ultra-quick freezing. Food Process. 22(6):48–50.

Anonymous. 1964. Nitrogen freezing arrives. Food Eng. 36(11):73–74.

Arpai, J. 1964. The recovery of bacteria from freezing. Z. Allg. Mikrobiol. 4:105–113.

Beuchat, L. R. 1975. Environmental factors affecting survival and growth of *Vibrio parahaemolyticus:* a review. J. Milk Food Technol. 38:476–480.

Christophersen, J. 1973. Basic aspects of temperature action on microorganisms. *In* H. Precht et al., Temperature and life, chap. 1. Springer-Verlag, New York.

Chung, B. H., R. Y. Cannon, and R. C. Smith. 1976. Influence of growth temperature on glucose metabolism of a psychrotrophic strain of *Bacillus cereus*. Appl. Environ. Microbiol. 31:39–45.

Doebbler, G. F., and A. P. Rinfret. 1963. Survival of microorganisms after ultrarapid freezing and thawing. J. Bacteriol. 85:485.

Eddy, B. P. 1960. Cephalotrichous, fermentative gram-negative bacteria: the genus *Aeromonas*. J. Appl. Bacteriol. 23:216–249.

Elliott, R. P., and H. D. Michener. 1960. Review of microbiology of frozen foods. *In* Conference on frozen food quality. USDA Agric. Res. Serv. ARS-74-21.

Elliott, R. P., and H. D. Michener. 1965. Factors affecting the growth of psychrophilic micro-organisms in foods: a review. USDA Agric. Res. Serv. Tech. Bull. 1320.

Fisher, F. E. (Chairman). 1962. Report of the committee on frozen food sanitation. J. Milk Food Technol. 25:55–57.

Genigeorgis, C., H. Riemann, and W. W. Sadler. 1969. Production of enteroxtin B in cured meats. J. Food Sci. 34:62–68.

Goldblith, S. A., L. Rey, and W. W. Rothmayr. 1975. Freeze drying and advanced food technology. Academic Press, Inc., London.

Gray, M. L., and A. H. Killinger. 1966. *Listeria monocytogenes* and listeria infections. Bacteriol. Rev. 30:309–382.

Gray, R. J. H., and T. Sorhaug. 1983. Response, regulation and utilization of microbial activities at low temperatures. *In* A. H. Rose (ed.), Food microbiology. Academic Press, Inc., New York.

Gunderson, M. F. 1961. Mold problem in frozen foods, pp. 299–310. *In* Proceedings low temperature microbiology symposium (Campbell Soup Co.).

Haines, R. B. 1935–1936. The freezing and death of bacteria. Rep. Food Invest. Board [Br.]. 1934:47; 1935:31–34.

Haines, R. B. 1938. The effect of freezing on bacteria. R. Soc. (Lond.) Proc. B124:451–463.

Hanna, M. O., J. C. Stewart, D. L. Zink, Z. L. Carpenter, and C. Vanderzant. 1977. Development of *Yersinia enterocolitica* on raw and cooked beef and port at different temperatures. J. Food Sci. 42:1180–1184.

Hucker, G. J., and E. R. David. 1957a. The effect of alternate freezing and thawing on the total flora of frozen chicken pies. Food Technol. 11:354–356.

Hucker, G. J., and E. R. David. 1957b. The effect of alternate freezing and thawing on the total flora of frozen vegetables. Food Technol. 11:381–383.

International Commission on Microbiological Specifications for Foods (ICMSF). 1980. Microbial ecology of foods. Volume 1. Factors affecting life and death of microorganisms. Academic Press, Inc., New York.

King, C. J. 1971. Freeze-drying of foods. Butterworth & Co. (Publishers), Ltd., London.

Krieg, N. R. (ed.). 1984. Bergey's manual of systematic bacteriology, vol. 1. The Williams & Wilkins Co., Baltimore.

Marth, E. H. 1973. Behavior of food microorganisms during freeze-preservation. *In* O. R. Fennema, W. D. Powrie, and E. H. Marth (eds.), Low-temperature preservation of foods and living matter, chap. 8. Marcel Dekker, Inc., New York.

Matches, J. R., and J. Liston. 1968. Low temperature growth of *Salmonella*. J. Food Sci. 33:641–645.

Michener, H. D., and R. P. Elliot. 1964. Minimum growth temperatures for food-poisoning, fecal-indicator, and psychrophilic microorganisms. Adv. Food Res. 13:349–396.

Mossel, D. A. A., M. Jansma, and J. de Waart. 1981. Growth potential of 114 strains of epidemiologically most common *Salmonellae* and *Arizonae* between 3 and 17c. *In* Psychrotrophic microorganisms in spoilage and pathogenicity. T. A. Roberts, G. Hobbs, J. H. Christian, and N. Skovgaard (eds.). Academic Press, Inc., New York.

Nickerson, J. T., and A. J. Sinskey. 1972. Microbiology of foods and food processing. American Elsevier Publishing Co., New York.

Olsvik, O., and G. Kapperud. 1982. Enterotoxin production in milk at 22 and 4°C by *Escherichia coli* and *Yersinia enterocolitica*. Appl. Environ. Microbiol. 43:997–1000.
Pennington, M. E., and D. K. Tressler. 1951. Food preservation by temperature control. *In* M. B. Jacobs (ed.), The chemistry and technology of food and food products, chap. 34. 2d ed. Interscience Publishers (Division of John Wiley & Sons, Inc.), New York.
Rogers, J. L. 1958. Quick frozen foods. Food Trade Press, London.
Schmidt, C. F., R. V. Lechowich, and J. F. Folinazzo. 1961. Growth and toxin production by type E *Clostridium botulinum* below 40°F. J. Food Sci. 26:626–630.
Simunovic, J., J. L. Oblinger, and J. P. Adams. 1985. Potential for growth of nonproteolytic types of *Clostridium botulinum* in pasteurized restructured meat products: a review. J. Food Prot. 48:265–276.
Stern, N. J., and M. D. Pierson. 1979. *Yersinia enterocolitica:* A review of the psychrotrophic water and foodborne pathogen. J. Food Sci. 44:1736-1742.
Straka, R. P., and J. L. Stokes. 1959. Metabolic injury to bacteria at low temperatures. J. Bacteriol. 78:181–185.
Tompkin, R. B. 1973. Refrigeration temperature as an environmental factor influencing the microbial quality of food: a review. Food Technol. 27(12):54–58.
Tressler, D. K., and C. F. Evers. 1968. The freezing preservation of foods. Volume I. Freezing of fresh foods. Volume II. Freezing of precooked and prepared foods. Volume III. Commercial freezing of fresh foods. Volume IV. Freezing of precooked frozen foods. 4th ed. AVI Publishing Co., Inc., Westport, Conn.
Woolrich, W. R., and E. R. Hallowell. 1970. Cold and freezer storage manual. AVI Publishing Co., Inc., Westport, Conn.
Wolstenholme, G. E. W., and M. O'Conner. 1970. The frozen cell. J. A. Churchill, Publishers, London.
Wright, R. C., D. H. Rose, and T. M. Whiteman. 1954. The commercial storage of fruits, vegetables, ornamentals and nursery stock. USDA Handb. 66.

PRESERVATION
BY DRYING

Preservation of foods by drying has been practiced for centuries. Some foods, e.g., grains, are sufficiently dry as harvested or with a little drying remain unspoiled for long periods under proper storage conditions. Most foods, however, contain enough moisture to permit action by their own enzymes and by microorganisms, so that to preserve them by dryness the removal or binding (e.g., by solutes) of moisture is necessary. Table 8-1 compares the moisture contents of several foods before and after drying to the level of moisture which would make the product stable.

Drying usually is accomplished by the removal of water, but any method that reduces the amount of available moisture, i.e., lowers the a_w, in a food is a form of drying. Thus, for example, dried fish may be heavily salted so that moisture is drawn from the flesh and bound by the solute and hence is unavailable to microorganisms. Sugar may be added, as in sweetened condensed milk, to reduce the amount of available moisture.

Moisture may be removed from foods by any of a number of methods, from the ancient practice of drying by the sun's rays to the modern artificial ones. Many of the terms used in connection with the drying of foods are rather inexact. A **sun-dried** food has had moisture removed by exposure to the sun's rays without any artificially produced heat and without controlled temperatures, relative humidities, or air velocities. A **dehydrated** or **desiccated** food has been dried by artificially produced heat under controlled conditions of temperature, relative humidity, and air flow. **Condensed** usually implies that moisture has been removed from a liquid food, and **evaporated** may have a similar meaning or may be used synonymously with the term dehydrated.

METHODS OF DRYING

Methods of drying will be mentioned only briefly; references on food technology should be consulted for details. The drying of individual foods will be discussed in the chapters on the preservation of these foods. Table 8-2 summarizes various forms of drying applied to several foods.

Solar Drying

Solar drying is limited to climates with a hot sun and a dry atmosphere and to certain fruits, such as raisins, prunes, figs, apricots, nectarines, pears, and peaches. The fruits are spread out on trays and may be turned during drying. Fish, rice, and other grains may also be sun-dried. Other special treatments will be discussed later.

Drying by Mechanical Dryers

Most methods of artificial drying involve the passage of heated air with controlled relative humidity over the food to be dried or the passage of the food through such air. A number of devices are used for controlled air circulation and for the reuse of air in some processes. The simplest dryer is the **evaporator** or **kiln,** sometimes used in the farm home, where the natural draft from the rising of heated air brings about the drying of the food. Forced-draft drying systems employ currents of heated air that move across the food, usually in

TABLE 8-1
MOISTURE CONTENT OF VARIOUS FOODS
BEFORE AND AFTER DRYING

Food	Moisture, before drying, %	Moisture, after drying, %
Milk		
Whole	87	5.0
Nonfat	90	5.0
Egg		
Whole	74	2.9
White	88	7.3
Yolk	51	1.1
Beef, lean, roasted	60	1.5
Chicken, broiled	61	1.6
Beans, snap, cooked	92	11.5
Corn, sweet, cooked	76	3.2
Potatoes, boiled	80	4.0
Apple juice	86	6.2
Figs, raw	78	3.6
Parsley, raw	84	5.3

Source: Condensed from Van Arsdel et al. (1973).

TABLE 8-2
TYPES OF DRYER USED FOR VARIOUS FOODS,
FOOD BY-PRODUCTS, AND WASTES

Product	Type of dryer
Vegetables, confectionery, fruits, pectin	Compartment and tunnel tray
Grass, grain, vegetables, fruit, nuts, breakfast cereals	Conveyor band
Grass, grain, apple pomace, lactose, poultry manure, peat, starch (vacuum)	Rotary
Coffee, milk, tea, fruit purees	Spray
Milk, starch, predigested infant foods, soups, brewery and distillery by-products	Film drum
Starch, fruit pulp, distillery waste products, crops	Pneumatic
Coffee, essences, meat extracts, malted and other confectioneries	Freeze dryers and vacuum dryers

Source: Williams-Gardner (1971).

tunnels. An alternative method is to move the food on conveyor belts or on trays in carts through the heated air.

Liquid foods, such as milk, juices, and soups, may be **evaporated** by the use of comparatively low temperatures and a vacuum in a vacuum pan or similar device; **drum-dried** by passage over a heated drum, with or without vacuum; or **spray-dried** by spraying the liquid into a current of dry, heated air.

Freeze Drying

Freeze drying, or the sublimation of water from a frozen food by means of a vacuum plus heat applied at the drying shelf, is being used for a number of foods, including meats, poultry, seafood, fruits, and vegetables. Frozen thin layers of foods of low sugar content may be dried without vacuum by sublimation of moisture during passage of dry carrier gas.

Drying during Smoking

As indicated in Chapter 9, most of the preservative effect of the smoking of foods is due to the drying of the food during the process. Indeed, some workers maintain that drying is the main preservative factor, especially drying at the surface of the food.

Other Methods

Electronic heating has been suggested for the removal of still more moisture from a food already fairly well dried. Foam-mat drying, in which liquid food is whipped to a foam, dried with warm air, and crushed to a powder, is receiving attention, as is pressure-gun puffing of partially dried foods to give a porous structure that facilitates further drying. Tower drying in dehumidified air at 30 C or lower has been successful with tomato concentrate, milk, and potatoes.

FACTORS IN THE CONTROL OF DRYING

A consideration of the proper control of dehydration includes the following factors.

  1 *The temperature employed.* This varies with the food and the method of drying.

  2 *The relative humidity of the air.* This, too, is varied with the food and the method of drying and also with the stage of drying. It usually is higher at the start of drying than it is later.

  3 *The velocity of the air.*

  4 *The time of drying.*

Improper control of these factors may cause **case-hardening** resulting from more rapid evaporation of moisture from the surface than diffusion from the interior, with a resulting hard, horny, impenetrable surface film that hinders further drying.

TREATMENTS OF FOODS BEFORE DRYING

Many of the pretreatments of foods to be dried are important in their effect on the microbial population, as will be indicated. These pretreatments may include (1) selection and sorting for size, maturity, and soundness, (2) washing, especially of fruits and vegetables, (3) peeling of fruits and vegetables by hand, machine, lye bath, or abrasion, (4) subdivision into halves, slices, shreds, or cubes, (5) alkali dipping, which is used primarily for fruits such as raisins, grapes, and prunes (for sun drying) and employs hot 0.1 to 1.5 percent lye or sodium carbonate, (6) blanching or scalding of vegetables and some fruits (apricots, peaches), and (7) sulfuring of light-colored fruits and certain vegetables. Fruits are sulfured by exposure to sulfur dioxide gas produced by the burning of sulfur so that a level of 1,000 to 3,000 ppm, depending on the fruit, will be absorbed. Vegetables may be sulfured after blanching in a similar manner or by dipping into or spraying with sulfite solution. Sulfuring helps maintain an attractive light color, conserve vitamin C and perhaps vitamin A, and repel insects; it also kills many of the microorganisms present.

PROCEDURES AFTER DRYING

The procedures after drying vary with the kind of dried food.

Sweating

"Sweating" is storage, usually in bins or boxes, for equalization of moisture or readdition of moisture to a desired level. It is used primarily with some dried fruits and some nuts (almonds, English walnuts).

Packaging

Most foods are packaged soon after drying for protection against moisture, contamination with microorganisms, and infestation with insects, although some dried foods (e.g., fruits and nuts) may be held as long as a year before packaging.

Pasteurization

Pasteurization is limited for the most part to dried fruits and kills any pathogens that may be present, as well as destroying spoilage organisms. The fruit usually is pasteurized in the package, and the treatment, varying with the fruit, is from 30 to 70 min at 70 to 100 percent relative humidity at 65.6 to 85 C.

MICROBIOLOGY OF DRIED FOODS

Before Reception at the Processing Plant

The microbiology of foods before their reception at the processing plant is likely to be similar whether the foods are to be dried, chilled, frozen, canned, or otherwise processed. Fruits and vegetables have soil and water organisms on them when harvested, plus their own natural surface flora, and spoiled parts contain the microorganisms causing the spoilage. Growth of some of these organisms may take place before the foods reach the processing plant if environmental conditions permit. Thus piled vegetables may heat and support the surface growth of slime-forming, flavor-harming, or even rot-producing organisms. Meats and poultry are contaminated by soil, intestinal contents, handlers, and equipment. Fish are contaminated by water and by their own slime and intestinal contents as well as by handlers and equipment, and growth may take place before the fish reach the processing plant. Eggs are dirtied by the hen, the nests, and the handler and, unless they are well and promptly handled, may support some microbial growth. Milk is subject to contamination from the time of its secretion by the cow to its reception at the processing plant and may support the growth of some psychrotrophic bacteria.

In the Plant before Drying

Growth of microorganisms that has begun on foods before they have reached the drying plant may continue in the plant up to the time of drying. Also, equipment and workers may contaminate the food. As will be noted, some of the pretreatments reduce numbers of organisms, and others may increase them, but the foods may be contaminated after any of these treatments.

The grading, selection, and sorting of foods, especially those such as fruits, vegetables, eggs, and milk, will influence the kinds and numbers of microorganisms present. The elimination of spoiled fruits and vegetables or of spoiled parts will reduce numbers of organisms in the product to be dried. The rejection of cracked, dirty, or spoiled eggs serves a similar purpose, as does the rejection of milk that does not conform to bacteriological standards of quality.

Washing fruits and vegetables removes soil and other adhering materials and serves to remove microorganisms. There also is the possibility of adding organisms if the water is of poor quality, and the moisture on the surface may encourage microbial growth if opportunity is given for it. Washing eggs may prove more harmful than helpful unless they are used promptly, for the moisture helps bacteria penetrate the shell.

Peeling fruits or vegetables, especially with steam or lye, should reduce numbers of microorganisms, since the majority of organisms usually are on the outer surface. Slicing or cutting should not increase numbers of organisms but will do so if equipment is not adequately cleansed and sanitized.

Dipping in alkali, as applied to certain fruits before sun drying, may reduce the microbial population.

Blanching or scalding vegetables reduces bacterial numbers greatly, as much as 99 percent in some instances. After blanching, numbers of bacteria may build up because of contamination from equipment and opportunities for growth.

Sulfuring of fruits and vegetables also causes a great reduction in numbers of microorganisms and serves to inhibit growth in the dried product.

During the Drying Process

Heat applied during a drying process causes a reduction in total numbers of microorganisms, but the effectiveness varies with the kinds and numbers of organisms originally present and the drying process employed. Usually all yeasts and most bacteria are destroyed, but spores of bacteria and molds commonly survive, as do vegetative cells of a few species of heat-resistant bacteria. As will be noted subsequently, improper conditions during drying may even permit the growth of microorganisms.

More microorganisms are killed by freezing than by dehydration during the freeze-drying process. Any method that involves abrupt and considerable changes in temperature, either an increase during drying by heat or a decrease during freeze drying, is likely to cause metabolic damage to some organisms, making them more demanding nutritionally.

After Drying

If the drying process and storage conditions are adequate, there will be no growth of microorganisms in the dried food. During storage there is a slow decrease in numbers of organisms, more rapid at first and slower thereafter. The microorganisms that are resistant to drying will survive best; therefore, the percentages of such organisms will increase. Especially resistant to storage under dry conditions are the spores of bacteria and molds, some of the micrococci, and microbacteria. There may be some opportunity for contamination of the dried food during packaging and other handling subsequent to drying.

Special treatments given some dry foods will influence microbial numbers. The sweating of dry fruits to equalize moisture may permit some microbial growth. Pasteurization of dry fruits will reduce numbers of microorganisms. Some products are repackaged for retail sale, e.g., figs in the near east, and are subject to contamination then.

The microbial content and the temperature of water used to rehydrate dried foods will affect the keeping quality of the rehydrated product. Bacteria in freeze-dried chicken meat are further reduced in numbers by rehydration with water at 50 C and are almost eliminated when the water is at 85 to 100 C. Growth of bacteria in the rehydrated meat will occur at favorable temperatures, but there is good shelf life (keeping time) at 4 C. *Staphylococcus aureus* has been found to survive freeze drying and rehydration at 60 C; therefore, rehydration at 100 C is recommended.

Microbiology of Specific Dried Foods

Dried Fruits The numbers of microorganisms on most fresh fruits range from comparatively few to many, depending on pretreatments, and on most dried fruits they vary from a few hundred per gram of fruit to thousands; in whole fruits they are mostly on the outer surfaces. Spores of bacteria and molds are likely to be the most numerous. When part of the fruit has supported growth and sporulation of mold before or after drying, mold spores may be present in large numbers.

Dried Vegetables Microbial counts on dried vegetables range from negligible numbers to millions per gram. The numbers on the vegetable just before drying may be high because of contamination and growth after blanching, and the percentage killed by the dehydrating process usually is lower than with the more acid fruits. If drying trays are improperly loaded, souring of such vegetables as onions and potatoes by lactic acid bacteria with a marked increase in numbers of bacteria may take place during the drying process. The risk is greater with onions because they are not blanched.

Chiefly bacteria are found on dried vegetables. A number of investigators have listed the genera of bacteria found (summarized by Vaughn, 1951) to include *Escherichia, Enterobacter, Bacillus, Clostridium, Micrococcus, Pseudomonas,* and *Streptococcus.* Vaughn found *Lactobacillus* and *Leuconostoc* species predominant in many samples of dehydrated vegetables.

Dried Eggs Dried eggs may contain from a few hundred microorganisms, mostly bacteria, per gram up to over 100 million, depending on the eggs broken and the methods employed. Since the contents of fresh eggs of good quality are normally free of microorganisms or include only a few, dried eggs should be low in microbial numbers. However, the inclusion of poorly washed eggs, those which have been permitted to sweat, dirty and cracked eggs, and those already invaded by microorganisms may add large numbers of organisms; also, contamination and growth may take place during breaking and other handling before drying. The drying process may reduce numbers ten- to a hundredfold but still permit large numbers to survive. A variety of kinds of organisms have been found in dried eggs, including micrococci, streptococci, coliforms, sporeformers, and molds. When egg white has been pretreated by a fermentation process, the counts on the dried product may be high. Egg yolk is a better culture medium than the white and is likely to have higher counts at breaking and to support growth better before drying.

Dried Milk   The number of microorganisms in dry milk may vary from a few hundred per gram to millions, depending on the milk being dried and the drying process. Roller or drum drying kills more organisms than does the spray process. The predominant kinds of organisms in dry milk are thermoduric streptococci, micrococci, and sporeformers.

INTERMEDIATE-MOISTURE FOODS

Numerous commercially prepared foods which contain 20 to 40 percent moisture and have nonrefrigerated shelf stability have been referred to as **intermediate-moisture products.** These include various soft candies, jams, jellies, honey, many dried fruits, some bakery items, and by definition even meat products such as pepperoni, country ham, jerky, and some dried fish. These products are low in moisture, can be eaten without preparation or rehydration, and yet do not taste like dehydrated products. The pet-food industry has demonstrated the most recent success of these products, stimulating interest throughout the food industry.

The stability of these products is in part a direct effect of a restrictive a_w. To be completely accurate these products are **reduced–water activity products.**

As was pointed out in Chapter 1, all microorganisms have an optimal and minimal water activity for growth. Adjusting the a_w of a fabricated product, by the addition of solutes or the removal of water, to a point below the minimal a_w of the normal spoilage flora results in a microbiological stable product. It should be noted that many of these products contain viable microorganisms and spores, which are not able to reproduce or germinate because of the restrictive a_w. In fabrication of a product with a reduced a_w, other factors which would affect the growth of organisms present must be considered, since the effect of a_w on microorganisms is influenced by pH, oxygen levels, temperature, nutrient content, and possibly food preservatives, either natural or added.

On a commercial scale full dependence for stability is not on an independent reduction of the a_w alone. For example, if the only factor were a_w reduction, the foods would have to have water activities of 0.65 to 0.70, and at this level they would resemble dehydrated products. The a_w of most intermediate-moisture products would be between 0.75 and 0.85. The a_w usually is adjusted by drying, by additives (solutes such as sugar, salt, and even glycerol), or by a combination of drying and additives. The moist pet food packaged in a flexible pouch and marketed nationwide exemplifies the success of intermediate-moisture-food technology. This specific product has an a_w of 0.83 to 0.85, is pasteurized, contains an antimycotic such as potassium sorbate, and has a moisture content of about 25 to 27 percent.

Brockmann (in Van Arsdel et al., 1973) has summarized the potential of reduced water activity in food preservation with the following considerations: (1) An a_w of 0.85 inhibits the most common food pathogens, (2) bacterial spore germination is inhibited at relatively high a_w values, (3) nonsporeformers, which can grow at an a_w below 0.95, are susceptible to pasteurizing temperatures, (4) suboptimal conditions of growth impose inhibition at higher levels of water activity, (5) organisms that will grow at low water activities multiply very slowly, and (6) yeasts and molds can be suppressed by antimycotics.

BIBLIOGRAPHY

Anonymous. 1962. Tumbling freeze drying. Food Process. 23(10):67.

Cruess, W. V. 1958. Commercial fruit and vegetable products, chaps. 17–19. 4th ed. McGraw-Hill Book Company, New York.

Fry, R. M., and R. I. N. Greaves. 1951. The survival of bacteria during and after drying. J. Hyg. 49:220–246.

Goldblith, S. A. 1963. Microbiological considerations in freeze-dehydrated foods. In S. A. Goldblith (ed.), Exploration in future food-processing techniques. The M.I.T. Press, Cambridge, Mass.

Goldblith, S. A., M. Karel, and G. Lusk. 1963. The role of food science and technology in the freeze dehydration of foods. Food Technol. 17:139–144, 258–264.

Gooding, E. G. B. 1962. The storage behaviour of dehydrated foods. Recent Adv. Food Sci. 2:22–40.

Great Britain Ministry of Agriculture, Fisheries and Food. 1961. The accelerated freeze-drying (AFD) method of food preservation. H.M. Stationery Office, London.

Harper, J. C., and A. L. Tappel. 1957. Freeze-drying of food products. Adv. Food Res. 7:172–234.

Hunziger, O. F. 1949. Condensed milk and milk powder. 7th ed. Published by author, La Grange, Ill.

International Commission on Microbiological Specifications for Foods (ICMSF). 1980. Microbial ecology of foods. Volume 1. Factors affecting life and death of microorganisms. Academic Press, Inc., New York.

Keey, R. B. 1972. Drying: principles and practice. Pergamon Press, Oxford.

Lazar, M. E., E. J. Bartha, and G. S. Smith. 1963. Dry-blanch-dry method for drying fruit (DBD). Food Technol. 17:1200–1202.

Masters, K. 1973. Spray drying. Leonard Hill Books, London.

May, K. N., and L. E. Kelly. 1965. Fate of bacteria in chicken meat during freeze-dehydration, rehydration, and storage. Appl. Microbiol. 13:340–344.

Rey, Louis. 1966. Advances in freeze-drying. Hermann Publishers, Paris.

Rockwell, W. C., E. Lowe, A. I. Morgan, Jr., R. P. Graham, and L. F. Ginnette. 1962. How foam-mat dryer is made. Food Eng. 34(8):86–88.

Scott, W. J. 1957. Water relations of food spoilage microorganisms. Adv. Food Res. 7:83–127.

Silverman, G. J., and S. A. Goldblith. 1965. The microbiology of freeze-dried foods. Adv. Appl. Microbiol. 7:305–334.

Van Arsdel, W. B., M. J. Copley, and A. I. Morgan (eds.). 1973. Food dehydration. Volume I. Drying methods and phenomena. AVI Publishing Co., Inc., Westport, Conn.

Vaughn, R. H. 1951. The microbiology of dehydrated vegetables. Food Res. 16:429–438.

Williams-Gardner, A. 1971. Industrial drying. CRC Press, Cleveland, Ohio.

Woodward, H. T. 1963. Freeze-drying without vacuum. Food Eng. 35(6):96–97.

Ziemba, J. V. 1962. Now—drying without heat. Food Eng. 35(7):84–85.

PRESERVATION
BY FOOD ADDITIVES

"A food additive is a substance or mixture of substances, other than the basic food stuff, which is present in food as a result of any aspect of production, processing, storage or packaging. The term does not include chance contamination" (WHO, 1965). This definition emphasizes one interpretation of a food additive; i.e., it is an intentional additive. Those food additives which are specifically added to prevent the deterioration or decomposition of a food have been referred to as **chemical preservatives.** These deteriorations may be caused by microorganisms, by food enzymes, or by purely chemical reactions. The inhibition of the growth and activity of microorganisms is one of the main purposes of the use of chemical preservatives. Preservatives may inhibit microorganisms by interfering with their cell membranes, their enzyme activity, or their genetic mechanisms. Other preservatives may be used as antioxidants to hinder the oxidation of unsaturated fats, as neutralizers of acidity, as stabilizers to prevent physical changes, as firming agents, and as coatings or wrappers to keep out microorganisms, prevent loss of water, or hinder undesirable microbial, enzymatic, and chemical reactions.

In addition to the chemicals intentionally added to foods or put on them or around them to help preserve them, there are many chemicals that get on or into foods during production, processing, or packaging. Residues of pesticides, herbicides, and fungicides on fruits and vegetables; residues of detergents used in washing foods; and residues of detergents and sanitizers used on utensils and equipment are likely to carry over into foods.

Factors that influence the effectiveness of chemical preservatives in killing microorganisms or inhibiting their growth and activity are similar to those considered in Chapter 6 in regard to the effectiveness of heating: (1) concentration of the chemical, (2) kind, number, age, and previous history of the organism,

(3) temperature, (4) time, and (5) the chemical and physical characteristics of the substrate in which the organism is found (moisture content, pH, kinds and amounts of solutes, surface tension, and colloids and other protective substances). A chemical agent may be bactericidal at a certain concentration, only inhibitory at a lower level, and ineffective at still greater dilutions.

THE IDEAL ANTIMICROBIAL PRESERVATIVE

The increased pressure on food supplies demands that food losses from product deterioration be kept at a minimum. Unfortunately, those countries experiencing food shortages and low food quality are the countries with inadequate technology of preservation. The use of a chemical preservative in this situation would have an immense impact.

Although many countries have advanced technology for preservation, methods either are not applied to their potential or are not completely effective. Chemical preservatives are depended on, either independently or in combination with other forms of preservation, to maintain a food in its original or fabricated state and to prevent excess losses from deterioration. Ideally, therefore, a chemical preservative should have a wide range of antimicrobial activity; should be nontoxic to human beings or animals; should be economical; should not have an effect on the flavor, taste, or aroma of the original food; should not be inactivated by the food or any substance in the food; should not encourage the development of resistant strains; and should kill rather than inhibit microorganisms. Most of the preservatives discussed in this chapter are inhibitory at acceptable concentrations, but only ethylene and propylene oxides and diethyl pyrocarbonate are lethal to microorganisms at normal concentrations of use. Needless to say, the ideal chemical preservative has not been found. Actually, many of the compounds most widely used are also the oldest preservatives. The new, simple, and "ideal" preservatives being suggested are few, and many of those suggested, for one reason or another, do not develop into a commercially acceptable additive.

ADDED PRESERVATIVES

The Federal Food, Drug, and Cosmetic Act, as amended by the Food Additives Amendment of 1958, defines a chemical preservative as

> any chemical which, when added to food, tends to prevent or retard deterioration thereof; but does not include common salt, sugars, vinegars, spices, or oils extracted from spices, or substances added by...woodsmoke.

The 1985 Code of Federal Regulations (Title 21, 1985) defined a food additive as follows:

> all substances not exempted by section 201(s) of the act, the intended use of which results or may reasonably be expected to result, directly or indirectly, either in their

becoming a component of food or otherwise affecting the characteristics of food. A material used in the production of containers and packages is subject to the definition if it may reasonably be expected to become a component, or to affect the characteristics, directly or indirectly, of food packed in the container. "Affecting the characteristics of food" does not include such physical effects, as protecting contents of packages, preserving shape, and preventing moisture loss. If there is no migration of a packaging component from the package to the food, it does not become a component of the food and thus is not a food additive. A substance that does not become a component of food but that is used, for example, in preparing an ingredient of the food to give a different flavor, texture, or other characteristic in the food, may be a food additive.

Antimicrobial preservatives added to foods can be grouped as follows:

1 *Those added preservatives not defined as such by law:* natural organic acids (lactic, malic, citric, etc.) and their salts, vinegars (acetic is a natural acid), sodium chloride, sugars, spices and their oils, woodsmoke, carbon dioxide, and nitrogen.

2 *Substances generally recognized as safe* (GRAS) *for addition to foods:* propionic acid and sodium and calcium propionates, caprylic acid, sorbic acid and potassium, sodium, and calcium sorbates, benzoic acid and benzoates and derivatives of benzoic acid such as methylparaben and propylparaben, sodium diacetate, sulfur dioxide and sulfites, potassium and sodium bisulfite and metabisulfite, and sodium nitrite. (Limitations on the use of some of these will be mentioned subsequently.)

3 *Chemicals considered to be food additives,* which would include all not listed in the first two categories. They can be used only when proved safe for humans or animals, and they then fall into group 4.

4 *Chemicals proved safe and approved by the Food and Drug Administration.*

Preservatives added to inhibit or kill microorganisms may be classified on various other bases, such as their chemical composition, mode of action, specificity, effectiveness, and legality. Some, e.g., sugar, are effective because of their physical action; others, e.g., sodium benzoate, because of their chemical action; and others, e.g., sodium chloride, because of a combination of these effects. Some preservatives are incorporated into foods and usually are antiseptic rather than germicidal, while others are used only to treat outer surfaces and may kill organisms as well as inhibit them. Some are employed to treat wrappers or containers for foods, while others are used as gases or vapors about the food. Some have been incorporated in ice used to chill foods such as fish. Preservatives may be fairly specific against microorganisms; e.g., they may be effective against molds or yeasts and less so against bacteria, or vice versa, and may act against definite groups or species of bacteria or other organisms.

Most of the more common antimicrobial additives used in foods are presented in Table 9-1. Current allowable levels for some of the preservatives are given in Table 9-2.

TABLE 9-1
USE OF ANTIMICROBIAL ADDITIVES IN VARIOUS FOODS*

Type of food product	Benzoic acid and sodium benzoate	Methyl- and propyl-paraben	Sorbates	Propionates	Sulfites	Acetates and diacetates	Nitrite and nitrate	Ethylene oxide	Propylene oxide
Carbonated beverages	+		+						
Beverage sirups	+	+	+						
Fruit drinks	+	+	+		+				
Fruit juices	+	+	+		+				
Wine and beer			+		+				
Cheese and cheese products		+	+	+					
Margarine	+		+			+			
Pie crust and pastries		+	+	+					
Pie fillings	+	+	+						
Sausage							+		
Preserved fish						+			
Salads, salad dressings	+	+	+						
Dried fruits and vegetables			+		+				
Fresh fruits and vegetables									
Pickles, relishes, olives, and sauerkraut	+	+	+						
Spices								+	+
Starch									+

*Maximum allowable concentrations vary.
Source: Condensed from the Handbook of Food Additives, T. E. Furia. The Chemical Rubber Co., 1972. Used by permission of The Chemical Rubber Co.,

147

TABLE 9-2
MAXIMUM LEVELS OF ANTIMICROBIALS PERMITTED IN FOODS

Preservative	Concentration allowed
Benzoic acid	0.1%, covered by good manufacturing practices (GMPs)
Methylparaben	0.1%, covered by GMPs
Propylparaben	0.1%, covered by GMPs
Ethylparaben	Not authorized for use
Sodium nitrate	500 ppm
Sodium nitrite	200ppm
Sorbates	Covered by GMPs
Acetates (acetic acid)	Covered by GMPs with concentrations from 0.25 to 9.0%
Propylene oxide	300 ppm cocoa, gums, starch, spices, processed nutmeats (except peanuts)
Ethylene oxide	Residues not to exceed 50 ppm
Sulfites	Covered by GMPs
Natamycin	200 to 300 ppm as a dip, spray, or solution

Source: From Code of Federal Regulations, Title 21, various subtitles, compiled January 1986.

Organic Acids and Their Salts

Lactic, acetic, propionic, and citric acids or their salts may be added to or developed in foods. Their development in foods during fermentation will be discussed in a following section. Citric acid is used in sirups, drinks, jams, and jellies as a substitute for fruit flavors and for preservation. Lactic and acetic acids are added to brines of various kinds, green olives, etc.

Propionates   Sodium or calcium propionate is used most extensively in the prevention of mold growth and rope development in baked goods and for mold inhibition in many cheese foods and spreads. Experimentally, or on a limited scale, they have been used in butter, jams, jellies, figs, apple slices, and malt extract.

They are effective against molds, with little or no inhibition of most yeast and bacteria. Their effectiveness decreases with an increase in pH, with an optimal upper limit of about pH 5 to 6, depending on the food item.

They appear to be ideal preservatives for bread and baked goods. Although the heat of baking destroys most molds, contamination of the loaves can occur during slicing and/or wrapping, hence the need for the propionates. Since they have little inhibitory effect on yeasts, they can be added to the dough of yeast-raised baked goods without interfering with leavening.

Propionic acid is a short-chain fatty acid (CH_3CH_2COOH) and, like some other fatty acids, perhaps affects the cell-membrane permeability, although its precise mode of fungistatic action is not known. Propionic acid is found naturally in Swiss cheese, as a developed preservative, at levels up to 1 percent.

Benzoates   The sodium salt of benzoic acid has been used extensively as an antimicrobial agent in foods. It has been incorporated into jams, jellies, margarine, carbonated beverages, fruit salads, pickles, relishes, fruit juices, etc.

Sodium benzoate is relatively ineffective at pH values near neutrality, and the effectiveness increases with increase in acidity, an indication that the undissociated acid is the effective agent. The pH at which sodium benzoate is most effective (2.5 to 4.0) is in itself enough to inhibit the growth of most bacteria, but some (not all) yeasts and molds are inhibited at pH levels that would otherwise permit their growth.

Two esters of p-hydroxybenzoic acid, methylparaben, and propylparaben, are also used extensively in foods, and to lesser extent the butyl and ethyl esters. These compounds are similar to benzoic acid in their effectiveness. Their distinct advantage is that they tend to be more effective at higher pH values than the other benzoates because the esterification of the carboxyl group means that the undissociated molecule is retained over a wider pH range; since it is the undissociated molecule that exerts inhibition, the esters are effective at higher pH values.

The mechanism of action of the benzoates is not clear; it is known, however, that the effectiveness of the benzoic acid esters increases with an increase in the chain length of the ester group.

Sorbates Sorbic acid, as the calcium, sodium, or potassium salt, is used as a direct antimicrobial additive in foods and as a spray, dip, or coating on packaging materials. It is widely used in cheeses, cheese products, baked goods, beverages, sirups, fruit juices, jellies, jams, fruit cocktails, dried fruits, pickles, and margarine.

Sorbic acid and its salts are known to inhibit yeast and molds but are less effective against bacteria. They are most effective at low pH values with a maximal level of use at about pH 6.5. These compounds are more effective than sodium benzoate at pH values above 4.0.

Acetates Derivatives of acetic acid, e.g., monochloroacetic acid, peracetic acid, dehydroacetic acid, and sodium diacetate, have been recommended as preservatives, but not all are approved by the Food and Drug Administration. Dehydroacetic acid has been used to impregnate wrappers for cheese to inhibit the growth of molds and as a temporary preservative for squash.

Acetic acid in the form of vinegar is used in mayonnaise, pickles, catsup, pickled sausages, and pigs' feet. Acetic acid is more effective against yeasts and bacteria than against molds, and its effectiveness increases with a decrease in pH, which would favor the presence of the undissociated acid.

Sodium diacetate has been used in cheese spreads and malt sirups and as treatment for wrappers used on butter.

Nitrites and Nitrates

Combinations of these various salts have been used in curing solutions and curing mixtures for meats. Nitrites decompose to nitric acid, which forms nitrosomyoglobin when it reacts with the heme pigments in meats and thereby forms a stable red color. Nitrates probably only act as a reservoir for nitrite, and their use is being restricted. Nitrites can react with secondary and tertiary amines to form nitrosamines, which are known to be carcinogenic. The assessment of the safety of nitrites in foods has been reviewed (Anonymous, 1981, 1982). The problem of possible carcinogenic nitrosamines may be greatest in bacon, and the extended future of nitrite use in foods will probably remain controversial. They are currently added in the form of sodium nitrite, potassium nitrite, sodium nitrate, and potassium nitrate.

Recent work has emphasized the inhibitory property of nitrites toward *Clostridium botulinum* in meat products, particularly in bacon and canned or processed hams. Nitrates have a limited effect on a limited number of organisms and would not be considered a good chemical preservative.

Sulfur Dioxide and Sulfites

The Egyptians and Romans burned sulfur to form sulfur dioxide as a means of sanitizing their wine-making equipment and storage vessels. Today sulfur dioxide and sulfites are used in the wine industry to sanitize equipment and to reduce the normal flora of the grape must.

In aqueous solutions, sulfur dioxide and various sulfites, including sodium sulfite, potassium sulfite, sodium bisulfite, potassium bisulfite, sodium metabisulfite, and potassium metabisulfite, form sulfurous acid, the active antimicrobial compound. The effectiveness of sulfurous acid is enhanced at low pH values. Many mechanisms for the action of sulfurous acid on microbial cells have been suggested, including the reduction of disulfide linkages, formation of carbonyl compounds, reaction with ketone groups, and inhibition of respiratory mechanisms.

The fumes of burning sulfur are used to treat most light-colored dehydrated fruits, while dehydrated vegetables are exposed to a spray of neutral bisulfites and sulfites before drying. Sulfur dioxide has also been used in sirups and fruit juices and, of course, wine making. Some countries permit the use of sulfites on meats and fish.

In addition to the antimicrobial action of sulfites, they are also used to prevent enzymatic and nonenzymatic changes or discoloration in some foods.

Ethylene and Propylene Oxide

Unlike the other chemical preservatives discussed, these two gases are sterilants. Ethylene oxide kills all microorganisms; propylene oxide, although it kills many microorganisms, is not as effective. They are thought to act as strong alkylating agents attacking labile hydrogens. The primary uses have been as sterilants for packaging materials, fumigation of warehouses, and "cold sterilization" of numerous plastics, chemicals, pharmaceuticals, syringes, and hospital supplies. They have also been used successfully in dried fruits, dried eggs, gelatin, cereals, dried yeast, and spices.

The FDA restricts the use of ethylene oxide to spices and other processed natural seasonings except mixtures containing added salt. Propylene oxide is permitted only as a package fumigant for dried prunes or glacé fruits and as a fumigant for cocoa, gums, spices, starch, and processed nutmeats (but not peanuts).

Sugar and Salt

These compounds lower the a_w and thus have an adverse effect on microorganisms. Sodium chloride is used in brines and curing solutions or is applied directly to the food. Enough may be added to slow or prevent the growth of microorganisms or only enough to permit an acid fermentation to take place. Salt has been reported to have the following effects: (1) It causes high osmotic pressure and hence plasmolysis of cells, the percentage of salt necessary to inhibit growth or harm the cell varying with the microorganism, (2) it dehydrates foods by drawing out and tying up moisture as it dehydrates microbial cells, (3) it ionizes to yield the chlorine ion, which is harmful to organisms, (4) it reduces the solubility of oxygen in the moisture, (5) it sensitizes the cell against carbon dioxide, and (6) it interferes with the action of proteolytic enzymes. The effectiveness of NaCl varies directly with its concentration and the temperature.

Sugars, such as glucose or sucrose, owe their effectiveness as preservatives to their ability to make water unavailable to organisms and to their osmotic effect. Examples of foods preserved by high sugar concentrations are sweetened condensed milk, fruits in sirups, jellies, and candies.

Alcohol

Ethanol, a coagulant and denaturizer of cell proteins, is most germicidal in concentrations between 70 and 95 percent. Flavoring extracts, e.g., vanilla and lemon extracts, are preserved by their content of alcohol. The alcoholic content of beer, ale, and unfortified wine is not great enough to prevent their spoilage by microorganisms but limits the types able to grow. Liqueurs and distilled liquors usually contain enough alcohol to ensure freedom from microbial attack. Methanol is poisonous and should not be added to foods; the traces added to foods by smoking are not enough to be harmful. Glycerol is antiseptic in high concentrations because of its dehydrating effect but is unimportant in food preservation. Propylene glycol has been used as a mold inhibitor and as a spray to kill airborne microorganisms.

Formaldehyde

The addition of formaldehyde to foods is not permitted, except as a minor constituent of woodsmoke, but this compound is effective against molds, bacteria, and viruses and can be used where its poisonous nature and irritating properties are not objectionable. Thus it is useful in the treatment of walls, shelves, floors, etc., to eliminate molds and their spores. Paraformaldehyde can be used to control bacterial and fungal growth in tapholes of maple trees. Formaldehyde probably combines with free amino groups of the proteins of cell protoplasm, injures nuclei, and coagulates proteins.

Woodsmoke

The smoking of foods usually has two main purposes: adding desired flavors and preserving. Other desirable effects may result, however, e.g., improvement in the color of the inside of meat and in the finish, or "gloss," of the outside and a tenderizing action on meats. The smoking process helps preservation by impregnating the food near the surface with chemical preservatives from the smoke, by combined action of the heat and these preservatives during smoking, and by the drying effect, especially at the surface. Commonly, smoke is obtained from the burning wood, preferably a hardwood such as hickory, but it may be generated from burning corncobs or other materials. Other woods used are apple, oak, maple, beech, birch, walnut, and mahogany. Sawdust is added to the fire to give a heavy smudge. Temperature and humidity are controlled at levels favorable to the product being smoked, and the duration of smoking depends on the kind of food. Smoking temperatures for meat vary from 43 to 71 C, and the smoking period lasts from a few hours to several days.

Woodsmoke contains a large number of volatile compounds that may have bacteriostatic and bactericidal effect. Formaldehyde is considered the most effective of these compounds, with phenols and cresols next in importance. Other compounds in the smoke are aliphatic acids from formic through caproic; primary and secondary alcohols, ketones, and acetaldehyde and other aldehydes; waxes; resins; guaiacol and its methyl and propyl isomers; and catechol, methylcatechol, and pyrogallol and its methyl ester. These compounds sometimes are grouped under the name pyroligneous acid. As would be expected, woodsmoke is more effective against vegetative cells than against bacterial spores, and the rate of germicidal action of the smoke increases with its concentration and the temperature and varies with the kind of wood employed. The residual effect of the smoke in the food has been reported to be greater against bacteria than against molds. The concentration of mycostatic materials from woodsmoke necessary to prevent mold growth increases with a rise in the humidity of the atmosphere of storage.

The application of "liquid smoke," a solution of chemicals similar to those in woodsmoke, to the outside of foods has little or no preservative effect although it contributes to flavor.

Spices and Other Condiments

Spices and other condiments do not have any marked bacteriostatic effect in the concentrations customarily used but may help other agents in preventing the growth of organisms in food. Different lots of spice vary in their effectiveness, depending on the source, the freshness, and whether they have been stored whole or ground up. The inhibitory effect of spices differs with the kind of spice and the microorganism being tested. Mustard flour and the volatile oil of mustard, for example, are very effective against *Saccharomyces cerevisiae* but are not as potent as cinnamon and cloves against most bacteria. The essential oils of spices are more inhibitory than the corresponding ground spices.

Cinnamon and cloves, containing cinnamic aldehyde and eugenol, respectively, usually are more bacteriostatic than are other spices. Ground peppercorn and allspice are less inhibitory, and mustard, mace, nutmeg, and ginger still less. Thyme, bay leaves, marjoram, savory, rosemary, black pepper, and others have only weak inhibitory power against most organisms and may even stimulate some, e.g., yeasts and molds. Fairly heavy concentrations of the more effective spices permit mycelial growth of some of the molds but inhibit the formation of asexual spores. Of the oils tested, the volatile oil of mustard is most effective against yeasts; oils of cinnamon and cloves are fairly effective, and oils of thyme and bay leaves are least effective.

Unless spices have been treated to reduce their microbial content, they may add high numbers and undesirable kinds of microorganisms to foods of which they are ingredients.

Other plant materials used in seasoning foods, such as horseradish, garlic, and onion, may be bacteriostatic or germicidal. Extracts of these plants, as well as of cabbage and turnip, have been shown to be inhibitory to *Bacillus subtilis* and *Escherichia coli*. Acrolein is supposedly the active principle in onions and garlic, and butyl thiocyanate in horseradish. These volatile compounds are lost from the condiment on exposure to the air, with a corresponding loss in bacteriostatic properties.

Others

Halogens are added to water for washing foods or equipment, for cooling, and for addition to some products, e.g., washing butter; water for drinking may be chlorinated by the direct addition of chlorine, or hypochlorites or chloramines may be used. Iodine-impregnated wrappers have been employed to lengthen the keeping time of fruits. Iodophors, which are combinations of iodine with nonionic wetting agents and acid, are being used in the sanitization of dairy utensils. Halogens kill organisms by oxidation, injury to cell membranes, or direct combination with cell proteins.

Hypochlorites, usually of calcium or sodium, yield hypochlorous acid, a powerful oxidizing agent, and are effective germicidal agents; their effectiveness is reduced by the presence of organic matter in any considerable amount. The hypochlorites are used in the treatment of water used in food plants for drinking, processing, and cooling and on plant equipment. They have been incorporated in ice for icing fish in transit and in water for washing the exterior of fruits and vegetables. Microorganisms are harmed by oxidation or by direct chlorination of cell proteins.

Phosphoric acid is used in some soft drinks, e.g., the colas.

The oxidizing agent hydrogen peroxide has been used as a preservative, usually in conjunction with heat. One method for the pasteurization of milk for cheese involves the addition of H_2O_2 and the use of a comparatively low heating temperature. Excess peroxide is decomposed by catalase. Thermophiles are destroyed in the processing of sugar by a combination of heat and H_2O_2. Other peroxides are used in foods but not for the prevention of microbial growth.

Gas storage of foods was mentioned in Chapter 7 in connection with preservation by chilling and will be discussed further in the chapters on the preservation of specific foods. Most often used is carbon dioxide in combination with chilling. Oxygen or air under pressure is combined with chilling, as in the Hofius process for milk. Nitrogen is used as an inert gas over foods that should not be exposed to air.

Boric acid and borates still are used in some countries as preservatives for foods, but their use is forbidden in the United States. Powdered boric acid has been dusted onto foods, e.g., meats, but it is a very weak antiseptic and is not considered healthful. Borax (sodium tetraborate) has been used to wash vegetables and whole fruits, such as oranges.

Other Groupings of Chemical Agents

Most of the oxidizing agents employed in food preservation have been mentioned under other headings. These include peroxides, bromine, chlorine, iodine, hypochlorites, chloramines, and ozone. Oxidizing agents used in bleaching flour, oxides of nitrogen, chlorine, nitrosyl chloride, nitrogen trichloride, and benzoyl peroxide may be bacteriostatic or even bactericidal, but that is not the reason for their addition.

The use of chemical agents for cleaning and sanitizing equipment will be discussed in Chapter 27. Most of these chemicals are antiseptic, and some are germicidal in the concentrations employed, but their main function in food preservation is to reduce the contamination of foods with microorganisms from the equipment touched by these foods. There should not be enough residual chemical carryover into the food to be of any significance in its preservation. Some of these chemicals are employed to remove dirt and remove or kill microorganisms on the outer surfaces of some foods, e.g., fruits, vegetables, and eggs, but none of these detergents or sanitizers would be incorporated in foods as preservatives.

It has been mentioned that chemical preservatives can be grouped on the basis of their specificity for certain microorganisms. Considerable attention has been paid to compounds that are effective against molds and related fungi. Mycostats previously mentioned include propionic acid and propionates, caprylic acid, acetic acid, dehydroacetic acid, monochloroacetic acid, sorbic acid and sorbates, and propylene glycol. Of these, only the propionates and sorbates have been incorporated in foods to any great extent. Chemical preservatives against molds have been applied in liquid form to the outside surfaces of foods or used as a vapor about them. Examples of mycostatic chemicals which have been tried in vapor or gaseous form about foods are propylene glycol, carbon dioxide, methyl bromide, and various derivatives of phenol. Antifungal antibiotics include griseofulvin, pimaricin, fulcine, actidione, rimocidin, and nystatin. Antimycotics permitted in food-packaging material (under specified conditions) are sodium and calcium propionates, sodium benzoate, sorbic acid and sorbates, and methyl-and propylparabens. Caprylic acid may be used in cheese wraps. Also recommended for impregnating wrappers for foods have been iodine, sulfites, o-phenylphenol or sodium o-phenylphenate, biphenyl, dimethylolurea, and many other substances. A large number of compounds (too many to list) have been recommended for the treatment of surfaces of fruits, vegetables, eggs, cheese, meats, and fish. They range from simple, inorganic compounds such as nitrites and sulfur dioxide (sulfurous acid) through organic acids (crotonic, sorbic, levulinic, etc.) and esters of organic acids, (e.g., esters of vanillic or benzoic acid) to complex phenolic compounds. Biphenyl and sodium o-phenylphenate plus ammonia, for example, have been applied to citrus fruits to reduce fungal spoilage. Most of these compounds cannot be used without the approval of the Food and Drug Administration.

Boiler-Water Additives

Boiler-water additives that have been approved by the Food and Drug Administration must be used for steam that comes in contact with foods (Anonymous, 1960).

Antibiotics

Most of the better-known antibiotics have been tested on raw foods, chiefly proteinaceous ones like meats, fish, and poultry, in an endeavor to lengthen the storage time at chilling temperatures. Aureomycin (chlortetracycline) has been found superior to other antibiotics tested because of its broad spectrum of activity. Terramycin (oxytetracycline) is almost as good for lengthening the time of preservation of foods. Some success also has been claimed with Chloromycetin (chloramphenicol). These three antibiotics inhibit protein synthesis in the cell. Streptomycin, neomycin, polymyxin, nisin, subtilin, bacitracin, and others are not as satisfactory, and penicillin is of little use. Nisin has been employed in Europe to suppress anaerobes in cheese and cheese products. Natamycin is effective against yeasts and molds; it is used, or tested, in orange juice, fresh fruits, sausage, and cheese.

Experimentally, antibiotics have been combined with heat in attempts to reduce the thermal treatment necessary for the preservation of low- and medium-acid canned foods. Most tests have been with the peptides, subtilin and nisin, and tylosin. It has been suggested that a botulinum cook, i.e., enough of a heat treatment to inactivate all spores of *Clostridium botulinum,* be given canned foods, combined with the addition of enough antibiotic to inhibit germination and outgrowth of surviving spores of the most heat-resistant thermophilic spoilage bacteria and putrefactive anaerobes. Subtilin supposedly has no effect on the heat resistance of bacterial spores but inhibits heat-damaged cells during outgrowth, whereas nisin apparently interferes with spore germination and with lysis of the spore coat. Tylosin may inhibit cell growth.

Although food bacteriologists realize the advantages of the preservation of raw foods by a nontoxic antibiotic or the use of one in combination with reduced amounts of heat in the processing of canned foods, they raise certain questions about the use of antibiotics as preservatives. They agree that antibiotics never should be substituted for good hygiene. The effect of an antibiotic on microorganisms is known to vary with the species or even with the strain of the organism; hence the antibiotic may be effective against some spoilage organisms but not others or against part of the population in a culture but not all organisms. Organisms are known to become adapted to increasing concentrations of an antibiotic so that new, resistant strains may develop. There also is the possibility that other organisms, not now significant in food spoilage but resistant to the antibiotic, may assume new importance in food spoilage. Then, too, there may be effects of the antibiotic on the consumer such as sensitization to it, changes in the intestinal flora, and the development of strains of pathogens in the body resistant to that antibiotic, although these effects probably would be minimized by the very low levels of antibiotics employed in foods compared with the amounts employed for therapy. It has been recommended that antibiotics selected for use in food preservation be other than those being used in the treatment of human diseases. Canners feel that when used in the processing of canned foods, the antibiotic plus the heat treatment must destroy all spores of *Clostridium botulinum* and allow a margin of safety, and preferably the treatment should destroy all spoilage organisms and their spores. If spores survive, the antibiotic must remain in sufficient concentration in the food to prevent germination, outgrowth, or vegetative growth of cells. This means that the antibiotic must persist in bacteriostatic or sporostatic concentration throughout the storage life of the canned food.

Attempts have been made to test the bactericidal effect of edible extracts of plants, e.g., of carrot, green bean, tomato, and celery plants, in combination with a milder heat treatment than usual, to destroy various bacteria and bacterial spores. The use of plant extracts in this manner would avoid most of the problems just discussed.

The Food and Drug Administration had approved the use of a chlortetracycline and oxytetracycline dip for preserving poultry, setting up a 7-ppm tolerance in the uncooked, dressed fowls. This quantity of antibiotic has been shown to double or triple the storage life of the poultry. Apparently approval had been granted because evidence was given to prove that (1) use of the material affords added protection to the consumer, (2) basic sanitation procedures are not replaced because of the method, and (3) the antibiotic is destroyed during cooking of the poultry, leaving no harmful end products. This permission for use by FDA has been revoked. Now it is permissible to use these tetracyclines at 5 ppm only on fresh fish, shucked scallops, and unpeeled shrimp. The antibiotic may be applied as a dip or an ice.

DEVELOPED PRESERVATIVES

Food fermentations may serve either or both of two purposes: (1) to produce new and desired flavors and physical characteristics and hence a different food product and (2) to help preserve the food. The relative importance of these two aims varies with the food and is difficult to evaluate. Certainly the first fermented milks and sauerkraut were empirical discoveries and served primarily to keep milk or cabbage over long periods of storage, but a taste for the fermented products developed, and now they are made as much for their palatability as for their keeping quality.

The preservatives produced in foods by microbial action are for the most part acids (chiefly lactic) and alcohol. The preservative effect of these substances nearly always is supplemented by one or more additional preservative agents, such as low temperature, heat, anaerobic conditions, sodium chloride, sugar, or added acid.

Developed acidity plays a part in the preservation of sauerkraut, pickles, green olives, fermented milk, cheese, and certain sausages and in various fermented foods of plant origin. Development of the full amount of acidity from the sugar available may be permitted in the pickle and green-olive fermentations, or the fermentation may be stopped by chilling or canning before the maximum acidity is attained in other fermentations, e.g., that for fermented milks or sauerkraut. The approximate acidity developed in some of these products, expressed as lactic acid, is sauerkraut, 1.7 percent; salt-stock or dill pickles and green olives, 0.9 percent; and fermented milks, 0.6 to 0.85 percent. The acidity of cheese usually is expressed in terms of hydrogen-ion concentration; most freshly made cheeses have a pH of about 5.0 to 5.2 and become more alkaline during curing.

The alcohol content of beer, ale, fermented fruit juices, and distilled liquors has a preservative effect but was not produced primarily for that purpose.

BIBLIOGRAPHY

Anonymous. 1960. FDA names 182 safe additives. Food Eng. 32(1): 81-82.
Anonymous. 1981. The health effects of nitrate, nitrite, and N-nitroso compounds. Assembly of Life Sciences, National Research Council, National Academy Press, Washington, D.C.
Anonymous. 1982. Alternatives to the current use of nitrite in foods. Assembly of Life Sciences, National Research Council, National Academy Press, Washington, D.C.
Bosund, O. 1962. The action of benzoic and salicylic acids on the metabolism of microorganisms. Adv. Food Res. 11:331–353.
Branen, A. L., and P. M. Davidson. 1983. Antimicrobials in foods. Marcel Dekker, Inc., New York.
Campbell, L. L., Jr., and R. T. O'Brien. 1955. Antibiotics in food preservation. Food Technol. 9:461–465.
Draudt, H. N. 1963. The meat smoking process: a review. Food Technol. 17:1557–1562.
Farber, L. 1959. Antibiotics in food preservation. Annu. Rev. Microbiol. 13:125–140.

Fine, S. D. 1970, 1973. Ethylene oxide, part 121, food additives, sec. 121.1231, Fed. Reg. 35(145):12062; sec. 121.1232, Fed. Reg. 38:5342.

Food Additives Amendment of 1958. Pub. L. 85–929, 85th Congr. H.R. 13254, Sept. 6, 1958.

Fulton, K. R. 1981. Surveys of industry on the use of food additives. Food Technol. 35:80.

Furia, T. E. 1972. Handbook of food additives. The CRC Press, Cleveland, Ohio.

Goldberg, H. S. 1964. Nonmedical uses of antibiotics. Adv. Appl. Microbiol. 6:91–117.

Gould, G. A. 1964. Gas sterilization of packaged, dried ingredients. Food Process. 25(9):96–97, 104–106.

Ingram, M., E. M. Barnes, and J. M. Shewan. 1956. Problems in the use of antibiotics for preserving meat and fish. Food Sci. Abstr. 28:121–136.

Mahoney, J. F. 1958. Food additives amendment enacted. Food Technol. 12:637–640.

Molin, N., and A. Erichsen (eds.). 1965. Microbial inhibitors in food. In IVth International Symposium on Food Microbiology. Almqvist and Wiskell, Stockholm.

Roberts, A. C., and D. J. McWeeny. 1972. The uses of sulphur dioxide in the food industry: a review. J. Food Technol. 7:221–238.

Title 21: Food and Drug. CFR, pts. 170–199, rev. Apr. 1, 1985.

Vandegraft, E. E., C. W. Hesseltine, and O. L. Shotwell. 1975. Grain preservatives: effect on aflatoxin and ochratoxin production. J. Cereal Chem. 52:79–84.

Vaughn, R. H., H. Ng, G. F. Stewart, C. W. Nagel, and K. L. Simpson. 1960. Antibiotics in poultry meat preservation: development *in vitro* of bacterial resistance to chlortetracycline. Appl. Microbiol. 8:27–30.

World Health Organization. 1965. Specifications of the identity and purity of food additives and their toxicological evaluation. WHO Tech. Rep. Ser. 38, Geneva.

World Health Organization. 1974. Toxicological evaluation of certain food additives with a review of general principles and of specifications. WHO Tech. Rep. Ser. 539, Geneva.

CHAPTER 10

PRESERVATION BY RADIATION

In their search for new, improved methods of food preservation, investigators have paid special attention to the possible utilization of radiations of various frequencies, ranging from low-frequency electrical current to high-frequency gamma rays (Figure 10-1). Much of this work has focused on the use of ultraviolet radiation, ionizing radiation, and microwave heating.

It is common to group the entire spectrum of radiation into two categories, one on each side of visible light. Low-frequency, long-wavelength, low-quantum-energy radiation ranges from radio waves to infrared. The effect of these radiations on microorganisms is related to their thermal agitation of the food. Conversely, the high-frequency, shorter-wavelength radiations have high quantum energies and actually excite or destroy organic compounds and microorganisms without heating the product. Microbial destruction without the generation of high temperatures suggested the term "cold sterilization."

When applied to the food industry, shorter-wavelength radiation can be further divided into two groups. Lower-frequency and lower-energy radiation, for example, the ultraviolet part of the spectrum, has sufficient energy only to excite molecules. This area of the spectrum is employed in the food industry and is covered in the section on ultraviolet irradiation. Radiations of higher frequencies have high energy contents and are capable of actually breaking individual molecules into ions, hence the term ionizing irradiation.

ULTRAVIOLET IRRADIATION

Of the various electromagnetic radiations, ultraviolet irradiation has been the most widely used in the food industry. Radiation with wavelengths near

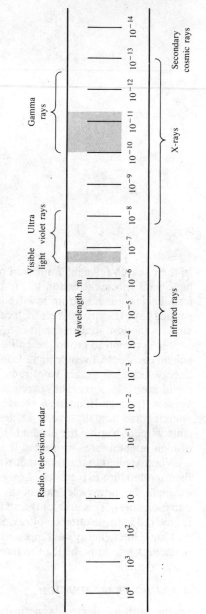

FIGURE 10-1
Chart of the electromagnetic spectrum, showing the location of various types of radiation. (*Courtesy of Westinghouse Electric Corporation, Bloomfield, N.J.*)

260 nm is absorbed strongly by purines and pyrimidines and is therefore the most germicidal. Ultraviolet radiation around 200 nm is strongly absorbed by oxygen, may result in the production of ozone, and is ineffective against microorganisms.

Germicidal Lamps

The usual source of ultraviolet radiation in the food industry is from quartz-mercury vapor lamps or low-pressure mercury lamps, which emit radiation at 254 nm. Radiation from these lamps includes rays in the visible range and those in the erythemic range, which have an irritating effect on skin and mucous membranes. The lamps are available in various sizes, shapes, and power. The newer types release only negligible amounts of ozone.

Factors Influencing Effectiveness

It should be emphasized that only direct rays are effective unless they come from special reflectors, and even then their effectiveness is reduced. The factors that influence the effectiveness of ultraviolet rays are as follows:

1 *Time*. The longer the time of exposure to a given concentration, the more effective the treatment.

2 *Intensity*. The intensity of the rays reaching an object will depend on the power of the lamp, the distance from the lamp to the object, and the kind and amount of interfering material in the path of the rays. Obviously, the intensity will increase with the power of the lamp. Intensity is usually measured as microwatts per square centimeter ($\mu W/cm^2$). The quantity or dose of irradiation actually absorbed by an organism or a product thus is expressed by the product of the time and intensity. Within the short distances common in industrial uses, the intensities of the rays vary inversely with distance from the lamp. A lamp is about 100 times as effective in killing microorganisms at 5 in, than at 8 ft from the irradiated object. Most tests are reported from a distance of about 12 in. Dust in the air or on the lamp reduces the effectiveness, as does too much atmospheric humidity. Over 80 percent relative humidity definitely reduces the penetration through air, but humidities below 60 percent have little effect.

3 *Penetration*. The nature of the object or material being irradiated has an important influence on the effectiveness of the process. Penetration is reduced even by clear water, which also exerts a protective effect on microorganisms. Dissolved mineral salts, especially of iron, and cloudiness greatly reduce the effectiveness of the rays. Even a thin layer of fatty or greasy material cuts off the rays. There is no penetration through opaque material. Therefore, the rays affect only the outer surface of most irradiated foods directly exposed to the lamp and do not penetrate to microorganisms inside the food. The lamps do serve, however, to reduce the number of viable organisms in the air surrounding the food.

Effects on Humans and Animals

Gazing at ultraviolet lamps produces irritation of the eyes within a few seconds, and longer exposure of the skin results in erythema, or reddening. The effect on animals is usually not as marked, although the eyes, especially of chicks, may be irritated.

Action on Microorganisms

As has been stated, the intensity of the rays when they reach the organism, the time in which they act, and the location of the organism determine the germicidal effect. Each microorganism has a characteristic resistance to ultraviolet irradiation. This can vary with the phase of growth and the physiological state of the cell. It takes as much as five times the exposure to kill vegetative cells of some bacteria compared with others, but in general the killing exposure does not vary widely among different species. The amount of ultraviolet radiation needed to destroy several different microorganisms is summarized in Table 10-1. The location of the organism during the tests has a marked influence. For example, 97 to 99 percent of *Escherichia coli* in air were killed in 10 sec at 24 in with a 15-watt lamp, but 20 sec at 11 in was necessary for bacteria on the surface of an agar plate. Capsulation or clumping of bacteria increases their resistance. Bacterial spores usually take from two to five times as much exposure as the corresponding vegetative cells. Some types of pigmentation also have a protective effect. Generally, yeasts are from two to five times as resistant as bacteria, although some are easily killed. The resistance of molds is reported to be from ten to fifty times that of bacteria. Pigmented molds are more resistant than nonpigmented molds, and spores are more resistant than

TABLE 10-1
ULTRAVIOLET RADIATION DOSES TO DESTROY
CERTAIN GROUPS OF MICROORGANISMS

Microorganism	Dose needed for 1 log cycle reduction or 1 D value (μW sec $\times 10^3$)
Gram-negative bacteria	
Facultative anaerobes	0.8–6.4
Aerobes	3.0–5.5
Phototrophic	5.0–6.0
Gram-positive bacteria	
Bacillus	5.0–8.0
Bacillus spores	8.0–10.0
Micrococcus	6.0–20.0
Staphylococcus	2.2–5.0
Molds	10.0–200.0
Yeasts	3.0–10.0

Source: Summarized from Ingram and Roberts (1980).

mycelium. The killing effect of ultraviolet rays is usually explained by the "target theory," which is described in the discussion of ionizing radiation.

Applications in the Food Industry

The use of ultraviolet irradiation in the food industry will be discussed in connection with the preservation of specific foods. Examples of the successful use of these rays include treatment of water used for beverages; aging of meats; treatment of knives for slicing bread; treatment of bread and cakes; packaging of sliced bacon; sanitizing of eating utensils; prevention of growth of film yeast on pickle, vinegar, and sauerkraut vats; killing of spores on sugar crystals and in sirups; storage and packaging of cheese; prevention of mold growth on walls and shelves; and treatment of air used for, or in, storage and processing rooms.

IONIZING RADIATIONS

Kinds of Ionizing Radiations

Radiation classified as ionizing includes x-rays or gamma rays, cathode or beta rays, protons, neutrons, and alpha particles. Neutrons result in residual radioactivity in foods, and protons and alpha particles have little penetration. Therefore, these rays are not practical for use in food preservation and will not be discussed.

X-rays are penetrating electromagnetic waves which are produced by bombardment of a heavy-metal target with cathode rays within an evacuated tube. They are not currently considered economical for use in the food industry.

Gamma rays are like x-rays but are emitted from by-products of atomic fission or from imitations of such by-products. Cobalt 60 and cesium 137 have been used as sources of these rays in most experimental work thus far, with cobalt 60 being the most promising for commercial applications.

Beta rays are streams of electrons (beta particles) emitted from radioactive material. **Electrons** are small, negatively charged particles of uniform mass that form part of the atom. They are deflected by magnetic and electric fields. Their penetration depends on the speed with which they hit the target. The higher the charge of the electron, the deeper its penetration.

Cathode rays are streams of electrons (beta particles) from the cathode of an evacuated tube. In practice, these electrons are accelerated by artificial means.

Definition of Terms

Before the utilization of ionizing radiations can be discussed, a few terms must be defined.

A **roentgen** (r) is the quantity of gamma or x-radiation which produces one electrostatic unit of electric charge of either sign in a cubic centimeter of air under standard conditions.

A **roentgen-equivalent-physical** (rep) is the quantity of ionizing energy which produces, per gram of tissue, an amount of ionization equivalent to a roentgen. A **megarep** is 1 million rep. One r, or 1 rep, is equivalent to the absorption of 83 to 90 erg per gram of tissue.

The **rad** now is employed chiefly as the unit of radiation dosage, being equivalent to the absorption of 100 erg per gram of irradiated material. A **megarad** (Mrad) is 1 million rad, and a **kilorad** (Krad) is 1,000 rad.

An **electronvolt** (eV) is the energy gained by an electron in moving through a potential difference of 1 volt. A **meV** is 1 million electronvolts.

A meV, then, is a measure of the intensity of the irradiation, and a rep is a measure of the absorbed energy that is effective within the food.

A **Gray** (Gy) equals 100 rads and is being used as a term to replace rads in some references.

Radappertization is a term used to define "radiation sterilization" which would imply high dose treatments, with the resulting product being shelf-stable.

Radurization refers to "radiation pasteurization" low-dose treatments, where the intent is to extend a product's shelf life.

Radicidation also is a low-dose "radiation pasteurization" treatment, but with the specific intent being the elimination of a particular pathogen.

Picowaved is a term used to label foods treated with low-level ionizing radiation.

X-Rays.

X-rays, gamma rays, and cathode rays are equally effective in sterilization for equal quantities of energy absorbed. X-rays and gamma rays have good penetration, while cathode rays have comparatively poor penetration. The greatest drawback at present to the use of x-rays in food preservation is the low efficiency and consequent high cost of their production, for only about 3 to 5 percent of the electron energy applied is used in the production of x-rays. For this reason, most recent research has concentrated on the application of gamma rays and cathode rays.

GAMMA RAYS AND CATHODE RAYS

Since these two types of rays are equally effective in sterilization for equal quantities of energy absorbed and apparently produce similar changes in the food being treated, they will be discussed together and compared where possible.

Sources

Chief sources of gamma rays are (1) radioactive fission products of uranium and cobalt, (2) the coolant circulated in nuclear reactors, and (3) other fuel elements used to operate a nuclear reactor. Cathode rays usually are accelerated by special electrical devices. The greater this acceleration (i.e., the more meV), the deeper the penetration into the food.

Penetration

Gamma rays have good penetration, but their effectiveness decreases exponentially with depth. They have been reported to be effective up to 20 cm in most foods, but this depth will depend on the time of exposure. Cathode rays, on the other hand, have poor penetration, being effective at only about 0.5 cm per meV when "cross firing," that is, irradiation from opposite sides, is employed. The absorption dose level in a material is not a uniformly decreasing fraction with depth but rather builds up to a maximum at a depth equal to about one-third of the total penetration and then decreases to zero.

Efficiency

Because cathode rays are directional, they can be made to hit the food and therefore are used with greater efficiency than are gamma rays, which are constantly emitted in all directions from the radioactive sources. Various estimates of the maximal efficiency of utilization of cathode rays range between 40 and 80 percent, depending on the shape of the irradiated material, but only a maximum of 10 to 25 percent utilization efficiency is estimated for gamma rays. Radioactive sources of gamma rays decay steadily and hence weaken with time.

Safety

The use of cathode rays presents fewer health problems than the use of gamma rays, since cathode rays are directional and less penetrating, can be turned off for repair or maintenance work, and present no hazard of radioactive materials after a fire, explosion, or other catastrophe. Gamma rays are emitted in all directions, are penetrating, are continuously emitted, and come from radioactive sources. Gamma rays require more shielding to protect workers. Tests thus far on animals and human volunteers have not indicated any ill effects from the eating of irradiated foods.

Effects on Microorganisms

The bactericidal efficacy of a given dose of irradiation depends on the following:

1 *The kind and species of organism.* The importance of this factor is illustrated by the data in Table 10-2.

2 *The numbers of organisms (or spores) originally present.* The more organisms there are, the less effective a given dose will be.

TABLE 10-2
APPROXIMATE KILLING DOSES OF IONIZING RADIATIONS IN KILOGRAYS

Organism	Approximate lethal dose	Organism	Approximate lethal dose
Humans	0.0056–0.0075	Bacteria (cells of saprophytes)	
Insects	.22–.93	Gram-negative	
Viruses	10–40	*Escherichia coli*	1.0–2.3
Yeasts (fermentative)	4–9	*Pseudomonas aeruginosa*	1.6–2.3
Saccharomyces		*Pseudomonas fluorescens*	1.2–2.3
cerevisiae	5	*Enterobacter aerogenes*	1.4–1.8
Torula cremoris	4.7	Gram-positive	
Yeasts (film)	3.7–18	*Lactobacillus* spp.	0.23–0.38
Hansenula sp.	4.7	*Streptococcus faecalis*	1.7–8.8
Candida krusei	11.6	*Leuconostoc dextranicum**	0.9
Molds (with spores)	1.3–11	*Sarcina lutea**	3.7
Penicillium spp.	1.4–2.5	Bacterial spores	3.1–37
Aspergillus spp.	1.4–3.7	*Bacillus subtilis*	12–18
Rhizopus sp.	10	*Bacillus coagulans*	10
Fusarium sp.	2.5	*Clostridium botulinum* (A)	19–37
Bacteria (cells of pathogens)		*Clostridium botulinum* (E)	15–18
Mycobacterium		*Clostridium perfringens*	3.1
tuberculosis	1.4	Putrefactive anaerobe	
Staphylococcus aureus	1.4–7.0	3679	23–50
Corynebacterium		*Bacillus stearothermo-*	
diphtheriae	4.2	*philus*	10–17
Salmonella spp.	3.7–4.8		

3 *The composition of the food.* Some constituents, e.g., proteins, catalase, and reducing substances (nitrites, sulfites, and sulfhydryl compounds), may be protective. Compounds that combine with the SH groups would be sensitizing. Products of ionization may be harmful to the organisms.

4 *The presence or absence of oxygen.* The effect of free oxygen varies with the organism, ranging from no effect to sensitization of the organism. Undesirable "side reactions," which will be discussed subsequently, are likely to be intensified in the presence of oxygen and to be less frequent in a vacuum or an atmosphere of nitrogen.

5 *The physical state of the food during irradiation.* Both moisture content and temperature affect different organisms in different ways.

6 *The condition of the organisms.* Age, temperature of growth and sporulation, and state—vegetative or spore—may affect the sensitivity of the organisms. These factors have been discussed previously in connection with other methods of processing foods.

The type of irradiation and, within limits, the pH of the food seem to have little influence on the dose needed to inactivate the organisms.

It has been stated by some workers that the resistance of a given species of microorganism to ionizing radiations parallels in general its resistance to conventional heat processing, although there are notable exceptions. Spores of *Clostridium botulinum,* for example, have been found to be more resistant to gamma rays than are spores of a flat sour bacterium (No. 1518) and a thermophilic anaerobe (T.A. No. 3814), although the latter two are more heat-resistant. Table 10-2 summarizes reports from various sources on the approximate dosages of radiation necessary to kill various types of microorganisms. These figures will vary with the conditions listed in the preceding paragraph. It is to be noted, however, that (1) humans are much more sensitive to radiations than are microrganisms, (2) bacterial spores are considerably more resistant than are vegetative cells, (3) gram-negative bacteria are, in general, less resistant than are gram-positive ones, and (4) yeasts and molds vary considerably, but some are more resistant than most bacteria. For example, *Candida krusei* (Table 10-2) is as resistant as many bacterial spores. Certain microorganisms are much more resistant than anticipated. For example, a radiation-resistant micrococcus resembling *Micrococcus roseus* has been found in irradiated meat. *Microbacterium* species in meat have been found to be especially resistant. There is, then, the possibility that resistant strains may be isolated from low-level-irradiated foods.

Preliminary gamma irradiation of bacterial spores has been found to make them more sensitive to heat, but preliminary heat shocking does not affect the lethal action of subsequent gamma irradiation. Previous ultrasonic treatment of organisms sensitizes them to radiation.

It is supposed that irradiated microorganisms are destroyed by passage of an ionizing particle or quantum of energy through, or in close proximity to, a sensitive portion of the cell, causing a direct "hit" on this target, ionization in this sensitive region, and subsequent death of the organism (this is called the target theory). It is assumed also that much of the germicidal effect results from ionization of the surroundings, especially of water, to yield free radicals, some of which may be oxidizing or reducing and therefore helpful in the destruction of the organisms. Irradiation also may cause mutations in the organisms present.

Effects on Foods

Radiation doses heavy enough to affect sterilization have been found to produce undesirable "side reactions," or secondary changes, in many kinds of foods, causing undesirable colors, odors, tastes, or even physical properties.

Some of the changes produced in foods by sterilizing doses of radiation include (1) in meat, a rise in pH, destruction of glutathione, and an increase in carbonyl compounds, hydrogen sulfide, and methyl mercaptan, (2) in fats and lipids, destruction of natural antioxidants, oxidation followed by partial polymerization, and increase in carbonyl compounds, and (3) in vitamins, reduction in most foods of levels of thiamine, pyridoxine, and vitamins B_{12}, C, D, E, and K; riboflavin and niacin are fairly stable. The lower the dosage of irradiation, of course, the less frequent the undesirable effects on the food. Destruction of many of the food enzymes requires five to ten times the dosage of rays needed to kill all the microorganisms. Enzyme action may continue after all microorganisms have been destroyed unless a special blanching treatment has preceded irradiation.

The chief effect on the healthfulness of foods is the destruction of vitamins. However, the general nutrition of an irradiated food would be as good as that of a food processed by other means to achieve the same shelf stability. There is no indication of production of radioactivity with electron beams below 11 meV or with gamma rays from cobalt 60.

Applications

Currently food irradiation has been approved only in a very limited way in the United States. Low-level irradiation ([1 kiloGray) can be used on fresh fruits and vegetables to kill insects and to inhibit spoilage. Dry or dehydrated vegetables (herbs and spices) can be irradiated at up to 30 kiloGray to kill insects

TABLE 10-3
APPLICATIONS OF FOOD IRRADIATION

Type of food	Radiation dose in kiloGrays	Effect of treatment
Meat, poultry, fish, shellfish, some vegetables, baked goods, prepared foods	20–70	Sterilization. Treated product can be stored at room temperature without spoilage. Treated product is safe for hospital patients who require micro-biologically sterile diets
Spices and other seasonings	8–30	Reduces number of microorganisms and insects. Replaces chemicals used for this purpose
Meat, poultry, fish	1–10	Delays spoilage by reducing the number of microorganisms in the fresh, refrigerated product. Kills some types of food poisoning bacteria
Strawberries and some other fruits	1–4	Extends shelf life by delaying mold growth
Grain, fruit, vegetables, and other foods subject to insect infestation	0.1–1	Kills insects or prevents them from reproducing. Could partially replace fumigants used for this purpose
Bananas, avocados, mangos, papayas, guavas, and certain other noncitrus fruits	0.25–0.35	Delays ripening
Potatoes, onions, garlic	0.05–0.15	Inhibits sprouting
Pork	0.08–0.15	Inactivates trichinae
Grain, dehydrated vegetables, other foods	Various doses	Desirable physical and chemical changes

Source: ACSH (1985).

and bacteria. Additionally, processes for irradiating pork (trichinae), wheat (insects), and potatoes (sprout formation) have been approved. However, renewed interest and regulatory proposals will probably result in expanded use in this country. Close to thirty countries now have approved some form of food irradiation. The specific applications of food irradiation are summarized in Table 10-3.

MICROWAVE PROCESSING

Microwave heating and processing of foods is becoming increasingly popular, particularly at the consumer level. Microwaves are electromagnetic waves between infrared and radio waves (Figure 10-1). Specific frequencies are usually at either 915 megacycles or 2,450 megacycles. The energy or heat produced by microwaves as they pass through a food is a result of the extremely rapid oscillation of the food molecules in an attempt to align themselves with the electromagnetic field being produced. This rapid oscillation, or intermolecule friction, generates heat. The preservative effect of microwaves or the bactericidal effect produced is really a function of the heat that is generated. In other words, the microwaves themselves do not result in any inactivation of foodborne microorganisms; rather, it is the heat produced by the excitation of food molecules that actually results in microbial destruction.

BIBLIOGRAPHY

ACSH. American Council on Science and Health. 1985. Irradiated foods. ACSH, Summit, N.J.

Anderson, A. W., K. E. Rash, and R. P. Elliker. 1961. Taxonomy of a recently isolated radiation-resistant micrococcus. Abstr. Bacteriol. Proc. (Soc. Amer. Bacteriol.) 1961:56.

Asselbergs, E. A. 1961. New developments in infra-red radiation. Food Can. 21(10): 36–38.

Bellamy, W. D. 1959. Preservation of foods and drugs by ionizing radiations. Adv. Appl. Microbiol. 1:49–73.

Bridges, B. A., and T. Horne. 1959. The influence of environmental factors on the microbicidal effect of ionising radiations. J. Appl. Bacteriol. 22:96–115.

Chandler, V. L., et al. and coworkers. 1956. Relative resistance of microorganisms to cathode rays. Appl. Microbiol. 4:143–152.

Copson, D. A. 1962. Microwave heating. AVI Publishing Co., Inc., Westport, Conn.

Dean, E. E., and D. L. Howie. 1963. Safety of food sterilization by ionizing radiations. U.S. Army Natick Labs. Activities Rep. 15(4th quarter):174–183.

Desrosier, N. W., and H. M. Rosenstock. 1960. Radiation technology in food, agriculture, and biology. AVI Publishing Co., Inc., Westport, Conn.

Food and Drug Administration. Irradiation in the production, processing, and handling of food: proposed rule. Fed. Reg. 49(31). Feb. 14, 1984.

Goldblith, S. A. (ed.). 1963. Exploration in future food-processing techniques. The M.I.T. Press, Cambridge, Mass.

Goldblith, S.A. 1964. Radiation. Food Technol. 18:1384–1391.

Goldblith, S. A., and B. E. Proctor. 1956. Radiation preservation of milk and milk products. I. Background and problems. J. Dairy Sci. 39:374–378.

Ingram, M., and T. A. Roberts. 1980. Ultraviolet irradiation. *In* J. H. Silliliker et al. (eds.), Microbial ecology of foods. Volume I. Factors affecting life and death of microorganisms. Academic Press, Inc., New York.

Ingram, M., and T. A. Roberts. 1980. Ionizing irradiation. *In* J. H. Silliliker et al. (eds.), Microbial ecology of foods. Volume I. Factors affecting life and death of microorganisms. Academic Press, Inc., New York.

Josephson, E. C., and M. S. Peterson (eds.). 1982 and 1983. Preservation of food by ionizing radiation, Volumes II and III. CRC Press, Inc., Boca Raton, Fla.

Lea, D. E. 1955. Action of radiation on living cells. 2d ed. Cambridge University Press, London.

Ley, F. J. 1983. New interest in the use of irradiation in the food industry. *In* T. A. Roberts and F. A. Skinner (eds.), Food microbiology: advances and projects. Academic Press, Inc., New York.

Maxcy, R. B. 1982. Irradiation of food for public health protection. J. Food Prot. 45:363–366.

Proctor, B. E., and S. A. Goldblith. 1951. Electromagnetic radiation fundamentals and their applications in food technology. Adv. Food Res. 3:119–196.

Sherman, V. W. 1946. Electronic heat in the food industries. Food Ind. 18:506–509, 628–630.

Thornley, M. J. 1963. Radiation resistance among bacteria. J. Appl. Bacteriol. 26:334–345.

PART

THREE

CONTAMINATION, PRESERVATION, AND SPOILAGE OF DIFFERENT KINDS OF FOODS

The fruit or vegetable is harvested, milk is drawn, eggs are gathered, fish and other products are obtained from natural waters, and animals are collected and slaughtered, all carrying contaminating microorganisms from natural sources (Chapter 4). In most instances, with the start of human handling further contamination begins, and it continues while the product is being handled and processed. The processor attempts to clean and sanitize equipment coming in contact with food to reduce contamination from that source and to employ packaging materials that will not add significant contamination. As has been stated, the term "sanitize" is used rather than "sterilize" because although an attempt is made to sterilize the equipment, i.e., free it all of all living organisms, sterility seldom is attained.

In Part Three, methods of preservation discussed in Chapters 5 to 10 are applied to the main kinds of foods, and the chief types of spoilage of these foods are considered.

CONTAMINATION, PRESERVATION, AND SPOILAGE OF CEREALS AND CEREAL PRODUCTS

Cereal products discussed in this chapter include the grains themselves, meals, flours, alimentary pastes, and breads, cakes, and other bakery products.

CONTAMINATION

The exteriors of harvested grains retain some of the microorganisms they had while growing plus contamination from soil, insects, and other sources. Freshly harvested grains contain a few thousand to millions of bacteria per gram and from none to several hundred thousand mold spores. Bacteria are mostly in the families Pseudomonadaceae, Micrococcaceae, Lactobacillaceae, and Bacillaceae. Scouring and washing the grains remove some of the microorganisms, but most of the microorganisms are removed with the outer portions of the grain during milling. The milling processes, especially bleaching, reduce numbers of organisms, but there then is a possibility of contamination during other procedures, such as blending and conditioning.

Bacteria in wheat flour include spores of *Bacillus,* coliform bacteria, and a few representatives of the genera *Achromobacter**, *Flavobacterium, Sarcina, Micrococcus, Alcaligenes,* and *Serratia*. Mold spores are chiefly those of aspergilli and penicillia, with also some of *Alternaria, Cladosporium,* and other genera. Numbers of bacteria vary widely from a few hundred per gram to millions. Most samples of white wheat flour from the retail market contain a few hundred to a few thousand bacteria per gram, twenty to thirty bacillus spores per

173

gram and 50 to 100 mold spores per gram. Patent flours usually give lower counts than straight or clear, and numbers decrease with storage of the flour. Higher counts usually are obtained from prepared flours, and still higher (8,000 to 12,000 per gram on the average) on graham and whole-wheat flours, which contain also the outer parts of the wheat kernel and are not bleached. Table 11-1 illustrates the normal microflora found on various cereal grains and cereal products.

Cornmeal and flour contain several hundred to several thousand bacteria and molds per gram. Species of *Fusarium* and *Pencillium* are the dominant molds. Because of incubation in a moist condition, malts contain high numbers of bacteria, usually in the millions per gram.

The surface of a freshly baked loaf of bread is practically free of viable microorganisms but is subject to contamination by mold spores from the air during cooling and before wrapping. During slicing, contamination may take place from microorganisms in the air, on the knives, or on the wrapper. Cakes are similarly subject to contamination. Spores of bacteria able to cause ropiness in bread will survive the baking process.

From a public health aspect, the contamination of grains and cereal products with molds has become a significant concern because of the possible presence of mycotoxins. The need to reduce contamination by mold and to avoid conditions which allow their growth is emphasized by the frequent isolation of *Aspergillus flavus* and *A. parasiticus,* which can produce aflatoxin. Other commonly isolated molds, such as fusaria and penicillia, are undesirable since certain species of these genera are also capable of producing mycotoxins (see Chapter 25). The distribution of aflatoxin B_1 in various corn fractions is shown in Table 11-2.

PRESERVATION

Most cereals and cereal products have such a restrictive a_w that there is little difficulty in preventing the growth of microorganisms as long as these products are kept dry. Such materials are stored in bulk or in containers to keep out vermin, resist fire, and avoid rapid changes in temperature and hence increase in moisture. A storage temperature of about 4.4 to 7.2 C is recommended for the dry products. Many bakery products, e.g., breads, rolls, cakes, pastries, pies, and canned mixes, contain enough moisture to be subject to spoilage unless special preservative methods are employed or turnover is rapid.

ASEPSIS

As in other food industries, the adequate cleaning and sanitization of equipment is essential for reasons of both sanitation and preservation. Improperly sanitized equipment may be a source of rope bacteria and the acid-forming bacteria that cause sourness of doughs. Bread, cakes, and other baked goods that

TABLE 11-1
MICROBIOLOGICAL PROFILE OF CEREAL GRAINS AND CEREAL PRODUCTS

Product category	Normal microflora	Quantitative range	Remarks
Raw cereal grains	Molds	10^2–10^4/g	Counts representative of "normal" grains in commercial channels; "mildewed" or "musty" or "spoiled" grain would obviously be beyond these ranges
	Yeasts and yeastlike fungi	10^2–10^4/g	
	Bacteria		
	Aerobic plate count	10^2–10^6/g	Related to amount of soil incorporated in grain sample
	Coliform group	10^2–10^4/g	
	E. coli	10–10^3/g	
	Actinomycetes	10^3–10^6/g	
Flour(s)*, cornmeal, corn grits, semolina	Molds	10^2–10^4/g	Microbial counts in flour can vary from one storage period to another depending on moisture content and storage conditions. The final observed count is a function of original bioload, proliferation, and dieoff. Counts frequently decrease during storage; however, increases have also been noted
	Yeast and yeastlike fungi	10–10^2/g	
	Bacteria		
	Aerobic plate count	10^2–10^6/g	
	Coliform group	0–10/g	Soy flours sometimes contain salmonellae; other flours rarely do
	"Rope" spores	0–10^2/g	
Breakfast cereals and "snacks"	Molds	0–10^3/g	
	Yeasts and yeastlike fungi	0–10^2/g	
	Bacteria		
	Aerobic plate count	0–10^2/g	
	Coliform group	0–10^2/g	
Refrigerated and frozen doughs	Molds	10^2–10^4/g	Yeast counts reflect inoculum intentionally added as part of the product formulation—do not represent "contamination"
	Yeast and yeastlike fungi	10^5–10^6/g	
	Bacteria		
	Aerobic plate count	10^2–10^6/g	The special case of "buttermilk biscuits" which contain 10^2–10^4 lactic acid producers have been omitted from this compilation.
	Coliform group	10–10^2/g	
	Psychrotrophs	10–10^3/g	

(Continued)

TABLE 11-1 *(continued)*
MICROBIOLOGICAL PROFILE OF CEREAL GRAINS AND CEREAL PRODUCTS

Product category	Normal microflora	Quantitative range	Remarks
Baked goods	Molds	$10–10^3$/g	
	Yeast and yeastlike fungi	$10–10^3$/g	
	Bacteria		
	Aerobic plate count	$10–10^3$/g	
	Coliform group	$10–10^2$/g	
Soy protein	Bacteria		Quantitative ranges reflect both original contamination and growth during storage of intermediate-moisture products
	Aerobic plate count	$10^2–10^5$/g	
	Coliform group	$10^2–10^3$/g	
	E. coli	$0–10^2$/g	
	Psychrotrophs	$10^2–10^4$/g	
	Cl. perfringens	$0–10^2$/g	
Pasta products	Bacteria		Wide ranges in bioloads of these products reflect difference between egg-based and macaroni-type products, which are all included in "pasta" category
	Aerobic plate count	$10^3–10^5$/g	
	Coliform group	$10–10^3$/g	
	Molds & yeasts	$10^2–10^5$/g	
Dry cereal mixes	Molds	$10^2–10^5$/g	
	Yeasts and yeastlike fungi	$10^2–10^5$/g	
	Bacteria		
	Aerobic plate count	$10^2–10^6$/g	
	Coliform group	$0–10^4$/g	

Table based on "routine" quality control tests normally performed on various items of specified category; data represent industrywide experience; data presented as "orders of magnitude" for illustrative purposes only.
Source: Condensed from Hobbs and Greene (1984).

TABLE 11-2
DISTRIBUTION OF AFLATOXIN B_1 IN VARIOUS CORN FRACTIONS

U.S. no.	Type of corn*	Weight of sample examined, kg	Total sample aflatoxin B_1, ppb	BCFM† Aflatoxin B_1, ppb‡	BCFM† Total, %	Fluorescing§ kernels and pieces Aflatoxin B_1, ppb	Fluorescing§ kernels and pieces Total, %	Fluorescence§ visible under seedcoat Aflatoxin B_1, ppb	Fluorescence§ visible under seedcoat Total, %	Discolored and damaged kernels Aflatoxin B_1, ppb	Discolored and damaged kernels Total, %	Outwardly sound kernels Aflatoxin B_1, ppb	Outwardly sound kernels Total, %	Origin
1	W	2.0	88	<1	<1	10	11	59	67	10	11	9	10	Ariz.
3	Y	1.0	144	2	1	7	5	51	35	51	35	33	23	S.C.
3	Y	2.0	150	8	5	32	21	38	25	47	31	25	17	Mo.
4	W	2.0	116	7	6	30	26	27	23	16	14	36	31	Tex.
4	W	2.0	132	14	11	27	20	33	25	37	28	21	16	Tex.
4	W	2.0	276	8	3	59	21	95	34	70	25	44	16	Mo.
5	Y	1.0	61	2	3	7	11	15	24	2	3	35	57	Va.
Sample Grade	Y	2.0	61	48	79	3	5	5	8	3	5	2	3	S.C.
Grade	W	2.1	145	4	3	32	22	33	23	29	20	47	32	Ala.
Grade	W	2.0	321	10	3	37	12	123	38	21	6	130	40	Mo.
Average					12		16		31		19		25	

*W=White; Y=Yellow.
†ppb of total sample weight
‡BCFM=broken corn—foreign material.
§BGY (blue-green-yellow) fluorescence under ultraviolet light (365 nm).
Source: Shotwell et al. (1974).

may be subject to spoilage by molds should be protected against contamination by mold spores. Protection of bread is especially important. The bread leaves the oven free of live mold spores and should be cooled promptly in an atmosphere free of them, sliced with spore-free knives, and wrapped without delay.

USE OF HEAT

Bakery products may be sold unbaked, partially baked, or fully baked. The complete baking process ordinarily destroys all bacterial cells, yeasts, and mold spores, but not spores of the rope-forming or other bacteria; yet it has been reported that mold spores in proofer cloths in bakeries can build up enough heat resistance to survive baking. Unbaked or partially baked products usually are kept on the retailer's shelf for only a short period or are kept cool during longer storage. Some special breads, e.g., Boston brown bread and nut bread, have been successfully canned.

USE OF LOW TEMPERATURES

Although ordinary room temperatures may be used by homemakers for short-term storage of baked goods, keeping times could be lengthened and risk of food poisoning lessened if really warm temperatures, like those of hot kitchens or summer weather, were avoided and the foods were stored in a cool place or even in the refrigerator.

The freezing-storage of bakery goods is on the increase. Unbaked or partially baked products, waffles, cheesecake, ice cream pie, and fish, poultry, and meat pies are usually frozen. Bread and rolls can be stored successfully for months in the frozen condition.

USE OF CHEMICAL PRESERVATIVES

Limited drying facilities or rainy weather may result in the storage of grain with a relatively high moisture content. Corn stored at moisture contents in excess of 20 percent, for example, is susceptible to mold growth and possible mycotoxin formation. In addition to insecticides and fumigants, ammonia and propionic acid have been evaluated for their effectiveness in preventing mold growth and mycotoxin production. Ammonia (2 percent) and propionic acid (1 percent) reduce mold growth in high-moisture corn.

A larger number of preservatives have been employed, particularly as mold inhibitors, in bread, rolls, cakes, and other bakery products. Sodium and calcium propionate, sodium diacetate, and sorbates are used extensively. Acidification of the dough with acetic acid has been used to combat rope.

USE OF IRRADIATION

In bakeries, ultraviolet rays have been used to destroy or reduce numbers of mold spores in dough and proof rooms, on the knives of slicing machines, in the room where the bread is packaged, and on the surface of bread, cakes, and other bakery products. The application of radio-frequency radiations to loaves of bread to reduce the likelihood of mold spoilage has been reported, and ionizing radiations, gamma and cathode rays, have been applied experimentally for the preservation of baked goods. Low-level irradiation can also be used to destroy insects in stored grains.

SPOILAGE

Cereal grains and meals and flours made from them should not be subject to microbial spoilage if they are prepared and stored properly because their moisture content is too low to support even the growth of molds. If, however, these products become moistened above the minimum for microbial growth, growth will follow. A little moistening will permit only growth of molds, but more moisture will allow the growth of yeasts and bacteria.

Although the microbial load of cereal grains, meals, and flours may not constitute a spoilage problem by itself, the numbers and types of microorganisms in such products are of concern since these products are used in the formulation of many other foods. The microbial contribution of cereal grains and flours to convenience foods is an important consideration from a public health aspect and as a source of possible spoilage agents.

CEREAL GRAINS AND MEALS

Since cereal grains and meals ordinarily are not processed to reduce their natural flora of microorganisms greatly, they are likely to contain molds, yeasts, and bacteria, which are ready to grow if enough moisture is added. In addition to starch, which is unavailable to many organisms, these grains contain some sugar and available nitrogen compounds, minerals, and accessory growth substances; and the amylases will release more sugar and proteinases will yield more available nitrogenous foods if the grains are moistened. A little added moisture will result in growth of molds at the surface, where air is available. A wet mash of the grains or a mash of the meals will undergo an acid fermentation, chiefly by the lactic acid and coliform bacteria normally present on plant surfaces. This may be followed by an alcoholic fermentation by yeasts as soon as the acidity has increased enough to favor them. Finally, molds (and perhaps film yeasts) will grow on the top surface, although acetic acid bacteria, if present, may oxidize the alcohol to acetic acid and inhibit the molds.

The major factors involved in the spoilage of stored grain by molds include microbial content, moisture levels above 12 to 13 percent, physical damage, and temperature. Numerous different molds can be involved, but the most common are species of *Aspergillus, Penicillium, Mucor, Rhizopus,* and *Fusarium.* As previously mentioned, many of these molds can produce mycotoxins. Grains spoiled by molds represent a potential animal or human health hazard as well as a great economic loss.

FLOURS

Dry cleaning and washing grains and the milling and sifting of flour reduce the content of microorganisms, but the important kinds still are represented in whole-grain flours, e.g., whole wheat or buckwheat, and the spoilage would be similar to that described for cereal grains and meals.

White wheat flour, however, usually is bleached by an oxidizing agent, such as an oxide of nitrogen, chlorine, nitrosyl chloride, or benzoyl peroxide, and this process serves to reduce microbial numbers and kinds. A moisture content of flour of less than 13 percent has been reported to prevent the growth of all microorganisms. Other workers claim that 15 percent permits good mold growth, and over 17 percent the growth of both molds and bacteria. Therefore, slight moistening of white flour brings about spoilage by molds. Because of the variations in microbial content of different lots of flour, the type of spoilage in a flour paste is difficult to predict. If acid-forming bacteria are present, an acid fermentation begins, followed by alcoholic fermentation by yeasts if they are there and then acetic acid by *Acetobacter* species. This succession of changes would be more likely in freshly milled flour than in flour that had been stored for a long period with a consequent reduction in kinds and numbers of microorganisms. In the absence of lactics and coliforms, micrococci have been found to acidify the paste, and in their absence species of *Bacillus* may grow, producing lactic acid, gas, alcohol, acetoin, and small amounts of esters and other aromatic compounds. It is characteristic of most flour pastes to develop an odor of acetic acid and esters.

BREAD

The fermentations taking place in the doughs for various kinds of bread will be discussed in Chapter 22, where it will be noted that some changes caused by microorganisms are desirable and even necessary in making certain kinds of bread. The acid fermentation by lactics and coliform bacteria that is normal in flour pastes or doughs may be too extensive if too much time is permitted, with the result that the dough and bread made from it may be too "sour." Excessive growth of proteolytic bacteria during this period may destroy some of the gas-holding capacity so essential during the rising of the dough and produce a sticky dough. Sticky doughs, however, are usually the result of overmixing or gluten breakdown by reducing agents, e.g., glutathione. There also is the possibility of the production by microorganisms of undesirable flavors other than the sourness.

Historically, the chief types of microbial spoilage of baked bread have been moldiness and ropiness, usually termed "mold" and "rope."

Mold

Molds are the most common and hence the most important cause of the spoilage of bread and most bakery products. The temperatures attained in the baking procedure usually are high enough to kill all mold spores in and on the loaf, so that molds must reach the outer surface or penetrate after baking. They can come from the air during cooling or thereafter, from handling, or from wrappers and usually initiate growth in the crease of the loaf and between the slices of sliced bread.

Chief molds involved in the spoilage of bread are the so-called bread mold, *Rhizopus stolonifer* (syn., *R. nigricans*), with its white cottony mycelium and black dots of sporangia; the green-spored *Penicillium expansum* or *P. stoloniferum; Aspergillus niger* (Figure 11-1) with its greenish- or purplish-brown to black conidial heads and yellow pigment diffusing into the bread; and *Monilia (Neurospora) sitophila,* whose pink conidia give a pink or reddish color to its growth. Species of *Mucor* or *Geotrichum* or any of a large number of species

FIGURE 11–1
Growth of mold (*Aspergillus*) on bread crust. (*Fleischmann Laboratories, Standard Brands Incorporated*).

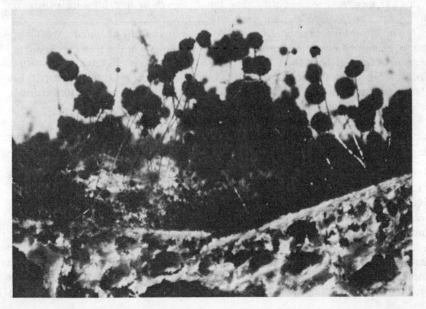

of other genera of molds may develop. Mold spoilage is favored by (1) heavy contamination after baking, due, for example, to air heavily laden with mold spores, a long cooling time, considerable air circulation, or a contaminated slicing machine, (2) slicing, in that more air is introduced into the loaf, (3) wrapping, especially if the bread is warm when wrapped, and (4) storage in a warm, humid place. There is little growth of commercial importance on bread crust in a relative humidity below 90 percent. Bread with 6 percent of milk solids retains moisture somewhat better than does milk-free bread, and hence there is less moisture between loaf and wrapper and hence less molding, but there is not enough of an effect to be of much practical importance. Molding often begins within a loaf of sliced bread, where more moisture is available than at the surface, especially in the crease.

Various methods are employed to prevent moldiness of bread:

1 *Prevention of contamination of bread with mold spores insofar as practicable.* The air about the bread is kept low in spores by removal of possible breeding places for molds, such as returned bread, or walls and equipment. Spore-laden flour dust from other parts of the bakery has been incriminated in causing increased moldiness of bread. Filtration and washing of air to the room and irradiation of the room and more especially the air by means of ultraviolet rays cut down contamination.

2 *Prompt and adequate cooling of the loaves before wrapping to reduce condensation of moisture beneath the wrapper.*

3 *Ultraviolet irradiation of the surface of the loaf and of slicing knives.*

4 *Destruction of molds on the surface by electronic heating.*

5 *Keeping the bread cool to slow mold growth or freezing and storage in the frozen condition to prevent growth entirely.*

6 *Incorporation in the bread dough of some mycostatic chemical.* Most commonly employed now is sodium or calcium propionate at the rate of 0.1 and 0.3 percent of the weight of the flour, a treatment that also is effective against rope. Sorbic acid, up to 0.1 percent, and sodium diacetate, up to 0.32 percent, are also used. An older remedy was the addition of vinegar or acetate to the dough or treatment of the exterior of the loaf with vinegar.

Rope

Ropiness of bread is fairly common in home-baked bread, especially during hot weather, but it is rare in commercially baked bread because of the preventive measures now employed. Ropiness is caused by a mucoid variant of *Bacillus subtilis* or *B. licheniformis,* formerly called *B. mesentericus*, B. panis*,* and other species names. The spores of these species can withstand the temperature of the bread during baking, which does not exceed 100 C, and can germinate and grow in the loaf if conditions are favorable. The ropy condition apparently is the result of capsulation of the bacillus, together with hydrolysis of the flour proteins (gluten) by proteinases of the organism and of starch by amylase to give sugars that encourage rope formation. The area of ropiness is yellow to brown in color and is soft and sticky to the touch. In one stage the slimy material can be drawn out into long threads when the bread is broken and pulled apart (see Figure 11-2). The unpleasant odor is difficult to characterize, although it has been described as that of decomposed or overripe melons. First the odor is evident, then discoloration, and finally softening of the crumb, with stickiness and stringiness.

A complete discussion of factors favoring rope formation and methods of prevention can be found in the second edition of this book (Frazier, 1967).

Red Bread

Red, or "bloody," bread is striking in appearance but rare in occurrence. The red color results from the growth of pigmented bacteria, usually *Serratia marcescens,* an organism that often is brilliantly red on starchy foods. In ancient times the mysterious appearance of apparent drops of blood was considered miraculous. Necessary for the phenomenon is the accidental contamination of the bread with the red organisms and unusually moist conditions to favor their growth. Molds, such as *Monilia (Neurospora) sitophila,* previously mentioned, may impart a pink to red color to bread. A red color in the crumb of dark bread has been caused by *Geotrichum aurantiacum* (syn. *Oidium aurantiacum*).

FIGURE 11-2
Ropy bread, showing stringy capsular material stretching between the halves of the loaf. (*Fleischmann Laboratories, Standard Brands Incorporated*).

Chalky Bread

Chalky bread, also uncommon, is so named because of white, chalklike spots. The defect has been blamed on the growth of yeastlike fungi, *Endomycopsis fibuligera* and *Trichosporon variable*.

CAKES AND BAKERY PRODUCTS

Molds are the chief cause of the microbial spoilage of cakes and other bakers' products, since the normal baking process destroys much of the original microflora. Methods of prevention are similar to those previously listed for bread. The microbiology of these products becomes more complicated when they are topped with frostings or fruits or filled with custard, imitation creams, or sauces. Usually the toppings or fillings are more prone to microbial spoilage than is the actual baked portion. It is not unusual for the fillings of many pasteries to support the growth of microorganisms. Frostings, because of their high sugar content, are quite stable but may be spoiled by molds or yeast upon storage. The deterioration of breads, cakes, pies, and other bakery products that is referred to as staling is due mostly to physical changes during holding and not to microorganisms.

PASTA, MACARONI, AND TAPIOCA

Pasta here is used to describe egg-based pastas usually containing flour, water, and eggs. Pasta is delivered and stored dry; therefore, there are seldom reports of spoilage in these products.

Macaroni usually contains only flour, water, and other nutrients. The swelling of moist macaroni has been reportedly caused by gas production by bacteria resembling *Enterobacter colacae*. During the drying of macaroni on paper a mold of the genus *Monilia* has been found responsible for purple streaks at contact points with the paper. The appearance of these defects is uncommon, however, despite the long, slow drying process of macaroni.

Tapioca, prepared from the root starch of cassava, will spoil if moistened. Spoilage by an orange-pigmented, starch-hydrolyzing bacterium has been described.

BREAKFAST CEREALS AND OTHER CEREAL SNACKS

According to Hobbs and Green (1984), there are three basic breakfast cereal manufacturing processes: These products are flaked, puffed, or extruded. In the initial steps of the manufacturing of these products there are high levels of moisture and, therefore, the possibility of microbial growth. However, in the finished state they usually represent products with low total numbers (Table 11-1).

PREPARED DOUGHS

A large number of products available at retail are essentially prepared, refrigerated, or frozen bakery product doughs. These convenience items may contain a yeast or a lactic acid bacteria inoculum. The level of contamination and the subsequent microbial quality would be a direct result of the quality of ingredients used and the sanitary practices employed during their manufacture. Microbial numbers (Table 11-1) may increase during refrigerated storage until the product receives its final "heat treatment" at the consumer level.

BIBLIOGRAPHY

Anonymous. 1937. Rope and mold. Standard Brands, Inc., New York.

Bothast, R. J., F. F. Rogers, and C. W. Hesseltine. 1974. Microbiology of corn and dry milled products. Cereal Chem. 51:829–831.

Bullerman, L. B., J. M. Baca, and W. T. Stott. 1975. An evaluation of potential mycotoxin-producing molds in corn meal. Cereal Foods World. 20:248–253.

Cathcart, W. H. 1951. Baking and bakery products, chap. 26: *In* M. B. Jacobs (ed.), The chemistry and technology of food and food products. 2d ed. Interscience Publishers (Division of John Wiley & Sons, Inc.), New York.

Christensen, C. M., and H. H. Kaufmann. 1965. Deterioration of stored grains by fungi. Annu. Rev. Phytopathol. 3:69–84.

Elliot, R. P. 1980. Cereals and cereal products. *In* J. H. Silliker, et al. (eds.), Microbial ecology of foods. Volume II. Food commodities. Academic Press, Inc., New York.

Frazier, W. C. 1967. Food microbiology. 2d ed. McGraw-Hill Book Co., New York.

Glabe, E. F. 1942. Preventing spoilage by mold and bacteria. Food Ind. 14(2):46–48.

Heath, B. 1947. Dehydrated foods and microorganisms. Aust. Food Manuf. 16(12): July 5.

Hesseltine, C. W., and R. R. Graves. 1963. Microbiological research on wheat and flour, pp. 170–199. 2d Natl. Conf. Wheat Util. Res., Peoria, Ill., North. Util. Res. Dev. Div., USDA.

Hobbs, W. E., and V. W. Greene. 1984. Cereal and cereal products. *In* M. L. Speck (ed.), compendium of methods for the microbiological examination of foods. 2d ed. American Public Health Association.

James, N., and A. R. Lejeune. 1952. Microflora and the heating of damp, stored wheat. Can. J. Bot. 30:1–8.

James, N., and K. N. Smith. 1948. Studies on the microflora of flour. Can. J. Res. 26C: 479–484.

Kent-Jones, D. W. 1937. Flour spoilage. Analyst. 62:649–653.

Knight, R. A., and E. M. Menlove. 1961. Effect of the bread-baking process on destruction of certain mould spores. J. Sci. Food Agr. 12:653–656.

Matz, S. A. (ed.). 1972. Baking technology and engineering. AVI Publishing Co., Inc., Westport, Conn.

Miller, F. W., Jr. 1942. The story of mold and rope. E. I. du Pont de Nemours & Co., Inc., Wilmington, Del.

Pyler, E. J. 1952. Baking science and technology, 2 vols. Seibel Publishing Co., Chicago.

Qasem, S. A., and C. M. Christensen. 1958. Influence of moisture content, temperature, and time on the deterioration of stored corn by fungi. Phytopathology. 48: 544–549.

Russ, J. J., W. R. Reeder, and D. W. Hatch. 1961. A rapid bacteriological method for predicting ropiness in bread. Cereal Sci. 6:89–91.

Shotwell, O. L., M. L. Goulden, and C. W. Hesseltine. 1974. Aflatoxin: distribution in contaminated corn. Cereal Chem. 51:492–500.

Shotwell, O. L., C. W. Hesseltine, and M. L. Goulden. 1973. Incidence of aflatoxin in southern corn. Cereal Sci. Today. 18:192–197.

Spicher, G. 1959. Sur la microflora des cereales. Meun. Fr. 148:23–30.

Tanner, F.W. 1944. Microbiology of foods. Ind. ed. The Garrard Press, Champaign, Ill.

Vandergraft, E. E., C. W. Hesseltine, and O. L. Shotwell. 1975. Grain preservatives: Effect on aflatoxin and ochratoxin production. Cereal Chem. 52:79–84.

Vojnovich, C., V. F. Pfeifer, and E. L. Griffin. 1970. Reducing microbial populations in dry-milled corn products. Cereal Sci. Today. 15:401–411.

Walter, A. H. 1964. Microbial resistance. *In* A. H. Woollen, London meeting unveils advances. Food Eng. 36:57–64.

Zottola, E. A. 1973. An introduction to the microbiology of cereal and cereal products. Bull. Ass. Oper. Millers. July. pp. 3375–3386.

CONTAMINATION, PRESERVATION, AND SPOILAGE OF SUGARS AND SUGAR PRODUCTS

Sugar products discussed in this chapter include sucrose (cane and beet sugar), molasses, sirups, maple sap and sugar, honey, and candy.

CONTAMINATION

SUCROSE

The raw juice expressed from sugarcane may become high in microbial content unless processing is prompt. The relevant microorganisms are those from the sugarcane and the soil contaminating it and therefore comprise slime producers, such as species of *Leuconostoc* and *Bacillus;* representatives of the genera *Micrococcus, Flavobacterium, Alcaligenes, Xanthomonas, Pseudomonas, Erwinia,* and *Enterobacter;* a variety of yeasts, chiefly in the genera *Saccharomyces, Candida,* and *Pichia;* and a few molds (Table 12-1). Much contamination may come from debris or fine particles on the sides or joints of troughs at the plant. If organisms grow to any extent, inversion of sucrose or even destruction of sugar may take place. Activity of the organisms continues from cutting of the cane through extraction to clarification of the juice, a process which kills yeasts and vegetative cells of bacteria. Bacterial spores are present from then on, through sedimentation, filtration, evaporation, crystallization, and centrifugation, but may be reduced in numbers by these processes, although spores of thermophiles may be added from equipment. Bagging of the raw sugar also may add some microorganisms. During the refining of the

187

raw sugar, contamination may come from equipment, and organisms are added during bagging.

In the manufacture of beet sugar, cleaned beets are sliced into thin slices and the sugar is removed by a diffusion process at 60 to 85 C. Sources of con-

TABLE 12-1
MICROBIOLOGICAL PROFILE OF SUGARCANE, CANE JUICE, RAW SUGAR, AND SUCROSE

Product	Microorganisms present	Approximate quantitative range
Sugarcane	Bacteria	10^2–10^8/g
	Enterobacter	
	Leuconostoc	
	Flavobacterium	
	Xanthomonas	
	Bacillus	
	Erwinia	
	Pseudomonas	
	Molds	10^2–10^4/g
	Yeast	10^2–10^4/g
Raw cane juice	Bacteria	10^4–10^8/ml
	as above plus	
	Micrococcus	
	Lactobacillus	
	Actinomyces	
	Molds	
	Aspergillus	
	Cladosporium	
	Monilia	
	Penicillium	
	Yeast	
	Saccharomyces	
	Candida	
	Pichia	
	Torulopsis	
Raw sugar	Bacteria	10^2–10^4/g
	Bacillus	
	Clostridium	
	Desulfotomaculum	
	Osmophilic yeast	
	Aspergillus	
	Penicillium	
	Osmophilic molds	
	Hansenula	
	Pichia	
	Saccharomyces	
Sucrose	Bacteria	10^1–10^2/g
	Mostly sporeformers, if any, and minimal yeast and molds	

tamination are flume waters and diffusion-battery waters. Thermophiles may grow in the latter up to 70 C. Contamination also may take place during refining and bagging of the sugar. Granulated sugar now on the market is very low in microbial content for the most part, containing from a few to several hundred organisms per gram, mostly bacterial spores.

MAPLE SIRUP

Sap of the sugar maple in the vascular bundles is sterile or practically so but becomes contaminated from outside sources in the tapholes and by the spout, plastic tubing, and buckets or other collection vessels. If a period of unusual warmth occurs before the sap is collected, considerable growth of yeasts and bacteria may take place in the sap.

Microorganisms entering sap between its flow from the tree and being boiled and concentrated are mostly psychrotrophic, gram-negative rods of *Pseudomonas, Alcaligenes,* and *Flavobacterium,* plus yeasts and molds. Paraformaldehyde taphole pellets are inserted into the drilled hole to prevent microbial growth from blocking the flow. In sugar-bush locations that are exposed to unusual dust and air contamination, collection of sap by a series of plastic tubes results in lower bacterial contamination. However, in a well-controlled sugar bush the microbial content of sap collected by tubing is not significantly different from that obtained by using individual pails. Sap-gathering tanks, usually mobile, must be sanitized regularly to prevent development of high numbers of bacteria in the sap when it reaches the evaporator. Bacterial counts in sap are usually less than 10,000 per milliliter, but higher numbers can develop as a result of warmer temperatures near the end of the season and poor sanitation.

HONEY

The chief sources of microorganisms in honey are the nectar of flowers and the honeybee. Yeasts have been shown to come from the nectar and from the intestinal content of the bee; bacteria also come from the latter source. Honey rarely contains staphylococci or enteric bacteria. Common isolates are usually acidophilic and glycolytic yeasts, which can damage the product. Honey has been found to contain lysozyme, an enzyme with a bacteriostatic as well as a lytic effect on most gram-positive bacteria. The use of antibiotics such as neomycin and streptomycin is widespread in beekeeping, and these antibiotics have been found in the honey obtained from treated larvae and bees. Traces of these antibiotics in the honey would, of course, have an effect on its microbial flora. Honey is one of the suspected food vehicles for the source of *C. botulinum* spores in cases of infant botulism (see Chapter 24). About 10 percent of the suspected honey samples contained viable spores.

A study by Ruiz-Argueso and Rodriguez-Navarro (1975) suggested that *Gluconobacter* and *Lactobacillus* are the two main groups of bacteria present during maturation of nectar to honey.

CANDY

Candies from retail markets contain from 0 to 2 million bacteria per piece, but most pieces harbor no more than a few hundred. Few coliform bacteria are found. The candies receive most of their contamination from their ingredients, although some contamination may be added to unwrapped pieces by air, dust, and handling. The several thousand types of candies and confections can be divided into two categories for microbiological consideration: (1) cold-processed and (2) hot-processed confections. Molded chocolate and chocolate coatings for creamed centers fall into the first category. Temperatures during processing may only approach pasteurization temperature. Examples of the second category include hard candy, jellies, caramels, and fudges. Processing temperatures for these items vary, but they all are exposed to a more severe heat treatment than are items in the first category.

Candies are infrequently associated with food-poisoning outbreaks, but chocolate candies have been incriminated in cases of salmonellosis. The problem appears to be one of cross contamination in the plant between raw and roasted cocoa beans, with the raw beans or environmental isolates serving as the source of contamination. Although temperatures of 60 C for 10 hr are not uncommon during processing and blending of milk chocolate, the low moisture content or the dryness of the chocolate apparently protects the salmonellae from heat.

PRESERVATION

Like cereals, sugars normally have a_w's so low that microorganisms cannot grow. Only when moisture has been absorbed is there any chance for microbial spoilage. Storage conditions should be such that vermin are kept out and the sugar remains dry. The recommended storage temperature is similar to that for cereals.

Cane or sugar beets may be stored in a controlled atmosphere. Fungal growth is inhibited by 6 percent carbon dioxide and 5 percent oxygen.

During the manufacture of raw sugar and the subsequent refining process the numbers of microorganisms present, which may have been large during extraction from cane or sugar beet, are reduced by most subsequent processes, e.g., clarification, evaporation, crystallization, centrifugation, and filtration. Chemical preservatives are effective in reducing microbial numbers during sugar refining. Special treatments to reduce numbers and kinds of organisms may be given during refining when the sugar is to be used for a special purpose, e.g., for soft drinks or canning. Care is taken to avoid buildup of organisms and their spores during processing, and numbers may be reduced by irradiation with ultraviolet rays or combined action of heat and hydrogen peroxide.

Because of their high sugar concentration and low a_w, most candies are not subject to microbial spoilage, although soft fillings of chocolate-covered candies may support the growth of microorganisms. The bursting of chocolates is prevented by a uniform and fairly heavy chocolate coating and use of a fondant or other filling that will not permit the growth of gas formers.

Sirups and molasses usually have undergone enough heating to destroy most microorganisms but should be stored at cool temperatures to prevent or slow chemical changes and microbial growth. Some molasses may contain enough sulfur dioxide to inhibit microorganisms, but most sirups and molasses contain no added preservatives and prevent microbial growth because of the high osmotic pressure of the sugar solution. The osmotic pressure increases with the extent of inversion (hydrolysis) of the sucrose. Mold growth on the surface is prevented by a complete fill of the container and is reduced by periodic mixing of the sirup or molasses.

The boiling process during evaporation of maple sap to maple sirup kills the important spoilage organisms. Such sirup, bottled hot and in a completely filled container, usually keeps well.

Honey distributed locally on a small scale usually is not pasteurized and therefore may be subject to crystallization and to possible spoilage in time by osmophilic yeasts. Commercially distributed honey usually is pasteurized at 71 to 77 C for a few minutes. A recommended treatment is to heat fairly rapidly to at least 71 C, hold there for 5 min, and cool promptly to 32.2 to 38 C.

SPOILAGE

The spoilage of sugars or concentrated solutions of sugars is limited to that caused by osmophilic or xerotolerant microorganisms. Certain yeasts, especially those of the genus *Saccharomyces*, and certain molds would be the principal spoilage flora. Some species of bacteria have also been suggested as possible spoilage problems, including species of *Bacillus* and *Leuconostoc*. As the sugar concentrations decrease, increasing numbers of kinds of organisms can grow, so that sap from a maple tree would show types of spoilage that maple sirup could not.

SUCROSE

During the manufacture of sugar, the original cane or beet juice becomes more and more purified toward sucrose and the concentration of sugar in solution becomes greater and greater until finally crystalline sugar is attained plus molasses that is high in sugar. The purer the product, the poorer it becomes as a culture medium for microorganisms; the more concentrated it gets, the fewer kinds of organisms can grow in it.

Raw Juice

The raw cane or beet juice is not high in sugar and contains a good supply of accessory foods for microorganisms; it therefore is readily deteriorated by the numerous organisms present if sufficient time is allowed. Until clarification, gum and slime may be formed, e.g., dextran by *Leuconostoc mesenteroides* or *L. dextranicum** and levan by *Bacillus* spp. or, less commonly, by yeasts or molds.

Sugar in Storage

Liquid sugar with sugar content as high as 67 to 72 brix will support the growth of yeasts (*Saccharomyces, Candida, Rhodotorula*) and molds which may enter from the air. Dilution by absorption of moisture at the surface may result in growth of microorganisms and hence deterioration of the product. This can be prevented by circulation of filtered sterile air across the top of the storage tank or exposure to ultraviolet lamps.

Molasses and Sirups

Microbial spoilage of molasses is not common, although it is difficult to sterilize by heat because of the protective effect of the sugar. Canned molasses or sirup may be subject to spoilage by osmophilic yeasts that survive the heat process. Molasses or sirup exposed to air will mold, in time, on the surface, and this also may occur at the surface of a bottled or canned sirup if air is left there and contamination has taken place prior to sealing. Some kinds of molasses are acid enough to cause hydrogen swells (see Chapter 19) upon long storage.

MAPLE SAP AND SIRUP

As previously stated, sap from the sugar maple becomes contaminated when drawn. Although a moderate amount of growth may improve flavor and color, the sap often stands under conditions that favor excessive growth of microorganisms and hence spoilage. Five chief types of spoilage are recognized: (1) ropy or stringy sap, usually caused by *Enterobacter aerogenes,* although *Leuconostoc* spp. may be responsible, (2) cloudy, sometimes greenish sap resulting from the growth of *Pseudomonas fluorescens,* with species of *Alcaligenes* and *Flavobacterium* sometimes contributing to cloudiness, (3) red sap, colored by pigments of red bacteria, e.g., *Micrococcus roseus,* or of yeasts or yeastlike fungi, (4) sour sap, a catchall grouping for types of spoilage not showing a marked change in color but having a sour odor and caused by any of a variety of kinds of bacteria or yeasts, and (5) moldy sap, spoiled by molds.

Maple sirup can be ropy because of *Enterobacter aerogenes,* yeasty as the result of growth of species of *Saccharomyces* yeasts, pink from the pigment of *Micrococcus roseus,* or moldy at the surface, where species of *Aspergillus, Penicillium,* or other genera may grow. The sirup may become dark because of alkalinity produced by bacteria growing in the sap and inversion of sucrose.

Maple sugar keeps well unless moistened, at which time molds may grow.

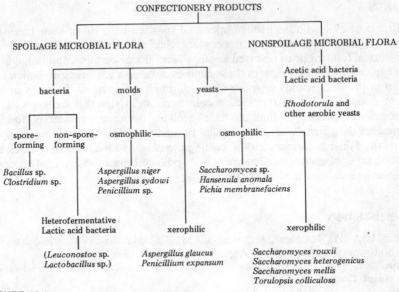

FIGURE 12-1
Spoilage flora of confectionery products. (*From Speck, 1976.*)

HONEY

Honey is variable in composition but must contain no more than 25 percent moisture. Because of its high sugar content, 70 to 80 percent, mostly glucose and levulose, and its acidity, pH 3.2 to 4.2, the chief cause of its spoilage is osmophilic yeasts: species of *Zygosaccharomyces,* such as *Z. mellis, richteri,* or *nussbaumeri,* or *Torula (Cryptococcus) mellis.* Most molds do not grow well on honey, although species of *Penicillium* and *Mucor* have developed slowly.

Most honey yeasts do not grow in the laboratory in sugar concentrations as high as those usually found in honey. Therefore, special theories for the initiation of growth of yeasts in honey have been advanced: (1) Honey, being hygroscopic, becomes diluted at the surface, where yeasts begin to multiply and soon become adapted to the high sugar concentrations, (2) crystallization of glucose hydrate from honey leaves a lowered concentration of sugars in solution, or (3) on long standing, yeasts gradually become adapted to the high sugar concentrations. The critical moisture content for the initiation of yeast growth has been placed at 21 percent. The degree of inversion of sucrose to glucose and levulose by the bees and the content of available nitrogen also are listed as factors determining the likelihood of growth. The fermentation process usually is slow, lasting for months, and the chief products are carbon dioxide, alcohol, and nonvolatile acids which give an off-flavor to the honey. Darkening and crystallization usually accompany the fermentation.

CANDY

Most candies are not subject to microbial spoilage because of their comparatively high sugar and low moisture content. Exceptions are chocolates with soft centers of fondant or of inverted sugar, which, under certain conditions, burst or explode. Yeasts growing in these candies develop a gas pressure which may disrupt the entire candy or more often will push out some of the sirup or fondant through a weak spot in the chocolate coating. Often this weak spot is on the poorly covered bottom of the chocolate, where a cylinder of fondant squeezes out. The defect is prevented by using a filling that will not support growth of the gas formers and by coating the candy with a uniformly thick and strong layer of chocolate. The microbial spoilage flora of many confectionery products is summarized in Figure 12-1.

BIBLIOGRAPHY

Allen, L. A., A. H. Cooper, A. Cairns, and M. C. C. Maxwell. 1946. Microbiology of beet-sugar manufacture. Soc. Appl. Bacteriol. Proc. 1946:5–9.

Cakebread, S. H. 1971. Chemistry of candy: factors in microbiological deterioration. Manuf. Confect. 51:45–49.

Casey, J. A. Sanitation of sugar factories. U.S. Patent 3,694,262.

Doolin, G. S. 1972. Quality control in the confectionery industry. J. Milk Food Technol. 35:424–431.

Guerin, B., M. S. Guerin, and M. Lolier. 1972. Emploi en sucrerie d'un nouvel inhibiteur de developpements microbiens. Sucr. Fr. 113:203–211.

Hayward, F. W., and C. S. Pederson. 1946. Some factors causing dark-colored maple sirup. N.Y. State Agr. Exp. Stn. Bull. 718.

Hucker, G. J., and R. F. Brooks. 1942. Gas production in storage molasses. Food Res. 7:481–494.

Hucker, G. J., and C. S. Pederson. 1942. A review of the microbiology of commercial sugar and related sweetening agents. Food Res. 7:459–480.

Karnik, V. V., D. K. Salunkhe, L. E. Olson, and F. J. Post. 1970. Physiochemical and microbiological studies on controlled atmosphere storage of sugar. J. Am. Soc. Sugar Beet Technol. 16:156–167.

Lochhead, A. G., and N. B. McMaster. 1931. Yeast infection of normal honey and its relation to fermentation. Sci. Agr. 11:351–360.

Mansvelt, J. W. 1964. Microbiological spoilage in the confectionery industry. Confectionery Prod. 30(1):33–35,37,39.

Marvin, G. E. 1928. Occurrence and characteristics of certain yeasts found in fermented honey. J. Econ. Entomol. 21:363–370.

Minifie, B. W. 1970. Chocolate, cocoa and confectionery: science and technology. AVI Publishing Co., Inc., Westport, Conn.

Mohrig, W., and B. Messner. 1968. Lysozyme as an antibacterial agent in honey and beer venom. Acta Biol. Med. Ger. 21:85–95.

Moroz, R. 1963. Microbiology of the sugar industry. In P. Honig (ed.), Principles of sugar technology. Volume III. Evaporation, centrifugation, microbiology, grading and classification of sugars and molasses, pp. 373–449. Elsevier Publishing Company, Amsterdam.

Naghski, J. 1953. The organisms of maple sirup: their effect and control. 2d Conf. Maple Prod. Proc. pp. 34–36.

Ostergren, B. 1974. Practical biological testing in confectionery plants. Manuf. Confect. 54:62–69.

Owens, W. L. 1958. The deterioration of raw sugars in storage. Sugar J. 21(5):22–25.

Pederson, C. S., and G. J. Hucker. 1948. The significance of bacteria in sugar mills. Int. Sugar J. 50:238–239.

Ruiz-Argueso, T., and A. Rodriguez-Navarro. 1975. Microbiology of ripening honey. Appl. Microbiol. 30:893–896.

Sheneman, J. M., and R. M. Costilow. 1959. Identification of microorganisms from maple tree tapholes. Food Res. 24:146–151.

Speck, M. L. (ed.). 1976. Compendium of methods for the microbiological examination of foods. American Public Health Association, Washington, D.C.

Speck, M. L. (ed.). 1984. Compendium of methods for the microbiological examination of foods. 2d ed. American Public Health Association, Washington, D.C.

Tysset, C., C. Durand, and Y. P. Taliercio. 1970. Contribution to the study of the microbiology and hygiene of commercial honey. Rec. Med. Vet. Paris. 146:1471–1492.

Underwood, J. C., and C. O. Willits. 1963. Research modernizes the maple sirup industry. Food Technol. 17:1380–1385.

U.S. Department of Agriculture. 1970. A survey of microbial contamination of maple sap in field collection systems. EU Publ. 3339. ARS 73-68.

U.S. Department of Health, Education, and Welfare, Public Health Service. 1974. Follow-up on *Salmonella eastbourne* outbreak. Cent. Dis. Control, Morbid. Mortal. Week. Rep. 23(10):89–90 (Mar. 9, 1974).

Weinzirl, J. 1922. The cause of explosion in chocolate candies. J. Bacteriol. 7:599–604.

CONTAMINATION, PRESERVATION, AND SPOILAGE OF VEGETABLES AND FRUITS

It has been estimated that one-fourth of all produce harvested is spoiled before consumption (Salunkhe, 1974). Spoilage of fresh fruits and vegetables usually occurs during storage and transport and while waiting to be processed. Unlike many other foods discussed in this book, fruits and vegetables after picking and before processing are "alive" for an extended time. The resulting respiration of these products and the normal ripening process complicate an independent discussion of the microbiological spoilage of fruits and vegetables. Many of the microbiological spoilage problems discussed are really "market diseases" of these products and are discussed in books on plant pathology. Vegetables and fruits may be fresh, dried, frozen, fermented, pasteurized, or canned. Spoilage of the canned products will be discussed in Chapter 19.

CONTAMINATION

As soon as fruits and vegetables are gathered into boxes, lugs, baskets, or trucks during harvesting, they are subject to contamination with spoilage organisms from each other and from the containers unless these have been adequately sanitized. During transportation to market or the processing plant, mechanical damage may increase susceptibility to decay and growth of microorganisms may take place. Precooling of the product and refrigeration during transportation will slow such growth.

Washing the fruit or vegetable may involve a preliminary soaking or may be achieved by agitation in water, or, preferably, by a spray treatment. Soaking and washing by agitation tend to distribute spoilage organisms from damaged to whole foods. Recirculated or reused water is likely to add organisms, and the washing process may moisten surfaces enough to permit growth of organisms during a holding period. Washing with detergent or germicidal solutions will reduce numbers of microorganisms on the foods.

Sorting spoiled fruits or vegetables or trimming spoiled parts removes microorganisms, but additional handling may result in mechanical damage and therefore greater susceptibility to decay. When these products are sold in the retail market without processing, they are not ordinarily subjected to much further contamination, except for storage in the market in contaminated bins or other containers, possible contact with decaying products, handling by salespeople and customers, and perhaps spraying with water or packing with chipped ice. This spraying gives a fresh appearance to the vegetables and delays decomposition but also adds organisms, e.g., psychrotrophs, from water or ice and gives a moist surface to encourage their growth on longer storage.

In the processing plant the fruits or vegetables are subjected to further contamination and chances for growth of microorganisms, or numbers and kinds of organisms may be reduced by some procedures. Adequate washing at the plant causes a reduction in numbers of microorganisms on the food, as do peeling by steam, hot water, or lye and blanching (heating to inactivate enzymes, etc.). Sweating of products during handling increases numbers. Processes such as trimming, mechanical abrasion or peeling, cutting, pitting or coring, and various methods of disintegration may add contaminants from the equipment involved. In fact, every piece of equipment coming in contact with food can be a significant source of microorganisms unless it has been cleaned and sanitized adequately. Modern metal equipment with smooth surfaces and without cracks, dead ends, etc., is made to facilitate such treatments. Examples of possible sources of contamination of foods with microorganisms are trays, bins, tanks, pipes, flumes, tables, conveyor belts and aprons, fillers, blanchers, presses, screens, and filters. Wooden surfaces are difficult to clean and sanitize and therefore are especially likely to be sources of contamination, as are cloth surfaces, e.g., on conveyor belts. Neglected parts of any food-handling system can build up numbers of microorganisms to contaminate the food. Hot-water blanching, although it reduces total numbers of organisms on the food, may cause the buildup of spores of thermophilic bacteria, causing the spoilage of canned foods, e.g., flat sour spores in peas.

Buildup of populations of microorganisms on equipment as the result of microbial growth in the exudates and residues from fruits and vegetables may greatly influence the amount of contamination of the foods and the growth of the contaminants. Not only is there the possibility of the addition of large numbers of organisms from this source, there is also the likelihood that these will be organisms in their logarithmic phase of growth and therefore able to continue rapid growth. This effect is especially evident on vegetables following blanching. This heat treatment reduces the bacterial content considerably, damages many of the surviving cells, and consequently lengthens their lag period. On the other hand, the actively growing contaminants from the equipment can attain large numbers if enough time is allowed before freezing, drying, or canning; such growth is usually the cause of very high bacterial counts.

Inclusion of decayed parts of fruits increases the numbers of microorganisms in fruit juices. Numbers in orange juice, for example, and numbers of coliforms are increased greatly by the inclusion of fruits with soft rots. Heating of grapes before extraction reduces numbers of organisms in the expressed juice, but pressing introduces contamination.

The kinds of microorganisms from equipment will depend on the product being processed, for that product will constitute the culture medium for the organisms. Thus pea residues would encourage bacteria that grow well in a pea medium and in tomatoes those organisms which can develop in tomato juice. As the equipment is used throughout the day, the organisms can continue to build up. At the end of the run, however, when equipment is cleaned and sanitized, the total numbers of microorganisms thereon are greatly reduced, and if the operation is efficient, only the resistant forms survive. Therefore, spores of bacteria are likely to survive, and if conditions for growth are present while the equipment is idle, these sporeformers may increase in numbers, especially in poorly cleaned parts. The thermophilic sporeformers so troublesome to canners of vegetables build up in this manner and add to the difficulty of giving the foods an adequate heat process. The numbers of such organisms on poorly cleaned and sanitized equipment may be high at the start of a day's run and decrease as the day progresses, but the reverse usually is true. A layoff during the run permits a renewed increase in numbers. It is obvious that the numbers of microorganisms that enter foods from equipment depend on the opportunities given these organisms for growth and that these opportunities are the result of inadequacy of cleaning and sanitizing combined with favorable conditions of moisture and temperature for an appreciable period of time. Added ingredients such as sugar and starch may add spoilage organisms, especially spores of thermophilic bacteria.

PRESERVATION OF VEGETABLES

Microorganisms on the surfaces of freshly harvested fruits and vegetables include not only those of the normal surface flora but also those from soil and water and perhaps plant pathogens (Table 13-1). Any of a number of kinds of molds also may be there, and sometimes a few yeasts. If the surfaces are moist or the outer surface has been damaged, growth of some microorganisms may take place between harvesting and processing or consumption of the vegetables. Adequate control of temperature and humidity will reduce such growth.

TABLE 13-1
GENERAL MICROBIOLOGICAL PROFILE OF HARVESTED FRUITS AND VEGETABLES*

Product	Microorganisms isolated	Approximate quantitative range

Vegetables†	Bacteria
	  Pseudomonas
	  Alcaligenes
	  Erwinia
	  Xanthomonas
		$10^3 - 10^7$/g
		(Splittstoesser, 1970)

	Other gram-negatives Micrococci Bacillus Lactic acid bacteria Coryneforms	

	Molds
	  Fusarium
	  Alternaria
	  Aureobasidium
	  Penicillium
	  Sclerotinia
	  Botrytis
	  Rhizopus
		$10^3 - 10^4$/g
		(Webb and Mundt, 1978)

Fruits	Bacteria: The inherent low pH of most fruits favors a predominance by molds; however, gram-negative species as above can be isolated	Usually less than 10^6/g

	Molds: As above plus
	  Cladosporium
	  Phoma
	  Trichoderma
		$10^3 - 10^4$/g
		(Webb and Mundt, 1978)

*There is considerable variation in the numbers and types of microorganisms present on vegetables and fruits. The species, the amount of adhering dirt or soil, the location, and the presence or absence of physical damage would all be significant variables.
†Counts on selected vegetables are listed by Splittstoesser (1970).

ASEPSIS

While a limited amount of contamination of vegetables will take place between harvesting and processing or consumption, gross contamination can be avoided. Boxes, lugs, baskets, and other containers should be practically free of the growth of microorganisms, and some will need cleaning and sanitation between uses. Examples are the lugs or other containers used for transporting peas to the processing plant. These containers may support a considerable amount of growth of bacteria on their moist interior and be a source of high numbers of organisms on the peas. Contact of vegetables undergoing spoilage with healthy vegetables will add contamination and may lead to losses. Contamination from equipment at the processing plant can be reduced by adequate cleaning and sanitizing. Especially feared is a buildup of heat-resistant spores of spoilage bacteria, e.g., the spores of flat sour bacteria, putrefactive anaerobes, or *Clostridium thermosaccharolyticum**.

Bacterial counts on fresh vegetables to be processed, upon arrival at the plant, may range from 10^2 to 10^7 per gram depending on the species and condition.

REMOVAL OF MICROORGANISMS

Thorough washing of vegetables removes most of the casual contaminants on the surface but leaves much of the natural microbial surface flora. Unless the wash water is of good bacteriological quality, it may add organisms, and subsequently growth may take place on the moist surface. Chlorinated water sometimes is used for washing, and detergents may be added to facilitate the removal of dirt and microorganisms. Part of the mold growth on strawberries, for example, can be removed by washing with a nonionic detergent solution.

USE OF HEAT

Vegetables to be dried or frozen, and some to be canned, are scalded or blanched to inactivate their enzymes. At the same time the numbers of microorganisms are reduced appreciably, perhaps by 1,000- to 10,000-fold (Splittstoesser, 1970). The heat processing of canned vegetables has been discussed in Chapter 6.

USE OF LOW TEMPERATURES

As has been indicated, a few kinds of vegetables that are relatively stable, such as root crops, potatoes, cabbage, and celery, can be preserved for a limited time by common or cellar storage (see Chapter 7).

Chilling

Most vegetables to be preserved without special processing are cooled promptly and kept at chilling temperatures. The chilling is accomplished by use of cold water, ice, or mechanical refrigeration or by vacuum cooling (moistening plus evacuation), as used for lettuce. In many cases precooling, i.e., cooling before normal cold storage, is done immediately after harvesting by use of a cold water spray, a practice referred to as **hydrocooling.** Each kind of vegetable has its own optimal temperature and relative humidity for chilling storage, as illustrated in Chapter 7 and as recommended in special bulletins and manuals. The "freshening" of leafy vegetables (lettuce, spinach) by a water spray will cool the products if cold water is employed and will aid in their preservation.

Control of the composition of the atmosphere in the storage of vegetables has not been used as much as with fruits. The addition of carbon dioxide or ozone to the air has been recommended by some workers. Ultraviolet rays have not been successful because the rays do not hit all surfaces of the vegetables as they are packaged and handled.

Sweet potatoes were mentioned in Chapter 7 as an example of a vegetable requiring special conditions of chilling storage. Ordinary potatoes turn sweet at temperatures below 2.2 to 4.4 C and are stored at higher temperatures if they are to be used for potato chips. Sweet potatoes and onions are subjected to special curing treatments before storage.

Freezing

The selection and preparation of vegetables, their blanching, their freezing, and the changes during these processes have been discussed in Chapter 7. On the surface of vegetables are the microorganisms of the natural flora, plus contaminants from soil and water. If the surfaces are moist, growth of some of these organisms will take place before the vegetable reaches the freezing plant. There, washing reduces the numbers of some organisms and adds some organisms, and scalding or blanching (86 to 98 C) brings about a great reduction in numbers, as much as 90 to 99 percent in some instances (see Table 13-2). But during the cooling and handling before freezing there is an opportunity for recontamination from equipment and for growth of organisms, so that under poor conditions 1 million or more organisms per gram of vegetable may be present at freezing. The freezing process reduces the number of organisms by a percentage that varies with the kinds and numbers originally present, but on the average about half of them are killed. Table 13-2 illustrates the changes in numbers of organisms on snap beans as they pass through various operations in a freezing plant. During storage in the frozen condition there is a steady decrease in numbers of organisms, but there are at least some survivors of most kinds of organisms after the usual storage period. The kind of bacteria most likely to grow on thawing will depend on the temperature and the elapsed time. Species of *Micrococcus** are predominant on thawing vegetables such as sweet corn and peas when the temperature of thawing is fairly low, although *Achromobacter** and *Enterobacter* spp. also are commonly present. Lactobacilli are also common on peas under such conditions. One species of *Micrococcus** may grow

TABLE 13-2
NUMBERS OF ORGANISMS PER GRAM ON SNAP BEANS AFTER
PASSING THROUGH UNIT OPERATIONS IN A FREEZING PLANT

Source of sample	Average plate count per gram*
Before cutter	740,000
After cutter and shaker	573,000
After blancher	1,000
After shaker, before sorting belt	188,000
Final package	36,000

*Average of seventeen samples during 9 days. Plates incubated at 32 C.

at first, followed by another species later. At higher temperatures, species of *Flavobacterium* also may multiply. As the small packages of quick-frozen vegetables usually are handled in the home, where the frozen food is placed directly into boiling water and cooked, there is no further opportunity for microbial growth. During freezing most vegetables wilt and become limp, and during storage frozen vegetables may undergo color changes.

When thawed vegetables are held at room temperature for any considerable period, there is a chance that food-poisoning bacteria may grow and produce toxin. Jones and Lochhead (1939), for example, found enterotoxin-forming staphylococci in frozen corn. Sterilized corn inoculated with staphylococci of the food-poisoning type, then frozen, and then thawed and held at a room temperature of 20 C for a total elapsed time of 1 day permitted growth of these cocci and the production of enough enterotoxin to cause symptoms of food poisoning. Enterotoxin produced in this way would not be entirely destroyed by the customary cooking of the vegetable. *Clostridium botulinum* has been found in frozen vegetables and can be assumed to be present often. Fortunately, the conditions for growth and toxin production would be unusual; power failure in freezers for several days during floods or hurricanes is an example of such conditions. Cooking frozen vegetables will not kill all spores of *Clostridium botulinum,* and such cooked food should not be allowed to stand at room temperature for any extended period of time.

Bacterial counts in frozen vegetables may range from a few to 10^5 per gram. Frequently, coliforms and enterococci can be recovered. The presence of *E. coli,* however, is unusual and can lead one to question sanitary practices.

DRYING

As the methods of drying vegetables and vegetable products have improved, public acceptance has increased, so that now a number of dried food products have wide sale. Dried vegetables and vegetable products are used in dried soups, and dried spices and condiments are used as flavoring materials.

Many vegetables can be dried by a process called **explosive puffing.** Usually small pieces of the diced, partially dehydrated vegetables are placed in a closed rotating chamber. Heat is applied, and the chamber is pressurized to a predetermined level; then the pressure is released instantaneously. This results in an additional loss of water, but more important, a porous network of capillaries is formed in the product. The increased porosity simplifies further drying and imparts good reconstituting ability.

Growth of the microorganisms surviving blanching may take place up to the time of drying and add to the count of the dried product. Drying by heat destroys yeasts and most bacteria, but spores of bacteria and molds usually survive, as do the more heat-resistant vegetative cells. Microbial counts on dried vegetables, either after drying or as purchased in the retail market, usually are considerably higher than on dried fruits, because there are likely to be higher numbers before drying and a greater percentage survival afterward. Most vegetables are less acid than fruits, and consequently the killing effect of the heat is less. Samples of dried vegetables from retail markets contain microorganisms in the hundreds of thousands or even millions per gram, although these dried foods can be produced so as to contain a much smaller number of organisms.

When dried vegetables are sulfured to preserve a light color, their microbial content is reduced.

If the vegetables are dried adequately and stored properly, there will be no growth of microorganisms in them. During storage there is a slow decrease in the number of viable organisms, more rapid during the first few months and slower thereafter. The spores of bacteria and molds, some of the micrococci*, and microbacteria are resistant to desiccation and will survive better than other microorganisms and will constitute an increasingly large percentage of the survivors as the storage time lengthens.

USE OF PRESERVATIVES

The addition of preservatives to vegetables is not common, although the surfaces of some vegetables may receive special treatment. Rutabagas and turnips sometimes are paraffined to lengthen their keeping time. Zinc carbonate has been reported to eliminate most mold growth on lettuce, beets, and spinach. Biphenyl vapors will control *Fusarium* on potatoes (McKee and Boyd, 1962). A controlled atmosphere of carbon dioxide or ozone about chilled vegetables . has been tried experimentally but has had little practical use.

Added Preservative

Sodium chloride is the only added chemical preservative in common use. The amount added to vegetables may vary from the 2.25 to 2.5 percent in making sauerkraut up to saturation for cauliflower. The lower concentrations of salt permit an acid fermentation by bacteria to take place; as the percentage of salt is increased, the rate of acid production becomes slower until a level of salt is reached that will permit no growth or production of acid.

Vegetables that are high in protein, such as green peas and lima beans, as well as some that soften readily, such as onions and cauliflower, are preserved by the addition of enough salt to prevent any fermentation: from 70 to 80° salometer (18.6 to 21.2 percent salt) up to saturation (26.5 percent salt, or 100° salometer).

It should be noted that upon the addition of brine or salt to vegetables, water is drawn from them and serves to decrease the salt concentration in the liquid.

The popularity of salad bars has resulted in an increased use of sulfites as salad fresheners, i.e., to prevent enzymatic browning of lettuce, cole slaw, and other salad items. Sulfite residues in foods may be associated with asthmatic attacks, and their levels in restaurant salads has been surveyed (Martin et al., 1986).

Developed Preservatives

At room temperature an acid fermentation is normal for shredded, chopped, or crushed vegetables containing sugar, but instead of a clean, acid flavor from the action of lactic acid bacteria, undesirable flavors and changes in body may result from growth of coliform bacteria, bacilli, anaerobes, proteolytic bacteria, and others. The addition of salt to such materials serves to reduce competition from undesirable organisms and hence to encourage the lactic fermentation. The salt also serves to draw the juice from the vegetables and bring about better distribution of the lactic acid bacteria. The amount of sugar in the vegetable affects the acidity that can be produced, while the amount of salt and the temperature determine the rate of acid production and the kinds of bacteria involved in it. In general, as the salt content is increased, the rate of acid formation becomes slower and the numbers of kinds of bacteria concerned become fewer. Some recipes call for a comparatively low salt content at the start, increasing amounts as the fermentation continues, and finally enough salt to prevent further growth of bacteria. This method is employed in the brining of vegetables such as string beans and corn. The fermentation of various vegetables is discussed in Chapter 22.

PRESERVATION BY IRRADIATION

Experimental treatment with gamma rays to inactivate microorganisms causing decay, followed by storage, has resulted in discoloration, softening, or other deterioration of most vegetables. However, irradiation has been used successfully to delay sprouting of potatoes, onions, and garlic and to kill insect reproduction on some vegetables (see Chapter 10).

PRESERVATION OF FRUITS AND FRUIT PRODUCTS

In general, principles similar to those for both vegetables and vegetable products are involved in the preservation of fruits and fruit products. The surfaces of healthy fruits include the natural flora plus contaminating microorganisms from soil and water and therefore have a surface flora much like that listed for vegetables; however, yeasts and molds will predominate. In addition, some fruits will contain plant pathogens or saprophytic spoilage organisms which may grow subsequent to harvesting. Such defective fruits should be sorted, and spoiled portions may be trimmed out. A few microorganisms are present in the interior of occasional healthy fruits.

ASEPSIS

Fruits, like vegetables, may be subject to contamination between harvesting and processing from containers and from spoiling fruits, and care should be taken to avoid such contamination as much as possible. Before harvest, fruits are usually exposed to insecticides and fungicides and may have their flora altered by such treatments.

REMOVAL OF MICROORGANISMS

Thorough washing of fruits serves to remove not only dirt and hence casual contaminating microorganisms but also poisonous sprays. Washing may be with water, detergent solutions, or even bactericidal solutions such as chlorinated water. Trimming also removes microorganisms. Clear fruit juices may be sterilized by filtration.

USE OF HEAT

Fruits seldom are blanched before other processing because blanching causes excessive physical damage.

The principles involved in the heat processing of canned fruits have been discussed in Chapter 6, and a few examples of the processes have been given. Note that the fruits are in one of two groups on the basis of their pH: the *acid* foods, such as tomatoes, pears, and pineapples, or the *high-acid* foods, such as berries. A steam-pressure sterilizer is not required for most fruits, since heating at about 100 C is sufficient and can be accomplished by flowing steam or boiling water. In general, the more acid the fruit, the less heat required for its preservation. Similar principles are involved in canning fruit juices.

USE OF LOW TEMPERATURES

A few fruits, such as apples, can be preserved for a limited time in common or cellar storage, but controlled lower temperatures usually are employed during most of the storage period of fruits.

Chilling

Each fruit has its own optimal temperature and relative humidity for chilling storage; even varieties of the same fruit may differ in their requirements. Fruits have been treated with various chemicals before or during storage to aid in their preservation. Thus hypochlorites, sodium bicarbonate, borax, propionates, biphenyl, *o*-phenylphenols, sulfur dioxide, thiourea, thiabendazole, dibromo-tetrachloroethane, and other chemicals have been recommended. Fruit also has been enclosed in wrappers treated with chemicals, e.g., sulfite paper on grapes, iodine paper on grapes and tomatoes, or borax paper on oranges. Waxed wraps, paraffin oil, paraffin, waxes, and mineral oil have been applied for mechanical protection.

There has been considerable research on the combination of the chilling storage of fruits with control of the atmosphere of the storage room. This control may consist merely of regulation of the concentrations of oxygen and carbon dioxide in the atmosphere or may involve the addition or removal of carbon dioxide or oxygen or the addition of ozone.

Controlled-atmosphere (CA) storage implies the altering of various gases from normal atmospheric concentrations. Usually this is done by increasing the CO_2 concentration and decreasing the O_2 concentration. A related term, **modified atmosphere** (MA), is defined similarly, but MA storage is usually used to describe CA conditions which are not accurately maintained or conditions where the air is intially replaced with gas but no further measures are taken to keep the gas atmosphere constant. "Gas storage" means CA or MA storage. Under certain circumstances only one gas is used, e.g., packaging a product in 100 percent N_2; this type of storage would more precisely be referred to as nitrogen gas storage. Several conditions of CA storage are compiled in Table 13-3. The optimal concentration of carbon dioxide and oxygen and proportion of these gases varies with the kind of fruit and even with the variety of fruit.

Although carbon dioxide storage has been employed chiefly with apples, it can be used successfully with pears, bananas, citrus fruits, plums, peaches, grapes, and other fruits.

Ozone in concentrations of 2 to 3 ppm in the atmosphere has been reported to double the storage time of loosely packed small fresh fruits, such as strawberries, raspberries, currants, and grapes, and of delicate varieties of apples.

Ethylene in the atmosphere is used to hasten ripening or produce a desired color change and is not considered preservative, although a combination of this gas and activated hydrocarbons has been suggested for the preservation of fruits.

Freezing

The surfaces of fruits contain the natural surface flora plus contaminants from soil and water. Any spoiled parts that are present will add molds or yeasts. During preparation of fruits for freezing, undesirable changes may take place,

TABLE 13-3
CONDITIONS OF CONTROLLED-ATMOSPHERE
STORAGE FOR SEVERAL FRUITS AND
VEGETABLES

Item	CO_2,%	O_2,%
Apples	1.5–10.0	2.5
Lettuce	2.5	2.5
Cabbage	2.5	5.0
Onions	5–10.0	3.0
Peaches	5.0	0

such as darkening, deterioration in flavor, and spoilage by microorganisms, especially molds. Washing the fruit removes most of the soil microorganisms, and adequate selection and trimming will reduce many of the molds and yeasts involved in spoilage. With proper handling there should be little growth of microorganisms before freezing. Some fruits are frozen in large drums (up to 50 lb); it would be mandatory to cool the fruit before filling the container to ensure that the product is frozen quickly. The freezing process reduces the numbers of microorganisms but also usually causes some damage to the fruit tissues, resulting in flabbiness and release of some juice. During storage in the frozen condition the physical changes described in Chapter 7 occur as well as a slow but regular decrease in numbers of microorganisms. Yeasts (*Saccharomyces, Cryptococcus*) and molds (*Aspergillus, Penicillium, Mucor, Rhizopus, Botrytis, Fusarium, Alternaria*, etc.) have been reported to be the predominant organisms in frozen fruits, although small numbers of soil organisms, e.g., species of *Bacillus, Pseudomonas, Achromobacter**, etc., survive freezing. Yeasts are most likely to grow during slow thawing.

Numbers of viable microorganisms in frozen fruits are considerably lower than in frozen vegetables. Large numbers of mold hyphae may be indicative of the freezing of inferior fruit that included rotten parts.

The numbers of microorganisms in frozen fruit juices depend on the condition of the fruit, the washing process, the method of filtration, and the opportunities for contamination and growth before freezing. There may be from a few hundred to over 1 million organisms per milliliter present in the juice at the time of freezing. The inclusion of rotten parts of the fruit increases the numbers of organisms markedly. The washing process, especially the kind of solution used for washing, has a considerable influence on the numbers of organisms, since those on the surface of fruits are difficult to remove. Numbers can build up in the washing solution, on moist surfaces of the washed fruit, and in the juice itself before freezing. In the plant, too, there is an opportunity for the addition of organisms from the equipment. The freezing process markedly reduces numbers, but added sugar or increased concentration of the juice has a protective effect against killing. The decrease in numbers of organisms during storage in the frozen condition is slow but is faster than in most neutral foods. The kinds of organisms are chiefly those of soil, water, and rots, together with the natural surface flora of the fruit. Prominent usually are coliforms, enterococci, lactics, e.g., *Leuconostoc* and *Lactobacillus* species, *Alcaligenes,* and yeasts.

Since coliform bacteria, mostly of the *Enterobacter aerogenes* type, form part of the natural flora of fruits, they are present in both fresh and frozen fruit juices. The use of decayed fruit for the juice increases the numbers of coliforms, but these organisms decrease during storage. Because coliforms normally are present, there are objections to the use of the presumptive test for coliforms to indicate sanitary quality of the juice. It has been suggested that tests be made for the fecal coliform, *Escherichia coli,* or *Streptococcus faecalis*.

DRYING

The drying of fruits has been discussed in Chapter 8, where it was noted that the numbers of microorganisms in dried fruits are comparatively low and that spores of bacteria and molds are likely to be the most numerous. An occasional sample may contain high numbers of mold spores, indicating that growth and sporulation of molds has taken place on the fruit before or after dehydration. Alkali treatment, sulfuring, blanching, and pasteurization reduce numbers of microorganisms.

USE OF PRESERVATIVES

The use of chemical preservatives to lengthen the keeping time of fruits has been discussed in Chapter 9, where it was noted that chemicals have been applied to fruits chiefly as a dip or spray or impregnated in wrappers for the fruits. Among substances that have been applied to the outer surfaces of fruit are waxes, hypochlorites, biphenyl, and alkaline sodium o-phenylphenate. Wrappers for fruits have been impregnated with a variety of chemicals including iodine, sulfite, biphenyl, o-phenylphenol plus hexamine, and others. As a gas or fog about the fruit, carbon dioxide, ozone, and ethylene plus chlorinated hydrocarbons have been tried. Sulfur dioxide and sodium benzoate are preservatives that have been added directly to fruits or fruit products. Most of the chemical preservatives mentioned have been primarily antifungal in purpose.

Green olives are the only fruits which are preserved on a commercial scale with assistance from an acid fermentation. Locally, other fermented fruits sometimes are prepared, such as fermented green tomatoes and Rumanian preserved apples. In all these products the lactic acid fermentation is of chief importance.

SPOILAGE

The deterioration of raw vegetables and fruits may result from physical factors, action of their own enzymes, microbial action, or combinations of these agencies. Mechanical damage resulting from action of animals, birds, or insects or from bruising, wounding, bursting, cutting, freezing, desiccation, or other mishandling may predispose toward increased enzymatic action or the entrance and growth of microorganisms. Previous damage by plant pathogens may make the part of the plant used as food unfit for consumption or may open the way for growth of saprophytes and spoilage by them. Contact with spoiling fruits and vegetables may bring about transfer of organisms, causing spoilage and increasing the wastage. Improper environmental conditions during harvesting, transit, storage, and marketing may favor spoilage. Most of the discussion to follow will be concerned with microbial spoilage, but it always should be kept in mind that the plant enzymes continue their activity in raw plant foods. If oxygen is available, the plant cells will respire as long as they are alive, and hydrolytic enzymes can continue their action after death of the cell. As stated in Chapter 4, the fitness of foods for consumption is judged partly on the basis of their maturity. If the desired stage of maturity is greatly exceeded, the food may be considered inedible or even spoiled. An example is an overripe banana, with its black skin and brown, mushy interior.

Diseases of vegetables and fruits may result from the growth of an organism that obtains its food from the host and usually damages it or from adverse environmental conditions that cause abnormalities in functions and structures of the vegetable or fruit. The diseases caused by pathogens and the decompositions caused by saprophytic organisms will be of chief interest in the following discussion, although clear distinction between these types of organisms is not possible. However, diseases not caused by organisms should be mentioned because they may sometimes be confused with those caused by organisms in that they may be rather similar in appearance. Examples of nonpathogenic diseases are brown heart of apples and pears, blackheart of potatoes, black leaf speck of cabbage, and red heart of cabbage.

No attempt will be made to deal with changes caused by plant pathogens growing on the plants, or on parts of the plants used for food, before harvesting; we shall instead consider those microbial changes which may take place during harvesting, grading, packing, transportation, storage, and handling by wholesaler and retailer, although some of these changes may begin before harvesting. Space will permit only a general treatment of the subject, and only from the viewpoint of the food microbiologist rather than the plant pathologist. The reader should consult references listed at the end of the chapter for more detail, especially the bulletins from the Bureau of Plant Industry USDA.

GENERAL TYPES OF MICROBIAL SPOILAGE

The most common or predominant type of spoilage varies not only with the kind of fruit or vegetable but also to some extent with the variety. Microbial spoilage may be due to (1) plant pathogens acting on the stems, leaves, flowers, or roots of the plant, on the fruits or other special parts used as foods, e.g., roots or tubers, or on several of these locations, or (2) saprophytic organisms, which may be secondary invaders after action of a plant pathogen or may enter a healthy fruit or vegetable, as in the case of various "rots," or grow on its surface, as when bacteria multiply on moist, piled vegetables. At times a saprophyte may succeed a pathogen or a succession of saprophytes may be involved in the spoilage. Thus, for example, coliform bacteria may grow as secondary invaders and be present in appreciable numbers in fruit and vegetable juices if rotten products have been included.

Although each fruit or vegetable has certain types of decomposition and kinds of microorganisms predominant in its spoilage, some general types of microbial spoilage are found more often than the rest in vegetables and fruits. The most commonly occurring types of spoilage are as follows:

1 Bacterial soft rot, caused by *Erwinia carotovora* and related species, which are fermenters of pectins. *Pseudomonas marginalis* and *Clostridium* and *Bacillus* spp. have also been isolated from these rots. It results in a water-soaked appearance, a soft, mushy consistency, and often a bad odor.

2 Gray mold rot, caused by species of *Botrytis*, e.g., *B. cinerea,* a name derived from the gray mycelium of the mold. It is favored by high humidity and a warm temperature.

3 Rhizopus soft rot, caused by species of *Rhizopus,* e.g., *R. stolonifer.* A rot results that often is soft and mushy. The cottony growth of the mold with small, black dots of sporangia often covers masses of the foods.

4 Anthracnose, usually caused by *Colletotrichum lindemuthianum, C. coccodes,* and other species. The defect is a spotting of leaves and fruit or seedpods (see Figure 13-1) .

5 Alternaria rot, caused by *Alternaria tenuis* and other species. Areas become greenish-brown early in the growth of the mold and later turn to brown or black spots.

6 Blue mold rot, caused by species of *Penicillium digitatum* and other species. The bluish-green color that gives the rot its name results from the masses of spores of the mold.

7 Downy mildew, caused by species of *Phytophthora, Bremia,* and other genera. The molds grow in white, woolly masses.

8 Watery soft rot, caused chiefly by *Sclerotinia sclerotiorum,* is found mostly in vegetables.

9 Stem-end rots, caused by species of molds of several genera, e.g., *Diplodia, Alternaria, Phomopsis, Fusarium,* and others, involve the stem ends of fruits.

FIGURE 13-1
Anthracnose on beans. (*Photography Division, USDA.*)

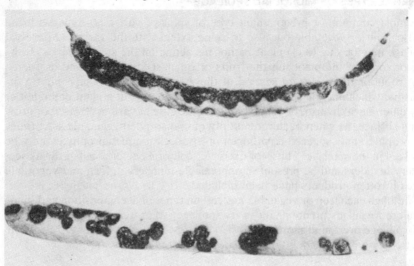

FIGURE 13-2
Black mold rot of onions. (*Photography Division, USDA.*)

10 Black mold rot, caused by *Aspergillus niger*. The rot gets its name from the dark-brown to black masses of spores of the mold, termed "smut" by the layperson (see Figure 13-2).

11 Black rot, often caused by species of *Alternaria* but sometimes of *Ceratostomella, Physalospora,* and other genera.

12 Pink mold rot, caused by pink-spored *Trichothecium roseum*.

13 Fusarium rots, a variety of types of rots caused by species of *Fusarium*.

14 Green mold rot, caused usually by species of *Cladosporium* but sometimes by other green-spored molds, e.g., *Trichoderma*.

15 Brown rot, caused chiefly by *Sclerotinia (Monilinia fructicola)* species.

16 Sliminess or **souring,** caused by saprophytic bacteria in piled, wet, heating vegetables.

Fungal spoilage of vegetables often results in water-soaked, mushy areas, while fungal rots of fleshy fruits such as apples and peaches frequently show brown or cream-colored areas in which mold mycelia are growing in the tissue below the skin and aerial hyphae and spores may appear later. Some types of fungal spoilage appear as "dry rots," where the infected area is dry and hard and often discolored. Rots of juicy fruits may result in leakage.

The composition of the fruit or vegetable influences the likely type of spoilage. Thus, bacterial soft rot is widespread for the most part among the vegetables which are not very acid, and among the fruits is limited to those which are not highly acid (Table 13-4). Because most fruits and vegetables are some-

TABLE 13-4
THE CHIEF MARKET DISEASES OF SEVERAL VEGETABLES AND FRUITS

Item	Market disease
Lily family	
Asparagus	Bacterial soft rot, fusarium rot, gray mold rot, phytophthera rot
Onions	Bacterial soft rot, black mold rot, gray mold rot
Garlic	Bacterial soft rot, black mold rot
Pulse or legume family	
Green beans	Bacterial soft rot, gray mold rot, rhizopus soft rot
Wax beans	
Lima beans	
Parsley family	
Carrots	Bacterial soft rot, black rot, fusarium rot, gray mold rot, watery soft rot
Parsnips	Bacterial soft rot, watery soft rot, gray mold rot
Celery	Bacterial soft rot, watery soft rot, gray mold rot
Parsley	Bacterial soft rot, watery soft rot
Beets	Bacterial soft rot, black rot, blue mold rot, fusarium rot
Endive	Bacterial soft rot, watery soft rot, downy mildew, gray mold rot
Globe artichokes	Gray mold rot
Lettuce	Bacterial soft rot
Rhubarb	Bacterial soft rot, gray mold rot
Small fruits	
Blackberries	Blue mold rot, gray mold rot, rhizopus rot
Grapes	Black mold rot, gray mold rot, rhizopus rot, blue mold rot
Strawberries	Gray mold rot, leather rot (*Phytophthera cactorum*), rhizopus rot
Citrus fruits	
Lemons	Alternaria rot, anthracnose, blue mold rots, stem-end rots
Limes	
Oranges	
Grapefruit	
Subtropical fruits	
Avocados	Anthracnose, rhizopus rot
Bananas	Anthracnose, *Fusarium, Gleoporium, Pestalozzia*
Figs	Alternaria rot, blue mold rot, cladosporium rot
Dates	Yeasts, various molds
Stone fruits	
Peaches	Alternaria (or green mold rot), gray mold rot, black mold rot;
Apricots	blue mold rot, brown rot, cladosporium rot, rhizopus rot
Plums	
Cherries	
Pomes	
Apples	Numerous molds
Pears	Black rot, blue mold rot, brown rot, gray mold, rhizopus rot
Spinach	Bacterial soft rot, gray mold rot
Sweet potatoes	Alternaria rot, black rot (*Ceratostomella fimbriata*), rhizopus soft rot
Potatoes	Fusarium tuber rots, bacterial ring rot, bacterial soft rot
Crucifers	
Cabbage	Bacterial soft rot, gray mold rot, black rot, watery soft rot
Brussel sprouts	Bacterial soft rot, gray mold rot, black rot, watery soft rot
Cauliflower	Bacterial soft rot, gray mold rot, black rot, watery soft rot

TABLE 13-4 *(continued)*

Item	Market disease
Crucifers *(continued)*	
Broccoli	Bacterial soft rot
Radishes	Bacterial soft rot, clubroot rot, rhizoctonia rot (*Rhizoctonia carotae*)
Turnips	Bacterial soft rot, clubroot rot, rhizoctonia rot
Rutabagas	Bacterial soft rot, gray mold rot, black rot, watery soft rot
Cucurbits	
Cucumber	Rhizopus soft rot, bacterial soft rot, blue mold rot, gray mold rot
Cantaloupe	Rhizopus soft rot, diplodia rot, bacterial soft rot, pink mold rot, fusarium rot
Pumpkin	Rhizopus soft rot, diplodia rot, phytophthera rot, gray mold rot
Squash	Rhizopus soft rot, gray mold rot
Watermelon	Rhizopus soft rot, gray mold rot, phytophthera rot, bacterial soft rot
Tomatoes	Alternaria rot, bacterial canker, bacterial spot, gray mold rot, green mold rot, rhizopus rot
Peppers	Alternaria rot, gray mold rot
Eggplant	Fruit rot (phomopsis rot)

what acid, are fairly dry at the surface, and are deficient in B vitamins, molds are the most common causes of spoilage. The composition, too, must determine the particular kinds of molds most likely to grow; thus some kinds of fruits or vegetables support a large variety of spoilage organisms and other kinds comparatively few.

The likelihood of the entrance of spoilage organisms also is important in influencing the possibility of spoilage and the kind that takes place. Damage by mechanical means, plant pathogens, or bad handling will favor entrance. The location of the plant part used also is important; thus underground parts such as roots, tubers, or bulbs as in radishes, beets, carrots, and potatoes are in direct contact with moist soil and become infected from that source. Fruits such as strawberries, cucumbers, peppers, and melons may be in direct contact with the surface of the soil. Leaves, stems, and flowers, as in lettuce, the greens, cabbage, asparagus, rhubarb, and broccoli, are especially exposed to contamination by plant pathogens or damage by birds and insects, as are most fruits, whether ordinarily classified as vegetables or "fruits."

The character of the spoilage will depend on the product attacked and the attacking organism. When the food is soft and juicy, the rot is apt to be soft and mushy and some leakage may result. There are, however, some kinds of spoilage organisms that have a drying effect so that dry or leathery rots or discolored surface areas may result. In some instances most of the mycelial growth of the mold is subsurface and only a rotten spot shows, as in most rotting of apples. In other types of spoilage the growth of the mold mycelium on the outside is apparent and may be colored by spores.

The identification of a type of spoilage of a fruit or vegetable makes possible the application of available methods for the prevention of such decay.

SPOILAGE OF FRUIT AND VEGETABLE JUICES

Juices may be squeezed directly from fruits or vegetables, may be squeezed from macerated or crushed material so as to include a considerable amount of pulp, or may be extracted by water, e.g., prune juice. These juices may be used in their natural concentrations or may be concentrated by evaporation or freezing, and may be preserved by canning, freezing, or drying.

Juices squeezed or extracted from fruits are more or less acid, depending on the product, the pH ranging from about 2.4 for lemon or cranberry juice up to 4.2 for tomato juice, and all contain sugars, the amounts varying from about 2 percent in lemon juice up to almost 17 percent in some samples of grape juice. Although molds can and do grow on the surface of such juices if the juices are exposed to air, the high moisture content favors the faster-growing yeasts and bacteria. Which of the latter will predominate in juices low in sugar and acid will depend more on the temperature than on the composition. The removal of solids from the juices by extraction and sieving raises the oxidation-reduction potential and favors the growth of yeasts. Most fruit juices are acid enough and have sufficient sugar to favor the growth of yeasts within the range of temperature that favors them, namely, from 15.6 to 35 C. The deficiency of B vitamins discourages some bacteria.

Therefore, the normal change to be expected in raw fruit juices at room temperatures is an alcoholic fermentation by yeasts, followed by the oxidation of alcohol and fruit acids by film yeasts or molds growing on the surface if it is exposed to air or the oxidation of the alcohol to acetic acid if acetic acid bacteria are present. The types of yeasts growing depend on the kinds predominant in the juice and on the temperature, but usually wild yeasts, such as the apiculate ones, producing only moderate amounts of alcohol and considerable amounts of volatile acid will carry out the first fermentation. At temperatures near the extremes of the range indicated (15.6 to 35 C), the undesirable yeasts are more likely to grow than those producing desirable flavors. At temperatures above 32.2 to 35 C lactobacilli would be likely to grow and form lactic and some volatile acids because these temperatures are too high for most yeasts. At temperatures below 15.6 C wild yeasts may grow, but the more the temperature drops toward freezing, the more likely the growth of bacteria and molds rather than yeasts. The acidity may be reduced by film yeasts and molds growing on the surface.

In addition to the usual alcoholic fermentation, fruit juices may undergo other changes caused by microorganisms: (1) the lactic acid fermentation of sugars, mostly by heterofermentative lactic acid bacteria such as *Lactobacillus pastorianus**, *L. brevis,* and *Leuconostoc mesenteroides* in apple or pear juice and by homofermentative lactic acid bacteria such as *Lactobacillus arabinosus**, *L. leichmanii**, and *Microbacterium*, (2) the fermentation of organic acids of the juice by lactic acid bacteria, e.g., *Lactobacillus pastorianus**, malic acid to lactic and succinic acids, quinic acid to dehydroshikimic acid, and citric acid to lactic and acetic acids, (3) slime production by *Leuconostoc mesenteroides,*

Lactobacillus brevis, and *L. plantarum* in apple juice and by *L. plantarum* and streptococci in grape juice.

Vegetable juices contain sugars but are less acid than fruit juices, having pH values in the range of 5.0 to 5.8 for the most part. Vegetable juices also contain a plentiful supply of accessory growth factors for microorganisms and hence support good growth of the fastidious lactic acid bacteria. Acid fermentation of the raw juice by these and other acid-forming bacteria would be a likely cause of spoilage, although yeasts and molds can grow.

Concentrates of fruit and vegetable juices, because of their increased acidity and sugar concentration, favor the growth of yeasts and of acid- and sugar-tolerant *Leuconostoc* and *Lactobacillus* species. Such concentrates usually are canned and then heat-treated or frozen. Heat processing kills the important microorganisms that could cause spoilage, and freezing prevents the growth of such organisms.

BIBLIOGRAPHY

Fruits and Vegetables

Bigelow, W. C., and P. H. Cathcart. 1921. Relation of processing to the acidity of canned foods. Natl. Canners Ass. Bull. 17-L.

Brooks, C., E. V. Miller, C. O. Bratley, P. V. Mook, and H. B. Johnson. 1932. Effect of solid and gaseous carbon dioxide upon transit diseases of certain fruits and vegetables. USDA Tech. Bull. 318.

Cruess, W. V. 1958. Commercial fruit and vegetable products. 4th ed. McGraw-Hill Book Company, New York.

Haard, N. F., and D. K. Salunkhe. 1975. Symposium: postharvest biology and handling of fruits and vegetables. AVI Publishing Co., Inc., Westport, Conn.

Holdsworth, S. D. 1971. Development in preservation. Food Proc. Ind. 40:27–31.

Martin, L. B., J. A. Nordlee, and S. Taylor. 1986. Sulfite residues in restaurant salads. J. Food Prot. 49:126–129.

McColloch, L. P., H. T. Cook, and W. R. Wright. 1968. Market diseases of tomatoes, peppers, and eggplants. USDA Agr. Res. Serv. Agr. Handb. 28.

Pantastico, E. B. (ed.). 1975. Postharvest physiology, handling and utilization of tropical and subtropical fruits and vegetables. AVI Publishing Co., Inc., Westport, Conn.

Rose, D. H., R. C. Wright, and T. M. Whiteman. 1949. The commercial storage of fruits, vegetables and florists' stocks. USDA Circ. 278.

Ryall, A. L., and W. J. Lipton. 1972. Handling transportation and storage of fruits and vegetables. Volume 1. Vegetables and melons. AVI Publishing Co., Inc., Westport, Conn.

Ryall, A. L., and W. T. Pentzer. 1974. Handling, transportation and storage of fruits and vegetables. Volume 2. Fruit and tree nuts. AVI Publishing Co., Inc., Westport, Conn.

Salunkhe, D. K. 1974. Developments in technology of storage and handling of fresh fruits and vegetables. Crit. Rev. Food Technol. April, pp. 15–54.

Splittstoesser, D. F. 1970. Predominate microorganisms on raw plant foods. J. Milk Food Technol. 33:500–505.

Splittstoesser, D. F., and J. O. Mundt. 1984. Fruits and vegetables. *In* M. Z. Speck (ed.), Compendium of methods for the microbiological examination of foods. American Public Health Association, Washington, D.C.

Starr, M. P., and A. K. Chatterjee. 1972. The genus *Erwinia:* enterobacteria pathogenic to plants and animals. Annu. Rev. Microbiol. 26:389–418.

Tomkins, R. G. 1951. The microbiological problems in the preservation of fresh fruits and vegetables. J. Sci. Food Agr. 2:381–386.

U.S. Department of Agriculture. 1932–1944. Market diseases of fruits and vegetables [series]. USDA Misc. Publ.

U.S. Department of Agriculture. 1966. Market "diseases" of asparagus, onions, beans, peas, carrots, celery, and related vegetables. USDA Agr. Res. Serv. Agr. Handb. 303.

Vaughn, R.H. 1963. Microbial spoilage problems of fresh and refrigerated foods. *In* L. W. Slanetz, et al. (eds.), Microbiological quality of foods. Academic Press, Inc., New York.

Von Schelhorn, M. 1951. Control of microorganisms causing spoilage of fruit and vegetable products. Adv. Food Res. 3:429–482.

Webb, T. A., and J. O. Mundt. 1978. Molds on vegetables at the time of harvest. Appl. Environ. Microbiol. 35:655–658.

Fruits

Cruess, W. V. 1938. Commercial fig products. Fruit Prod. J. 17:337–339, 343.

Esau, P., and W. V. Cruess. 1933. Yeasts causing "souring" of dried prunes and dates. Fruit Prod. J. 12:144.

Harvey, J. M., and W. T. Pentzer. 1960. Market diseases of grapes and other small fruits. Agricultural Marketing Service. USDA Handb. 189.

Luepschen, N. S., and M. A. Smith. 1962. Watermelon diseases on the Chicago market, 1960–1961. Plant Dis. Rep. 46:41–42.

Miller, M. W., and H. J. Phaff. 1962. Successive microbial populations in Calimyrna figs. Appl. Microbiol. 10:394–400.

Pierson, C. F., M. J. Ceponis, and L. P. McColloch. 1971. Market diseases of apples, pears, and quinces. USDA Agr. Res. Serv. Agr. Handb. 376.

Woodroof, J. G., and B. S. Luh. 1975. Commercial fruit processing. AVI Publishing Co., Inc., Westport, Conn.

Vegetables

Edmond, J. B., and G. R. Ammerman. 1971. Sweet potatoes: production, processing, marketing. AVI Publishing Co., Inc., Westport, Conn.

Hucker, G. J., R. F. Brooks, and A. J. Emery. 1952. The source of bacteria in processing and their significance in frozen vegetables. Food Technol. 6:147–155.

Jones, A. H., and A. G. Lochhead. 1939. A study of micrococci surviving in frozen-pack vegetables and their enterotoxic properties. Food Res. 4:203–216.

Luh, B. S., and J. G. Woodroof. 1975. Commercial vegetable processing. AVI Publishing Co., Inc., Westport, Conn.

Lynch, L. J., R. S. Mitchell, and D. J. Casimir. 1959. The chemistry and technology of the preservation of green peas. Adv. Food Res. 9:61–151.

McKee, R. K., and A. E. W. Boyd. 1962. Dry rot disease of potato. IX. The effect of diphenyl vapor on dry rot infection of potato tubers. Ann. Appl. Biol. 50:89–96.

Smith, O. 1968. Potatoes: production, storing, processing. AVI Publishing Co., Inc., Westport, Conn.

Splitstoesser, D. F., and D. A. Corlett, Jr. 1980. Aerobic plate counts of frozen blanched vegetables processed in the United States. J. Food Prot. 43:717–719.

Splittstoesser, D. F., W. P. Wettergreen. 1964. The significance of coliforms in frozen vegetables. Food Technol. 18:392–394.

Splittstoesser, D. F., W. P. Wettergreen, and C. S. Pederson. 1961. Control of microorganisms during preparation of vegetables for freezing. I. Green beans. II. Peas and corn. Food Technol. 15:329–331; 332–334.

White, A., and H. R. White. 1962. Some aspects of the microbiology of frozen peas. J. Appl. Bacteriol. 25:62–71.

Juices

Berry, J. M., L. D. Witter, and J. F. Folinazzo. 1956. Growth characteristics of spoilage organisms in orange juice and concentrate. Food Technol. 10:553–556.

Bowen, J. F., and F. W. Beech. 1964. The distribution of yeasts on cider apples. J. Appl. Bacteriol. 27:333–341.

Carr, J. G. 1958. Lactic acid bacteria as spoilage organisms of fruit juice products. J. Appl. Bacteriol. 21:267–271.

Carr, J. G. 1959. Some special characteristics of the cider lactobacilli. J. Appl. Bacteriol. 22:377–383.

Faville, L. W., and E. C. Hill. 1952. Acid-tolerant bacteria in citrus juices. Food Res. 17:281–287.

Hays, G. L., and D. W. Riester. 1952. The control of "off-odor" spoilage in frozen concentrated orange juice. Food Technol. 6:386–389.

Lüthi, H. 1959. Microorganisms in noncitrus juices. Adv. Food Res. 9:221–284.

Marshall, C. R., and V. T. Walkley. 1952. Some aspects of microbiology applied to commercial apple juice production. III. Isolation and identification of apple juice spoilage organisms. IV. Development characteristics and viability of spoilage organisms in apple juice. Food Res. 17:123–131; 197–203.

Murdock, D. I., and W. S. Hatcher, Jr. 1975. Growth of microorganisms in chilled orange juice. J. Milk Food Technol. 38:393–396.

Rushing, N. D., and V. J. Senn. 1964. Shelf life of chilled orange juice with heat treatment and preservatives. Food Technol. 18:112–114.

Tressler, D. K., and M. A. Joslyn. 1971. Fruit and vegetable juice processing technology. 2d ed. AVI Publishing Co., Inc., Westport, Conn.

CONTAMINATION, PRESERVATION, AND SPOILAGE OF MEATS AND MEAT PRODUCTS

Meats may be fresh, cured, dried, or otherwise processed. Spoilage of the canned products will be discussed in Chapter 19.

CONTAMINATION

The healthy inner flesh of meats has been reported to contain few or no microorganisms, although they have been found in lymph nodes, bone marrow, and even flesh. Staphylococci, streptococci, *Clostridium,* and *Salmonella* have been isolated from the lymph nodes of red-meat animals. Normal slaughtering practices would remove the lymph nodes from edible parts. The important contamination, however, comes from external sources during bleeding, handling, and processing. During bleeding, skinning, and cutting, the main sources of microorganisms are the exterior of the animal (hide, hooves, and hair) and the intestinal tract. Recently approved "humane" methods of slaughter—mechanical, chemical, and electrical—have little effect on contamination, but each method is followed by sticking and bleeding, which can introduce contamination. As with the older methods of use of a knife on hogs and poultry, any contaminating bacteria on the knife soon will be found in meat in various parts of the carcass, carried there by blood and lymph. The exterior of the animal harbors large numbers and many kinds of microorganisms from soil, water, feed, and manure, as well as its natural surface flora, and the intestinal contents contain the intestinal organisms (see Table 14-1). Knives, cloths, air, and hands and clothing of the workers can serve as intermediate sources of contaminants. During the handling of the meat thereafter, contamination can come from carts,

TABLE 14-1
AVERAGE NUMBERS OF MICROORGANISMS CONTAMINATING BEEF IN PACKING-PLANT
SLAUGHTER ROOM (EMPEY AND SCOTT, 1939)

Sample	Bacteria	Yeasts	Molds
Beef, dressed, on floor	6,400–830,000/cm^2		
Soil from animals (dry)	110,000,00/g	50,000/g	120,000/g
Animal feces (fresh)	90,000,000/g	200,000/g	60,000/g
Rumen content	2,000,000,000/g	180,000/g	1,600/g
Room air	140/cm^2 of plate		2/cm^2
Water, washing beef	20–10,000/ml		
Water, washing floor	1,000–16,000/ml		

Source: Empey and Scott (1939).

boxes, or other containers; other contaminated meat; air; and personnel. Especially undesirable is the addition of psychrotrophic bacteria from any source, e.g., from other meats that have been in chilling storage. Special equipment such as grinders, sausage stuffers and casings, and ingredients in special products, e.g., fillers and spices, may add undesirable organisms in appreciable numbers. Growth of microorganisms on surfaces touching the meats and on the meats themselves increases their numbers.

Because of the varied sources, the kinds of microorganisms likely to contaminate meats are many (Table 14-2). Molds of many genera may reach the surfaces of meats and grow there. Especially important are species of the genera *Cladosporium, Sporotrichum, Geotrichum, Thamnidium, Mucor, Penicillium, Alternaria,* and *Monilia*. Yeasts, mostly asporogenous ones, often are present. Bacteria of many genera are found, among which some of the more important are *Pseudomonas, Acinetobacter, Moraxella, Alcaligenes, Micro-*

TABLE 14-2
FREQUENTLY ISOLATED MICROORGANISMS FROM MEATS

Product	Microorganisms isolated

Fresh and refrigerated meat	Bacteria
	  Acinetobacter, Moraxella, Pseudomonas, Aeromonas, Alcaligenes,
	  and *Micrococcus*
	Molds
	  Cladosporium, Geotrichum, Sporotrichum, Mucor, and *Thamnidium*
	Yeasts
	  Candida, Torulopsis, Debaryomyces, and *Rhodotorula*

Processed and cured meats	Bacteria
	  Lactobacillus and other lactic acid bacteria, *Acinetobacter, Bacillus,*
	  Micrococcus, Serratia, and *Staphylococcus*
	Molds
	  Aspergillus, Penicillium, Rhizopus, and *Thamnidium*
	Yeasts
	  Debaryomyces, Torula, Torulopsis, Trichosporon, and *Candida*

coccus, Streptococcus, Sarcina, Leuconostoc, Lactobacillus, Proteus, Flavo-bacterium, Bacillus, Clostridium, Escherichia, Campylobacter, Salmonella, and *Streptomyces.* Many of these bacteria can grow at chilling temperatures. There also is the possibility of the contamination of meat and meat products with human pathogens, especially those of the intestinal type.

In the retail market and in the home additional contamination usually takes place. In the market knives, saws, cleavers, slicers, grinders, chopping blocks, scales, sawdust, and containers as well as the market operators may be sources of organisms. In the home refrigerator containers used previously to store meats can serve as sources of spoilage organisms.

PRESERVATION

The preservation of meats, as of most perishable foods, usually is accomplished by a combination of preservative methods. The fact that most meats are very good culture media—high in moisture, nearly neutral in pH, and high in nutrients—coupled with the fact that some organisms may be in the lymph nodes, bones, and muscle and contamination with spoilage organisms is almost unavoidable makes the preservation of meats more difficult than that of most kinds of food. Unless cooling is prompt and rapid after slaughter, meat may undergo undesirable changes in appearance and flavor and may support the growth of microorganisms before being processed in some way for its preservation. Long storage at chilling temperatures may allow some increase in numbers of microorganisms.

ASEPSIS

Asepsis, or keeping microorganisms away from meats as much as practicable during slaughtering and handling, permits easier preservation by any method. Storage time under chilling conditions may be lengthened, aging for tenderizing becomes less of a risk, curing and smoking methods are more certain, and heating processes are more successful.

Asepsis begins with avoidance, as much as possible, of contamination from the exterior of the animal. Water spraying of the animal before slaughter has been recommended to remove as much gross dirt as possible from hair and hide, and a foot bath may be used to remove dirt from the hoofs. Even so, the hide and hair of the animal are important sources of contamination of the surfaces of the carcass during skinning. The knife used to bleed animals after slaughter may contribute microorganisms to the still-circulating bloodstream and also introduce organisms while penetrating the hide. Organisms may be added to the hide and lungs of hogs during scalding. There is contamination not only from the hide during skinning but also from knives and from workers and their clothes. During evisceration, contamination may come from the animal's intestine; the air; the water for washing and rinsing the carcass; cloths and brushes employed on the carcass; the various knives, saws, etc., used; and the hands and clothing of the workers. Some organisms may come from walls touched by the carcass or from splash or mist from the floors. Meat in the chill room may be subject to contamination from air, walls, floors, and workers. Of special interest as a source of mold spores is the sawdust usually spread on the floor. Further contamination during cutting and trimming comes from knives, saws, conveyors, tables, air, water, and workers.

The fact that the microorganisms added from these sources normally include practically all the organisms involved in the spoilage of meats, many in appreciable numbers, emphasizes the importance of aseptic methods.

Once meat is contaminated with microorganisms, their removal is difficult. Gross soil may be washed from surfaces, but the wash water may add organisms. The use of hot water or sanitizer sprays under pressure is an effective way of decreasing the total numbers of bacteria on the surfaces of the carcass and perhaps of lengthening its refrigerated shelf life. Moldy or otherwise spoiled surface areas of large pieces of meat, especially "hung," or aged, meat, may be trimmed off, but this should not be considered effective as a preservative method.

Films used to wrap meats keep out bacteria and affect the growth of those already there. These films differ considerably in their penetrability to water, oxygen, and carbon dioxide. Meats have been reported to have a shorter storage life in films less permeable to water. Fresh meats keep their red color better in an oxygen-permeable film without evacuation. With an oxygen-impermeable film, more carbon dioxide from bacteria is retained, resulting in a poorer color but favoring lactic acid bacteria, *Lactobacillaceace,* and *Brochothrix thermosphacta.* Cured meats preferably are packed in an oxygen-tight film with evacuation. Evacuation helps restrict the growth of aerobes, especially molds, reduces the rate of growth of staphylococci, and favors the growth of lactics but apparently does not favor the growth of *Clostridium botulinum* any more than plain overwrapping does.

USE OF HEAT

The canning of meat is a very specialized technique in that the procedure varies considerably with the meat product to be preserved. Most meat products are low-acid foods that are good culture media for any surviving bacteria. Rates of heat penetration range from fairly rapid in meat soups to very slow in tightly packed meats and in pastes. Chemicals added to meats, such as spices, salt, or nitrates and nitrites in curing processes, also affect the heat processing, usually making it more effective. Nitrates in meat help kill spores of anaerobic bacteria by heat and inhibit germination of surviving spores.

Commercially canned meats can be divided into two groups on the basis of the heat processing used: (1) meats that are heat-processed in an attempt to make the can contents sterile or at least "commercially sterile," as for canned meats for shelf storage in retail stores, and (2) meats that are heated enough to kill part of the spoilage organisms but must be kept refrigerated to prevent spoilage. Canned hams and loaves of luncheon meats are so handled.

Meats in group 1 are referred to as shelf-stable canned meats, and those in group 2 are called non-shelf-stable, or "keep refrigerated," canned meats. The canned cured meats owe their microbial stability to the heat process and various curing salts. The processing temperature for shelf-stable canned cured meats is 98 C, and the size of container is usually less than 1 lb. The non-shelf-stable cured meats are packed in containers up to 22 lb and are processed at temperatures of about 65 C.

Heat may be applied to meat products in other ways than canning. Treatment of meat surfaces with hot water to lengthen the keeping time has been suggested, although this may lessen nutrients and damage color. Cooking wieners at the packing plant by steam or hot water reduces the numbers of microorganisms and helps preservation. Heat applied during the smoking of meats and meat products helps reduce microbial numbers. The precooking or tenderizing of hams reduces bacterial numbers somewhat but does not sterilize. Such products should be refrigerated, for they are perishable and they may support the growth of food-poisoning organisms if they are held at room temperatures. Similar considerations hold for cooked sausages such as frankfurters and liver sausage, which also are spiced but should be kept refrigerated. The cooking of meats for direct consumption greatly reduces the microbial content and hence lengthens the keeping time. Precooked frozen meats should contain few viable microorganisms.

USE OF LOW TEMPERATURES

More meat is preserved by the use of low temperatures than by any other method, and much more by chilling than by freezing.

Chilling

Modern packing-house methods involve chilling meat promptly and rapidly to temperatures near freezing and chilling storage at only slightly above the freezing point. The more prompt and rapid this cooling, the less opportunity there will be for growth of mesophilic microorganisms. The principles concerned in chilling storage, discussed in Chapter 7, apply to meats as well as other foods. Storage temperatures vary from −1.4 to 2.2 C, with the lower temperatures preferred. The time limit for chilling storage of beef is about 30 days, depending on the numbers of microorganisms present, the temperature, and the relative humidity; for pork, lamb, and mutton, 1 to 2 weeks; and for veal, a still shorter period. Uncooked sausage, like uncured pork sausage in bulk or in links, must be preserved by refrigeration. It was emphasized in Chapter 7 that the relative humidity usually is lowered with an increase in storage temperature. Storage time can be lengthened by storage of meats in an atmosphere containing added carbon dioxide or ozone, or the temperature and relative humidity can be raised without shortening storage time. Although considerable experimental work has been done on the gas storage of meats, this method has not been used extensively. Ships equipped for storage of meat in a controlled atmosphere of carbon dioxide have been employed successfully. Increasing amounts of carbon dioxide in the atmosphere inhibit microorganisms but also hasten the formation of metmyoglobin and hence the loss of "bloom," or natural color (see Figure 14-1). The storage life of meat has been doubled, according to reports, by such gas storage. Experts do not agree on the optimal concentration of carbon dioxide, with recommendations varying from 10 to 30 percent for most meats and up to 100 percent for bacon.

Storage time also can be increased by the presence of 2.5 to 3 ppm ozone in the atmosphere. Storage up to 60 days at 2.2 C and 92 percent relative humidity without development of molds or slime has been reported. Ozone is an active oxidizing agent, however, that may give an oxidized or tallowy flavor to fats. It has been observed that while the levels of ozone cited will inhibit microorganisms, much higher concentrations are necessary to stop growth that already has begun.

The microorganisms that give trouble in the chilling storage of meats are the psychrotrophic bacteria, chiefly those of the genus *Pseudomonas*, although bacteria of the genera *Acinetobacter, Moraxella, Alcaligenes, Micrococcus, Lactobacillus, Streptococcus, Leuconostoc, Pediococcus, Flavobacterium*, and *Proteus* and yeasts and molds can grow in meats at low temperatures.

Freezing

Most meat sold in retail stores has not been frozen, but freezing often is used to preserve meats during shipment over long distances or for holding until times of shortage, and, of course, considerable quantities of meat now are frozen in home freezers. Large pieces of meat, e.g., halves and quarters, are sharp-frozen, while hamburger and smaller, fancier cuts may be quick-frozen in wrapped packages. The preservation of frozen meats is increasingly effective as the storage temperature drops from −12.2 toward −28.9 C.

Meats for freezing are subject to the same risks of contamination and growth of microorganisms as meats for any other purpose. The freezing process kills about half the bacteria, and numbers decrease slowly during storage. The low-temperature bacteria that grow on meat during chilling, species of *Pseudomonas, Acinetobacter, Moraxella, Alcaligenes, Micrococcus, Lactobacillus, Flavobacterium*, and *Proteus*, can resume growth during the thawing of meat if this is done slowly. If directions are followed, packaged quick-frozen meats are thawed too rapidly for appreciable growth of microorganisms.

USE OF IRRADIATION

Irradiation with ultraviolet rays has been used in conjunction with chilling storage to lengthen the keeping time. It has been employed chiefly on large, hung pieces of meat in plant storage rooms. The rays serve to reduce numbers of microorganisms in the air and to inhibit or kill them on the surfaces of the meat reached directly by the rays. To be affected, the microorganisms must be on the immediate surface, unprotected by fatty or opaque materials.

Irradiation has been used in the rapid aging of meats that are "hung" at higher than the usual chilling temperatures to reduce the growth of microorganisms, especially molds, on the surface. The aging, or hanging, process tenderizes the meat by its own proteolytic enzymes and is used especially for obtaining tender steaks and other fancy cuts. Ordinary aging is for several weeks at 2.2 to 3.3 C with the relative humidity between 80 and 90 percent and an air movement of 10 to 30 fpm, but with exposure to ultraviolet rays the time is reduced to 2 to 3 days at 18 C in a relative humidity of 85 to 90 percent. Some oxidation, favored by ultraviolet rays, and hydrolysis of fats may take place during aging.

Gamma irradiation of meats still is limited and in the experimental stage. When sterilization is effected, doses of 20 to 70 KiloGrays are applied and undesirable changes in color and flavor may appear.

PRESERVATION BY DRYING

Drying meats for preservation has been practiced for centuries. Jerky, or sundried strips of beef, was a standard food of American pioneers. Some types of sausage are preserved primarily by their dryness. In dried beef, made mostly from cured, smoked beef hams, growth of microorganisms may take place before processing and may develop in the "pickle" during curing, but numbers of organisms are reduced by the smoking and drying process. Organisms may contaminate the dried ham during storage and the slices during cutting and packing.

Meat products such as dry sausages, dry salamis, and dry cervelats are preserved chiefly by their low moisture content, for some varieties are not smoked. A dry outer surface on the casing of any sausage is protective.

Older methods of drying meats are usually combined with salting and smoking. During World War II pieces of freshly cooked beef and pork were dried by heat. Another method of drying pork involves a short nitrate-nitrite cure before drying and the addition of lecithin as an antioxidant and stabilizer. Drying may be by vacuum, in trays, or by other methods. The final product keeps without refrigeration.

Freeze drying of meats is on the increase, with greater success with processed products such as meat patties, meatballs, and stew than with fresh meats. The efficiency of the process is being improved enough to reduce costs to where production for retail sale has become practicable for specialized markets, e.g., hikers, campers, and backpackers.

Meat for drying should be of good bacteriological quality, without previous development of appreciable numbers of microorganisms or of undesirable flavor.

USE OF PRESERVATIVES

The utilization of a controlled atmosphere containing added carbon dioxide or ozone in the chilling storage of meats has been discussed. Preservation by heavy salting is an old method that usually results in an inferior product. Ordinarily salting is combined with curing and smoking in order to be effective.

Curing

The curing of meats is limited to beef and pork, either ground meat or certain cuts such as hams, butts, jowls, sides, loins, and bellies of hogs and the hams, brisket, and leg muscles of beef. Originally, curing of meats was for the purpose of preserving by salting without refrigeration, but most cured meats of the present day have other ingredients added and are refrigerated, and many also are smoked and hence dried to some extent. The curing agents permitted are sodium chloride, sugar, sodium nitrite, and vinegar, but only the first three are commonly used. The functions of the ingredients are as follows:

Sodium chloride, or common salt, is used primarily as a preservative and flavoring agent. The cover pickle, used for immersing the meat, may contain about 15 percent of salt, in contrast to the pumping pickle, injected into the meat, which has a higher concentration, approximating 24 percent. Its primary purpose is to lower the a_w.

Sugar adds flavor and also serves as an energy source for nitrate-reducing bacteria in the curing solution or pickle. Sucrose is used chiefly, but glucose can be substituted if a short cure is employed, or no sugar may be added.

Sodium nitrate is indirectly a color fixative and is bacteriostatic in acid solution, especially against anaerobes. It has also served as a reservoir from which nitrite can be formed by bacterial reduction during the long cure.

Sodium nitrite is the source of nitric oxide, which is the real color fixative (Figure 14-1) and has some bacteriostatic effect in acid solution.

Most of the preservative effect of the curing agents, then, is attributed to the sodium chloride, with some bacteriostatic effect from the nitrite and little effect from the nitrate. The salts, sugar, and meat protein combine to lower the a_w value of the cured meats, e.g., of hams to about 0.95 to 0.97. Other preservative factors are the low curing temperature and smoking.

Nitrate also plays a role in the color of meats. For example, purplish-red color of meats (Figure 14-1) is due to blood hemoglobin and muscle myoglobin; oxygenation of these compounds produces oxyhemoglobin and oxymyoglobin, which are bright red. Under acid and reducing conditions in the presence of nitrite, the red nitric oxide myoglobin and nitrosohemoglobin are produced from

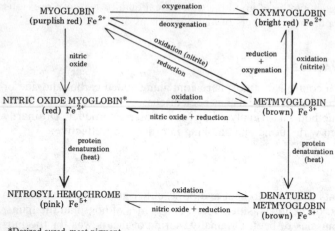

*Desired cured–meat pigment

FIGURE 14-1
Chemical changes of myoglobin during meat processing and curing.
(*From John C. Forrest et al., Principles of Meat Science. W. H. Freman and Company. Copyright © 1975.*)

myoglobin and hemoglobin (see Figure 14-1). The acid condition is produced by the meat itself, the reduced condition by the bacteria, and the nitric oxide for the reaction by reduction of the nitrite.

There are four methods for introducing curing agents into meat: (1) the dry cure, in which dry ingredients are rubbed into the meat, as in curing belly bacon, (2) the pickle cure, in which the meats are immersed in a solution of the ingredients, (3) the injection cure, in which a concentrated solution of the ingredients is injected by needle into the arteries and veins of the meat via an artery or into the muscular tissue in various parts of the meat, as is done with pork hams, and (4) the direct-addition method, in which the curing agents are added directly to finely ground meats, such as sausage, and aid in their preservation.

The curing temperature, especially with a pickling solution, usually is about 2.2 to 3.3 C, and the time of the cure varies with the methods used and the meats to be cured. The older methods of curing in the pickle require several months, but the newer "quick cure," in which the pickling solution is pumped into the meat, greatly shortens that time.

Most meats are smoked after curing to aid their preservation; others, such as corned beef, are not smoked but must be refrigerated.

Some types of sausage, such as Thuringer, cervelat, Lebanon bologna, the salamis, and the dry and semidry summer sausages, undergo an acid fermentation, preferably of a mixed lactic acid kind, during their curing. This not only has a preservative effect, preventing undesirable fermentations, but also adds a desired tangy flavor. Many processors carry over the mixed lactic flora from a previous lot of sausage, but the use of pure cultures such as *Pediococcus cerevisiae** have added increased control of the desired fermentation and have shortened the fermentation time. A summary of the various bacteria reported in fermented and cured meats is presented in Table 14-3.

Vinegar is added to the pickling solution in the preservation of foods such as pickled pigs' feet, pickled spiced beef, and souses. Pigs' feet are cured in a solution of salt, sodium nitrate, and sodium nitrite, cooked, and then held in a brine of salt and vinegar. Then they are packed into jars or other containers and covered with a fresh salt-vinegar brine, and the jar is sealed. Unless the acidity is unduly low, the product will not spoil.

Microbiology of Meat-Curing Brines   The microorganisms in curing brines and on immersed meats in them vary with the initial condition of the meat and the method of curing employed. The microbial content of the salt seems to have little significance except on salted meat, which after removal from brine or after dry salting sometimes develops red surface colonies of halophilic bacteria like those carried by the salt. In modern American short methods of curing meats, such as ham, bacteria in the brine apparently have little to do with changes that occur in the meat, for they do not reach high numbers and are killed mostly on the meat by the smoking that follows. Such brines contain principally lactic acid bacteria, except at the surface, where micrococci and yeasts may develop. The lactics are chiefly lactobacilli and pediococci. In the old long cure, bacteria, especially micrococci, functioned in reducing nitrate to nitrite, thus fixing the red color in the meat.

Foreign methods of curing bacon usually involve immersion in fairly concentrated brines and use of these brines for a long period. The brines appear to build up, besides micrococci, a special mixture of cocci and gram-positive and

TABLE 14-3
MICROORGANISMS REPORTED IN CURED MEATS

Meat	Microorganism
Sausages	
Salami	Homofermentative lactobacilli
Big bologna	*Leuconostoc mesenteroides,* heterofermentative lactobacilli
Smoked links	*Leuconostoc mesenteroides,* heterofermentative lactobacilli
Frankfurters	Streptococci, pediococci, leuconostocs, lactobacilli, micrococci*, sporeformers, yeasts
Fresh pork	Leuconostocs, microbacteria, lactobacilli, pseudomonads
Bacon	
Sliced, packaged	Mostly lactobacilli; also micrococci*, enterococci
Wiltshire	Micrococci*, lactobacilli
Vacuum-wrapped	Streptococci, leuconostocs, pediococci, lactobacilli
Ham	
Raw	Lactobacilli, micrococci*, microbacteria, enterococci, leuconostocs
Sliced, packaged	*Streptococcus faecium, Microbacterium* spp.
Pressed, spiced	Heterofermentative lactobacilli, leuconostocs
Canned	Enterococci, bacilli, micrococci*
Irradiated	Enterococci
Heated, irradiated	Bacilli, clostridia

gram-negative rods that, for the most part, form tiny colonies on agar media. They are halotolerant to halophilic and reduce nitrates to nitrites. When hog bellies are treated with the dry curing mixture and compressed in boxes, growth of salt-tolerant, nitrate-reducing psychrotrophs is permitted. Some beef-curing brines have been found to contain micrococci, lactobacilli, streptococci, *Achromobacter**, vibrios, and perhaps pediococci, plus other bacteria in small numbers. Species of *Micrococcus** are active in many of the pickling solutions and have been found especially in those of high salt concentration used in curing British and Canadian bacons.

Smoking

Use of wood smoke as a preservative was discussed in Chapter 9, where it was pointed out that smoking has two main purposes: to add desired flavors and to aid in preservation. It was noted that the preservative substances added to the meat, together with the action of the heat during smoking, have a germicidal effect and that the drying of the meat, together with chemicals from the smoke, inhibits microbial growth during storage.

Older methods of curing and smoking, where high salt concentrations were used in curing and greater drying and incorporation of preservative chemicals was accomplished in smoking, produced hams, dried beef, etc., that would keep without refrigeration. Many of the newer methods, however, yield a perishable product that must be refrigerated. Precooked or tenderized hams and sausages of high moisture content are examples.

Spices

Spices and condiments added to meat products such as meat loaves and sausages are not in concentrations high enough to be preservative, but they may add their effect to those of the other preservative factors. Certainly products such as bologna, Polish, and frankfurter and other sausages owe their keeping quality to the combined effect of spicing, curing, smoking (drying), cooking, and refrigerating.

Antibiotics

Although in this country the only permitted use of antibiotics in flesh foods now is in fish (chlortetracycline at 7 ppm in ice), experiments have indicated that antibiotics can be used successfully in meats to prolong storage life at chilling or higher temperatures. The antibiotics most often recommended have been chlortetracycline, oxytetracycline, nisin, and chloramphenicol. The antibiotics may be applied to meats in various ways: (1) The antibiotic may be fed to the animal over a long period, (2) it may be fed more intensively for a short period before slaughter, (3) it may be infused into the carcass or into parts of it, or (4) it may be applied to the surface of pieces of meat or mixed with comminuted meat. Feeding an antibiotic brings about a selection of microorganisms in the animal's intestinal tract, presumably reducing the numbers of spoilage bacteria there and therefore reducing the numbers that are likely to reach the meat from that source during slaughter and dressing. It has been suggested that injection of antibiotic before slaughter might be employed to prolong the keeping time of carcasses at atmospheric temperatures before they reach the refrigerator or to hold beef briefly at temperatures that will favor tenderization of special cuts as well as lengthen the keeping time of meats held at chilling temperatures. Infusion of an antibiotic into the carcass immediately after slaughter or into special parts would serve similar purposes. The storage life of meats could be lengthened by means of an antibiotic dip or by inclusion of an antibiotic in ground meats.

SPOILAGE

Raw meat is subject to change by its own enzymes and by microbial action, and its fat may be oxidized chemically. A moderate amount of autolysis is desired in the tenderizing of beef and game by hanging, or aging, but is not encouraged in most other raw meats. Autolytic changes include some proteolytic action on muscle and connective tissues and slight hydrolysis of fats. The defect caused by excessive autolysis has been called "souring," an inexact term that is applied to a variety of kinds of spoilage of food and to in fact almost any kind that gives a sour odor. Souring due to autolysis is difficult to separate or distinguish from defects caused by microbial action, especially from simple proteolysis. However, this preliminary hydrolysis of proteins by the meat enzymes undoubtedly helps microorganisms start growing in the meat by furnishing the simpler nitrogen compounds needed by many microorganisms that cannot attack complete native proteins.

GENERAL PRINCIPLES UNDERLYING MEAT SPOILAGE

It has been pointed out that during slaughter, dressing, and cutting, microorganisms come chiefly from the exterior of the animal and its intestinal tract but that more are added from knives, cloths, air, workers, carts, boxes, and equipment in general. A great variety of kinds of organisms are added, and so it can be assumed that under ordinary conditions most kinds of potential spoilage organisms are present and will be able to grow if favorable conditions present themselves.

Invasion of Tissues by Microorganisms

Upon the death of the animal, invasion of the tissues by contaminating microorganisms takes place. Factors that influence that invasion include the following:

1 *The load in the gut of the animal.* The greater the load, the greater the invasion of tissues. For that reason starvation for 24 hr before slaughter has been recommended.

2 *The physiological condition of the animal immediately before slaughter.* If the animal is excited, feverish, or fatigued, bacteria are more likely to enter the tissues, bleeding is apt to be incomplete, thus encouraging the spread of bacteria, and chemical changes may take place more readily in the tissue, such as those due to better bacterial growth because of a higher pH, earlier release of juices from the meat fibers, and more rapid denaturation of proteins. Because glycogen is used up in fatigue, the pH will not drop from 7.2 to about 5.7, as it would normally.

3 *The method of killing and bleeding.* The better and more sanitary the bleeding, the better the keeping quality of the meat. Little has been reported on the effect of humane methods of slaughter on the keeping quality of meat, although it has been claimed that more greening was found in pork and bacon from electrically stunned animals than from those killed with carbon dioxide.

4 *The rate of cooling.* Rapid cooling will reduce the rate of invasion of the tissues by microorganisms.

Microorganisms are spread in the meat through the blood and lymph vessels and connective-tissue interspaces, and in ground meat by grinding.

Growth of Microorganisms in Meat

Meat is an ideal culture medium for many organisms because it is high in moisture, rich in nitrogenous foods of various degrees of complexity, and plentifully supplied with minerals and accessory growth factors. Also, it usually has some fermentable carbohydrate (glycogen) and is at a favorable pH for most microorganisms.

The factors that influence the growth of microorganisms and hence the kind of spoilage are those mentioned in Chapter 4. Briefly, these factors are as follows.

1 *The kind and amount of contamination with microorganisms and the spread of these organisms in the meat.* For example, meat with a contaminating flora that is high in percentage of psychrotrophs would spoil at chilling temperatures more rapidly than meat with a low percentage of these psychrotrophic organisms.

2 *The physical properties of the meat.* The amount of exposed surface of the flesh has considerable influence on the rate of spoilage because the greatest load of organisms usually is there and air is available for aerobic organisms. Fat may protect some surfaces but is subject to spoilage itself, chiefly enzymatic and chemical. Grinding meat greatly increases the surface and encourages microbial growth for this reason and because it releases moisture and distributes bacteria throughout the meat. Skin on meat serves to protect the meat inside, although microorganisms grow on it.

3 *Chemical properties of the meat.* It has been pointed out that meat in general is a fine culture medium for microorganisms. The moisture content is important in determining whether organisms can grow and what kinds can grow, especially at the surface, where drying may take place. Thus the surface may be so dry as to permit no growth, a little moist to allow mold growth, still moister to encourage yeasts, and very moist to favor bacterial growth. The relative humidity of the storage atmosphere is important in this regard. Food for microorganisms is plentiful, but the low content or absence of fermentable carbohydrate and the high protein content tend to favor the nonfermenting types of organisms, those which can utilize proteins and their decomposition products for nitrogen, carbon, and energy. The pH of raw meat may vary from about 5.7 to over 7.2, depending on the amount of glycogen present at slaughter and subsequent changes in the meat. A higher pH value favors microbial growth; a lower one usually makes it slower and may be selective for certain organisms, such as yeasts.

4 *Availability of oxygen.* Aerobic conditions at the surface of meat are favorable to molds, yeasts, and aerobic bacteria. Within the solid pieces of meat, conditions are anaerobic and tend to remain that way because the potential is strongly poised at a low level, although oxygen will diffuse slowly into ground meat and slowly raise the O-R potential unless the casing or packaging material is impervious to oxygen. True putrefaction is favored by anaerobic conditions.

5 *Temperature.* Meat should be stored at temperatures not far above freezing, where only low-temperature microorganisms can grow. Molds, yeasts, and psychrotrophic bacteria grow slowly and produce characteristic defects to be discussed later. True putrefaction is rare at these low temperatures but is likely at room temperature. As for most foods, the temperature is most important in selecting the kinds of organisms to grow and the types of spoilage to result. At chilling temperatures, for example, psychrophiles are favored and proteolysis is likely, caused by a dominating species of bacterium, followed by utilization of peptides and amino acids by secondary species. At ordinary atmospheric temperatures, mesophiles would grow, such as coliform bacteria and species of *Bacillus* and *Clostridium,* with the production of moderate amounts of acid from the limited amounts of carbohydrates present.

General Types of Spoilage of Meats

The common types of spoilage of meats can be classified on the basis of whether they occur under aerobic or anaerobic conditions and whether they are caused by bacteria, yeasts, or molds.

Spoilage under Aerobic Conditions   Under aerobic conditions bacteria may cause the following:

1 *Surface slime*, which may be caused by species of *Pseudomonas, Acinetobacter, Moraxella, Alcaligenes, Streptococcus, Leuconostoc, Bacillus,* and *Micrococcus.* Some species of *Lactobacillus* can produce slime. The temperature and the availability of moisture influence the kind of microorganisms causing surface slime. At chilling temperatures, high moisture will favor the *Pseudomonas-Alcaligenes* group; with less moisture, as on frankfurters, micrococci and yeasts will be encouraged; and with still less moisture, molds may grow.

At higher temperatures, up to that of the room, micrococci* and other mesophiles compete well with the pseudomonads and related bacteria. The numbers of microorganisms necessary before detection of off-odor or slime in meats and other proteinaceous foods are shown in Table 14-4. Numbers in the millions per square centimeter or gram are required.

2 *Changes in color of meat pigments* (see Figure 14-1). The red color of meat, called its "bloom," may be changed to shades of green, brown, or gray as a result of the production of oxidizing compounds, e.g., peroxides, or of hydrogen sulfide, by bacteria. Species of *Lactobacillus* (mostly heterofermentative) and *Leuconostoc* are reported to cause the greening of sausage.

3 *Changes in fats*. The oxidation of unsaturated fats in meats takes place chemically in air and may be catalyzed by light and copper. Lipolytic bacteria may cause some lipolysis and also may accelerate the oxidation of the fats. Some fats, such as butterfat, become tallowy on oxidation and rancid on hydrolysis, but most animal fats develop oxidative rancidity when oxidized, with off-odors due to aldehydes and acids. Hydrolysis adds the flavor of the released fatty acids. Rancidity of fats may be caused by lipolytic species of *Pseudomonas* and *Achromobacter** or by yeasts.

4 *Phosphorescence*. This rather uncommon defect is caused by phosphorescent or luminous bacteria, e.g., *Photobacterium* spp., growing on the surface of the meat.

5 *Various surface colors due to pigmented bacteria*. Thus "red spot" may be caused by *Serratia marcescens* or other bacteria with red pigments. *Pseudomonas syncyanea** can impart a blue color to the surface. Yellow discolorations are caused by bacteria with yellow pigments, usually species of *Micrococcus** or *Flavobacterium*. *Chromobacterium lividum* and other bacteria give greenish-blue to brownish-black spots on stored beef. The purple "stamping-ink" discoloration of surface fat is caused by yellow-pigmented cocci and rods. When the fat becomes rancid and peroxides appear, the yellow color changes to a greenish shade and later becomes purplish to blue.

6 *Off-odors and off-tastes*. "Taints," or undesirable odors and tastes, that appear in meat as a result of the growth of bacteria on the surface often are

TABLE 14-4
NUMBERS OF MICROORGANISMS AT TIME OF APPEARANCE OF ODOR AND SLIME IN PROTEINACEOUS FOODS

Food	Numbers	
	When odor evident	When slime evident
Poultry meat	$2.5–100 \times 10^6/cm^2$	$10–60 \times 10^6/cm^2$
Beef	$1.2–100 \times 10^6/cm^2$	$3–300 \times 10^6/cm^2$
Frankfurters	$100–130 \times 10^6/cm^2$	$130 \times 10^6/cm^2$
Processed meats		$10–100 \times 10^6/cm^2$
Wiltshire bacon		$1.5–100 \times 10^6/cm^2$
Fish	$1–130 \times 10^6/cm^2$	
Shell or liquid eggs	$10 \times 10^6/g$	

evident before other signs of spoilage. "Souring" is the term applied to almost any defect that gives a sour odor that may be due to volatile acids, e.g., formic, acetic, butyric, and propionic, or even to growth of yeasts. "Cold-storage flavor" or taint is an indefinite term for a stale flavor. *Actinomycetes* may be responsible for a musty or earthy flavor.

Under aerobic conditions yeasts may grow on the surface of meats, causing sliminess, lipolysis, off-odors and tastes, and discolorations—white, cream, pink, or brown—due to pigments in the yeasts.

Aerobic growth of molds may cause the following:

1 *Stickiness*. Incipient growth of molds makes the surface of the meat sticky to the touch.

2 *Whiskers*. When meat is stored at temperatures near freezing, a limited amount of mycelial growth may take place without sporulation. Such white, fuzzy growth can be caused by a number of molds, including *Thamnidium chaetocladioides,* or *T. elegans; Mucor mucedo, M. lusitanicus,* or *M. racemosus; Rhizopus;* and others. Controlled growth of a special strain of *Thamnidium* has been recommended for improvement in flavor during aging of beef.

3 *Black spot*. This usually is caused by *Cladosporium herbarum,* but other molds with dark pigments may be responsible.

4 *White spot. Sporotrichum carnis* is the most common cause of white spot, although any mold with wet, yeastlike colonies, e.g., *Geotrichum,* can cause white spot.

5 *Green patches*. These are caused for the most part by the green spores of species of *Penicillium* such as *P. expansum, P. asperulum,* and *P. oxalicum.*

6 *Decomposition of fats*. Many molds have lipases and hence cause hydrolysis of fats. Molds also aid in the oxidation of fats.

7 *Off-odors and off-tastes*. Molds give a musty flavor to meat in the vicinity of their growth. Sometimes the defect is given a name indicating the cause, e.g., "thamnidium taint."

Spots of surface spoilage by yeasts and molds usually are localized to a great extent and can be trimmed off without harm to the rest of the meat. The time that has been allowed for diffusion of the products of decomposition into the meat and the rate of that diffusion will determine the depth to which the defect will appear. Extensive bacterial growth over the surface may bring fairly deep penetration. Then, too, facultative bacteria may grow inward slowly.

Spoilage under Anaerobic Conditions   Facultative and anaerobic bacteria are able to grow within the meat under anaerobic conditions and cause spoilage. The terminology used in connection with this spoilage is inexact. Most used are the words "souring," "putrefaction," and "taint," but these terms apparently mean different things to different people.

1 *Souring*. The term implies a sour odor and perhaps taste. This could be caused by formic, acetic, butyric, propionic, and higher fatty acids or other organic acids such as lactic or succinic. Souring can result from (*a*) action of

the meat's own enzymes during aging or ripening, (b) anaerobic production of fatty acids or lactic acid by bacterial action, or (c) proteolysis without putrefaction, caused by facultative or anaerobic bacteria and sometimes called "stinking sour fermentation." Acid and gas formation accompany the action of the "butyric" *Clostridium* species and the coliform bacteria on carbohydrates. Vacuum-packed meats, especially those in gastight wrappers, commonly support the growth of lactic acid bacteria.

2 *Putrefaction.* True putrefaction is the anaerobic decomposition of protein with the production of foul-smelling compounds such as hydrogen sulfide, mercaptans, indole, skatole, ammonia, and amines. It usually is caused by species of *Clostridium*, but facultative bacteria may cause putrefaction or assist in its production, as evidenced by the long list of species with the specific names *putrefaciens, putrificum, putida**, etc., chiefly in the genera *Pseudomonas* and *Alcaligenes*. Also, some species of *Proteus* are putrefactive. The confusion in the use of the term "putrefaction" arises from the fact that any type of spoilage with foul odors, whether from the anaerobic decomposition of protein or from the breakdown of other compounds, even nonnitrogenous ones, may erroneously be termed putrefaction. Thus, for example, trimethylamine in fish and isovaleric acid in butter are described as putrid odors. Gas formation accompanies putrefaction by clostridia, the gases being hydrogen and carbon dioxide.

3 *Taint.* "Taint" is a still more inexact word applied to any off-taste or off-odor. The term "bone taint" of meats refers to either souring or putrefaction next to the bones, especially in hams. Usually it means putrefaction.

Not only air but temperature has an important influence on the type of spoilage to be expected in meat. When meat is held at temperatures near 0 C, as recommended, microbial growth is limited to that of molds, yeasts, and bacteria able to grow at low temperatures. These include many of the types that produce sliminess, discoloration, and spots of growth on the surface and many that can cause souring, such as *Pseudomonas, Acinetobacter Moraxella, Alcaligenes, Lactobacillus, Leuconostoc, Streptococcus,* and *Flavobacterium* species. Most true putrefiers, like those in the genus *Clostridium*, require temperatures above those of the refrigerator.

SPOILAGE OF DIFFERENT KINDS OF MEATS

The processing of meats by curing, smoking, drying, or canning usually changes them and their microbial flora enough to encourage types of spoilage not undergone by fresh meats.

Spoilage of Fresh Meats

The spoilage of fresh meats has been covered in the preceding discussion of general types of spoilage. Normally, upon extended refrigeration, *Pseudomonas, Acinetobacter,* and *Moraxella* species spoil fresh meats.

Lactic acid bacteria, chiefly of the genera *Lactobacillus, Leuconostoc, Streptococcus, Brevibacterium,* and *Pediococcus,* are present in most meats, fresh or cured, and can grow even at refrigerator temperatures. Ordinarily their limited growth does not detract from the quality of the meat; on the contrary, in certain types of sausage, such as salami, Lebanon, and Thuringer, the lactic fermentation is encouraged. However, the lactic acid bacteria may be responsible for three types of spoilage: (1) slime formation at the surface or within, especially in the presence of sucrose, (2) production of a green discoloration, and (3) souring, when excessive amounts of lactic and other acids have been produced.

Fresh Beef   Fresh beef undergoes the changes in color mentioned: (1) changes in the hemoglobin and myoglobin, the red pigment in the blood and muscles, respectively, so as to cause loss of bloom and the production of reddish-brown methemoglobin and metmyoglobin and the green-gray-brown oxidation pigments by action of oxygen and microorganisms, (2) white, green, yellow, and greenish-blue to brown-black spots and purple discolorations due to pigmented microorganisms, (3) phosphorescence, and (4) spots due to various bacteria, yeasts, and molds. Beef also is subject to sliminess on the surface due to bacteria or yeasts, stickiness due to molds, whiskers resulting from mycelial growth of molds, and souring and putrefaction by bacteria. Pseudomonads usually predominate in beef held at 10 C or lower, but at 15 C or above micrococci* and pseudomonads grow in about equal numbers.

Hamburger   Hamburger held at room temperature usually putrefies, but at temperatures near freezing it acquires a stale, sour odor. The sourness at low temperatures is caused chiefly by species of *Pseudomonas, Acinetobacter,* and *Moraxella,* with help from lactic acid bacteria. *Alcaligenes, Micrococcus*,* and *Flavobacterium* species may grow in some samples. A large number of kinds of microorganisms have been found in hamburger held at higher temperatures, but no distinction has been made between mere presence and actual growth. Among the genera reported are *Bacillus, Clostridium, Escherichia, Enterobacter, Proteus, Pseudomonas, Alcaligenes, Lactobacillus, Leuconostoc, Streptococcus, Micrococcus,* and *Sarcina* of the bacteria and *Penicillium* and *Mucor* of the molds. A few yeasts also have been found.

Fresh Pork Sausage   Fresh sausage is made mostly of ground fresh pork to which salt and spices have been added. It may be sold in bulk or in natural or artificial casings. Pork sausage is a perishable food that must be preserved by refrigeration and then can be kept only a relatively short time without spoilage. Souring, the most common type of spoilage at refrigerator temperatures of 0 to 11 C, has been attributed to growth and acid production by lactobacilli and leuconostocs, although *Microbacterium* and *Micrococcus** organisms may grow at higher storage temperatures. The encased pork sausages, especially the "little-pig" type, are subject to slime formation on the outside of the casing on long storage or to variously colored spots due to mold growth. Thus *Alternaria* has been found to cause small dark spots on refrigerated links.

Spoilage of Cured Meats

Most of the cured meats are pork, although some cuts of beef may be cured. The inhibitory effect of nitrite against anaerobes has been mentioned previously. Sodium nitrite is alleged to favor lactic acid bacteria in sausages such as Thuringer and Essex that support a lactic fermentation. Curing salts make meats more favorable to growth of gram-positive bacteria, yeasts, and molds than to the gram-negative bacteria which usually spoil meats. They also reduce the thermal processing necessary to produce stable heated meat foods, such as pork luncheon meats. Some meats, e.g., bulk chipped beef, are preserved by their high content of sodium chloride.

The load of microorganisms on the piece of meat to be cured and any deterioration that has taken place will influence the success of the curing operation. Thus undesirable changes in the meat pigments will result in a discolored cured product, incipient spoilage will give an inferior appearance and flavor to the product, and large numbers of spoilage bacteria may interfere with the cure.

Dried Beef or Beef Hams Beef hams are made spongy by species of *Bacillus,* sour by a variety of bacteria, red by *Halobacterium salinarium* or a red *Bacillus* species, and blue by *Pseudomonas syncyanea*, Penicillium spinulosum* (purplish), and species of *Rhodotorula* yeasts. The major factor is the water content and relative humidity. As the relative humidity increases and the product absorbs water, there is a decrease in shelf life.

Gas in jars of chipped dried beef has been attributed to a denitrifying aerobic organism that resembles *Pseudomonas fluorescens.* The gases are oxides of nitrogen. *Bacillus* species have been known to produce carbon dioxide in the jars.

Sausage In encased sausages, spoilage microorganisms may grow on the outside of the casing, between the casing and meat, or in the interior.

Growth of organisms can take place on the outside of the casings only if sufficient moisture is available. If moisture is available, micrococci* and yeasts can form a slimy layer, as often occurs on frankfurters that have become moist because of removal from refrigerator to warmer temperatures. With less moisture, molds may produce fuzziness and discoloration. Carbon dioxide, produced mostly by heterofermentative lactic acid bacteria, may swell packages of wieners or breakfast sausages when they are packaged in gastight flexible film.

Growth between the casing and the meat is favored by an accumulation of moisture there during cooking if the casing is penetrable to water; when two casings are employed, the inner casing may be wetted before the outer casing is applied, trapping water between them. The slime at the surface of the meat or between the casings is formed chiefly by acid-producing micrococci*. The penetrability of the inner casing to soluble nutrients favors the bacterial growth.

Various kinds of bacteria have been reported able to grow within sausages on long chilling storage or at storage temperatures above 10.5 C. Acid-forming micrococci* such as *Micrococcus candidus** may grow in liver sausage and bologna, and species of *Bacillus* have been found growing in liver sausage. Psychrotrophic leuconostocs and lactobacilli also can grow and cause a souring that is not encouraged in most sausage but is favored in certain varieties, such as Lebanon, Thuringer, and Essex sausages. Fading of the red color of sausage to a chalky gray has been attributed to oxygen and light and may be hastened by bacteria. Various causes have been suggested for "chill rings," such as oxidation, the production of organic acids or reducing substances by bacteria, excessive water, and undercooking.

The greening of sausage may appear as a green ring not far from the casing, a green core, or a green surface. The cause of greening is probably the production of peroxides, e.g., hydrogen peroxide, by heterofermentative species of *Lactobacillus* and by *Leuconostoc* or other catalase-negative bacteria, according to Niven (1961). Jensen (1954) stated that hydrogen sulfide also may be involved. Greening is favored by a slightly acid pH and by the presence of small amounts of oxygen. The green ring below the surface of large sausages or green core in small sausages develops within 12 to 36 hr after the sausage has been processed, even under refrigeration; it is evident as soon as the sausage is cut and usually is not accompanied by surface slime. Bacterial growth and the production of heat-stable peroxide have taken place before smoking and cooking, and the peroxide continues to act to produce greening after the processing. Green cores in large sausage, e.g., big bologna, develop usually after 4 or more days of holding and within 1 to 12 hr after slicing, after large numbers of causative bacteria develop as a result of underprocessing and inadequate refrigeration. Greening of a cut surface indicates contamination with, and growth of, salt-tolerant, peroxide-forming bacteria (probably lactics) which can grow at low temperatures. Surface sliminess often accompanies the greening. The defect can be spread from sausage to sausage.

Production of nitric oxide gas in sausage by nitrate-reducing bacteria has been reported. Unless the casing or packaging material permits the passage of carbon dioxide, carbon dioxide may accumulate as the result of the action of heterofermentative lactics and cause swelling. This also can take place in packaged sliced, cured meats; in sandwich spreads; and in similar products in plastic casings or packages.

Bacon   Since the parts of the hog used for bacon and the curing processes vary in different parts of the world, the types of spoilage and the organisms concerned also vary. The bellies employed in the American process usually are subject to little change and are reported to emerge from the smokehouse comparatively free from molds and yeasts and low in bacteria. Because of its salt tolerance and ability to grow at low temperatures, *Streptococcus faecalis* often is present. The surface flora of bacon may also contain micrococci* and staphylococci. Molds are the chief spoilage organisms on the cured bacon, especially on the sliced, packaged (air-permeable) bacon when stored in the home refrigerator. Most trouble is encountered in late summer and early fall with species of *Aspergillus, Alternaria, Monilia, Oidium, Fusarium, Mucor, Rhizopus, Botrytis,* and *Penicillium*. Few microbiological problems are encountered with dry-salt bellies and Oxford-style bellies. Any rancidity that develops usually is due to chemical changes. Sliced bacon may be deteriorated by oxidizing and lipolytic bacteria on long storage, although chemical oxidation also may take place. Oxidizing and sulfide-forming bacteria also may be concerned in producing a poor color in the flesh part of bacon, although wrong concentrations of nitrite are more often responsible, and chromogenic bacteria may cause discolored areas. A yellowish-brown discoloration, showing the presence of tyrosine, has been blamed on proteolytic bacteria. Gumminess of pickle and bellies, now uncommon, results from the formation of gum by any of a large number of species of bacteria and yeasts.

An extensive study of the bacteriology of Wiltshire bacon has been made in Canada. In the manufacture of this bacon, the sides of the hog are cured in a very concentrated brine for a short time (6 to 8 days) at a low temperature (3.3 to 4.5 C), permitting the growth of only psychrotrophic, salt-tolerant bacteria. Little growth takes place in the curing pickle, but marked increases in bacteria take place on the sides of meat, sometimes enough to give sliminess to the surface. Visible growth or slime usually appears when the count is over 71.5 million per square centimeter. Micrococci are most common in the brine, but other organisms, unable to grow in the cold brine, may grow before brining or during the storage of the pickled sides after baling.

Unopened, packaged (air-impermeable) sliced bacon is spoiled mostly by lactobacilli, but micrococci* and fecal streptococci may grow, especially if the wrapper is somewhat permeable to oxygen. Opened bacon may be spoiled by molds.

As a means of reducing levels of nitrite in bacon, the Wisconsin process has been proposed (Tanaka et al., 1985). Bacon prepared with 40 or 80 ppm sodium nitrite, 0.7% sucrose, and a *Lactobacillus plantarum* had a greater antibotulinal effect than bacon made with 120 ppm sodium nitrite only.

Ham The term "souring," as used for the spoilage of hams, covers all important types of spoilage from a comparatively nonodorous proteolysis to genuine putrefaction with its very obnoxious odors of mercaptans, hydrogen sulfide, amines, indole, etc., and may be caused by a large variety of psychrotrophic, salt-tolerant bacteria. Jensen (1954) listed a number of genera, the species of which may cause souring: *Alcaligenes, Bacillus, Pseudomonas, Lactobacillus, Proteus, Serratia, Bacterium**, *Micrococcus, Clostridium,* and others, as well as some unnamed, hydrogen sulfide–producing streptobacilli that cause flesh-souring of ham. The types of souring are classified according to their location as sours of shank or tibial marrows, body or meat, aitchbone, stifle joint, body-bone or femur marrow, and butt. "Puffers," or gassy hams, are not encountered commercially but occur occasionally when inexpert curing is done.

The common, or quick-cure, method for curing hams, in which the curing solution is pumped into the ham by way of the veins, has reduced greatly the incidence of souring. The reduction of bacterial contamination and growth by proper slaughter and bleeding of hogs, adequate refrigeration, sealing of the marrows by sawing in the right places, prompt handling, use of bacteriologically satisfactory pickling solution, and good overall sanitation has helped reduce the amount of souring.

Tenderized hams are really precooked and are given a mild cure. Such hams are perishable and should be protected from contamination and refrigerated during storage to prevent their deterioration by microorganisms. Improperly handled tenderized hams may be spoiled by any of the common meat-spoilage bacteria, among which *Escherichia coli, Proteus* spp., and food-poisoning staphylococci (*Staphylococcus aureus*) have been reported.

Refrigerated Packaged Meats   Packaging films, permitting good penetration of oxygen and hence of carbon dioxide, favor the more aerobic bacteria, such as *Pseudomonas, Acinetobacter,* and *Moraxella,* and their production of off-flavors, slime, and even putrefaction. This spoilage is much like that in the unwrapped meat. Films with poor gas penetration encourage lactic acid bacteria, especially when combined with vacuum packing. These bacteria in time cause souring, slime, and atypical flavors. Spoilage of canned meats is discussed in Chapter 19.

Curing Solutions or Pickles   Spoilage of the pickle or curing solution for ham and other cured meats is likely in the presence of available sugar and a pH well above 6.0. Spoilage of multiuse brines usually is putrefactive and is caused by *Vibrio, Alcaligenes,* or *Spirillum*. Souring can be caused by *Lactobacillus* and *Micrococcus,* and slime by *Leuconostoc* or *Micrococcus lipolyticus**.

Turbid and ropy vinegar about pickled pigs' feet or sausages are caused chiefly by lactic acid bacteria from the meats, although yeasts may be responsible for cloudiness. Black spots on pickled pigs' feet may be caused by hydrogen sulfide–producing bacteria, and gas in vacuum-packed pickles may come from heterofermentative lactic acid bacteria or yeasts.

BIBLIOGRAPHY

Allen, J. R., and E. M. Foster. 1960. Spoilage of vacuum-packed, sliced processed meats during refrigerated storage. Food Res. 25:19–25.

American Meat Institute Foundation. 1960. The science of meat and meat products. W. H. Freeman and Company, San Francisco.

Anderton, J. I. 1963. Pathogenic organisms in relation to pasteurized cured meats. Sci.

Technol. Surv. 40. The British Food Manufacturing Industries Research Association, Leatherhead, Surrey.

Ayres, J. C. 1955. Microbiological implications in the handling, slaughtering, and dressing of meat animals. Adv. Food Res. 6:110–161.

Ayres, J. C. 1960a. Temperature relationships and some other characteristics of the microbial flora developing on refrigerated beef. Food Res. 25:1–18.

Ayres, J. C. 1960b. The relationship of organisms of the genus *Pseudomonas* to the spoilage of meat, poultry and eggs. J. Appl. Bacteriol. 23:471–486.

Brown, M. H. (ed.). 1982. Meat microbiology. Applied Science Publications, New York.

Brown, W. L., C. Vinton, and C. E. Gross. 1960. Radiation resistance of natural bacterial flora of cured ham. Food Technol. 14:622–625.

Cavett, J. J., 1962. The microbiology of vacuum packed sliced bacon. J. Appl. Bacteriol. 25:282–289.

Drake, S. D., J. B. Evans, and C. F. Niven, Jr. 1959. The identity of yeasts in the surface flora of packaged frankfurters. Food Res. 24:243–246.

Draudt, H. N. 1963. The meat smoking process: a review. Food Technol. 17:1557–1562.

Dyett, E. J. 1963. Microbiology of raw materials for the meat industry. Chem. Ind. 6: 234–237.

Eddy, B. P. (ed.). 1958. Microbiology of fish and meat curing brines. *In* II Int. Symp. Food Microbiol., Proc. H.M. Stationery Office, London.

Empey, W. A., and W. J. Scott. 1939. Investigations on chilled beef. I. Microbial contamination acquired in the meatworks. Council Sci. Ind. Res. [Aust.] Bull. 126.

Evans, J. B., and C. F. Niven, Jr. 1955. Slime and mold problems with prepackaged processed meat products. Am. Meat Inst. Found. Bull. 24.

Food Engineering Staff. 1962. Humane slaughter. Food Eng. 34(2):52.

Gardner, G. A. 1981. *Brochotrix thermosphacta (Microbacterium thermosphacta)* in the spoilage of meats. *In* T. A. Roberts, G. Hobbs, J. H. Christian, and N. Skovgaard (eds.), Psychrotrophic microorganisms in spoilage and pathogenicity. Academic Press, Inc., New York.

Haines, R. B. 1937. Microbiology in the preservation of animal tissues. G.B. Dept. Sci. Ind. Res. Food Invest. Spec. Rep. 45.

Halleck, F. E., C. O. Ball, and E. F. Stier. 1958. Factors affecting quality of prepackaged meat. IV. Microbiological studies. B. Effect of package characteristics and of atmospheric pressure in package upon bacterial flora of meat. C. Effects of initial bacteria count, kind of meat, storage time, storage temperature, antioxidants, and antiobiotics on the rate of bacterial growth in packaged meat. Food Technol. 12: 301–306; 654–659.

Ingram, M. 1960. Bacterial multiplication in packed Wiltshire bacon. J. Appl. Bacteriol. 23:206–215.

Ingram, M., and B. Simosen. 1980. Meat and meat products. *In* J. H. Silliker (ed.), Microbial ecology of foods. Volume II. Food commodities. Academic Press, Inc., New York.

Jaye, M., R. S. Kittaka, and Z. J. Ordal. 1962. The effect of temperature and packaging material on the storage life and bacterial flora of ground beef. Food Technol. 16(4):95–98.

Jensen, L. B. 1954. Microbiology of meats. 3d ed. The Garrard Press, Champaign, Ill.

Johnston, R. W., and R. B. Tompkin. 1984. Meat and poultry products. *In* M. L. Speck (ed.), Compendium of methods for the microbiological examination of foods. American Public Health Association, Washington, D.C.

Kempton, A. G., and S. R. Bobier. 1970. Bacterial growth in vacuum-packed luncheon meats. Can. J. Microbiol. 16:287–297.

Kitchell, A. G. 1962. Micrococci and coagulase negative staphylococci in cured meats and meat products. J. Appl. Bacteriol. 25:416–431.

Leistner, L. 1960. Microbiology of ham curing. 12th Res. Conf. Am. Meat Inst. Found. Proc. Circ. 61:17–23.

Miller, W. A. 1961. The microbiology of some self-service packaged luncheon meats. J. Milk Food Technol. 24:374–377.

Miller, W. A. 1964. The microbiology of self-service, prepackaged, fresh pork sausage. J. Milk Food Technol. 27:1–3.

Niinivaara, F. P., M. S. Pohja, and S. E. Komulainen. 1964. Some aspects about using bacterial pure cultures in the manufacture of fermented sausages. Food Technol. 18: 147–153.

Niven, C. F., Jr. 1951. Influence of microbes upon the color of meats. Am. Meat Inst. Found. Circ. 2.

Niven, C. F., Jr. 1956. Vinegar pickled meats. A discussion of bacterial and curing problems encountered in processing. Am. Meat Inst. Found. Bull. 27.

Niven, C. F., Jr. 1961. Microbiology of meats. Am. Meat Inst. Found. Circ. 68.

Nottingham, P. M. 1960. Bone-taint in beef. II. Bacteria in ischiatic lymph nodes. J. Sci. Food Agr. 11:436–441.

Ordal, Z. J. 1962. Anaerobic packaging of fresh meat. 14th Res. Conf. Am. Meat Inst. Found. Proc., Circ. 70:39–45.

Palumbo, S. A., C. N. Huhtanen, and J. L. Smith. 1974. Microbiology of the frankfurter process: *Salmonella* and natural aerobic flora. Appl. Microbiol. 27:724–732.

Phillips, A. W., H. R. Newcomb, T. Robinson, F. Bach, W. L. Clark, and A. R. Whitehill. 1961. Experimental preservation of fresh beef with antibiotics and radiation. Food Technol. 15:13–15.

Riemann, H. 1963. Safe heat processing of canned cured meats with regard to bacterial spores. Food Technol. 17:39–49.

Roberts, T. A. 1980. Contamination of meat. Royal Soc. Health J. 100:3–9.

Shank, J. L., and B. R. Lundquist. 1963. The effect of packaging conditions on the bacteriology, color, and flavor of table-ready meats. Food Technol. 17:1163–1166.

Shank, J. L., J. H. Silliker, and P. A. Goeser. 1962. The development of a nonmicrobial off-condition in fresh meat. Appl. Microbiol. 10:240–246.

Sharpe, M. E. 1962. Lactobacilli in meat products. Food Manuf. 37:582–589.

Steinke, P. K. W., and E. M. Foster. 1961. Effect of temperature of storage on microbial changes in liver sausage and bologna. Food Res. 16:372–376.

Steinkraus, K. H., and J. C. Ayres. 1964. Biochemical and serological relationships of putrefactive anaerobic sporeforming rods isolated from pork. J. Food Sci. 29:100–104.

Surkiewicz, B. F., M. E. Harris, and R. W. Johnston. 1973. Bacteriological survey of frozen meat and gravy produced at establishments under federal inspection. Appl. Microbiol. 26:574–576.

Surkiewicz, B. F., R. W. Johnston, and J. M. Carosella. 1976. Bacteriological survey of frankfurters produced at establishments under federal inspection. J. Milk Food Technol. 39:7–9.

Surkiewicz, B. F., R. W. Johnston, R. P. Elliott, and E. R. Simmons. 1972. Bacteriological survey of fresh pork sausage produced at establishments under federal inspection. Appl. Microbiol. 23:515–520.

Tanaka, N. L., M. P. Doyle, L. Meske, E. Traisman, D. W. Thayer, and R. W. Johnston. 1985. Plant trials of bacon made with lactic acid bacteria, sucrose and lowered sodium nitrite. J. Food Prot. 48:679–686.

Wang, S. Y., T. R. Dockerty, R. A. Ledford, and J. R. Stouffer. 1985. Shelf-life extension of vacuum packaged frankfurters made from beef inoculated with *Streptococcus lactis*. J. Food Prot. 49:130–134.

Zottola, E. A. 1972. Introduction to meat microbiology. American Meat Institute, Chicago.

CONTAMINATION, PRESERVATION, AND SPOILAGE OF FISH AND OTHER SEAFOODS

Seafoods discussed in this chapter include fresh, frozen, dried, pickled, and salted fish as well as various shellfish. Freshwater fish are also considered.

CONTAMINATION

The flora of living fish depends on the microbial content of the waters in which they live. The slime that covers the outer surface of fish has been found to contain bacteria of the genera *Pseudomonas, Acinetobacter, Moraxella, Alcaligenes, Micrococcus*, Flavobacterium, Corynebacterium, Sarcina, Serratia, Vibrio,* and *Bacillus*. The bacteria on fish from northern waters are mostly psychrophiles, whereas fish from tropical waters carry more mesophiles. Freshwater fish carry freshwater bacteria, which include members of most genera found in salt water plus species of *Aeromonas, Lactobacillus, Brevibacterium, Alcaligenes,* and *Streptococcus*. In the intestines of fish from both sources are found bacteria of the genera *Alcaligenes, Pseudomonas, Flavobacterium, Vibrio, Bacillus, Clostridium,* and *Escherichia*. Boats, boxes, bins, fish houses, and fishers soon become heavily contaminated with these bacteria and transfer them to the fish during cleaning. The numbers of bacteria in slime and on the skin of newly caught ocean fish may be as low as 100 and as high as several million per square centimeter, and the intestinal fluid may contain from 1,000 to 100 million per milliliter. Gill tissue may harbor 1,000 to 1 million per gram. Washing reduces the surface count.

243

Oysters and other shellfish that pass large amounts of water through their bodies pick up soil and water microorganisms in this way, including pathogens if they are present. *Alcaligenes, Flavobacterium, Moraxella, Acinetobacter,* and some gram-positive bacteria will be found.

Shrimps, crabs, lobsters, and similar seafood have a bacteria-laden slime on their surfaces that probably resembles that of fish. Species of *Bacillus, Micrococcus, Pseudomonas, Acinetobacter, Moraxella, Flavobacterium, Alcaligenes,* and *Proteus* have been found on shrimp.

The numbers of microorganisms on the skin of fish can be influenced by the method of catching. For example, trawling fish nets along the bottom for long periods results in exposure of the fish to high bacterial counts in the disturbed bottom sediment, and this can be reflected in the initial microbial load on the fish.

Fish cakes and fish sticks or similar products represent a large percentage of the consumed seafood in the United States. Products of this type have additional sources of contamination. In the manufacture of fish cakes various other products, including potatoes, spices, and flavorings, are mixed with the fish and then the product is molded, coated with batter and bread crumbs, packed, and usually frozen if not used immediately. Fish sticks are mechanically sliced from frozen blocks of fish, coated with batter and bread crumbs, packed, and frozen for distribution. Many fish-stick items are precooked in hot oil at temperatures of 204 to 232 C. The cooking process is short (2 min or less), and the inside of the product remains frozen. The microbial content of these products would, of course, be quite different from fresh fish as a result of contamination from the ingredients, increased handling, machinery contact, and packaging.

PRESERVATION

Of all the flesh foods, fish is the most susceptible to autolysis, oxidation and hydrolysis of fats, and microbial spoilage. Its preservation therefore involves prompt treatment by preservative methods, and often these methods are rigorous compared with those used on meats. When fish are gathered far from the processing plant, preservative methods must be applied even on the fishing boat. Evisceration should be done promptly to stop active digestive enzymes in the gut. Advantages gained by gutting may be offset by a possible delay in rapid cooling of the fish.

Rigor mortis is especially important in the preservation of fish, for it retards postmortem autolysis and bacterial decomposition. Therefore, any procedure that lengthens rigor mortis lengthens keeping time. It is longer if the fish have had less muscular activity before death and have not been handled roughly and bruised during catching and later processing, and it is longer in some kinds of fish than in others. The ultimate pH of the flesh after death is related to the amount of glycogen available at death. The more glycogen present, the lower the pH. The less muscular activity before death, the higher the level of glycogen, or the lower the ultimate pH. Reducing the holding temperature will lengthen the period.

Aseptic methods to reduce the contamination of seafood are difficult to apply, but some of the gross contamination before processing can be avoided by general cleaning and sanitization of boats, decks, holds, bins, or other containers and processing equipment in the plant and by use of ice of good bacteriological quality. The removal of soil from contaminating surfaces and from the fish by adequate cleaning methods, including effective detergent solutions, helps greatly to reduce the microbial load on the fish.

The removal of organisms is difficult, but the fact that most of the contamination is on the outer surface of the fish and other seafood permits the removal of many of the microorganisms by washing off slime and dirt.

USE OF HEAT

Live crabs are cooked in retorts at temperatures up to 121 C to facilitate removing the meat from the shell. Hand picking and hand packing of the meat is common. Processing times and temperatures for canned crabmeat range from 85.6 to 87.2 C for 92 to 150 min (Dickerson and Berry, 1974). These processes are considered pasteurization, and cans are preserved by refrigeration. Some seafoods, e.g., oysters, are "canned" by packing into cans or jars and are not heat-processed but are preserved by refrigeration.

Most canned seafoods, however, are heat-processed so that they are sterile, or at least "commercially sterile." Like meats, seafoods are low-acid foods and for the most part have a slow rate of heat penetration and hence are difficult to heat-process. Also, some kinds of seafoods soften considerably or even fall apart when sterilization in the can is attempted.

The process varies with the product being canned and the size and shape of the container. In general, the heat processes are more severe than those used for meats, but some special products are lightly processed. Canning practices carried out in accordance with the FAO code of practice (FAO, 1973) minimize health hazards arising from canned seafoods.

USE OF LOW TEMPERATURES

It is only after death of the fish or other sea animal that autolysis gets under way, with softening and production of off-flavor, and microbial growth becomes uncontrolled; as has been stated, these changes are delayed by rigor mortis. Oysters in their shells, for example, will not decompose so long as they remain alive, and life is lengthened by chilling storage of shell oysters. Carp seined from mid western lakes have been kept alive and hence in good condition by shipment in tanks to the New York market. "Feedy" fish, that is, those stuffed with food, seem to decompose faster than normal fish.

Chilling

Because fish flesh autolyzes and the fats become oxidized at temperatures above freezing—rapidly at summer temperatures and more slowly as the temperature is dropped toward freezing—preservation by chilling temperatures is at best temporary. When fish or other seafood is obtained at some distance from the receiving plant, the necessity for chilling on the boat depends on the kind of fish, whether it is dressed there, and the atmospheric temperature. In general, small fish are more perishable than large ones, and dressed fish autolyze more slowly than whole fish but are spoiled more readily by bacteria. When outside temperatures are warm and distances of transportation are great, it becomes necessary to chill the fish and related foods on the fishing boat by packing in crushed ice or by mechanical refrigeration in order to slow autolysis and microbial growth until the products are marketed or are processed for longer preservation. The incorporation of preservatives in the ice used for chilling fish will be discussed subsequently. The time allowable for holding in ice or in chilling storage will vary considerably with the kind of fish or other seafood but will not be long in most instances. In general, chilling storage on shore is useful only when retail markets are near at hand and turnover is rapid. Otherwise, some other method of preservation is applied, such as freezing, salting, drying, smoking, canning, or combinations of these methods.

Freezing

Most of the modern methods of freezing foods initially were developed for freezing fish. In earlier days, ice with added salt was employed. With the advent of mechanical refrigeration, sharp freezing was employed and the fish were "glazed"; i.e., a layer of ice was frozen around the outside. Whole fish, especially the larger ones, usually are sharp-frozen in air or in a salt brine. Quick freezing is applied to wrapped fillets or steaks, although whole smaller fish may be so frozen. Like meats, quick-frozen fish may thaw to more like their original condition than fish frozen more slowly. During storage the fats of frozen fish are subject to hydrolysis and oxidation. Fatty fish deteriorate more rapidly than lean ones, probably because of more hydrolysis.

Decapitated raw shrimp are frozen and glazed, and some cooked shrimp are frozen. Other seafoods preserved by freezing include scallops, clams, oysters, spiny lobster tails, and cooked crab and lobster meat. Most of these products are packaged before freezing.

As with meats, freezing kills some but not all of the microorganisms present, and growth will take place after thawing if time permits. Fish carry a flora of psychrotrophic bacteria, most of which survive freezing and are ready to grow on thawing, e.g., *Pseudomonas, Acinetobacter, Moraxella, Alcaligenes,* and *Flavobacterium* species. Spores of type E *Clostridium botulinum* will survive freezing and storage and may grow and produce toxin when temperatures reach 3.3 C or above. Frozen raw seafoods contain few enterococci, coliforms, or staphylococci. Numbers of these organisms may be increased in the processing plant by cutting, breading, and battering operations. Precooking reduces only coliforms to any extent.

USE OF IRRADIATION

Preservation of fish by ultraviolet rays has been tried but not put into practice. Experiments have indicated that gamma or cathode irradiation of some kinds of fish may be successful.

PRESERVATION BY DRYING

The dry-salting of fish or immersion in brine constitutes a method of drying, in that moisture is removed or tied up. Oxidation of fish oils is not retarded and may cause deterioration. Salting of fish is being done to a lesser extent in the United States but still is used widely throughout the world. Salt cod is prepared by a combination of salting and air drying. The flesh is then removed from bones and skin.

Sun drying of fish, either of small fish or of strips of flesh, is not practiced extensively in the United States.

Part of the preservative effect of smoking is a result of the drying of the fish.

USE OF PRESERVATIVES

The salting or marination of fish by dry salt or in brine is effective not only because of the drying effect mentioned in the preceding section but also because of the effect of the sodium chloride as a chemical preservative. This method is used to a considerable extent in many countries. The chemical and bacteriological qualities of the salt are important, for impurities such as calcium and magnesium salts may hinder the penetration of the sodium chloride, and halophilic or salt-tolerant bacteria that are introduced may cause discolorations of the fish.

Because of the great perishability of fish, investigators have tried numerous chemicals as preservatives, either applied directly to the fish or incorporated in the ice used in chilling them.

Preservatives Used on Fish

In the intensive search for chemical preservatives that could be applied directly or as dips to round fish or fillets, a large number of chemicals have been tried, ranging from those which most control agencies would approve to those whose use would be questionable. Sodium chloride, an acceptable preservative, has been discussed.

Fish may be dry-salted so as to contain 4 to 5 percent salt. The salt contributes halophiles which may discolor the fish (e.g., a red color from *Serratia salinaria**). Species of *Micrococcus** usually grow on the fish, and there is a decrease in *Flavobacterium, Alcaligenes, Pseudomonas,* and others. Curing of fish may be "mild," i.e., with light salting, or may be in heavy brine or with solid salt and may be followed by smoking. Benzoic acid and benzoates have been only moderately successful as preservatives. Sodium and potassium nitrites and nitrates have been reported to lengthen the keeping time and are permitted in some countries. Sorbic acid has been found to delay spoilage of smoked or salted fish. Boric acid has been used in Europe with some improvement in the keeping quality, but its use is illegal in the United States. Other chemicals for which claims of success have been made but whose use is contraindicated include formaldehyde, hypochlorites, hydrogen peroxide, sulfur dioxide, undecylenic acid, capric acid, p-oxybenzoic acid, and chloroform.

Antibiotics also have been tried experimentally, usually in a dip or in ice. Of those tested, chlortetracycline and oxytetracycline seemed best, and now their use is permitted. Chloramphenicol is fairly effective, and penicillin, streptomycin, and subtilin are poor or useless.

Storage of fish in an atmosphere containing increased levels of carbon dioxide has been found to lengthen the keeping time. The normal spoilage flora is replaced with lactobacilli and others, and the product "sours" when it begins to spoil.

Pickling of fish may mean salting or acidification with vinegar, wine, or sour cream. Herring is treated in various ways: salted, spiced, and acidified. Various combinations of these treatments, coupled with an airtight container, preserve the fish, although refrigeration also must be employed for some products.

Formerly, fish was smoked primarily for its preservation, and the smoking was heavy, but now that canning, chilling, and freezing are available to lengthen keeping time, much of the smoking of fish is primarily for flavor and hence is light. The smoke treatment and other preservative methods combined with it vary with the kind of fish, the size of pieces, and the keeping time desired. Fish to be smoked usually are eviscerated and decapitated but may be in the round, split, or cut into pieces. Commonly, salting, light or heavy, precedes smoking and serves not only to flavor the fish but also to improve its keeping quality by reducing the moisture content. Drying may be aided by air currents. The smoking may be done at comparatively low temperatures (26.7 to 37.8 C) or at high temperatures such as 63 to 92 C which result in partial cooking of the fish.

The principles of preservation involved in smoking fish are similar to those discussed in Chapter 9.

Microbiology of Fish Brines Numbers of bacteria in fish-curing brines vary with the concentration of salt, the temperature of the brine, the kind and amount of contamination from the fish introduced, and the duration of use of the brine and range from 10,000 to 10 million bacteria per milliliter. Salt concentrations usually are between 18 percent and saturation but may be lower, especially after fish are introduced. The higher the temperature of the brine, the more salt necessary to prevent its spoilage. Contamination comes from the fish, which ordinarily introduce species of *Pseudomonas, Acinetobacter, Moraxella, Alcaligenes,* and *Flavobacterium;* from ice, which introduces these genera plus *Corynebacterium* and cocci; and from mechanically introduced sources, e.g., dust, which add cocci. On continued use of the brine, numbers of organisms increase, because of addition from successive lots of fish and because of growth of salt-tolerant bacteria such as the micrococci*. As the brine ages, there is a decrease in numbers and an increase chiefly in corynebacteria in low-salt brines and in micrococci* in high-salt brines.

Preservatives Incorporated in Ice

So-called germicidal ices are prepared by adding a chemical preservative to water before freezing. These ices are **eutectic** when the added chemical is uniformly distributed throughout, as with sodium chloride, or **noneutectic** when distribution is not uniform, as with sodium benzoate. Noneutectic ice is finely crushed for use on fish so as to get the chemical evenly spread in it.

Many investigators have sought the ideal chemical to be incorporated in ice for icing fish and have tested with some success a large number of chemicals, including hypochlorites, chloramines, benzoic acid and benzoates, colloidal silver, hydrogen peroxide, ozone, sodium nitrite, sulfonamides, antibiotics, propionates, levulinic acid, and many others. Both the American and Canadian governments and those of other nations now permit the incorporation of the tetracyclines at up to 7 ppm in ice to be used by fishers to preserve fish on trawlers and during transportation.

The purpose of the application of preservative chemicals to fish either directly or as dips or germicidal ices is to kill or inhibit microorganisms on the surfaces of the fish, where at first they are most numerous and active.

Antioxidants

Fats and oils of many kinds of fish, especially the fatter ones, such as herring, mackerel, mullet, and salmon, are composed to a great extent of unsaturated fatty acids and hence are subject to oxidative changes producing oxidative rancidity and sometimes undesirable alterations in color. To counteract these undesirable changes, antioxidants may be applied as dips, coatings, glazes, or gases. Good results have been reported with nordihydroguaiaretic acid, ethyl gallate, ascorbic acid, and other compounds and with storage in carbon dioxide.

SPOILAGE

Like meat, fish and other seafood may be spoiled by autolysis, oxidation, or bacterial activity or most commonly by combinations of these. Most fish flesh, however, is considered more perishable than meat because of more rapid autolysis by the fish enzymes and because of the less acid reaction of fish flesh that favors microbial growth. Also, many of the unsaturated fish oils seem to be more susceptible to oxidative deterioration than are most animal fats. The experts agree that the bacterial spoilage of fish does not begin until after rigor mortis, when juices are released from the flesh fibers. Therefore, the more this is delayed or protracted, the longer the keeping time of the fish. Rigor mortis is hastened by struggling of the fish, lack of oxygen, and warm temperature and is delayed by a low pH and adequate cooling of the fish. The pH of the fish flesh has an important influence on its perishability, not only because of its effect on rigor mortis but also because of its influence on the growth of bacteria. The lower the pH of the fish flesh, the slower in general bacterial decomposition will be. Lowering of the pH of the fish flesh results from the conversion of muscle glycogen to lactic acid.

FACTORS INFLUENCING KIND AND RATE OF SPOILAGE

The kind and rate of spoilage of fish vary with a number of factors:

1 *The kind of fish.* The various kinds of fish differ considerably in their perishability. Thus some flat fish spoil more readily than round fish because they pass through rigor mortis more rapidly, but a flat fish like the halibut keeps longer because of the low pH (5.5) of its flesh. Certain fatty fish deteriorate rapidly because of oxidation of the unsaturated fats of their oils. Fishes high in trimethylamine oxide soon yield appreciable amounts of the "stale-fishy" trimethylamine.

2 *The condition of the fish when caught.* Fish that are exhausted as the result of struggling, lack of oxygen, and excessive handling spoil more rapidly than those brought in with less ado, probably because of the exhaustion of glycogen and hence smaller drop in pH of the flesh. "Feedy" fish, i.e., those full of food when caught, are more perishable than those with an empty intestinal tract.

3 *The kind and extent of contamination of the fish flesh with bacteria.* These may come from mud, water, handlers, and the exterior slime and intestinal content of the fish and are supposed to enter the gills of the fish, from which they pass through the vascular system and thus invade the flesh, or to penetrate the intestinal tract and thus enter the body cavity. Even then, growth probably is localized for the most part, but the products of bacterial decomposition penetrate the flesh fairly rapidly by diffusion. In general, the greater the load of bacteria on the fish, the more rapid the spoilage. This contamination may take place in the net (mud), in the fishing boat, on the docks, or, later, in the plants. Fish in the round, i.e., not gutted, have not had the flesh contaminated with intestinal organisms, but it may become odorous because of decay of food in the gut and diffusion of decomposition products into the flesh. This process is hastened by the digestive enzymes attacking and perforating the gut wall and the belly wall and viscera, which in themselves have a high rate of autolysis.

Gutting the fish on the boat spreads intestinal and surface-slime bacteria over the flesh, but thorough washing will remove most of the organisms and adequate chilling will inhibit the growth of those left. Any damage to skin or mucous membranes will harm the keeping quality of the product.

4 *Temperature.* Chilling the fish is the most commonly used method for preventing or delaying bacterial growth and hence spoilage until the fish is used or is otherwise processed. The cooling should be as rapid as possible 0 to −1 C, and this low temperature should be maintained. Obviously, the warmer the temperature, the shorter the storage life of the fish. Prompt and rapid freezing of the fish is still more effective in its preservation.

5 *Use of an antibiotic ice or dip.*

EVIDENCES OF SPOILAGE

Since the change is gradual from a fresh condition to staleness and then to inedibility, it is difficult to determine or agree on the first appearance of spoilage. A practical test to determine the quality of fish has been sought for many years, but none has proved entirely satisfactory. A chemical test for trimethylamine is backed by most workers for use on saltwater fish, although some support other methods, such as an estimate of volatile acids or volatile bases or a test for pH, hydrogen sulfide, ammonia, etc. Bacteriological tests are too slow to be useful.

Reay and Shewan (1949) described the succession of external changes in a fish as it spoils and finally becomes putrid. The bright characteristic colors of the fish fade, and dirty, yellow, or brown discolorations appear. The slime on the skin of the fish increases, especially at the flaps and gills. The eyes gradually sink and shrink, the pupil becoming cloudy and the cornea opaque. The gills turn a light pink and finally grayish-yellow color. Most marked is the softening of the flesh, so that it exudes juice when squeezed and becomes easily indented by the fingers. The flesh is easily stripped from along the backbone, where a reddish-brown discoloration develops toward the tail and is a result of the oxidation of hemoglobin.

Meanwhile a sequence of odors is evolved: first the normal, fresh, seaweedy odor, then a sickly sweet one, then a stale-fishy odor due to trimethylamine, followed by ammoniacal and final putrid odors due to hydrogen sulfide, indole, and other malodorous compounds. Fatty fish also may show rancid odors. Cooking will bring out the odors more strongly.

BACTERIA CAUSING SPOILAGE

The bacteria most often involved in the spoilage of fish are part of the natural flora of the external slime of fishes and their intestinal contents. The predominant kinds of bacteria causing spoilage vary with the temperatures at which the fish are held, but at the chilling temperatures usually employed, species of

Pseudomonas are most likely to predominate, with *Acinetobacter, Moraxella,* and *Flavobacterium* species next in order of importance. Appearing less often, and then at higher temperatures, are bacteria of the genera *Micrococcus* and *Bacillus.* Reports in the literature list other genera as having species involved in fish spoilage, such as *Escherichia, Proteus, Serratia, Sarcina,* and *Clostridium.* Most of these would grow only at ordinary atmospheric temperatures and probably would do little at chilling temperatures.

Normally pseudomonads increase in numbers on chilled fish during holding, achromobacters* decrease, and flavobacteria increase temporarily and then decrease. The bacteria grow first on the surfaces and later penetrate the flesh. Fish have a high content of nonprotein nitrogen, and autolytic changes caused by their enzymes increase the supply of nitrogenous foods (e.g., amino acids and amines) and glucose for bacterial growth. From these compounds the bacteria make trimethylamine, ammonia, amines (e.g., putrescine and cadaverine), lower fatty acids, and aldehydes, and eventually hydrogen and other sulfides, mercaptans, and indole, which products are indicative of putrefaction. A musty or muddy odor and taste of fish has been attributed to the growth of *Streptomyces* species in the mud at the bottom of the body of water and the absorption of the flavor by the fish.

As has been indicated, discolorations of the fish flesh may occur during spoilage; yellow to greenish-yellow colors caused by *Pseudomonas fluorescens,* yellow micrococci, and others; red or pink colors from growth of *Sarcina, Micrococcus,* or *Bacillus* species or by molds or yeasts; and a chocolate-brown color by an asporogenous yeast. Pathogens parasitizing the fish may produce discolorations or lesions.

SPOILAGE OF SPECIAL KINDS OF FISH AND SEAFOODS

The previous discussion has been limited for the most part to the spoilage of fish preserved by chilling. Salt fish are spoiled by salt-tolerant or halophilic bacteria of the genera *Serratia, Micrococcus, Bacillus, Alcaligenes, Pseudomonas,* and others, which often cause discolorations, a red color being common. Molds are the chief spoilage organisms on smoked fish. Marinated (sour pickled) fish should present no spoilage problems unless the acid content is low enough to permit growth of lactic acid bacteria or the entrance of air permits mold growth. Frozen fish, too, should present no bacteriological problems after freezing, but of course their quality depends on what has happened to the fish before freezing. The spoilage of canned fish and other seafood will be discussed in Chapter 19. Japanese fish sausage is subject to souring caused by volatile acid production by bacilli or to putrefaction, despite the addition of nitrite and permitted preservatives.

In general, shellfish are subject to types of microbial spoilage similar to those for fish. However, in chilled shrimp *Acinetobacter, Moraxella,* and *Vibrio* are chiefly responsible for spoilage, although there may be a temporary increase in pseudomonads and a decrease in *Flavobacterium, Micrococcus*,* and *Bacil-*

lus. Crabmeat is deteriorated by *Pseudomonas, Acinetobacter,* and *Moraxella* at chilling temperatures and mainly by *Proteus* at higher temperatures. Species of *Pseudomonas, Alcaligenes, Flavobacterium,* and *Bacillus* have been incriminated in the spoilage of raw lobsters. Crabs and oysters may contain species of *Vibrio,* including *V. parahaemolyticus.* The levels in these products fluctuate with seasonal temperature changes.

Oysters remain in good condition as long as they are kept alive in the shell at chilling temperature, but they decompose rapidly when they are dead, as in shucked oysters. The type of spoilage of the shucked oysters depends on the temperature at which they are stored. Oysters are not only high in protein but also contain sugars, which result from the hydrolysis of glycogen. At temperatures near freezing, *Pseudomonas, Acinetobacter,* and *Moraxella* species are the most important spoilage bacteria, but *Flavobacterium* and *Micrococcus** species also may grow. The spoilage is termed "souring" although the changes are chiefly proteolytic. At higher temperatures the souring may be the result of the fermentation of the sugars by coliform bacteria, streptococci, lactobacilli, and yeast to produce acids and a sour odor. Early growth of *Serratia, Pseudomonas, Proteus,* and *Clostridium* may take place. An uncommon type of spoilage by an asporogenous yeast causes pink oysters.

BIBLIOGRAPHY

Akamatsu, M. 1959. Bacteriological studies on the spoilage of fish sausage. I. Number of bacteria present in the meat of fish sausage on the market. Jap. Soc. Sci. Fish. Bull. 25:545–548.

Borgstrom, G. (ed.). 1961. Fish as food. Volume I. Production, biochemistry, and microbiology. Academic Press, Inc., New York.

Borgstrom, G. (ed.). 1962. Fish as food. Volume II. Nutrition, sanitation, and utilization. Academic Press, Inc., New York.

Chichester, C. O., and H. D. Graham. 1973. Microbial safety of fishery products. Academic Press, Inc., New York.

Colwell, R. R., and J. Liston. 1960. Microbiology of shellfish: bacteriological study of the natural flora of Pacific oysters (*Crassostrea gigas*). Appl. Microbiol. 8:104–109.

Dickerson, R. W., and M. R. Berry. 1974. Temperature profiles during commercial pasteurization of meat from the blue crab. J. Milk Food Technol. 37:618–621.

Eddy, B. P. (ed.). 1958. Microbiology of fish and meat curing brines. II Int. Symp. Food Microbiol. Proc. H.M. Stationery Office, London.

Evelyn, T. P. T., and L. A. McDermott. 1961. Bacteriological studies of fresh-water fish. I. Isolation of aerobic bacteria from several species of Ontario fish. Can. J. Microbiol. 7:375–382.

FAO. 1973. Code of practice for canned fishery products. FAO Fish. Circ. 315.

Hess, E. 1950. Bacterial fish spoilage and its control. Food Technol. 4:477–480.

Licciardello, J. J., and W. S. Hill. 1978. Microbiological quality of commercial frozen minced fish blocks. J. Food Prot. 41:948–952.

Maclean, D. P., and Camille Walander. 1960. The preservation of fish with ionizing radiation: bacterial studies. Food Technol. 14:251–254.

Masurovsky, E. B., J. S. Voss, and S. A. Goldblith. 1963. Changes in the microflora of haddock fillets and shucked soft-shelled clams after irradiation with ^{60}Co gamma rays and storage at 0 C and 6 C. Appl. Micribiol. 11(3):229–234.

Post, L. S., D. A. Lee, M. Solberg, D. Furgang, J. Specchio, and C. Graham. 1985. Development of botulinal toxin and sensory deterioration during storage of vacuum and modified atmosphere packaged fish fillets. J. Food Sci. 50:990–996.

Reay, G. A., and J. M. Shewan. 1949. The spoilage of fish and its preservation by chilling. Adv. Food Res. 2:343–398.

Shewan, J. M. 1971. The microbiology of fish and fishery products—a progress report. J. Appl. Bacteriol. 34:299–308.

Shewan, J. M., and G. Hobbs. 1967. The bacteriology of fish spoilage and preservation. Prog. Ind. Microbiol. 6:169–208.

Silliker, J. H., and S. K. Wolfe. 1980. Microbiological safety considerations in controlled atmosphere storage of meats. Food Technol. 34:59–63.

Spencer, R. 1959. The sanitation of fish boxes. I. The quantitative and qualitative bacteriology of commercial wooden fish boxes. J. Appl. Bacteriol. 22:73–84.

Spencer, R., and R. B. Hughes. 1963. Recent advances in fish processing technology. Food Manuf. 38:407–412.

Stansby, M. E. 1962. Speculations on fishy odors and flavors. Food Technol. 16(4):28–32.

Tanikawa, E. 1963. Fish sausage and ham industry in Japan. Adv. Food Res. 12:367–424.

Tarr, H. L. A. 1954. Microbiological deterioration of fish post mortem, its detection and control. Bacteriol. Rev. 18:1–15.

Tomiyasu, Y., and B. Zentani. 1957. Spoilage of fish and its preservation by chemical agents. Adv. Food Res. 7:42–82.

Wentz, B. A., A. P. Duran, A. Swartzentruber, A. H. Schwab, and R. B. Read, Jr. 1983. Microbiological quality of fresh blue crabmeat, clams and oysters. J. Food Prot. 46:978–981.

World Health Organization. 1974. Fish and shellfish hygiene. Geneva.

U.S. Department of Health, Education, and Welfare, Public Health Service, National Shellfish Sanitation Program. 1965. Manual of Operations. Washington.

CONTAMINATION, PRESERVATION, AND SPOILAGE OF EGGS

Although only hens' (chickens') eggs are discussed here, it is assumed that the microbiology of the eggs of other domestic poultry will be similar.

CONTAMINATION

Most freshly laid eggs are sterile, at least inside, but the shells soon become contaminated by fecal matter from the hen, by the cage or nest, by wash water if the eggs are washed, by handling, and perhaps by the material in which the eggs are packed. The total number of microorganisms per shell of a hen's egg has been reported to range from 10^2 to 10^7 with a mean of about 10^5. The types of microorganisms recovered from the shell are diverse. A comparison of the flora of the shell (Table 16-1) and the flora isolated from spoiled eggs (Table 16-2) suggest a high number of gram-positive organisms in the former but a low number in the latter. Therefore, those organisms which frequently spoil or "rot" the egg are in relatively low numbers initially on the shell.

Salmonella spp. may be on the shell or in the egg as laid, build up during processing, and appear in significant numbers in frozen or dried eggs.

PRESERVATION

Methods for the preservation of eggs have received considerable attention because eggs are so perishable. "What manufacturer would be so foolhardy as to

TABLE 16-1
INCIDENCE OF MICROORGANISMS ON THE SHELL OF HENS' EGGS

| | | Percent of the flora | |
Type	Farms	Egg-breaking plants*	Packaging station*
Streptococcus		8(5)	
Staphylococcus	5	30	9(16)
Micrococcus*	18	23(20)	37(94)
Sarcina	2	20	
Arthrobacter			5(23)
Bacillus	30	(18)	(2.5)
Pseudomonas	6		22.5(36.5)
Achromobacter*	19		1.5(3)
Alcaligenes			(2)
Flavobacterium	3		
Cytophaga			(1)
Coli-aerogenes	5	19(12)	10.5(11.5)
Aeromonas		20(20)	1
Proteus	1	20(50)	
Serratia		10(20)	
Molds	7		
Unclassified			12(11)

*Numbers represent data from clean eggs; numbers in parentheses, data from soiled or cracked eggs.
Source: Condensed From Board (1969).

attempt to pack a perishable commodity in a semipermeable membrane within a fragile, porous shell and have it distributed and marketed under uncontrolled conditions?'' Board (1969) continues, ''This is what the hen appears to have done.''

The egg has various ways of protecting itself from microbial invasion. The shell and the thin surface layer of proteinaceous material known as the **cuticle** or **bloom** are the first line of defense and serve to retard entry. However, the

TABLE 16-2
TYPES OF ORGANISMS ISOLATED FROM SPOILED EGGS

Organism	Haines (1939)	Alford et al. (1950)	Florian and Trussell (1957)	Board (1965)	Board and Board (1968)
Gram-positive	−	−	±	±	±
Coli-aerogenes	+	+	+	+	+
Proteus	+	+	+	+	+
Aeromonas	−	−	+	+	+
Pseudomonas	+	+	+	+	+
Alcaligenes	+	+	+	+	+
Achromobacter*	+	+	+	+	+

+=isolated on many occasions; ±=isolated occasionally;−=not isolated.
Source: Condensed From Board (1969).

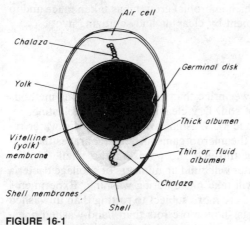

FIGURE 16-1
Internal structure of an egg. (*Courtesy of Poultry and Egg National Board, Chicago.*)

shell is porous for gas exchange during embryonic development. The membranes inside the shell (Figure 16-1) also tend to serve as a mechanical barrier. This barrier is probably only temporary and also offers no protection against the infiltration of mold hyphae through the shell and membrane pores. This fact emphasizes the need to store eggs in a way that will avoid accumulation of moisture on the surface of the shell. A rapid change in storage temperature may permit bacteria to overcome the physical barrier of the shell and its membrane. For example, if a warm egg is placed in a cold environment, microorganisms on the shell surface may be drawn in through the pores upon contraction of the egg contents. Changes in the membranes occur with aging and favor more rapid bacterial multiplication. The rates of physical and chemical changes in the eggs depend on the time and temperature of holding, the relative humidity, and the composition of the atmosphere about the eggs.

In addition to the physical barrier of the shell and its membranes, numerous studies have shown that the albumen is an inadequate growth medium for many microorganisms. The characteristics of albumen that hinder microbial growth include a pH of 9 to 10 that may be reached during storage; low levels of simple nitrogenous compounds; apoprotein, which ties up riboflavin; avidin, which ties up biotin; antiproteolytic factors, which might prevent bacterial proteinases from releasing nitrogenous compounds necessary for growth; conalbumin (ovotransferrin), which chelates iron; and lysozyme, an enzyme which degrades the cell walls of gram-positive bacteria.

ASEPSIS

Great care is taken to reduce the contamination of the outside of the shell by hen feces and dirt from the nests. When eggs are broken for drying or freezing, care is taken to discard those in which microbial growth has taken place and to reduce contamination from equipment by cleaning and sanitizing it.

REMOVAL OF MICROORGANISMS

Because dirty eggs command a lower price than clean ones, various methods have been tried for the removal of soil. Dry cleaning, as by sandblasting, removes dirt and also the bloom (mucin). Washing with warm, plain water removes dirt, the bloom, and part of the microorganisms but encourages the penetration of bacteria into the egg through the pores in the shell. Unless precautions are taken, the wash water will build up numbers of spoilage bacteria so that increased contamination will take place during washing. Experiments have shown that hand-washed eggs are more subject to rotting than unwashed ones and that machine-washed eggs show more rots than hand-washed ones. The amount of rotting that results varies with the kind of washing machine and the kind of washing solution. Attempts to reduce contamination with rot bacteria by cleaning the machines and by disinfecting with 1% hypochlorite solution have not always been successful, but use of that disinfectant solution as the wash water has reduced the percentage of rots in the washed eggs. The use of 1 to 3% acetic acid was effective in removing the flora but resulted in a reduction of shell thickness and egg quality (Heath and Wallace, 1978). Lye, acids, formalin, hypochlorites, quaternary ammonium compounds, various detergents, and detergent-sanitizer combinations have been tried in washing solutions. These solutions are used at temperatures ranging from 32.2 to 60 C, depending on the chemicals employed. A warm washing solution is essential to prevent the liquid from being drawn into the cool egg. A properly operating mechanical egg washer will remove essentially all of the shell flora.

USE OF HEAT

The heat coagulability of the egg white determines to a great extent the maximal heat treatment that can be given shell eggs. Salton et al. (1951) have determined the maximal time at different temperatures for heating in water in order to just avoid coagulation, for example, 800 sec at 57.5 C; 320 sec at 60 C or above resulted in some coagulation of the white when heat treatments were employed that would control rotting. Rotting was well controlled, for instance, by heating at 60 C for 320 sec. Heating in water was superior to heating in oil.

Treatments suggested include heating shell eggs in oil for 10 min at 60 C or in water for 30 min at 54.4 C; heating of egg contents at 61.7 C for 30 min; immersion of shell eggs in boiling water for a few seconds or in hot oil (57.2 C) with or without a vacuum; and immersion of eggs in a hot detergent-sanitizer solution (43.3 to 54.4 C) (the sanitizer being a quaternary ammonium compound). A **thermostabilization** method of dipping eggs into hot water reduces evaporation of moisture from the egg by a slight coagulation of the outermost part of the egg albumen.

Heat treatments employed in the United States for the elimination of salmonellae are as follows: (1) whole egg liquid, 60 C for at least 3.5 min, (2) plain yolk liquid, 61.1 C for at least 3.5 min or 60 C for at least 6.2 min, (3) yolk with carbohydrate, 63.3 C for at least 3.5 min, or 62.2 C for at least 6.2 min, (4) yolk with salt, 63.3 C for at least 3.5 min or 62.2 C for at least 6.2 min. Treatments used in other countries are similar but vary slightly.

Pasteurization is required for most egg products. One exception is salt yolk for use in salad dressings. This product is exempt if it contains at least 1.4 percent acetic acid (pH 4.1 or lower). Because of the heat coagulability of eggs, a stabilization process is required before pasteurization. This includes the addition of aluminum salts and adjustment of the pH.

USE OF LOW TEMPERATURES

The most common method of preservation of eggs is the use of low temperatures including chilling temperatures for shell eggs and freezing for egg "meats." Oiling, gas storage, or treatment with chemical preservatives may be combined with the chilling of shell eggs.

Chilling

Most shell eggs are preserved by chilling. They are selected for storage on the basis of their general appearance and the result of **candling.** To candle an egg, it is held and rotated in front of a light to examine it for defects such as cracks, rots, molds, blood, developing embryo, crusted or sided yolk, weak white, or large air cell. The eggs should be cooled as promptly as practicable after production and held at a temperature and relative humidity that depend on the anticipated time of storage. The lower the relative humidity below 99.6 percent, the more rapidly the egg will lose moisture and hence weight and the larger the air cell will become. The higher the relative humidity, the more likely the microbial spoilage of the egg. The higher the temperature above −1.67 C, the more rapid the penetration of microorganisms into the egg and growth there and the greater the physical and chemical changes, e.g., thinning of the white and weakening of the yolk membrane. For commercial storage for 6 months or longer, a temperature of −1.7 to −0.55 C and a relative humidity of 70 to 80 percent are recommended. Air circulation in the storage room is important to maintain the desired relative humidity around the eggs, and a constant storage temperature is essential to avoid the condensation of moisture on the eggshells.

Special treatments given eggs can improve their keeping quality during chilling storage. Impregnation of the eggshell with a colorless and odorless mineral oil is a common method that keeps out moisture, slows desiccation and air penetration, retains carbon dioxide, and retards physical and chemical changes within the egg. Eggs are sprayed lightly with the oil, particularly eggs to be stored commercially for long periods, with little apparent effect on rates of microbial changes within the egg.

Freezing

The chief bacteriological problems in the freezing of egg "meats" or "pulp" are in connection with the selection and the preparation of the egg contents for freezing. Like other frozen foods, the frozen egg is no better than the egg before it was frozen. Many of the eggs broken for freezing or drying are defective in some way that lowers their grade as shell eggs but does not affect the quality of the contents, e.g., off-sized, dirty, cracked, and weak-shelled eggs.

The eggs first are selected by candling and then are washed mechanically with a final rinse in 200 to 500 ppm chlorine (iodine is also effective) and then broken on automatic breaking machines. The use of automatic machine breaking demands strict control over quality of the whole eggs and inspection of broken eggs before mixing or "pooling" of large quantities. The eggs are broken, and the contents fall into inspection cups. During inspection the yolks and whites are being separated by the action of the cup.

The careful elimination of spoiled eggs has a very important influence on the kinds and numbers of bacteria in the frozen product, as does sanitation throughout the breaking process. All equipment that touches the shell eggs or their contents must be cleaned and sanitized daily or more often. The egg meats, whole or separated, are filtered to remove pieces of shell and stringy material (chalazae), mixed or churned, standardized as to solids content, and frozen in 30- or 50-lb tin cans or other containers, usually by a sharp-freezing process. Yolks frozen separately and stored frozen form a jelly which does not become fluid on thawing. This difficulty is avoided by the incorporation of 5 percent or more of sugar, salt, or glycerol before freezing. The frozen eggs are stored at −17.8 to −20.5 C.

Unless proper precautions are taken, frozen eggs may contain high numbers of bacteria, up to millions per gram. These large numbers may result from the use of heavily contaminated egg pulps, contamination from pieces of shell and from equipment in the breaking room, and growth before freezing. Bacteria that spoil eggs stored at low temperatures, especially *Pseudomonas* organisms, are likely to be numerous, as well as bacteria of the genera *Alcaligenes, Proteus,* and *Flavobacterium.* Gram-positive cocci and rods and coliforms from the eggshell occur in smaller numbers, and possibly anaerobes and other bacteria as chance contaminants. Occasionally, salmonellae may be in eggs from infected hens or contamination. The freezing process reduces numbers, but some of each kind of organism present are likely to survive. The numbers decrease slowly during storage in the frozen condition. If thawing is done at too high a temperature or the thawed eggs are held unduly long before use, numbers of bacteria will increase as a result of growth of the predominating psychrotrophic bacteria. Thawing at temperatures in excess of 2 to 3 C should be for as short a time as possible. Some suggested combinations of time and temperature (for 30-lb cans) are 10 to 15 C for 8 to 15 hr or 2 to 3 C for 48 to 72 hr.

PRESERVATION BY DRYING

In the preparation of whole pulp, white, or yolk of eggs for drying, the principles involved are similar to those just discussed in the preparation of these materials for freezing. Egg white requires some additional treatment before drying to retain its whipping properties. Removal of glucose, one of the reactants in the Browning or Maillard reaction, must be done prior to drying. Several methods of glucose removal have been suggested, including fermentation by group D streptococci, *Enterobacter aerogenes,* or *Saccharomyces cerevisiae* and an enzyme process using glucose oxidase. In the latter glucose is converted into gluconic acid, with added hydrogen peroxide serving as the oxygen donor. A cold desugaring process using glucose oxidase at 10 C has the advantage of producing a product with a low bacteria count.

Most of the drying of eggs in the United States utilizes the spray dryer, where the liquid is sprayed into a current of dry, heated air. Another method is the roller or drum process, in which the liquid egg is passed over a heated drum, with or without vacuum. Air drying is accomplished by means of open pans, as used by the Chinese, or by the belt system, where the egg liquid is on a belt that passes through a heated tunnel (60 to 71.1 C). Spray drying or pan drying, combined with tunnel drying, is used for egg white. Formerly, eggs were dried to a moisture of about 5 percent, but the keeping quality of dried white or whole egg is improved as the moisture content is decreased toward 1 percent, and the trend is in that direction.

The most commonly used drying equipment is similar to the spray-drying equipment used in the dairy industry for drying milk, and similar problems are evident. A major concern in both processes is the bacteriological quality of the air to which the product is exposed during the drying operation. The use of absolute filters and preheating of the air has had significant effects. In addition, the heat applied during drying cannot be depended on for complete reduction of bacterial numbers in the final product or even as a pasteurization technique. Therefore monitoring or prepasteurization of the original product is a necessary safeguard. Whole-egg and yolk products can be pasteurized before drying, while a secondary heat treatment is usually applied to egg white following drying. The bulk packages of egg white are exposed to temperatures of 52 to 54 C for 7 to 10 days, depending on the percentage of moisture of the final product.

Dried eggs may contain from a few hundred microorganisms per gram up to over 100 million, depending on the eggs broken and the methods of handling employed. The same reasons for high numbers hold as for large numbers in frozen eggs. The drying process may reduce the microbial content ten- to a hundredfold from the numbers in the liquid egg but still permit large numbers to survive. A variety of organisms have been found in dried eggs, including micrococci*, streptococci (enterococci), coliform bacteria, salmonellae species, spore-forming bacteria, and molds. Cocci and the gram-positive rods are likely to be present as a result of contamination from the shell during breaking or from handlers or equipment rather than from spoiled eggs. Salmonellae can come from infected hens; however, they are not usually present, and most buyers specify "salmonella-free" products. When the egg white has been pretreated by a fermentation process, the dry product may have a high content of micro-organisms. Adequately dried egg products contain too little moisture for growth of microorganisms. In fact, during storage the numbers of organisms in dry egg will decrease, more rapidly at first and gradually later. Organisms resistant to desiccation, such as micrococci* and spores of bacteria and molds, will make up an increasing percentage of the survivors as storage continues. The more the moisture content of the dry egg has been reduced from 5 percent, the faster the death of bacteria will be.

USE OF PRESERVATIVES

Preservatives may be used on the shells of eggs, in the atmosphere around them, or on wraps or containers for eggs. An enormous number of different substances have been applied to the surface of the shells of eggs or used as packing material about eggs to aid in their preservation. Some of these substances are used primarily to keep the shell dry and reduce penetration of oxygen into the egg and passage of carbon dioxide and moisture out; waxing, oiling the shells, and otherwise sealing are examples. Other materials inhibit the growth of microorganisms, and some are germicidal. Materials used for the dry packing of eggs in the home include salt, lime, sand, sawdust, and ashes. Immersion in water glass, a solution of sodium silicate, long has been a successful home method of preservation. The solution is inhibitory because of its alkalinity. Other inhibitory chemicals that have been tried are borates, permanganates, benzoates, salicylates, formates, and a host of other compounds. The utilization of warm or hot solutions of germicides in the washing of eggs has been mentioned, such as solutions of hypochlorites, lye, acids, formalin, quaternary ammonium compounds, and detergent-sanitizer combinations. Sealing the shell with a solution of dimethylolurea has been found effective in inhibiting mold growth.

Some attempts have been made to reduce spoilage of eggs by molds during storage by treatment of the flats and fillers of storage cases with a mycostatic or mold-inhibiting chemical. Sodium pentachlorophenate and related compounds have been used with some success.

Fumigation of eggs with gaseous ethylene oxide before storage has been reported to protect them against bacterial spoilage.

The only two gases that are added to the atmosphere about eggs to improve their keeping quality are carbon dioxide and ozone, although nitrogen has been used experimentally. Recommendations vary concerning the optimal concentration of carbon dioxide in the air for this purpose. A low concentration, 2.5 percent, for example, slows physical and chemical changes in the egg that accompany the rise in pH as carbon dioxide escapes from the egg but has little effect on microbial growth, particularly of molds. Concentrations as high as 60 percent will markedly delay microbial spoilage, especially if the temperature is near freezing, even if the relative humidity approaches saturation, but the white becomes thinner and an unpleasant flavor develops. Thus the recommendations vary from 0.5 to 0.6 percent at -1 C and from 2.5 to 5 percent at 0 C up to a 15 percent maximum. There has been some disagreement about the effectiveness of ozone. It has been claimed that from 0.6 ppm of ozone (for clean eggs) to 1.5 ppm (for dirty eggs) at -0.55 C and 90 percent relative humidity will keep eggs fresh for 8 months and that 3.5 ppm will not injure them, but some workers claim that 0.5 to 1.5 ppm have little effect on microorganisms. Low concentrations of ozone are reported to improve the flavor of stored eggs because of the deodorizing effect of the gas.

USE OF IRRADIATION

Experiments have indicated that pathogens (e.g., *Salmonella*) in liquid, frozen, and dried eggs can be inactivated by means of ionizing radiation. However, damage by relatively light dosages has also been observed.

SPOILAGE

Some of the defects of eggs are obvious from their general appearance, others are shown by candling with transmitted light, and some show up only in the broken egg.

DEFECTS IN THE FRESH EGG

Fresh eggs may exhibit cracks, leaks, loss of bloom or gloss, or stained or dirty spots on the exterior as well as "meat spots" (blood clots), general bloodiness, or translucent spots in the yolk when candled. From among these, any breaks in the shell or dirt on the egg will favor spoilage on storage.

CHANGES DURING STORAGE

The changes that take place in eggs while they are being held or stored may be divided into those due to nonmicrobial causes and those resulting from the growth of microorganisms.

Changes Not Caused by Microorganisms

Untreated eggs lose moisture during storage and hence lose weight. The amount of shrinkage is shown to the candler by the size of the air space or air cell at the blunt end of the egg, a large cell indicating much shrinkage. Of more importance is the change in the physical state of the contents of the egg, as shown by candling or by breaking out the egg. The white of the egg becomes thinner and more watery as the egg ages, and the yolk membrane becomes weaker. The poorer the egg, the more movement there is of the yolk and the nearer it approaches the shell when the egg is twirled during candling. When an old egg is broken onto a flat dish, the thinness of the white is more evident and the weakness of the yolk membrane permits the yolk to flatten out or even break. By contrast, a broken fresh egg shows a thick white and a yolk that stands up strongly in the form of a hemisphere. During storage, the alkalinity of the white of the egg increases from a normal pH of about 7.6 to about 9.5. Any marked growth of the chick embryos in fertilized eggs also serves to condemn the eggs.

Changes Caused by Microorganisms

To cause spoilage of an undamaged shell egg, the causal organisms must do the following: (1) contaminate the shell, (2) penetrate the pores of the shell to the shell membranes (usually the shell must be moist for this to occur), (3) grow through the shell membranes to reach the white (or to reach the yolk if it touches the membrane), (4) grow in the egg white, despite the previously mentioned unfavorable conditions there, to reach the yolk, where they can grow readily and complete spoilage of the egg. Bacteria unable to grow in the white can reach the yolk and flourish there only when the yolk touches the inner cell membrane.

The time required for bacteria to penetrate the shell membranes varies with the organisms and the temperature but may take as long as several weeks at refrigerator temperatures. The special set of environmental conditions, the selective egg-white medium, and the low storage temperature of about 0 C combine to limit the number of kinds of bacteria and molds that can cause spoilage chiefly to those to be mentioned.

In general, more spoilage of eggs is caused by bacteria than by molds. The types of bacterial spoilage, or "rots," of eggs go by different names. Alford et al. (1950) list five groups of rots that are found in Australian eggs for export. Among the three chief ones are the **green rots**, caused chiefly by *Pseudomonas fluorescens,* a bacterium that grows at 0 C; the rot is so named because of the bright-green color of the white during early stages of development. This stage is noted with difficulty in candling but shows up clearly when the egg is broken. Later the yolk may disintegrate and blend with the white so as to mask the green color. Odor is lacking or is fruity or "sweetish." The contents of eggs so rotted fluoresce strongly under ultraviolet light. A second important group of rots are the **colorless rots**, which may be caused by *Pseudomonas, Acinetobacter, Alcaligenes,* certain coliform bacteria, or other types of bacteria. These rots are detected readily by candling, for the yolk usually is involved, except in very early stages, and disintegrates or at least shows a white incrustation. The odor varies from a scarcely detectable one to fruity to "highly offensive." The third important group of rots are the **black rots**, where the eggs are almost opaque to the candling lamp because the yolks become blackened and then break down to give the whole-egg contents a muddy-brown color. The odor is putrid, with hydrogen sulfide evident, and gas pressure may develop in the egg. Species of *Proteus* most commonly cause these rots, although some species of *Pseudomonas* and *Aeromonas* can cause black rots. *Proteus melanovogenes** causes an especially black coloration in the yolk and a dark color in the white. The development of black rot and of red rot usually means that the egg has at some time been held at temperatures higher than those ordinarily used for storage. **Pink rots** occur less often, and **red rots** are still more infrequent. Pink rots are caused by strains of *Pseudomonas* and may at times be a later stage of some of the green rots. They resemble the colorless rots, except for a pinkish precipitate on the yolk and a pink color in the white. **Red rots,** caused by species of *Serratia,* are mild in odor and are not offensive.

Florian and Trussell (1957) have listed rots by ten different species of the genera *Pseudomonas, Alcaligenes, Proteus, Flavobacterium,* and *Paracolobactrum**. These rots have been characterized as fluorescent, green and yellow, custard, black, red, rusty red, colorless, and mixed. These authors also list secondary invaders in the genera *Enterobacter, Alcaligenes, Escherichia, Flavobacterium,* and *Paracolobactrum**. These bacteria can grow in the egg but cannot initiate penetration.

The spoilage of eggs by fungi goes through stages of mold growth that give the defects their names. Very early mold growth is termed **pin-spot molding** because of the small, compact colonies of molds appearing on the shell and usually just inside it. The color of these pin spots varies with the kind of mold; *Penicillium* species cause yellow or blue or green spots inside the shell, *Cladosporium* species give dark-green or black spots, and species of *Sporotrichum* produce pink spots. In storage atmospheres of high humidity a variety of molds may cause **superficial fungal spoilage,** first in the form of a fuzz or "whiskers" covering the shell and later as more luxuriant growth. When the eggs are stored at near-freezing temperatures, as they usually are, the temperatures are high enough for slow mycelial growth of some molds but too low for sporulation, while other molds may produce asexual spores. Molds causing spoilage of eggs include species of *Penicillium, Cladosporium, Sporotrichum, Mucor, Thamnidium, Botrytis, Alternaria,* and other genera. The final stage of spoilage by molds is **fungal rotting,** after the mycelium of the mold has grown through the pores or cracks in the egg. Jelling of the white may result, and colored rots may be produced, e.g., fungal red rot by *Sporotrichum* and a black color by *Cladosporium,* the cause of black spot of eggs as well as of other foods. The hyphae of the mold may weaken the yolk membrane enough to cause its rupture, after which the growth of the mold is stimulated greatly by the food released from the yolk.

Off-flavors sometimes are developed in eggs with little other outward evidence of spoilage. Thus mustiness may be caused by any of a number of bacteria, such as *Achromobacter perolens**, *Pseudomonas graveolens**, and *P. mucidolens*. The growth of *Streptomyces* on straw or elsewhere near the egg may produce musty or earthy flavors that are absorbed by the egg. Molds growing in the shell also give musty odors and tastes. A hay odor is caused by *Enterobacter cloacae*, while fishy flavors are produced by certain strains of *Escherichia coli*. The "cabbage-water" flavor mentioned in connection with type II black rot of Haines may appear before rotting is obvious. Off-flavors, such as the "cold-storage taste," may be absorbed from packing materials.

BIBLIOGRAPHY

Alford, L. R., N. E. Holmes, W. J. Scott, and J. R. Vickery. 1950. Studies in the preservation of shell eggs. I. The nature of wastage in Australian export eggs. Aust. J. Appl. Sci. 1:208–214.

Board, P. A., and R. G. Board. 1968. A diagnostic key for identifying organisms recovered from rotten eggs. Br. Poult. Sci. 9:111–120.

Board, R. G. 1965. The properties of and classification of the predominant bacteria occurring in rotten eggs. J. Appl. Bacteriol. 28:437–453.

Board, R. G. 1969. The microbiology of the hen's egg. Adv. Appl. Microbiol. 11:245–281.

Board, R. G., and J. C. Ayres. 1965. Influence of temperature on bacterial infection of the hen's egg. Appl. Microbiol. 13:358–364.

Board, R. G., J. C. Ayres, A. A. Kraft, and R. H. Forsythe. 1964. The microbiological contamination of egg shells and egg packing materials. Poult. Sci. 43:584–595.

Board, R. G., and R. Fuller. 1974. Non-specific antimicrobial defenses of the avian egg, embryo and neonate. Biol. Rev. 49:15–49.

Brooks, J. 1960. Mechanism of the multiplication of *Pseudomonas* in the hen's egg. J. Appl. Bacteriol. 23:499–509.

Florian, M. L. E., and P. C. Trussell. 1957. Bacterial spoilage of shell eggs. IV. Identification of spoilage organisms. Food Technol. 11:56–60.

Forsythe, R. H. 1970. Egg processing technology: progress and sanitation programs. J. Milk Food Technol. 33:64–73.

Fromm, D. 1960. Permeability of the egg shell as influenced by washing, ambient temperature changes and environmental temperature and humidity. Poult. Sci. 39:1490–1495.

Garibaldi, J. A. 1960. Factors in egg white which control growth of bacteria. Food Res. 25:337–344.

Garibaldi, J. A., and H. G. Bayne. 1962. Iron and the bacterial spoilage of shell eggs. J. Food Sci. 27:57–59.

Haines, R. B. 1939. Microbiology in the preservation of the hen's egg. G.B. Dep. Sci. Ind. Res. Food Invest. Spec. Rep. 47.

Hartung, T. E., and W. J. Stadelman. 1962. Influence of metallic cations on the penetration of the egg shell membranes of *Pseudomonas fluorescens*. Poult. Sci. 41: 1590–1596.

Hartung, T. E., and W. J. Stadelman. 1963. Penetration of egg shell membranes by *Pseudomonas fluorescens* as influenced by shell porosity, age of egg and degree of bacterial challenge. Poult. Sci. 42:147–150.

Heath, J. L., and J. Wallace. 1978. Dilute acid immersion as a method of cleaning shell eggs. Poult. Sci. 57:149–155.

Kraft, A. A., E. H. McNally, and A. W. Brant. 1958. Shell quality and bacterial infection of shell eggs. Poult. Sci. 37:638–644.

Lifshitz, A., R. C. Baker, and H. B. Naylor. 1964. The relative importance of chicken egg exterior structures in resisting bacterial penetration. J. Food Sci. 29:94–99.

Miller, W. A. 1957. A comparison of various wash-water additives in preventing microbial deterioration in washed eggs that formerly were dirty. Poult. Sci. 36:579–584.

Murdock, C. R., E. L. Crossley, J. Robb, M. E. Smith, and B. C. Hobbs. 1960. The pasteurization of liquid whole egg. Month. Bull. Med. Res. Coun. 19:134–152.

Northolt, M. D., N. Wiegersman, and M. Van Schothorst. 1978. Pasteurization of dried egg white by high temperature storage. J. Food Technol. 13:25–30.

Salton, M. R. J., W. J. Scott, and J. R. Vickery. 1951. Studies in the preservation of shell eggs. VI. The effect of pasteurization on bacterial rotting. Aust. J. Appl. Sci. 2:205–222.

Thatcher, F. S., and J. Montford. 1962. Egg-products as a source of salmonellae in processed foods. Can. J. Public Health 53:61–69.

CONTAMINATION, PRESERVATION, AND SPOILAGE OF POULTRY

The discussion of poultry is concerned mostly with chicken meat, but the principles apply to meat of other fowl, such as turkey, goose, duck, and squab.

CONTAMINATION

Sources of contamination discussed for meats apply to poultry as well. The skin of live birds may contain numbers of bacteria averaging 1,500 per square centimeter. These numbers probably reflect the natural flora of the skin plus other organisms that could be derived from feet, feathers, and feces. Contamination of the skin and the lining of the body cavity occurs during washing, plucking, and evisceration. Table 17-1 shows microbial counts obtained during various stages of processing. A comparison of Table 17-1 with Table 17-2 suggests that the final product microbial loads are not that different. Obviously processing procedures have changed since 1956. Chickens are currently processed by a fully automated conveyor or track line with vacuum evisceration.

Bacterial numbers vary considerably on the surface of chickens. This variation, however, is greater between birds than it is between different areas of the same bird. The types of organisms isolated depend on where samples are taken and on the stage of processing. Isolates from poultry and poultry products include members of numerous genera (Table 17-3), The giblets (gizzards, hearts and livers) are processed separately, and numbers and types of microorganisms present may differ from those of the carcass.

The incidence of salmonellae on poultry carcasses and the role of poultry processing in transmitting salmonellosis have received considerable attention.

TABLE 17-1
NUMBERS OF MICROORGANISMS ON
POULTRY AND IN PROCESSING WATERS

Point of sampling	Usual range ($\times 10^3$)*
Skin of live bird	0.6–8.1
Scald water (58.3–60 C)	5.9–17
Fresh chill water	50–210
Aerated chill water	34–240
Skin, after rough pick	8.1–45
After neck pick	3.3–32
After pinning	10–84
After singe	13–210
After evisceration	11–93
Cavity after evisceration	1.4–12
In chill tank	50–600
After aeration	3.4–240
Final product	4–330

*Counts on waters are per milliliter, on surfaces per square centimeter.
  Source: Walker and Ayres (1956).

The incidence of salmonella-positive birds has been reported to range from 0 to 50 percent. There is also a high incidence of *Campylobacter jejuni* in poultry processing plants and on the processed bird.

PRESERVATION

Most of the principles of preservation discussed for meats in Chapter 14 apply likewise to poultry, although the plucking and dressing of the fowls raise different problems. As in the slaughter of animals for meat, the method of killing

TABLE 17-2
GEOMETRIC MEANS ($\log_{10}$) OF AEROBIC
PLATE COUNTS PER GRAM OF NECK SKIN
AT DIFFERENT STAGES OF PROCESSING*

Stage	Plant 1†	Plant 2‡
After picking	5.24	4.60
After eviseration	5.42	4.92
After spray washing	5.15	4.64
After immersion chilling	4.51	—
After air chilling	—	4.54
After packaging	4.72	4.52

*The report summarizes many plants; only two are presented for illustrative purposes.
  †This plant was using a countercurrent immersion chiller.
  ‡This plant was using tunnel air chilling.
  Source: Commission of European Communities (1976).

TABLE 17-3
MICROBIOLOGICAL PROFILE OF POULTRY

Product	Microorganisms isolated	Approximate quantative range
Incoming birds	Bacteria *Acinetobacter, Corynebacterium, Moraxella, Pseudomonas, Flavobacterium, Staphylococcus,* and *Micrococcus*	10^2–10^3/cm^2
After processing	Bacteria *Pseudomonas, Acinetobacter, Flavobacterium, Cytophaga, Enterobacter, Alcaligenes, Salmonella, Campylobacter,* and many others Yeast *Trichosporon, Torulopsis, Candida,* and *Rhodotorula* Molds *Penicillium, Alternaria, Aspergillus,* and others	10^3–10^5/cm^2

and bleeding the fowl has an important effect on the quality of the product.Modern methods involve severing of the jugular vein while the bird is suspended by its feet and draining the blood.

If the trachea is left intact, it is referred to as an **outside cut**; a **kosher cut** severs the trachea. When the birds are scalded, they may gasp, drawing scald water into the air sac. Apparently the kosher cut minimizes inhalation of scald water because the cut end of the trachea is drawn under the skin. The method of picking or plucking has some influence on the keeping quality of the bird. Dry-plucked birds are more resistant to decomposition than are semiscalded or scalded ones because the skin is less likely to be broken but more pinfeathers are left. Most picking is by means of the semiscald method, in which the fowl is immersed in water at about 55 C for 2 min. Experiments have shown that the water in the semiscald method is not an important source of contaminating microorganisms if reasonable precautions are taken to change the water. Although the total numbers of bacteria might increase in the scald water during processing, the contamination to birds is minimized by (1) the temperature of the scald water, (2) the low initial count on some birds, and (3) a dilution effect of adding fresh water to the scald tank (Brune and Cunningham, 1971). The USDA requires a minimum of 1 qt per bird per minute.

Steam scalding of birds is more effective than hot water in reducing numbers of bacteria, including coliforms and salmonellae.

ASEPSIS

Comparatively little can be done to keep microorganisms from contaminating the dressed poultry. The sanitation of the housing of the birds before killing has some influence on the numbers of microorganisms on the skin at dressing, but even under the best conditions enough spoilage organisms contaminate the skin to permit microbial deterioration if conditions of handling and storage are not good. Contamination of the lining of the body cavity of the bird can be prevented if the fowl is not eviscerated until sold in the retail market, but visceral taints may develop unless the birds are adequately refrigerated. The shackles holding the feet and head of the fowl may be a source of heavy contamination. Contamination can be reduced if equipment is adequately cleaned and sanitized at intervals.

USE OF HEAT

Dressed chickens and other fowls may be canned, whole or dissected, in their own juices or in jelly. Heat processes are analogous to those for canned meats (Chapter 14). The chicken or other fowl may be salted in a weak brine before being packed into the glass jars or cans.

USE OF LOW TEMPERATURES

Most poultry is preserved by either chilling or freezing. Of prime importance in either method of storage is a rapid chilling process immediately after the birds have been eviscerated and drawn (if that is done). Various commercial methods of submerging the birds in cold water, ice water, or ice slush are used. Variations include counterflow vat-type, counterflow tumbler-type, and oscillating vat-type chiller, agitated ice and water, and blasts of cold air or CO_2 or sprays of refrigerant or solid CO_2. The chill tanks can serve as a source of contamination if not properly controlled. A counterflow system would be better in preventing the buildup of microbial numbers, since fresh potable water added to the chiller would flow against the movement of the carcasses. Chlorine can be added to chill-tank water to reduce numbers of organisms. The effect of chlorine on the shelf life of the carcasses, however, is debatable. Chilling by blasts of cold air would leave the birds relatively dry compared with those from chill tanks. The moisture added to the carcasses may not only add organisms but also favor their growth.

Chilling

Chilling storage of poultry is for only a short period, usually less than a month; birds to be stored longer should be frozen. Packing the dressed birds in ice has been used for short periods of holding and where mechanical refrigeration is not available. The lower the temperature of storage, the longer the birds can be stored without undesirable changes. In tests on cut-up chicken, Ayres (1959) found that compared with room temperature, storage life was extended 2 days at 10 C, 6 days at 4.4 C, and 14 days at 0 C.

Freezing

Poultry can be kept in good condition for months if freezing is prompt and rapid and the storage temperature is low enough. Fairly rapid freezing is desirable since it produces a light-appearing bird because fine ice crystals are formed within the fibers. Slow freezing, on the other hand, causes large crystals to accumulate outside the fibers and causes the flesh to appear darker. A bird that is frozen rapidly while fresh will have smaller crystals than one frozen after a delay. Most chickens frozen commercially are packed ten to a box lined with moistureproof and airproof paper and for the most part are dressed but not drawn.

Poultry should be frozen fast enough to retain most of the natural bloom or external appearance of a freshly dressed fowl. The storage temperature should be below −17.8 C and the relative humidity above 95 percent to reduce surface drying. Most poultry is sharp-frozen at about −29 C or less in circulating air or on a moving belt in a freezing tunnel. For quick freezing, a smaller package is necessary, usually a whole bird, a cut-up one, or a boned fowl, packed in a special watertight and almost airtight wrapper. Actually, a large chicken would not freeze fast enough to measure up to the definition of quick freezing in Chapter 7.

Although some of the bacteria are killed by the freezing process and numbers decrease slowly during storage, enough remain to cause spoilage when the bird is thawed. The growth of bacteria can take place during picking, dressing, drawing, chilling, and also during the freezing process until the temperature of the bird drops below 0 C. Deterioration that has developed due to bacterial growth, diffusion of taints from the viscera, and activity of enzymes of the bird before freezing will carry over into the frozen product. Although bacterial growth has been stopped, some of the enzymatic action will continue unless the storage temperature is very low.

Unless adequate sanitary precautions are taken, a marked increase in bacteria will take place during the removal of the bones of cooked fowl for subsequent canning or quick freezing. Low-temperature bacteria of the genera *Proteus* and *Alcaligenes,* as well as coliform bacteria, have been found in considerable numbers. Canning will destroy them, but quick freezing permits many to survive.

USE OF PRESERVATIVES

Feeding antibiotics to birds may lead to increased percentages of resistant microorganisms in the fecal matter and hence on the birds, although low levels of antibiotic may be deposited in the flesh. Low levels of antibiotic in the meat of treated birds are mostly destroyed by cooking.

Soaking cut-up poultry in solutions of organic acids (acetic, adipic, succinic, etc.) at pH 2.5 has also been reported to lengthen shelf life.

Turkey sometimes is cured in a solution of salt, sugar, and sodium nitrate for several weeks at about 3.3 C, washed, dried, and then smoked. Usually a light smoking process is used, more for flavor than for preservation. Recommended temperatures during smoking range from 43.3 to 60 C, and the time ranges from a few hours to several days.

CARBON DIOXIDE ATMOSPHERE

Increasing carbon dioxide concentrations (10 to 20 percent) in the atmosphere of stored chickens inhibits the growth of psychrotrophs. Dry ice packed with the carcasses may serve as the source of the carbon dioxide. The use of films of both high and low gas permeability in combination with a carbon dioxide atmosphere shows that the carbon dioxide atmosphere is the significant factor in reducing microbial counts.

USE OF IRRADIATION

Irradiation of poultry with cathode or gamma rays could be a successful preservation method since the rays apparently produce less objectionable change in appearance and flavor than in some other foods, but to date the method has not been practiced commercially. Radiation doses of 1 to 10 kilograys would reduce the microbial flora and extend the product's refrigerated shelf life. Chicken carcasses have been treated with 2.5 kilograys to effectively destroy salmonellae (Mulder et al., 1977).

SPOILAGE

While the enzymes of the fowl contribute to the deterioration of the dressed bird, bacteria are the chief cause of spoilage, with the intestines a primary source of these organisms. The work done on the bacterial spoilage of poultry has indicated that most bacterial growth takes place on the surfaces, i.e., the skin, the lining of the body cavity, and any cut surfaces, and the decomposition products diffuse slowly into the meat. A surface odor has been noted when the bacterial count on the skin was about 2.5 million per square centimeter. This took about 4 weeks at 0 C and 5 weeks at 1.1 C in one set of experiments. Eviscerated poultry held at 10 C or below is spoiled mostly by *Pseudomonas* and to a lesser degree by yeasts, e.g., *Torulopsis* and *Rhodotorula*. Above 10 C, micrococci* usually predominate, and there also is growth of *Alcaligenes* and *Flavobacterium*. In time the surface of the meat usually becomes slimy. Small amounts (1 to 5 ppm) of iron in the wash water may favor bacterial growth on the surface and production of the fluorescent pigment pyoverdine by pseudomonads; more iron will reduce pigmentation. About 100 ppm of magnesium is optimal for pigment production by *P. fluorescens*.

Iced, cut-up poultry often develops a slime that is accompanied by an odor described as "tainted," "acid," "sour," or "dishraggy." This defect is caused chiefly by species of *Pseudomonas,* although *Alcaligenes* also may be con-

TABLE 17-4
MAJOR BACTERIA INVOLVED IN THE SPOILAGE OF REFRIGERATED POULTRY

Product	Bacteria	Reference
Raw eviserated carcasses	*Pseudomonas fluorescens, P. putida, Acinetobacter, Moraxella*	
Dark meat, pH 6.4–6.7	*Acinetobacter, Alteromonas, Pseudomonas*	Barnes and Impey (1968)
White meat, pH 5.7–5.9	*Pseudomonas* and others	Barnes and Impey (1968)
Chicken wrapped in oxygen-impermeable films	Microaerophilic bacteria, lactic acid bacteria, and others	
Vacuum-packed chicken	*Enterobacter* and others	Arafa and Chen (1975)

cerned. Similar bacteria grow whether the temperature is as low as 0 C or as high as 10 C, and enormous numbers must be present, about 10^8 per square centimeter, before the odor becomes evident. The major species involved in spoilage are summarized in Table 17-4.

It should be kept in mind that chemical changes in poultry meat other than those caused by microorganisms occur during refrigerated storage and will in time reduce the quality.

BIBLIOGRAPHY

Arafa, A. S., and T. C. Chen. 1975. Effect of vacuum packaging on microorganisms, on cut-up chickens and in chicken products. J. Food Sci. 40:50–52.

Ayres, J. C. 1959. Effect of sanitation, packaging and antibiotics on the microbial spoilage of commercially processed poultry. Iowa State J. Sci. 54:27–46.

Ayres, J. C., W. S. Ogilvy, and G. F. Stewart. 1950. Post mortem changes in stored meats. I. Microorganisms associated with development of slime on eviscerated cut-up poultry. Food Technol. 4:199–205.

Barnes, E. M., and C. S. Impey. 1968. Psychrophilic spoilage of poultry. J. Appl. Bacteriol. 31:97–107.

Brune, H. E., and F. E. Cunningham. 1971. A review of microbiological aspects of poultry processing. World's Poult. Sci. J. 27:(3)223–240.

Bryan, F. L. 1980. Poultry and poultry meat products. *In* J. H. Silliker, et al. (eds.), Microbial ecology of foods. Volume II. Factors affecting life and death of microorganisms. Academic Press, Inc., New York.

Clark, D. S., and C. P. Lentz. 1969. Microbiological studies in poultry processing plants in Canada. Can. Inst. Food Tech. J. 2:33–38.

Coleby, B., M. Ingram, and H. J. Shepherd. 1960. Treatment of meats with ionizing radiation. III. Radiation pasteurization of whole eviscerated chicken carcasses. J. Sci. Food Agr. 11:61–71.

Commission of European Communities. 1976. Evaluation of hygienic problems related to the chilling of poultry carcasses. Information on Agric. No. 22. EEC, Brussels.

Eklund, M. W., J. V. Spencer, E. A. Sauter, and M. H. George. 1961. The effect of different methods of chlortetracycline application on the shelf-life of chicken fryers. Poult. Sci. 40:924–928.

Elliot, R. P., R. P. Straka, and J. A. Garibaldi. 1964. Polyphosphate inhibition of growth of pseudomonads from poultry meat. Appl. Microbiol. 12:517–522.

Essary, E. O., W. E. C. Moore, and C. Y. Kramer. 1958. Influence of scald temperatures, chill time, and holding temperatures on the bacterial flora and shelf-life of freshly chilled, tray-pack poultry. Food Technol. 12:684–687.

Gunderson, M. F., H. W. McFadden, and T. S. Kyle. 1954. The bacteriology of commercial poultry processing. Burgess Publishing Company, Minneapolis, Minn.

Hamdy, M. K., N. D. Barton, and W. E. Brown. 1964. Source and portal of entry of bacteria found in bruised poultry tissue. Appl. Microbiol. 12:464–469.

Kotula, A. W., and J. A. Kinner. 1964. Airborne microorganisms in broiler processing plants. Appl. Microbiol. 12:179–184.

Kraft, A. A., and J. C. Ayres. 1965. Development of microorganisms and fluorescence of poultry chilled in water containing iron or magnesium. J. Food Sci. 30:154–159.

Lillard, H. S. 1985. Bacterial cell characteristics and conditions influencing their adhesion to poultry skin. J. Food Prot. 48:803–807.

May, K. N. 1962. Bacterial contamination during cutting and packaging chicken in processing plants and retail stores. Food Technol. 16:89-91

Mulder, R. W. A., S. Notermans, and E. H. Kampelmacher. 1977. Inactivation of salmonellae on chilled and deep frozen broiler carcasses by irradiation. J. Appl. Bacteriol. 42:179–185.

Nagel, C. W., K. L. Simpson, H. Ng, R. H. Vaughn, and G. F. Stewart. 1960. Microorganisms associated with spoilage of refrigerated poultry. Food Technol. 14:21–23.

Oosterom, J., S. Motermans, H. Karman, and G. B. Engels. 1983. Origin and prevelence of *Campylobacter jejuni* in poultry processing. J. Food Prot. 46:339–344.

Stevenson, J. R., and S. A. Edgar. 1968. Shelf life and microflora of broiler carcasses and parts. Poul. Sci. 47:1722–1729.

Surkiewicz, B. F., R. W. Johnston, A. B. Moran, and G. W. Krumm. 1969. A bacteriological survey of chicken eviscerating plants. Food Technol. 23:1066–1070.

Thomson, J. E. 1970. Microbial counts and rancidity of fresh fryer chickens as affected by packaging materials, storage atmosphere, and temperature. Poult. Sci. 49: 1104–1109.

Thomson, J. E., and A. W. Kotula. 1959. Contamination of the air sac areas of chicken carcasses and its relationship to scalding and method of killing. Poult. Sci. 38: 1433–1437.

Wabeck, C. J., C. E. Parmelee, and W. J. Stadelman. 1968. Carbon dioxide preservation of fresh poultry. Poult. Sci. 47:468–474.

Walker, H. W., and J. C. Ayres. 1958. Antibiotic residuals and microbial resistance in poultry treated with tetracyclines. Food Res. 23:525–531.

Walker, H. W., and J. C. Ayres. 1958. Incidence and kinds of microorganisms associated with commercially dressed poultry. Appl. Microbiol. 4:345–349.

Walker, H. W., and J. C. Ayres. 1959. Characteristics of yeasts isolated from processed poultry and the influence of tetracyclines on their growth. Appl. Microbiol. 7:251–255.

Wetzler, T. F., P. Musick, H. Johnson, and W. A. Mackenzie. 1962. The cleaning and sanitizing of poultry processing plants. Am. J. Public Health 52:460–471.

Wilkerson, W. B., J. C. Ayres, and A. A. Kraft. 1961. Occurrence of enterococci and coliform organisms on fresh and stored poultry. Food Technol. 15:286–292.

CONTAMINATION, PRESERVATION, AND SPOILAGE OF MILK AND MILK PRODUCTS

Dairy products include market milk and cream, butter, frozen desserts, cheese, fermented milks, and condensed and dried milk products.

CONTAMINATION

ON THE FARM

Milk contains relatively few bacteria when it leaves the udder of a healthy cow, and generally these bacteria do not grow in milk under the usual conditions of handling. However, micrococci and streptococci have been recovered from aseptically drawn milk. During the normal milking operation, however, milk is subject to contamination from the animal, especially the exterior of the udder and adjacent areas. Bacteria found in manure, soil, and water may enter from this source. Such contamination is reduced by clipping the cow, especially the flanks and udder, grooming the cow, and washing the udder with water or a germicidal solution before milking. Contamination of the cow with soil, water, and manure is reduced by paving and draining barnyards, keeping cows from stagnant pools, and cleaning manure from the barns or milking parlors.

Probably the two most significant sources of contamination are dairy utensils and milk-contact surfaces, including the milk pail or milking machines, as the case may be, strainers, milk cans or pipelines, and the bulk-milk cooler. If dairy utensils or the milk-contact surfaces are inadequately cleaned, sanitized, and dried, bacteria may develop in large numbers in the dilute milklike residue and enter the next milk to touch these surfaces. Undesirable bacteria from these sources include lactic streptococci, coliform bacteria, psychrotrophic gram-negative rods, and **thermodurics,** those which survive pasteurization, e.g., micrococci*, enterococci, bacilli, and brevibacteria*. In general, these bacteria grow well in milk and hence endanger its keeping quality. When they are cleaned and sanitized properly, utensils and milk-contact surfaces add few bacteria per milliliter of milk, but under very poor conditions these sources may increase the bacterial content of milk by millions per milliliter. Application of quaternary ammonium compounds as sanitizing agents tends to increase the percentage of gram-negative rods on the utensils (psychrotrophs, coliforms), whereas hypochlorides favor gram-positive bacteria (micrococci*, bacilli). Modern dairy utensils and milk-contact surfaces, particularly milking machines, pipelines, and bulk-milk coolers, are designed to provide easy access for cleaning, sanitizing, and drying. Farm bulk-milk coolers are also equipped with excellent refrigeration capacity and agitation to ensure proper cooling of the milk.

Other possible sources of contamination are the hands and arms of the milker or dairy workers, the air of the barn or milking parlor, and flies. Normally these sources would contribute very few bacteria, but they might be a source of pathogens or spoilage microorganisms. The quality of the farm water supply used in the milking parlor for cleaning, rinsing, etc., will have some effect on the quality of the milk.

The numbers of bacteria per milliliter of milk added from the various sources depends on the care taken to avoid contamination. For example, the exterior of the cow contributes comparatively few organisms if precautions are taken and a milking machine is used, but under very poor conditions thousands per milliliter could enter the milk. Table 18-1 lists the approximate range of microorganisms usually found in milk at different points of sampling.

IN TRANSIT AND AT THE MANUFACTURING LEVEL

Other sources of contamination after the milk leaves the farm include the tanker truck, transfer pipes, sampling utensils, and the equipment at the market-milk plant, cheese factory, condensery, or other processing plant. Again, the most significant sources of contamination are the milk-contact surfaces. Pipelines, vats, tanks, pumps, valves, separators, clarifiers, homogenizers, coolers, strainers, stirrers, and fillers may serve as possible sources of bacteria. The amount or level of

TABLE 18-1
ESTIMATED NUMBERS OF
MICROORGANISMS IN MILK

Point of sampling	Usual range*
Aseptically drawn milk	500–1,000
Milk pail or milking machine	1,000–10,000
Bulk-milk tank (farm)	5,000–20,000

*Standard plate counts per milliter.

contamination from each of these sources depends on cleaning and sanitizing methods. In addition, the employees, particularly their hands and arms, are a possible source of contamination and pathogens. The paper stock used for packaging fluid milk is also an important source of contamination.

It should be kept in mind that the number and types of organisms in milk or other dairy products may be increased either by contamination or by growth of the organisms already present. Methods of production, handling, storage, and manufacture are designed to prevent both.

PRESERVATION

Milk is such a delicately flavored, easily changed food that many preservative methods cannot be used without causing an undesirable change or, at best, making a different food product. In fact, most of the products made from milk or cream evolved for the purpose of improving the keeping quality. Thus nomadic tribes found that milk that had undergone a lactic acid fermentation could be kept for long periods, although now we produce fermented milks for their characteristic body and flavor. Treatment of the curd from milk in various ways was found to lengthen the keeping time; now we produce different kinds of cheese for their individual characteristics. Milk and milk products, which serve to illustrate most of the principles of preservation and spoilage of foods, have had more research done on them than have most foods, and numerous texts and reference books have been published on the subject. These references, some of which are listed at the end of this chapter, should be consulted for more detail than can be presented here.

ASEPSIS

The prevention as far as is practical of the contamination of milk is important in its preservation. Keeping quality is usually improved when smaller numbers of microorganisms are present, especially those which grow readily in milk. Although the type of microorganisms present is extremely important, in general, the lower the initial total microbial load, the better the keeping quality of the milk. For example, a low microbial load, particularly the number of spores present, is an important consideration in the milk to be processed by ultrahigh-temperature or commercial sterilization processes.

Since numbers of bacteria in milk are indicative of the sanitary precautions and careful handling employed during the production, the bacterial content of milk is used to measure its sanitary quality, and historically milk has been graded on the basis of some method of estimating bacterial numbers. The exterior of the cow and milk-contact surfaces have been emphasized as possible sources of both high numbers and undesirable kinds of microorganisms. Especially undesirable in market milk are bacteria that grow well in milk, e.g., the lactics and the coliforms; the psychrotrophs, those which grow well at refrigeration temperatures, at which milk is usually stored; the thermodurics, those which survive the pasteurization treatment of milk; and, of course, human pathogens. When the milk is to be used as the substrate for microbial fermentation, as in the manufacture of fermented milks or cheese, microorganisms that are able to compete with the starter bacteria and produce defects in the product are extremely important. Thus the coliform bacteria, anaerobes, and yeast can cause gasiness and off-flavors in these products. Other organisms may inhibit the desirable starter culture or cause defects in body, texture, or flavor. The presence of heat-resistant microorganisms or spores may be a potential source of spoilage in high-heat-treatment milks, such as evaporated milk and sweetened condensed milk.

Packaging serves to keep microorganisms from bottled milk, fermented milks, packaged butter, canned milk, dry milk, and packaged cheese, and so do coatings of plastic, wax, or other protective substances on finished cheeses. The bacteriological quality of the paper stock used in the fabrication of paper milk cartons has been examined. Normally the packaging material contributes very little to the total microbial load in the finished product.

REMOVAL OF MICROORGANISMS

After microorganisms have entered milk, it is difficult to remove them effectively. The process of centrifugation, as in clarifying or separating, will remove some microorganisms from milk. High-speed centrifugation (at 10,000 g) removes about 99 percent of the spores and more than half of the vegetative cells of bacteria plus some protein. However, the centrifugal procedure used for removing bacteria from milk, known as **bactofugation,** is not used extensively on a commercial basis. Molds can be removed physically from the surface of some kinds of cheese during the curing process by scraping or periodic washing, but aside from these limited instances, physical removal is difficult.

USE OF HEAT

Pasteurization and Ultrapasteurization

Because milk and cream are so readily changed by heat, the mild heat treatment called pasteurization (review Chapter 6) is used for their preservation. Historically, milk first received heat treatments to increase its shelf life. When it became evident that milk could serve as a source of food-borne illness, pasteurization became a necessary safeguard. The objectives of market-milk pasteurization are to (1) kill all the pathogens that may enter the milk and be transmitted to people and (2) improve the keeping quality of milk. Ideally, this heat treatment should be accomplished without deleteriously affecting the flavor, appearance, nutritional properties, or creaming of the milk. When milk is pasteurized for the manufacture of cheese or cream is pasteurized for making butter, a third objective is to destroy microorganisms that would interfere with the activities of desirable organisms, such as the starter culture, or cause inferiority or spoilage of the product. The cheese maker is also concerned that the heat treatment does not harm the curdling properties of the milk. The heat treatment of cream also destroys lipases that may cause deterioration of butter during storage.

The first widely used pasteurization process for milk involved heating the milk in large tanks or vats to 60 C for at least 20 min. This holding method was subsequently changed to 61.7 C for 30 min and finally to 62.8 C for 30 min to eliminate *Coxiella burnetii,* a rickettsia responsible for Q fever which can be transmitted in milk. This was not a continuous process and was referred to as **vat pasteurization.** The use of plate heat exchangers and a continuous operation involves the high-temperature–short-time (HTST) pasteurization process at a temperature of at least 72 C for at least 15 sec. The HTST system is the most widely used commercial pasteurization process today. Most processors, however, heat their product above the minimum temperature and time. For example, many pasteurize milk at temperatures approaching 79 C for as long as 20 to 25 sec. The main objective is to decrease total microbial load and thereby increase the shelf life of the product. Recent disease outbreaks attributed to milk and other dairy products have implicated *Listeria monocytogenes* as the causative agent (see Chapter 24). There was some question as to whether minimum times and temperature of HTST pasteurization were adequate to eliminate *L. monocytogenes* from milk and other dairy products.

Heat-treatment processes in excess of pasteurization for milk and milk products have been designated as very high temperature (VHT) systems and ultrahigh-temperature (UHT) systems. There does not appear to be a precise definition for a VHT system. According to the International Dairy Federation, UHT processes usually refer to pasteurization techniques with temperatures of at least 130 C in a continuous flow, with holding times of approximately 1 sec or more. UHT systems have been more extensively used in Europe than in the United States for fluid milk. Current federal standards of identity stipulate that a product must have been heated to 137.8 C or above and held there for at least 2 sec to be labeled "ultrapasteurized." Products such as cream for whipping, coffee cream, and half and half are processed by UHT systems. The current drawback to UHT systems is that the severe heating needed could affect or alter the nutritive and organoleptic properties of the product. The most popular of the UHT systems are the direct-heating methods, including a steam-injection-into-milk process and a milk-injected-into-steam process, referred to as a **steam-injection technique** and a **steam-infusion technique,** respectively. In both these systems the added steam or excess water is removed following the heat treatment in a sterile vacuum chamber. The combination of this type of heat treatment with aseptic packaging results in a category of products usually referred to as "sterilized milk" or "sterilized cream." This designation does not imply absolute sterility but a sterile product in the commercial sense. These products have an extremely long shelf life. The sterilized fluid milk or milk product would have to be packaged in containers that would maintain the "sterility" of the product and its shelf life. Some processors in the United States guarantee that their sterilized milk products have a shelf life in excess of 6 weeks. With a proper combination of efficient sterilization, aseptic packaging, and adequate refrigeration, it would not be unusual for these types of products to last longer than 90 days.

The efficiency of milk pasteurization or the percentage of reduction of numbers of microorganisms in milk during pasteurization depends on (1) the temperature of pasteurization, (2) the holding time, (3) the total numbers of bacteria, and (4) the proportion of the total microbial load that are sporeformers or thermoduric organisms. In general, the conventional HTST system may reduce the number of microorganisms in milk by at least 90 to 99 percent. Following pasteurization, milk is cooled rapidly to at least 7.2 C or less. As will be discussed later, the shelf life of pasteurized milk depends on the temperature of storage and the numbers and types of microorganisms surviving the pasteurization process.

Cream for butter making is given a greater heat treatment during pasteurization than is market cream. Heating is at 71.1 C or above for 30 min by the holding method or 87.7 to 93.3 C for a few seconds by the HTST method. Cream is more protective to organisms than is milk, and cream for butter making is likely to contain a higher population of microorganisms than most lots of milk. Rapid heating of cream is accomplished by injecting steam or by a combination of steam injection and evaluation in a process known as **vacreation.**

The forewarming at 71 to 100 C for 10 to 30 min and evaporation processes at 48.9 to 57.2 C in the manufacture of sweetened condensed milk are in effect pasteurization processes that kill all pathogens and should destroy all organisms that could spoil the final canned product.

What amounts to a high-temperature pasteurization is applied to bulk condensed milk. Forewarming the milk at 65.6 to 76.7 C before evaporation kills many of the organisms present, and superheating of the condensed product, which is concentrated more than evaporated milk, at higher temperatures (82.2 to 93.3 C) destroys still more. Such a product must be cooled rapidly, stored at a chilling temperature, and used fairly soon. Preheating of milk before drying, as mentioned subsequently, is in effect pasteurization.

The cooking at 65.6 C or higher in the melting and blending of cheese during the manufacture of processed cheese is in effect a pasteurization process that kills most of the microorganisms present in the original cheeses. Phosphates, citrates, and tartrates are added as emulsifiers.

Conventional pasteurization should kill all yeasts and molds and most vegetative cells of bacteria in the milk. The surviving bacteria, termed thermodurics, belong to a number of different groups of bacteria, of which only a few of the more important ones will be mentioned. Most important of the non-spore-forming bacteria are (1) the high-temperature lactics, e.g., the enterococci; *Streptococcus thermophilus,* high-temperature lactobacilli, such as *Lactobacillus bulgaricus**, and *L. lactis*;* and species of *Microbacterium,* and (2) certain species of *Micrococcus**. Some species of *Streptococcus* and *Lactobacillus* are thermophilic as well as thermoduric. The spore-forming thermodurics fall into two main groups: (1) species of *Bacillus,* i.e., aerobic to facultative spore-forming bacilli, of which *B. cereus* (proteolytic) usually is the most numerous but *B. licheniformis, B. subtilis* (proteolytic),

B. coagulans (thermophilic), *B. polymyxa* (gas-forming), and other species some-times are of importance, and (2) species of *Clostridium,* anaerobic, spore-forming rods, some of which are saccharolytic, e.g., *C. butyricum,* and others proteolytic and saccharolytic, e.g., *C. sporogenes.* Most of those growing in milk also form gas. Other miscellaneous bacteria may survive pasteurization but do not grow well in milk.

As processors continue to raise pasteurization temperatures to increase shelf life, the presence of spore-forming bacteria becomes increasingly significant.

Steam under Pressure

Evaporated milk is canned and then heat-processed by steam under pressure, of-ten with accompanying rolling or agitation. The forewarming of the milk at about 93 to 100 C or higher before evaporation kills all but the more resistant bacterial spores. Sealed cans of evaporated milk are processed at about 115 to 118 C for 14 to 18 min, which results in a commercially sterile product. Some of the heat-cool-fill methods, e.g., the Martin process mentioned in Chapter 6, have been applied to the processing of canned whole milk, cream, and whole milk concentrate.

USE OF LOW TEMPERATURES

With the exception of canned milk and dry milk, most dairy products require the use of low temperatures as one factor in their preservation; often this is the most important factor.

Refrigerated Storage

For the production of milk of good quality it is essential that it be cooled promptly after it is withdrawn from the cow. The Grade A Pasteurized Milk Ordinance of the United States Public Health Service stipulates that Grade A raw milk for pas-teurization shall be cooled to 10 C or less within 2 hr after being drawn and kept that cold until processed. Newly pasteurized milk is to be cooled to 7.2 C or less and maintained there. It is preferable, of course, to cool it to temperatures well below 7.2 C. For example, the bulk-milk coolers on farms can rapidly cool milk to 3.0 to 4.5 C or lower and hold that temperature, except for short periods when fresh milk is entering, and then the temperature usually does not exceed 7.2 C. Also, it is not unusual to find the temperature of milk as it is being filled into milk cartons or bottles approaching 2 to 3 C.

Milk is held at refrigeration temperatures during storage on the farm, in the truck or tank during transportation to the plant or receiving station, and during storage there. Refrigeration temperatures are recommended for the milk or related prod-ucts during storage in the plant or in the retail market and during delivery and in the home or restaurant until consumption. Fermented milks and unripened cheeses are chilled after their manufacture and kept chilled until they reach the consumer.

Most kinds of ripened cheese also are stored at chilling temperatures after their ripening is complete. Table 18-2 lists some recommended storage temperatures for various dairy products.

Freezing

Ice cream and other frozen dairy desserts are frozen as part of the manufacturing process and are stored at low temperatures in the frozen state, where microbial multiplication is impossible. The microbial content of the ingredients—milk, cream, sugar, eggs, stabilizers, and flavoring and coloring materials—along with contamination picked up during processing will determine the numbers and kinds of microorganisms in the mix and the microbial content after pasteurization of the mix and freezing. Pasteurization, of course, reduces numbers and kinds of microorganisms, but freezing kills relatively few of the organisms, and storage in the frozen state permits survival of most of the microorganisms for long periods.

Butter in storage is held at -17 to -18 C or lower, where no microbial growth can take place. Frozen cream is stored in considerable amounts at a similar temperature. Milk, concentrated to one-third its volume, can be frozen at -17 to -18 C and stored at -23 to -24 C or lower and can be held for several weeks without deterioration. Frozen milk can be concentrated by freeze-drying methods. Pasteurized whole milk has been frozen at about -28 to -29 C and shipped and stored in the frozen state.

TABLE 18-2
STORAGE CONDITIONS AND SHELF LIFE OF VARIOUS
DAIRY PRODUCTS

Product	Temperature, C	RH, %	Approximate storage period
Cheese			
Blue	0–1.1	70	3–6 months
Cheddar	0–1.1	70	12 months
Cream	0–1.1	70	4 weeks
Pasteurized processed	0–4.4		6–10 months
Swiss	0–4.4	70	8–12 months
Milk			
Evaporated and condensed	0		+1 year
	4.4		6–12 months
	10		Few months
	21.1		Few weeks
HTST	1.6–4.4		2–3 weeks
	4.4–7.2		1–2 weeks
UHT	1.6–4.4		+1 month
Nonfat dry milk	4.4	60	10 months
	21.1	60	5 months
	37.7	60	2 months

Source: Adapted in part from The Refrigeration Research Foundation (1974).

DRYING

Various milk products are made by removing different percentages of water from whole or skim milk. Only in the manufacture of dry products is enough moisture removed to prevent the growth of microorganisms. The reduction in moisture and consequent increase in the concentration of dissolved substances in liquid condensed-milk products inhibits the growth of some kinds of bacteria.

Condensed Products

Evaporated milk is made by removing about 60 percent of the water from whole milk, so that about 11.5 percent lactose would be in solution, plus twice the amount of soluble inorganic salts in whole milk. This high concentration of sugar is inhibitory to the growth of some bacteria and might retard or prevent the growth of some survivors of the heat treatments described previously. Bulk condensed milk is more condensed than evaporated milk and is a still poorer culture medium for organisms not tolerant of high sugar concentrations. Condensed whey, called **whey semisolids,** is another concentrated dairy product, as is condensed buttermilk, called **semisolid buttermilk,** which has its concentration of acid and other solutes increased by the condensation process.

In the preparation of the product from whole milk, enough sugar (mostly sucrose but occasionally glucose) is added to milk before evaporation to form sweetened condensed milk with a total average sugar content (lactose plus added sugar) of about 54 percent, and in the liquid part of over 64 percent. The product from skim milk contains about 58 percent total sugar and about 66 percent in the liquid part of the condensed product. These very high concentrations of sugar plus the increased percentage of soluble inorganic salts tie up the moisture, making it unavailable to any but osmophilic microorganisms. Therefore, drying, both by removal of water and by tying it up, is a main preservative factor. With the evacuation of the can and the aseptic effect of the sealed can, a product of good keeping quality results.

Dry Products

Among the dairy products prepared in the dry form are milk, skim milk, cream, whey, buttermilk, ice cream mix, and malted milk. Since for the most part similar principles apply to all these products, dry skim milk or nonfat dry milk solids will be discussed as a typical example. Most dry milk is prepared either by the roller process, with or without vacuum, or by the spray process mentioned in Chapter 8. Preliminary to the final drying process, the milk is concentrated three to five times for the roller process, and two to three times for the spray process. Usually the milk is preheated before drying (to 65 to 85 C for the roller process and to 68.8 to 93.3 C for the spray process). This preheating process pasteurizes the milk and kills the less heat-resistant microorganisms. Modern processing methods for the manufacturing of nonfat dry milk optimize conditions to result in a product that is most acceptable on the basis of solubility and flavor. Some of the drying processes involve an instantization step, in which the dry powder is wetted and then redried. In this process the product is actually exposed to contact with the air at nine different stages. A large salmonellosis outbreak involving powdered milk was shown to have resulted from air contamination during this instantizing process.

The microbial content of the heat-dried dairy product depends on the content of the liquid product to be dried, the temperature and time of preheating, the evaporation process (if used), contamination and growth in storage tanks and pipes, the method of drying, and contamination from air sources. Preheating kills organisms as pasteurization would and hence destroys all but the thermodurics. Evaporation, especially a continuous process, may result in increases in thermodurics and bacteria that are thermophilic. If the evaporated or concentrated product is stored, an increase in numbers of microorganisms may take place since the temperature of evaporation is not high and the milk soon cools. The high temperature of the roller process without vacuum destroys almost all organisms except bacterial spores. The acutal spray-drying process, not considering the lethal effect of preheating or evaporation and concentration, cannot be depended on to eliminate microorganisms from the finished product. In general, thermoduric bacteria are most numerous in the dry product, i.e., heat-resistant streptococci, micrococci, aerobic and anaerobic sporeformers, and microbacteria. Numerous outbreaks of food poisoning attributed to salmonellae or staphylococci from milk powder provide evidence that these pathogens do on occasion survive in the final product.

USE OF PRESERVATIVES

Added Preservatives

The addition of preservatives to dairy products is permitted only to a limited extent. The use of sorbic or propionic acid or one of their salts is permitted in cottage cheese, yogurt, and some of the hard cheeses and processed cheeses. The primary objective in adding a preservative to hard cheeses or preserved cheeses is to prevent the surface growth of molds. Likewise, the addition of preservatives to cottage cheese and yogurt is done to prevent the growth of molds on the surface of the product and to extend its shelf life.

Added sugar acts as a preservative of sweetened condensed milk; it reduces the a_w, thereby making moisture unavailable to microorganisms. Sodium chloride or common salt is added in the manufacture of various kinds of cheese, but usually it is more for flavor or for controlling the growth of microorganisms during manufacturing and curing than for preservation of the finished product.

The sodium chloride in salted butter is in a concentration in a liquid phase sufficient to prevent the growth of many bacteria and to cause a decrease in the number of those which are not salt-tolerant. In butter with 16.34 percent moisture and 2.35 percent salt, the water phase would be about 12.6 percent salt brine.

Cheese is smoked primarily for the addition of flavor, although the drying, especially of the rind, and the chemical preservatives from the smoke may improve the keeping quality. Mold spoilage of cheese is usually delayed or prevented when sorbic acid, sorbates, propionic acid, or propionates are added or incorporated in the wrapper.

The addition of hydrogen peroxide combined with a mild heat treatment has been used for pasteurization of milk for certain kinds of cheese (e.g., Swiss and Cheddar). The excess peroxide is usually destroyed by added catalase.

Developed Preservatives

Most fermented products are microbiologically more stable or have a longer shelf life than the initial substrate. Fermented milks and cheese are preserved partly by the developed acidity produced by the bacterial culture and therefore have a longer shelf life than fluid milk. Fermented dairy products are discussed further in Chapter 22.

Other Methods

Although an effect equivalent to pasteurization can be obtained by the treatment of milk with ultraviolet rays, this method is not used in the preservation of milk because only a thin layer of milk can be successfully irradiated and, unless great care is taken, a "burnt" flavor will result. Other uses of ultraviolet light in the dairy industry include irradiation of rooms to reduce the numbers of microorganisms in the air in processing rooms where sweetened condensed milk is being prepared or cut cheese is being packaged and in cheese-curing rooms. The rays inhibit mold growth on the sides of the curing cheese exposed to them directly but are not effective on the shaded side. Ultraviolet light is also used in storage tanks containing liquid sugar or corn-sirup solids (ingredients in ice cream) to prevent mold growth on the surface.

Several preservative factors are involved in the preservation of milk and its products. Milk for market sale or for the manufacture of dairy products is produced as aseptically as practicable, is cooled promptly, and is kept chilled. It is pasteurized, and then packaged to keep out microorganisms. Cream is treated similarly. Fermented milks owe most of their keeping qualities to the acid formed during the fermentation but require chilling and packaging for their preservation. Butter is preserved primarily by low temperatures, chilling for short-time storage or freezing temperatures for long-time storage. The low moisture and the salt content also aid in the preservation, as does packaging or sealing to prevent contamination. Cheese is preserved by the acidity produced during its making, by chilling, and by impervious rinds or by packaging. Dry milk, if properly prepared, has too little moisture for microbial growth but requires packaging to prevent contamination. Evaporated milk is processed by steam under pressure to kill all or most microorganisms and is sealed in cans to keep out contaminants. Sweetened condensed milk undergoes a pasteurization during its preparation, contains a high concentration of sugars, and is protected by the sealed can.

SPOILAGE

As has been indicated, milk and products made from it are preserved in a number of different ways, some of which involve killing only part of the microorganisms present and inhibiting the growth of the remainder. Some products therefore have a limited keeping time, and many spoil readily if the methods of preservation are inadequate.

MILK AND CREAM

Milk is an excellent culture medium for many kinds of microorganisms, being high in moisture, nearly neutral in pH, and rich in microbial foods. A plentiful supply of food for energy is present in the form of milk sugar (lactose), butterfat, citrate, and nitrogenous compounds in many forms (proteins, amino acids, ammonia, urea, and other compounds), and the accessory foods and minerals required by microorganisms are available. Some inhibitory substances (lactoperoxidase and agglutinins) are present in freshly drawn milk but soon become comparatively ineffective. Because of the fermentable sugar, an acid fermentation by bacteria is most likely under ordinary conditions in raw milk, but other changes may take place if conditions are unfavorable to the acid formers or if they are absent. With a trend toward higher pasteurization temperatures, the spoilage flora of pasteurized milk is more frequently becoming heat-resistant, spore-forming bacilli which can be psychrotrophic.

When milk sours, it usually is considered spoiled, especially if it curdles. The evidences of acid formation are first a sour flavor and then coagulation of the milk to give a solid jellylike curd or a weaker curd that releases clear whey. The lactic acid fermentation is most likely to take place in raw milk held at room temperatures.

In raw milk at temperatures from 10 to 37 C, *Streptococcus lactis* is most likely to cause the souring, with possibly some growth of coliform bacteria, enterococci, lactobacilli, and micrococci*. At higher temperatures, e.g., from 37 to 50 C, *S. thermophilus* and *S. faecalis* may produce about 1 percent acid and be followed by lactobacilli, such as *Lactobacillus bulgaricus*, which will produce more acid. Some of the lactobacilli can grow at temperatures above 50 C but produce less acid there. Thermophilic bacteria can grow at still higher temperatures, e.g., *L. thermophilus*. Little formation of acid takes place in milk held at temperatures near freezing, but proteolysis may take place.

The pasteurization of milk kills the more active acid-forming bacteria but may permit the survival of heat-resistant lactics (e.g., enterococci, *Streptococcus therm-*

ophilus, and lactobaciɯɯ), which will cause a lactic acid fermentation if the subsequent storage temperature is high enough.

Many bacteria other than those termed lactics can cause an acid fermentation in milk, especially if conditions are unfavorable for the lactic acid bacteria. The coliform bacteria produce some lactic acid and considerable amounts of volatile products, such as hydrogen, carbon dioxide, acetic acid, formic acid, alcohol, etc. Species of *Micrococcus*, Microbacterium,* and *Bacillus* can produce acid in milk, mostly lactic, but ordinarily cannot compete with the lactics.

Butyric acid may be produced in milk by action of *Clostridium* spp. under conditions that prevent or inhibit the normal lactic acid formation. Thus after a heat treatment which destroys all vegetative cells of bacteria but allows the survival of spores of *Clostridium,* milk may undergo butyric acid fermentation with the production of hydrogen and carbon dioxide gas.

Gas Production

Gas production by bacteria usually is accompanied by acid formation and with few exceptions is undesirable in milk and milk products. The chief gas formers are the coliform bacteria, *Clostridium* spp., gas-forming *Bacillus* species that yield both hydrogen and carbon dioxide, and the yeasts, propionics, and heterofermentative lactics that produce only carbon dioxide. The production of gas in milk is evidenced by foam at the top if the milk is liquid and is supersaturated with the gas, by gas bubbles caught in the curd or furrowing it, by floating curd containing gas bubbles, or by a ripping apart of the curd by rapid gas production, causing the so-called stormy fermentation of milk.

The likelihood of gas formation and the type of microorganisms causing it depend on the pretreatment of the milk and the temperature of holding. In raw milk the coliform bacteria are most apt to be the main gas formers. Heterofermentative lactics also may produce gas, but usually not enough to be evident in the milk. Yeasts (lactose-fermenting) usually are absent or in low numbers in milk and do not compete well with the bacteria.

Gas-forming *Clostridium* and *Bacillus* do not compete well with acid formers at higher temperatures but may function if the acid formers are absent or comparatively inactive. Thus in milk heated at pasteurizing temperatures or above, the chief acid formers will be killed, the spores of *Clostridium* and *Bacillus* species will survive, and gas formation by the sporeformers may take place.

Propionic acid–forming bacteria are not active in milk but form gas (carbon dioxide) in cheese, as discussed subsequently.

Proteolysis

The hydrolysis of milk proteins by microorganisms usually is accompanied by the production of a bitter flavor caused by some of the peptides released. Proteolysis is favored by storage at a low temperature, by the destruction of lactics and other acid formers by heat, and by the destruction of formed acid in the milk by molds and film yeasts or the neutralization of acids by products of other organisms.

The types of change produced by proteolytic microorganisms include (1) acid proteolysis, in which acid production and proteolysis occur together, (2) proteolysis with little acidity or even with alkalinity, (3) sweet curdling, which is caused by renninlike enzymes of the bacteria at an early stage of proteolysis, (4) slow proteolysis by intracellular enzymes of bacteria after their autolysis, and (5) residual proteolytic activity of heat-stable proteinase. For example, *Pseudomonas fluorescens* produces a proteinase that will survive pasteurization even though the bacterium does not.

Acid proteolysis causes the production of a shrunken curd and the expression of much whey. This is followed by a slow digestion of the curd, which changes in appearance from opaqueness to translucency and may be completely dissolved by some kinds of bacteria. Sometimes separate curd particles are formed that shrink so small that they are barely visible in the large amount of whey. Acid proteolysis may be caused by several species of *Micrococcus**, some of which grow in the udder of the cow and cause acid proteolysis of aseptically drawn milk. One of the intestinal streptococci or enterococci, *Streptococcus faecalis* var. *liquefaciens**, is a lactic acid organism that also is actively proteolytic. It is thermoduric, like the other enterococci, and may cause acid proteolysis in pasteurized milk. Spores of lactose-fermenting, proteolytic strains of some species of *Bacillus* can survive pasteurization or a more rigorous heat treatment of milk and cause acid proteolysis.

Proteolysis by bacteria unable to ferment lactose varies with the bacterium involved, from obvious digestion of the casein to slight proteolysis that is detectable only by chemical tests. Little if any acidity is produced by most of these bacteria; in fact, the milk usually becomes alkaline in time from products of protein decomposition. Many of these bacteria "sweet-curdle" the milk (coagulation but little acid) before digesting the casein, but others hydrolyze the protein so rapidly that no curdling is evident and finally a fairly clear liquid remains with no sign of casein or curd. Actively proteolytic bacteria are found among the species of *Micrococcus**, *Alcaligenes, Pseudomonas, Proteus, Flavobacterium*, and *Serratia*, all of which are genera of non-spore-forming bacteria, and of the genera *Bacillus* and *Clostridium* of the sporeformers. Some species of the genera *Micrococcus**, *Pseudomonas, Alcaligenes*, Flavobacterium*, and *Bacillus* can grow at low temperatures and hence are likely to cause some proteolysis and/or bitterness of milk held at chilling temperatures. *Bacillus cereus* has been implicated in sweet curdling of pasteurized milk. This spoilage condition is becoming more common in milk because of (1) higher pasteurization temperatures, (2) psychrotrophic capacity of some bacilli, and (3) longer holding or shelf-life times. Coagulation or curd formation usually begins at the bottom of the carton and may not even be evident to the consumer in its early stages.

Slow proteolysis by intracellular enzymes of bacteria after their autolysis is of no significance in milk under ordinary circumstances but is significant when a long time is allowed for their action, as in curing cheese or in products with a long shelf life.

Ropiness

Ropiness and sliminess can occur in milk, cream, or whey but are important mostly in market milk and cream. Nonbacterial ropiness or sliminess may be due to (1) stringiness caused by mastitis and in particular by fibrin and leukocytes from the cow's blood (in contrast to ropiness produced by bacteria, it is present when the milk is drawn, not developed during holding of the milk), (2) sliminess resulting from the thickness of cream, e.g., at the top of a bottle, (3) stringiness due to thin films of casein or lactalbumin during cooling, as sometimes is observed on surface coolers. This effect is only temporary.

Bacterial ropiness is caused by slimy capsular material from the cells, usually gums or mucins, and ordinarily develops best at low storage temperatures. The ropiness usually decreases as the acidity of the milk or cream increases. There are two main types of bacterial ropiness, one in which the milk is most ropy at the top and the other in which the milk becomes ropy throughout. Surface ropiness is caused most often by *Alcaligenes viscolactis**, an organism chiefly from water or soil that can grow fairly well in the vicinity of 10 C. Some of the thermoduric micrococci, e.g., *Micrococcus freudenreichii**, can cause surface ropiness. Ropiness throughout the milk may be caused by any of a number of kinds of bacteria:

1 *Enterobacter aerogenes, E. cloacae, Klebsiella oxytoca,* and rarely *Escherichia coli.* Ropiness caused by *Enterobacter* usually is worse near the top of the milk.

2 *Certain strains of some of the common species of lactic acid bacteria. Streptococcus lactis* var. *hollandicus* causes ropiness in milk, and is used in making a Scandinavian fermented milk. *Lactobacillus casei, L. bulgaricus**, and *L. plantarum* occasionally produce ropiness, as do strains of *Streptococcus cremoris*. Most of these lactic bacteria can grow in long chains, a characteristic that supposedly contributes to the stringy condition of the milk.

3 *Miscellaneous other bacteria* among the alkali formers, micrococci*, streptococci, and bacilli. Ordinarily these bacteria would be suppressed by the acid formers.

Since the sources of the bacteria causing ropiness are water, manure, utensils, and feed, the reduction or elimination of contamination from these sources helps prevent ropiness. Adequate pasteurization of milk readily destroys most of these kinds of bacteria.

Changes in Milkfat

Milkfat may be decomposed by various bacteria, yeasts, and molds that do not constitute distinct groups on the basis of other characteristics. The bacteria are for the most part aerobic or facultative, proteolytic, and non-acid-forming. The following changes in the milkfat take place:

1 *Oxidation of the unsaturated fatty acids,* which, coupled with other decomposition, yields aldehydes, acids, and ketones and results in tallowy odors and tastes. The reaction is favored by metals, sunlight, and oxidizing microorganisms.

2 *Hydrolysis of the butterfat* to fatty acids and glycerol by the enzyme lipase. The lipase may have been in the original milk or may be microbial.

3 *Combined oxidation and hydrolysis* to produce rancidity.

Species of lipase-forming bacteria are found in many of the bacterial genera, e.g., *Pseudomonas, Proteus, Alcaligenes, Bacillus, Micrococcus*, Clostridium,* and others. Many of the molds and some species of yeasts are lipolytic.

Pseudomonas fragi and *Staphylococcus aureus* produce fairly heat-resistant lipases which may survive pasteurization if present in the raw milk.

Alkali Production

The group of alkali formers includes bacteria which cause an alkaline reaction in milk without any evidence of proteolysis. The alkaline reaction may result from the formation of ammonia, as from urea, or of carbonates, as from organic acids such as citric acid. Most of these bacteria grow from moderate to low temperatures, and many can survive pasteurization. Examples of alkali formers are *Pseudomonas fluorescens* and *A. viscolactis**.

Flavor Changes

The flavor of milk as drawn is low, delicate, and easily altered. Since individuals differ in their ability to detect flavors and disagree in their description of them, a number of more or less descriptive terms have been suggested to name the off-flavors.

As drawn from the cow, milk may be abnormal in flavor because of the individual cow, mastitis, the stage of lactation of the cow, or feed.

Some of the off-flavors caused by microorganisms are described as follows.

Sour or Acid Flavor   The acidity may be described as "clean," as produced by *Streptococcus lactis* and other lactics; as "aromatic," when lactic streptococci and aroma-forming *Leuconostoc* species are growing together; and as "sharp," when appreciable amounts of volatile fatty acids (formic, acetic, or butyric) are produced by coliform bacteria, *Clostridium* spp., and other organisms. Clean and aromatic flavors are desired in fermented milk products, but sharp flavors are undesirable.

Bitter Flavors   Bitterness usually results from proteolysis but may follow lipolysis or even fermentation of lactose. Milk from cows late in their lactation period sometimes is slightly bitter. Microorganisms causing proteolysis and hence bitterness have been mentioned in a previous paragraph. Other organisms causing bitterness are certain strains of coliform bacteria and of asporogenous yeasts.

Some cocci cause very bitter milk, and actinomycetes sometimes give bitter-musty flavors.

Burnt or Caramel Flavor   Certain strains of *Streptococcus lactis* var. *maltigenes* produce this flavor, which resembles the cooked flavor of overheated milk.

Miscellaneous Other Flavors   Other flavors that are found less commonly make up a long list, only part of which will be mentioned: a barny flavor by *Enterobacter oxytocum**; soapiness by ammonia formers like *Pseudomonas sapolactica**; a turniplike flavor by *Escherichia coli* and *P. fluorescens;* a malty flavor by yellow micrococci from the udder; fruity flavor by *P. fragi;* a potatolike flavor by *P. mucidolens,* fishiness by *Aeromonas hydrophila* or various cocci that produce trimethylamine from lecithin; earthy or musty flavors by actinomycetes; fruity, esterlike, and alcoholic flavors by yeasts; an amyl alcohol flavor by white and orange micrococci; and putrefaction by species of *Clostridium, P. putrefaciens**, and other putrefactive bacteria. Other flavors have been termed unclean, stale, astringent, oily, weedy, carroty, etc.

Inadequately cooled raw milk that has been held in a tightly covered can so that volatile products of bacterial metabolism have collected above the milk has an undesirable odor that varies in nature. Milk in this condition is termed **smothered.**

Color Changes

The color of milk or cream is affected by its physical and chemical composition, e.g., by the amount and yellowness of the butterfat, the thinness of the milk, the content of blood and pus, and the feed of the animal. Color changes caused by microorganisms may occur along with other changes previously discussed, but some special changes in color should be mentioned. The color may be due to the surface growth of pigmented bacteria or molds in the form of a scum or ring or may be present throughout the milk.

Blue Milk   *Pseudomonas syncyanea** produces a bluish-gray to brownish color in milk in pure culture but when growing with an acid former like *Streptococcus lactis* causes a deep-blue color. This defect and the blue color produced by actinomycetes or species of the mold *Geotrichum* are rare.

Yellow Milk   *Pseudomonas synxantha** may cause a yellow color in the cream layer of milk, coincident to lipolysis and proteolysis. Species of *Flavobacterium* can also give yellowness.

Red Milk   Red milk usually is caused by species of *Serratia,* e.g., *S. marcescens,* but is rare because other bacteria ordinarily outgrow the red-pigmented species. *Brevibacterium erythrogenes** produces a red layer at the top of the milk, followed by proteolysis. *Micrococcus roseus* may grow and produce a red sediment, and yeast may produce pink or red colonies on the surface of sour milk or cream. Blood in milk will give it a red color. The red blood cells settle out or can be centrifuged out.

Brown Milk A brown color may result from *Pseudomonas putrefaciens**
or by the enzymic oxidation of tyrosine by *P. fluorescens.*

Spoilage of Milk at Different Temperatures

At any given storage temperature most samples of raw milk undergo a typical series of changes caused by a succession of microorganisms. At refrigeration temperatures, proteolysis may be initiated by psychrotrophic bacteria such as *Pseudomonas,* and molds may then appear. At room temperatures, an acid fermentation is most probable, first by lactic streptococci and coliform bacteria and then by the acid-tolerant lactobacilli. Then molds or film yeasts on the surface lower the acidity, permitting the formation of more acid. Eventually, when most of the acid has been destroyed, proteolytic or putrefactive bacteria complete the decomposition.

Pasteurization as applied commercially in HTST systems kills yeasts, molds, most psychrotrophic bacteria, the coliforms, and rapid acid producers such as *Streptococcus lactis.* The spoilage of pasteurized milk then depends on:

1 The bacteria that survive pasteurization, the "thermodurics" and spore-formers
2 The bacteria that enter the milk following pasteurization, postpasteurization contamination from equipment, filling operation, and the package itself
3 The possible presence of heat-resistant residual microbial enzymes
4 The temperature of storage

Of course, once the milk is pasteurized and sealed in the carton, the microbial flora present is established unless the carton loses its integrity. Therefore, the storage temperature dictates which organism will predominate and the rate of spoilage for that particular carton. Likewise, the initial number and types present following pasteurization affect the spoilage rate if the temperature of storage is fixed. Since milk is refrigerated, spoilage usually results from psychrotrophic organisms. Growth at low temperatures is slow but significant. Assuming a generation time of 8 hr at 7 C, 1 cell could become 1 million in 20 generations, or about 6 to 7 days, or 2 million in 7 to 8 days, or 1 billion in 10 days.

Considering the excellent refrigeration to which milk (raw and pasteurized) is currently exposed and the continuing trend toward higher pasteurization temperatures, it is reasonable to expect very heat resistant psychrotrophic organisms to be a problem in pasteurized milk. Current spoilage problems of pasteurized milk are related to spore-forming psychrotrophic bacilli.

CONDENSED AND DRY MILK PRODUCTS

Under this heading are included evaporated milk (unsweetened), bulk condensed milk, frozen milk, sweetened condensed milk, condensed whey or buttermilk, and condensed sour skim milk and dry milk. The quality of all of these products depends on the quality of the starting material dried or condensed, since defects in the raw material carry over to the condensed or dried product. All the condensed products have a fairly high concentration of solutes that inhibits the growth of some bacteria. Dry milk is so low in moisture that it offers no microbial spoilage problems when properly handled. Moisture contents over 8 percent might permit some mold growth. The only spoilage of condensed buttermilk and sour skim milk is by molds when the surface is exposed to air. The high concentration of acid and solutes prevents the growth of bacteria or yeasts.

Bulk Condensed Milk

The forewarming temperatures employed in the making of plain condensed milk are equivalent to no more than pasteurization, and the evaporating process is at a temperature low enough to permit the growth of thermophiles. Therefore, although refrigerated, this product has only a short storage life and is subject to spoilage by thermoduric bacteria that tolerate the increased concentration of solutes in the condensed product. In superheated condensed milk the temperature of the milk is raised to 65.6 to 76.7 C during the introduction of steam, a process that probably destroys most of the vegetative cells of bacteria but not the spores. This product, too, has a short storage life.

Evaporated Milk

Unsweetened evaporated milk is canned and heat-processed under steam pressure in an attempt to destroy all the microorganisms present. Spoilage can take place only when the heat process is inadequate or defects in the can permit the entrance of organisms. Bacterial spores that survive the heat process may be the cause of can swelling, milk coagulation, or development of a bitter flavor.

Swelling of the can is caused primarily by gas-forming anaerobic sporeformers (*Clostridium*), although overfilling of the can with cold milk may cause swelling. Acid constituents of milk acting on the iron of the can may produce hydrogen gas and cause bulging on long storage.

Coagulation of the milk in the can may vary from a few flakes to a solid curd. Species of *Bacillus* usually are to blame, either mesophiles, such as *B. cereus, B. subtilis,* and *B. megaterium;* a facultative thermophile, *B. coagulans;* or an obligate thermophile, *B. calidolactis**. The extent of the curd in the milk depends to some extent on the amount of air in the can. Spoilage by the thermophiles should cause no trouble if the milk is cooled promptly and kept cool, but it can cause trouble in the tropics.

Bitterness usually results from proteolysis by species of *Bacillus* and less commonly by species of *Clostridium*. Some of the latter may cause putrefaction in rare instances.

Spoilage resulting from leakage, as indicated by the presence of nonspore-formers, may result in gas and swelling caused by coliform bacteria or yeasts, coagulation by streptococci, or bitterness caused by cocci.

Sweetened Condensed Milk

Sweetened condensed milk has been subjected to a fairly high temperature (71.1 to 100 C) during forewarming and to a milder heat treatment (48.9 to 54.4 C) during condensing, so that the yeasts, molds, and most of the vegetative cells of bacteria are destroyed. In addition, there is a high concentration of sugar, about 55 to 60 percent of total sugar (lactose plus added sugar). Also, the can is evacuated and sealed. Spoilage, then, is due primarily to organisms that have entered after the heat treatments, especially if air is present. The chief types of spoilage are (1) gas formation by sucrose-fermenting yeasts or, more rarely, by coliform bacteria, (2) thickening caused by micrococci, which probably produce renninlike enzymes, and (3) "buttons," which are mold colonies growing on the milk surface. The size of these buttons is determined by the amount of air in the can. Species of *Aspergillus,* e.g., *A. repens,* and of *Penicillium* have been incriminated.

FROZEN DESSERTS

Frozen desserts include ice cream, ice milk, frozen custards, sherbets, and ices. The ingredients may be various combinations of milk, cream, evaporated milk, condensed milk, dried milk, coloring materials, flavors, fruits, nuts, sweetening agents, eggs and egg products, and stabilizers. Any of these may contribute microorganisms to the product and affect the quality of the dessert as judged by its bacterial content or its content of specific kinds of bacteria such as the coliforms. The desserts are not ordinarily subject to spoilage, however, as long as they are kept frozen. The only important types of spoilage take place in the ingredients before they are mixed or in the mix before it is frozen. Since the mix is pasteurized before it is frozen, no spoilage problems should result unless it is held at temperatures above freezing for a considerable time, when souring by acid-forming bacteria can take place.

BUTTER

Many of the defects of butter originate in the cream from which it is made, especially when the cream has been held for several days on the farm before collection by the creamery. During this time lactic acid bacteria, gas formers, and other spoilage organisms may grow and be followed by molds, e.g., *Geotrichum candidum*. Lactose-fermenting yeasts, which are present only occasionally, may develop high gas pressures in the can of cream. In fact, most of the types of spoilage described for milk in the early part of this chapter could occur in the cream and affect the butter made from it.

The probability and type of spoilage will depend on the kind of butter and the environment in which it is kept. Because of the high salt concentration in the small amount of moisture present, salted butter is less likely to support microbial growth than is unsalted butter. In general, sweet-cream butter keeps better than sour-cream butter. Today most butter in this country is made from pasteurized cream, in which most of the spoilage organisms have been destroyed. Also, butter commonly is kept refrigerated, and during commercial storage is kept at about −17.8 C, where no microbial growth can take place. For these reasons bacteria usually do not grow in butter, and when they do, their growth is not extensive. The flavor of good butter is so delicate, however, that relatively small amounts of growth may cause appreciable damage to the flavor.

Flavor Defects

As has been indicated, undesirable flavors may come from the cream, which may receive such flavors from the feed of the cow, absorb them from the atmosphere, or develop them during microbial growth. Feeds such as onions, garlic, French weed, peppergrass, and poor silage contribute off-flavors to the cream. Volatile products that may be absorbed from the air are odors from the barn and from the chemicals used there, e.g., kerosene, gasoline, fly sprays, disinfectants, etc. Growth of microorganisms in the cream and in the milk from which it is separated may result in any of the following bad flavors:

1 Cheesiness, caused by lactobacilli
2 Rancidity, resulting from lipolytic bacteria and molds and perhaps by lipase in the cream
3 Barny flavor, produced by species of *Enterobacter*
4 Malty flavor, produced by *Streptococcus lactis* var. *maltigenes**
5 Yeasty flavor, produced by yeasts
6 Musty flavors, caused by molds and actinomycetes
7 Metallic flavors, caused by dissolved metals in highly acid cream
8 Flat flavor, resulting from the destruction of diacetyl by bacteria like some of the *Pseudomonas* species
9 Highly acid flavor, when the cream has excessive acidity
10 "Unclean" flavor, caused by coliform bacteria

Unsatisfactory processing methods may cause a cooked flavor from over-pasteurization of the cream or a "neutralizer" flavor if too much of the neutralizing compound is used, if it is unevenly distributed in the cream, or if pasteurization takes place before a balance is reached.

Like cream, butter readily absorbs volatile materials from the air. Microorganisms in the butter can cause the following defects:

1 *Surface taint,* also called "rabbito" and "putridity," which is blamed on *Pseudomonas putrefaciens*,* introduced usually by the wash water, churns, or equipment. It is worse in unsalted or low-salt butter. The "sweaty-feet" odor is due chiefly to isovaleric acid.

2 *Fishiness,* caused by *Aeromonas hydrophila.*

3 Esterlike flavors, resulting from the action of *P. fragi.*

4 *Skunklike flavors,* caused by *P. mephitica.*

5 *Roquefortlike flavors,* produced by molds.

Chemically produced flavors include (1) rancidity produced by lipase in the cream, (2) tallowiness from oxidations of unsaturated fats catalyzed by copper and bacterial enzymes and favored by a low pH, low-temperature pasteurization, salt, air, and ozone, and (3) fishiness, where trimethylamine is produced from lecithin. This defect is favored by high acidity, salt, overworking of the butter, and the presence of copper.

Color Defects

Some color defects not caused by microorganisms are mottling because of improper working, a pink color caused by the sulfur dioxide refrigerant on the butter color, surface darkening resulting from the loss of water from surface layers, and bleaching that accompanies tallowiness.

Discolorations, chiefly at the surface, may be caused by molds, yeasts, or bacteria that come from churns, wrappers, liners, circles, tubs, the air, or the cream if it is unpasteurized. Colored growths of molds result in the smudged or *Alternaria* type of discoloration, with dark, smoky, or (rarely) greenish areas where *Alternaria* or *Cladosporium* species have grown, or small black spots of *Stemphylium. Penicillium* produces green coloration, *Phoma* or *Alternaria* molds brown areas, and *Geotrichum* (syn. *Oospora*) species produce orange or yellow spots. *Fusarium culmorum* can cause bright reddish-pink areas. Yeasts sometimes grow in pink colonies. *Pseudomonas nigrifaciens** causes the reddish-brown "black smudge" in mildly salted butter.

BIBLIOGRAPHY

Aggarwal, M. L. 1974. Commercial sterilization and aseptic packaging of milk products. J. Milk Food Technol. 37:250–254.

American Public Health Association. 1985. Standard methods for the examination of dairy products. 15th ed. New York.

Cook, D. J. 1963. Radiations for the dairy industry. II. Effects of radiation in milk and milk products. Dairy Ind. 28:465–470, 536–540.

Cuthbert, W. A. 1964. The significance of thermoduric organisms in milk. Int. Dairy Fed. Annu. Bull. 1964. (4):10–22.

Elliker, P. R. 1949. Practical dairy bacteriology. McGraw-Hill Book Company, New York.

Flake, J. C., A. E. Parker, J. B. Smathers, A. K. Saunders, and E. H. Marth. 1972. Methods for production of high-quality raw milk. International Association of Milk, Food, and Environmental Sanitarians, Inc., Shelbyville, Ind.

Forss, D. A. 1964. Fishy flavor in dairy products. J. Dairy Sci. 47:245–250.

Foster, E. M., F. E. Nelson, M. L. Speck, R. D. Doetsch, and J. C. Olson, Jr. 1957. Dairy microbiology. Prentice-Hall, Inc., Englewood Cliffs, N.J.

Houran, G. A. 1964. Utilization of centrifugal force for removal of microorganisms from milk. J. Dairy Sci. 47:100–101.

International Dairy Federation. 1980. Factors influencing the bacteriological quality of raw milk. Doc. No. 120, IDF, Brussels, Belgium.

International Dairy Federation. 1981. New monograph on UHT milk. Doc. No. 133, IDF, Brussels, Belgium.

Johns, C. K. 1971. Bacteriological testing of milk for regulatory purposes: usefulness of current procedures and recommendations for change. II. Bacteriological testing of raw milk for regulatory purposes. J. Milk Food Technol. 34:173–180.

Keogh, B. P. 1971. Reviews of the progress of dairy science. Bacteriology. The survival of pathogens in cheese and milk powder. J. Dairy Res. 38:91–111.

Martin, J. H. 1974. Significance of bacterial spores in milk. J. Milk Food Technol. 37:94–98.

Maxcy, R. B. 1971. Bacteriological testing of milk for regulatory purposes: usefulness of current procedures and recommendations for change. IV. Quality at the point of consumption. J. Milk Food Technol. 34:264–267.

Milk pasteurization controls and tests. 1974. U.S. Department of Health, Education and Welfare, Public Health Service, Food and Drug Administration, Cincinnati.

Morse, P. M., H. Jackson, C. H. McNaughton, A. G. Leggatt, G. B. Landerkin, and C. K. Johns. 1968a. Investigation of factors contributing to the bacterial count of bulk-tank milk. I. Influence of two-day storage on results of preliminary incubation. J. Dairy Sci. 51:1182–1187.

Morse, P. M., et al. 1968b. Investigation of factors contributing to the bacterial count of bulk-tank milk. II. Bacteria in milk from individual cows. J. Dairy Sci. 51:1188–1191.

Morse, P. M., et al. 1968c. Investigation of factors contributing to the bacterial count of bulk-tank milk. III. Increase in count, from cow to bulk tank and effects of refrigerated storage and preliminary incubation. J. Dairy Sci. 51:1192–1206.

Olson, H. C. 1971. Bacteriological testing of milk for regulatory purposes—usefulness of current procedures and recommendations for change. V. Pasteurized milk. J. Milk Food Technol. 34:279–281.

Plastridge, W. N. 1958. Bovine mastitis: a review. J. Dairy Sci. 41:1141–1181.

Read, R. B. 1971. Bacteriological testing of milk for regulatory purposes: usefulness of current procedures and recommendations for change. I. The problem. J. Milk Food Technol. 34:172–173.

Refrigeration Research Foundation. 1974. Commodity storage manual. Refrigeration Research Foundation, Washington.

Reinbold, G. W. 1971. Bacteriological testing of milk for regulatory purposes: usefulness of current procedures and recommendations for change. III. Raw milk quality: where do we go from here? J. Milk Food Technol. 34:260–263.

Robinson, R. K. (ed.). 1981. Dairy microbiology. Volume 1. The microbiology of milk. Applied Science Publishers, London.

Robinson, R. K. (ed.). 1981. Dairy microbiology. Volume 2. The microbiology of milk products. Applied Science Publishers, London.

Sunga, F. C. A., D. R. Heldman, and T.I. Hedrick. 1970. Microorganisms from arms and hands of dairy plant workers. J. Milk Food Technol. 33:178–181.

Thomas, S. B. 1964. Investigations on the bacterial content and microflora of farm dairy equipment. J. Soc. Dairy Technol. 17:210–215.

Thomas, S. B., R. G. Druce, and K. Elson. 1960. Ropy milk. Dairy Ind. 25:202–207.

Thomas, S. B., P. M. Hobson, and K. Elson. 1964. The microflora of milking equipment cleansed by chemical methods. J. Appl. Bacteriol. 27:15–26.

Thomas, S. B., M. Jones, P. M. Hobson, G. Williams, and R. G. Druce. 1963. Microflora of raw milk and farm dairy equipment. Dairy Ind. 28:212–219.

Torres-Anjel, M. J., and T. I. Hedrick. 1971. Spore removal by centrifugation and its effect on ultra-high temperature commercial sterilization of milk. J. Dairy Sci. 54:326–330.

White, C. H., and R. T. Marshall. 1973. Reduction of shelf-life of dairy products by a heat-stable protease from *Pseudomonas fluorescens* P26. J. Dairy Sci. 56:849–853.

SPOILAGE OF HEATED CANNED FOODS

It was pointed out in Chapter 6 that the heat treatments given foods for their preservation may vary from a mild pasteurization treatment, as for milk or fruit juice, to commercial sterilization by pressurized steam, as for canned vegetables or soups. Obviously, the milder the heat treatment, the less heat-resistant the microorganisms will need to be to survive and the greater the numbers and kinds of survivors. There is always the possibility that a surviving organism may grow and cause spoilage if environmental conditions permit.

CAUSES OF SPOILAGE

Spoilage of heated foods may have a chemical cause or a biological cause or both. The most important kind of chemical spoilage of canned foods is **hydrogen swell,** resulting from the pressure of hydrogen gas released by the action of the acid of a food on the iron of the can. Hydrogen swells are favored by (1) increasing acidities of foods, (2) increasing temperatures of storage, (3) imperfections in the tinning and lacquering of the interior of the can, (4) a poor exhaust, and (5) the presence of soluble sulfur and phosphorus compounds. Other defects, caused by interaction between the steel base of the can and the contained food include (1) discoloration of the inside of the can, (2) discoloration of the food, (3) production of off-flavors in the food, (4) cloudiness of liquors or sirups, (5) corrosion or perforation of the metal, and (6) loss in nutritive value.

Biological spoilage of canned foods by microorganisms may result from either or both of two causes: (1) survival of organisms after the administration of the heat treatment and (2) leakage of the container after the heat process, permitting the entrance of organisms. Mild heat treatments may be only enough to permit the successful storage of the foods for limited periods with the help of another preservative method such as refrigeration. Surviving microorganisms are likely to be of several kinds and may even include vegetative cells. Processing of meat loaves and pasteurization of milk are examples of such mild heat processes. Acid foods, such as fruits, are processed at temperatures approaching 100 C, treatments which result in killing all vegetative cells of bacteria, yeasts, and molds and their spores and some bacterial spores. The only survivors ordinarily are spores of bacteria, which cannot grow in a very acid food. Any survivors of heat treatments by steam under pressure are very heat resistant bacterial spores, usually only one or two kinds.

Microorganisms entering through leaks in containers may be of various kinds and are not necessarily heat-resistant. Leakage and subsequent spoilage of canned food may be a result of mechanical damage of the empty cans so that side and end seams are defective; rough handling of filled cans may also result in damage. Microorganisms may enter from outer surfaces of filled cans that have become contaminated from equipment, especially if the cans are wet, or they may enter from contaminated cooling water after the heat process. Leakage also may cause a loss in can vacuum, thus encouraging chemical and microbial deterioration of the food. Spoilage resulting from container leakage will be caused by the organisms that happen to enter. The presence of organisms known to be of low heat resistance, and especially many species, indicates leakage.

APPEARANCE OF THE UNOPENED CONTAINER

Normally the ends of a can of food are termed **flat,** which means that they are actually slightly concave; and a partial vacuum exists in the container. If pressure develops inside, the can goes through a series of distortions as a result of increasing pressures (Figure 19-1) and is called successively a flipper, springer, soft swell, or hard swell. A **flipper** has flat ends, one of which will become convex when the side of the can is struck sharply or the temperature of the contents is increased. A **springer** has both ends of the can bulged, but one or both ends will stay concave if pushed in; or if a swollen end is pushed in, an opposite flat end will pop out. The terms "flipper" and "springer" are used by some to designate slight pressures in the can not caused by gas production but by such things as a poor exhaust, overfilling, denting of the can, changes in temperature, etc., but the can may have the same outward characteristics at the start of gas production from either a microbial or a chemical cause or both. A **soft swell** has both ends of the can bulged, but the gas pressure is low enough to permit the ends to be dented by manual pressure. A **hard swell** has such high gas pressure from within that the ends are too hard to dent by hand. Often the high gas pressures distort or buckle the ends or side seam of the cans. The final step is the bursting of the can, usually through the side seam, but sometimes through the seals at the ends. A **breather** is a can with a minute

FIGURE 19-1
Normal can of food and swells: (A) normal can with concave ends, (B) swollen can with ends bulged out, (C) swollen can with leakage where seams are breaking, (D) a burst can. (*In Microbiology: General and Applied, 2d ed., by William Bowen Sarles, William Carroll Frazier, Joe Bransfield Wilson, and Stanley Glenn Knight. Copyright © 1951, 1956 by Harper & Row, Publishers, Inc. By permission of the publisher.*)

leak that permits air to move in or out but does not necessarily allow microorganisms to enter.

Other defects in the general appearance of the can are noted before and after it is opened: dents, which may be responsible for a flipper; rust; perforations; defective side seam or end seals; and corrosion.

The glass container of food under gas pressure may have its cover bulged or popped off or may show leakage of food through the broken seal. Of course, it is possible to see evidence of microbial growth through the glass sides, such as gas bubbles, cloudiness, and films of growth.

GROUPING OF CANNED FOODS ON THE BASIS OF ACIDITY

The acidity of canned foods is important in determining the heat process necessary for their sterilization and the type of spoilage to be expected if the process is inadequate or leakage takes place. Various groupings of canned foods have been made by the National Food Processors Association, always with a division into the low-acid foods, with the pH above 4.5, and a high-acid group, with the pH below 4.5 (see Chapter 6).

TYPES OF BIOLOGICAL SPOILAGE OF CANNED FOODS

Types of spoilage of canned foods by microorganisms usually are divided into those caused by the thermophilic bacteria and those caused by mesophilic microorganisms. Other methods of classification of kinds of spoilage are based on the kinds of changes produced in the food, e.g., putrefaction, acid production, gas formation, and blackening. Types of spoilage also may be grouped on the basis of the kinds of foods involved.

The three most important kinds of biological spoilage of commercially canned foods (described subsequently) are flat sour spoilage, TA spoilage, and putrefaction. A fourth important kind of spoilage, caused by action of food acid on the iron of the can, results in a **hydrogen swell.**

Types of Spoilage by Thermophilic Spore-forming Bacteria

Most spoilage of commercially heat processed canned foods resulting from under-processing is caused by thermophilic bacteria because their spores are more heat-resistant than those of most mesophilic bacteria. The three chief types of spoilage by thermophiles are flat sour spoilage, TA spoilage, and sulfide spoilage, or "sulfide stinker."

Flat Sour Spoilage   This kind of spoilage derives its name from the fact that the ends of the can of food remain flat during souring, or the development of lactic acid in the food by the flat sour bacteria. Because the can retains a normal outward appearance, this type of spoilage cannot be detected by examination of the unopened can but must be detected by cultural methods. The spoilage occurs chiefly in low-acid foods, such as peas and corn (group I), and is caused by species of *Bacillus*. Flat sour spoilage of acid foods, e.g., tomatoes or tomato juice, is caused by a special facultatively thermophilic species, *B. coagulans*. The various species of *Bacillus* that are able to form acid without gas in food may be mesophiles, facultative thermophiles, or obligate thermophiles. The spores of the mesophiles are the least heat-resistant and are usually killed by the heat processing and hence are rarely concerned with flat sour spoilage of low-acid foods. The spores of the thermophiles, on the other hand, are considerably more heat-resistant and may survive the heat process to cause flat sour spoilage. Surviving thermophiles, such as *B. stearothermophilus,* would not cause spoilage unless the food were held hot for a while, as in slow cooling or storage in the tropics, but facultative thermophiles could grow at ordinary temperatures. The immediate source of the flat sour bacteria is usually the plant equipment, e.g., the blanchers, but they may come originally from sugar, starch, or soil.

The ability of *B. coagulans* to grow in tomato juice depends on the number of spores present, the availability of oxygen, and the pH of the juice. The organism, which is homofermentative under almost anaerobic conditions and heterofermentative under aerobic conditions, can grow in low concentrations of oxygen.

TA Spoilage   The bacterium causing this type of spoilage has been nicknamed TA, which is short for "thermophilic anaerobe not producing hydrogen sulfide," or for the species *Clostridium thermosaccharolyticum*. This is a thermophilic spore-forming anaerobe that forms acid and gas in foods. The gas, a mixture of carbon dioxide and hydrogen, swells the can if it is held long enough at a high temperature and may eventually cause bursting. The spoiled food usually has a sour or "cheesy" odor. Sources are the same as for flat sour bacteria.

Sulfide, or "Sulfur Stinker," Spoilage This spoilage, caused by *Desulfotomaculum nigrificans,* is found, and then uncommonly, in low-acid foods such as peas and corn. The spores of this bacterium have considerably less heat resistance than those of flat sour and TA bacteria; hence their appearance in canned foods is indicative of gross underprocessing. The organism is an obligate thermophile and therefore also requires poor cooling of the heat-processed foods or hot storage for its development. It is detected by means of the black (FeS) colonies it forms in an iron sulfite agar at 55 C. Hydrogen sulfide, formed in the canned peas or corn, is evident by odor when the can is opened. In corn, a bluish-gray liquid is evident in which blackened germs and gray kernels of corn float. Peas usually give the H_2S odor but without any marked discoloration. Sources of the spores are similar to those for flat sour and TA bacteria, but manure can also be an original source.

Types of Spoilage by Mesophilic Spore-Forming Bacteria

Most spoilage by mesophilic microorganisms that results from underprocessing is caused by spore-forming bacteria of the genera *Bacillus* and *Clostridium,* but lightly heated foods, e.g., some acid ones, may permit the survival of, and spoilage by, non-spore-forming bacteria or even yeasts or molds.

Spoilage by Mesophilic *Clostridium* Species Species of *Clostridium* may be sugar-fermenting, e.g., *C. butyricum* and *C. pasteurianum,* and cause the butyric acid type of fermentation in acid or medium-acid foods, with swelling of the container by the carbon dioxide and hydrogen gas produced. Other species, such as *C. sporogenes, C. putrefaciens,* and *C. botulinum,* are proteolytic or putrefactive, decomposing proteins with the production of malodorous compounds such as hydrogen sulfide, mercaptans, ammonia, indole, and skatole. The putrefactive anaerobes also produce carbon dioxide and hydrogen, causing the can to swell. The spores of some of the putrefactive anaerobes are very heat resistant; therefore, putrefaction joins flat sour and TA spoilage in constituting the chief types of biological spoilage of canned foods resulting from underprocessing.

Because the spores of the saccharolytic clostridia, sometimes called "butyrics," have a comparatively low heat resistance, spoilage by these anaerobes takes place most commonly in canned foods which have been processed at 100 C or less, as are many of the commercially canned acid foods and home-canned foods processed by the hot-water, flowing-stream, or oven methods. Thus canned acid foods such as pineapple, tomatoes, and pears have been found spoiled by *C. pasteurianum.* Such spoilage is more likely when the pH of the food is above 4.5. Home-canned foods heated to about 100 C may be spoiled by the saccharolytic bacteria with the production of butyric acid, carbon dioxide, and hydrogen.

The putrefactive anaerobes grow best in the low-acid canned foods, such as peas, corn, meats, fish, and poultry, but on rare occasions may spoil other foods.

One of the putrefiers, *C. botulinum*, is a cause of food poisoning and will be discussed in Chapter 24.

Spoilage by Mesophilic *Bacillus* Species   Spores of various species of *Bacillus* differ considerably in their heat resistance, but in general the spores of the mesophiles are not as resistant as those of the thermophiles. Spores of many of the mesophiles are killed in a short time at 100 C or less, but a few kinds can survive the heat treatments employed in steam-pressure processing. The spores that survive do not necessarily cause spoilage, since conditions in the can of food may be unfavorable for germination and growth. Many species of *Bacillus* are aerobic and therefore cannot grow in a well-evacuated container. The food may be too acid for the bacteria, or the medium may be unfavorable otherwise. There have been reports, however, of *B. subtilis*, *B. mesentericus**, and other species growing in low-acid home-canned foods that had been given a heat processing at 100 C. Commercially canned foods have been spoiled by *Bacillus* species, especially in poorly evacuated cans. Foods so spoiled have been mostly canned seafood, meats, and evaporated milk. The aerobacilli, or gas-forming *Bacillus* species (*B. polymyxa* and *B. macerans*), have been reported to cause spoilage of canned peas, asparagus, spinach, peaches, and tomatoes, but there is some doubt whether they survived the heat process. Entrance may have been through a leak in the container. Spores of these bacteria have about the same heat resistance as those of *Clostridium pasteurianum*.

Spoilage by Non-Spore-Forming Bacteria

If viable non-spore-forming bacteria are found in canned foods, either a very mild heat treatment was used or the bacteria entered the container through a leak. Vegetative cells of some kinds of bacteria are fairly heat resistant in that they can withstand pasteurization. Among these thermoduric bacteria are the enterococci, *Streptococcus thermophilus*, some species of *Micrococcus* and *Lactobacillus*, and *Microbacterium**. Acid-forming *Lactobacillus* and *Leuconostoc* species have been found growing in underprocessed tomato products, pears, and other fruits. The heterofermentative species may release enough CO_2 gas to swell the can. Micrococci* have been reported in meat pastes and in similar products with very poor heat penetration, and *S. faecalis* or *S. faecium* is often present in canned hams that are only partially sterilized and may be responsible for spoilage on storage.

Usually, however, the presence of viable non-spore-forming bacteria in heat-processed canned foods indicates leakage of the container. Since the cooling water is most frequently the source of contamination, types of bacteria commonly found in water usually cause spoilage of the leaky cans. Some of these, e.g., the coliform bacteria, produce gas which swells the cans. The tiny orifice through which the bacteria enter apparently becomes tightly plugged by a food particle, permitting the accumulation of gas pressure in the can. It should be noted that spore-forming bacteria also can enter the can through a leak, so that the aerobacilli (*B. macerans* and *B. polymyxa*) or the clostridia could be responsible for the gas formation. Often non-gas-forming bacteria are found growing in the food in leaky cans, along with the gas former or by themselves. It is possible, of course, that only one kind of bacterium may enter, so that an apparently pure culture would be growing. Non-spore-forming, non-gas-forming bacteria that may enter include those in the genera *Pseudomonas, Alcaligenes, Micrococcus, Flavobacterium, Proteus,* and others. Less common nonsporeformers other than those of water may enter through leaks in the cans and cause spoilage.

Spoilage by Yeasts

Since yeasts and their spores are killed readily by most pasteurization treatments, their presence in canned foods is the result of either gross underprocessing or leakage. Canned fruits, jams, jellies, fruit juices, sirups, and sweetened condensed milk have been spoiled by fermentative yeasts, with swelling of the cans by the CO_2 produced. Film yeasts may grow on the surface of jellied pickled pork, repacked pickles or olives, and similar products, but their presence indicates recontamination or lack of heat processing, plus poor evacuation.

Spoilage by Molds

Molds probably are the most common cause of the spoilage of home-canned foods, which they enter through a leak in the seal of the container. Jams, jellies, marmalades, and fruit butters will permit mold growth when sugar concentrations are as high as 70 percent and in the acidity usually present in these products. It has been claimed that adjustment of the soluble extract of jam to 70 to 72 percent sugar in the presence of a normal 0.8 to 1.0 percent acid will practically remove the risk of mold spoilage. Strains of *Aspergillus, Penicillium,* and *Citromyces,* found growing in jellies and candied fruits, are able to grow in sugar concentrations up to 67.5 percent. Acidification to pH 3 prevented growth of the first two molds, and heating the foods at 90 C for 1 min killed all strains. Some molds are fairly resistant to heat, especially those forming the tightly packed masses of mycelium called sclerotia. *Byssochlamys fulva,* a pectin-fermenting mold, has ascospores that have resisted the heat processing of bottled and canned fruits and have caused spoilage. The high sugar content of sirups about fruits helps protect microorganisms against heat, and this protective effect is increased if the sugar and fruit are added to the can separately, localizing the sugar during processing.

Spoilage of Canned Foods of Different Acidities

The previous discussion has indicated that the grouping of commercially canned foods on the basis of pH divides them also on the basis of the chief types of spoilage to be expected. Thus the low-acid foods with a pH above 5.3 are especially subject to flat sour spoilage and putrefaction. Foods with a pH between 5.3 and 4.5 are likely to undergo TA spoilage. High-acid foods with a pH between 4.5 and 3.7 usually are spoiled by a special flat sour bacterium or by a saccharolytic anaerobe. High-acid foods with a pH below 3.7 ordinarily do not undergo spoilage by microorganisms, but in cans may become hydrogen swells (as may other high-acid foods).

Spoilage of Canned Meats and Fish

In general, canned meats and fish exhibit two chief types of spoilage: (1) by *Bacillus* species, resulting in softening and souring, and (2) by *Clostridium* species (e.g., *C. sporogenes*), producing putrid swells. Less commonly, bacilli may produce acid and gas and swell the cans. Even nonsporeformers have been found in some pastes. Besides spoilage by these organisms, mostly sporeformers that have survived the heat process, there may be spoilage by organisms entering through leaks.

Canned cured meats which are given a heat process insufficient for sterilization, such as ham or luncheon meats, may be subject to production of carbon dioxide, nitrogen oxides, or nitrogen gas by species of *Bacillus* (e.g., *B. licheniformis, B. coagulans, B. cereus,* or *B. subtilis*) from the nitrate, sugar, and meat, or they may be subject to putrefaction with gas produced by *Clostridium* species. Such spoilage ordinarily is prevented by adequate refrigeration. Gas also may be produced by heterofermentative lactic acid bacteria (e.g., leuconostocs), but only after inadequate processing. Spoilage without gas production but with souring and changes in color and texture may be caused by species of *Bacillus* and by homofermentative lactic acid bacteria (e.g., *Streptococcus faecium* or *faecalis*).

Unusual Types of Spoilage of Canned Foods

Certain types of spoilage seem to be limited to one or two kinds of food. Sulfide spoilage has been reported only for peas and sweet corn. Black beets are caused by the mesophilic *Bacillus betanigrificans** in the presence of a high content of soluble iron. This is distinct from the darkening resulting from a deficiency of boron in the soil. *Bacillus* species can cause bitterness, acidity, and curdling in canned milk, cream, and evaporated milk. The only important alkaline canned vegetable, hominy (pH 6.8 to 7.8), undergoes flat sour spoilage which is characterized by a sweetish taste. Canned poultry is more often spoiled by putrefactive than by saccharolytic clostridia, chiefly because of the lower heat resistance of spores of the latter.

Canned sweetened condensed milk may become gassy because of growth of yeasts or coliform bacteria, may become thickened by a *Micrococcus** species, or may exhibit buttons, which consist of small masses of mold mycelium and coagulated milk usually on the surface of the milk. The size of the buttons is limited by the quantity of free oxygen in the head space of the can.

Sometimes, as the result of **autosterilization,** no viable organisms can be found in cans of food that have undergone obviously biological spoilage. All vegetative cells have died, including those of sporeformers which did not sporulate.

A scheme for the diagnosis of the cause of spoilage of a canned food is outlined in Figure 19-2. This scheme applies only to common types of spoilage.

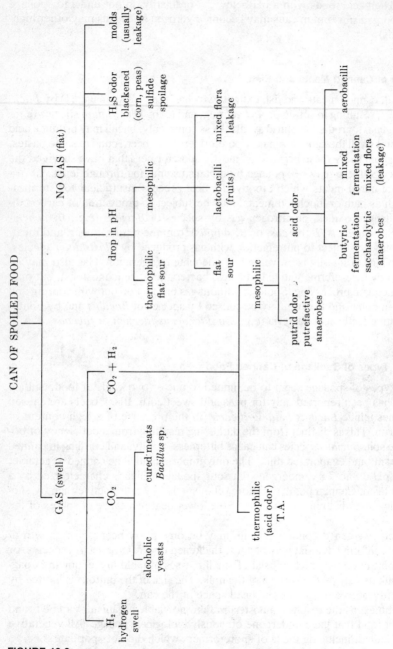

FIGURE 19-2
Scheme for diagnosis of cause of spoilage of a canned food.

BIBLIOGRAPHY

Aschehoug, V., and E. Jansen. 1950. Studies on putrefactive anaerobes as spoilage agents in canned foods. Food Res. 15:62–67.

Ayres, J. C., and A. T. Adams. 1953. Occurrence and nature of bacteria in canned beef. Food Technol. 7:318–323.

Bowen, J. F., C. C. Strachan, and A. W. Moyls. 1954. Further studies of butyric fermentations in canned tomatoes. Food Technol. 8:471–473.

Buttiaux, R., and H. Beerens. 1955. Gas-producing mesophilic clostridia in canned meats, with improved techniques for their identification. J. Appl. Bacteriol. 18:581–590.

Cameron, E. J., and J. R. Esty. 1940. Comments on the microbiology of spoilage in canned foods. Food Res. 5:549–557.

Corlett, D. A. Jr., and C. B. Denny. 1984. Canned foods—tests for cause of spoilage. *In* M. L. Speck (ed.), Compendium of methods for the microbiological examination of foods. 2d ed. American Public Health Association, Washington, D.C.

Dakin, J. C., and P. M. Day. 1958. Yeasts causing spoilage in acetic acid preserves. J. Appl. Bacteriol. 21:94–96.

Fields, M. L. 1970. The flat sour bacteria. Adv. Food Res. 18:163–217.

Goldblith, S. A., M. A. Joslyn, and J. T. R. Nickerson (eds.). 1961. An introduction to the thermal processing of foods. AVI Publishing Co., Inc., Westport, Conn. (Contains reproductions of early papers on bacteriological spoilage of canned foods.)

Herson, A. C., and E. D. Hulland. 1964. Canned foods: an introduction to their microbiology. Chemical Publishing Company, Inc., New York.

Hunwicke, R. F. 1928. Bacteria and the canning industry. Food Manuf. 1:19–20; 2:179–180, 184.

Jarvis, N. D. 1940. Spoilage in canned fishery products. Canning Age 21:434–436, 444, 476–477.

Jensen, L. B. 1954. Microbiology of meats, chaps. 11–13. 3d ed. The Garrard Press, Champaign, Ill.

National Canners Association. 1968. Laboratory manual for food canners and processors, vols. I and II. AVI Publishing Co., Inc., Westport, Conn.

Potter, R. S. 1935. Jam troubles. Food Manuf. 10:232–233.

Rangaswami, G., and R. Venkatesan. 1959. Studies on the microbial spoilage of canned food. I. Isolation and identification of some spoilage bacteria. Indian Acad. Sci. Proc., Sec. B. 50:349–359.

Riemann, H. 1957. Bacteriology of canned fish. Food Manuf. 32:265–267, 333–335.

Schmitt, H. P. 1966. Commercial sterility in canned foods, its meaning and determination. Ass. Food Drug Off. U.S. Q. Bull. 30:141–151.

Tanikawa, E. 1958. Studies on the technical problems in the processing of canned salmon. Mem. Fac. Fish. Hokkaido Univ. 6:67–138.

Vaughn, R. H., I. H. Kreulevitch, and W. A. Mercer. 1952. Spoilage of canned foods caused by the *Bacillus macerans-polymyxa* group of bacteria. Food Res. 17:560–570.

MISCELLANEOUS FOODS

Foods not in previously discussed groups are included in this chapter: fatty foods, salad dressings, essential oils, bottled soft drinks, spices and other condiments, salt, and nutmeats.

Food products compounded from combinations of the different groups of foods also would combine their microbial contents, and the new product may furnish a good culture medium for microorganisms that previously had little chance to grow. Thus yeasts from sugar added to bottled soft drinks may spoil the product. The bottlers of carbonated beverages have bacteriological standards for sugar: not over 200 mesophilic bacteria per 10 g and not more than 10 yeasts or molds. The water and flavoring materials also are potential sources of contamination. Spices and other condiments added to foods may be important sources of microorganisms, although spices may be treated with propylene oxide gas or may be irradiated to give them a low microbial content. Microorganisms are added to salad dressings by ingredients such as spices, condiments, eggs, and pickles. Salt (sodium chloride), especially solar salt, may add halophilic and salt-tolerant bacteria to salted fish and other salted or brined products.

FATTY FOODS

Fats and Oils

The fatty parts of foods, the foods made up chiefly of fats and oils, and the fats and oils themselves are subject more often to chemical than to microbial spoilage. Besides the fatty glycerides, natural fats and oils usually contain small amounts of fatty acids, glycerol or other liquid alcohols, sterols, hydrocarbons, proteins and other nitrogenous compounds, phosphatides, and carotenoid pigments. The chief types of spoilage result from hydrolysis, oxidation, or combinations of the two processes. The terms applied to the different types of spoilage often are used rather loosely, although when applied to the deterioration of a specific kind of fat or oil they may have a definite meaning. The term **rancidity** sometimes is used for the result of any change in fats or oils that is accompanied by undesirable flavors, regardless of the cause. The spoilage due to oxidation, chemical or microbial, is termed **oxidative rancidity,** as distinguished from changes resulting from hydrolysis, by lipases originally present or by those from microorganisms, causing **hydrolytic rancidity.** Extensive oxidation, usually following hydrolysis and the release of fatty acids, can result in **ketonic rancidity. Flavor reversion** is defined as the appearance of objectionable flavors from less oxidation than is needed to produce rancidity. Oils that contain linolenic acid, fish oils, and vegetable oils, for example, are subject to flavor reversion.

The oxidation of fats and oils may be catalyzed by various metals and rays and by moisture as well as by microorganisms; such oxidation is prevented or delayed by natural or added antioxidants. Hydrolysis by lipases results in fatty acids and glycerol or other alcohols. Fats subjected to either or both of these types of changes may contain fatty oxy and hydroxy acids, glycerol and other alcohols, aldehydes, ketones, and lactones; in the presence of lecithin, they may include trimethylamine, with its fishy odor.

Butterfat and meat fats become "tallowy" as the result of oxidation, but butterfat is called rancid when only hydrolysis to fatty acids and glycerol has taken place.

Some of the pigments produced by microorganisms are fat-soluble and therefore can diffuse into fat, producing discolorations ranging through yellow, red, purple, and brown. Best known is the "stamping-ink" discoloration of meat fat that Jenson (1937) and others have shown to be caused by yellow-pigmented micrococci* and bacilli. The fat-soluble pigment is an O-R indicator that changes from yellow to green to blue and finally to purple as the fat becomes more oxidized by the peroxides formed by the bacteria. Yellow, pink, and red fat-soluble pigments may be produced by various bacteria, yeasts, and molds.

Bacteriostatic and bactericidal properties have been claimed for many of the fixed vegetable and animal oils, but most of them, like the fats, can be hydrolyzed and oxidized by microorganisms. These fatty materials ordinarily are very low in moisture, a condition that favors molds more than other microorganisms. Molds cause both oxidative and hydrolytic decomposition that results in rancidity. Bacteria causing rancidity of butter cause a similar defect in olive oil. Among the bacteria that can decompose fats are species of *Pseudomonas, Micrococcus*, Bacillus, Serratia, Achromobacter*,* and *Proteus;* and among the molds, species of *Geotrichum, Penicillium, Aspergillus, Cladosporium,* and *Monilia.* Some yeasts, especially film yeasts, are lipolytic. Copra and cocoa butter may be spoiled by molds.

Salad Dressings

Salad dressings contain oil, which may become oxidized or hydrolyzed, and enough moisture to permit microbial growth. For the most part, however, their acidity (about pH 3 to 4) is too great for most bacteria but favorable for yeasts or molds. Egg or egg products, pickles, relish, pimientos, sugar, starch, gums, gelatin, spices, and other ingredients may add microorganisms, sometimes in appreciable numbers, and may make the dressings better media for microbial growth. The three types of spoilage of mayonnaise and similar dressings are (1) separation of the oil or water from the emulsion, (2) oxidation and hydrolysis of the oils by chemical or biological action, and (3) growth of microorganisms to produce gas, off-flavors, or other defects. Darkening often takes place.

The decomposition of salad dressings and related products can be caused by bacteria, yeasts, or molds. The acidity, coupled with the sugar content, about 4.5 percent on the average in the water phase of mayonnaise, is most favorable to yeasts, which have been reported to cause gassiness. Species of *Zygosaccharomyces* and *Saccharomyces* have spoiled mayonnaise, salad dressing, and French dressing. Bacteria would have to be acid-tolerant to spoil most types of dressing. Therefore, it is not unexpected to learn of a heterofermentative lactobacillus resembling *Lactobacillus brevis* causing gas in a salad dressing. More surprising is the report of species of *Bacillus,* e.g., *B. subtilis* and *B. megaterium,* as organisms causing gas, rancidity, and separation, since they are not acid-tolerant. Yeasts growing with *B. megaterium* could account for the gas. Darkening and separation of Thousand Island dressing with a pH of 4.2 to 4.4 by *B. vulgatus** from the pepper and paprika have been reported. Molds can grow on salad dressings if air is available and are favored by the addition of starch or pectin to the dressing. A comprehensive review on the microbiology of mayonnaise and salad dressing by Smittle (1977) should be consulted for greater detail.

ESSENTIAL OILS

Essential oils or volatile oils are products obtained from the plant kingdom in which the odoriferous and flavoring characteristics are concentrated. These present no spoilage problems but on the contrary may have some preservative effect as ingredients of foods, e.g., mustard, cinnamon, garlic, and onion oils. Most of them do not affect the heat resistance of microorganisms.

BOTTLED BEVERAGES

The spoilage of alcoholic beverages will be discussed in Chapter 22. The ease with which the nonalcoholic beverages spoil and the type of spoilage depend on the composition of the soft drink. Carbonation is inhibitory or even germicidal to some microorganisms, and the acidity resulting from carbonation and the addition of acids, e.g., citric, lactic, phosphoric, tartaric, and malic, inhibits the growth of organisms not tolerant to acidity. Also benzoic acid (75 mg/kg) may be added as a preservative. Nonacid drinks such as root beer are better culture media for spoilage organisms than are acid drinks such as the cola drinks, ginger ale, and fruit-flavored drinks. The ingredients of soft drinks not only affect the suitability for microbial growth but also can affect the kinds and numbers of microorganisms present and hence the likelihood of spoilage organisms being added. In addition, the bottles and closures are possible sources of contamination. The water for soft drinks is purified in regard to carbonate and mineral content and is filtered. The filtration process may remove microorganisms or, if the filter is badly contaminated, add them. Ultraviolet irradiation sometimes is used to destroy microorganisms in the water. Discoloration of water and a flocculent precipitate may be caused by growth of algae. Treatment with chlorine or chlorine dioxide has been recommended to kill the algae, and filtration, e.g., through diatomaceous earth, to remove the flocculent dead cells.

Yeasts, chiefly *Torulopsis* and *Candida,* are the most likely causes of spoilage of soft drinks, for most such beverages are acid and contain sugar. One worker found that 85 percent of 1,500 spoiled samples of carbonated beverages had been spoiled by yeasts. Since the sugars are a possible source of yeasts, the American Bottlers of Carbonated Beverages have set a standard of not more than ten yeasts per 10 g of dry sugar. Fruit concentrates are another possible source of yeasts.

Cloudiness and ropiness are types of spoilage of soft drinks. Cloudiness results from marked growth of various yeasts or bacteria and ropiness from the development of capsulated bacteria, most of which seem to be of the genus *Bacillus.* Bacteria may enter from ingredients, bottles, or closures. Occasionally, *Gluconobacter, Lactobacillus,* or *Leuconostoc* may be isolated from spoiled soft drinks. An *Achromobacter** species was found responsible for a musty odor and taste in root beer.

Since molds must have air, they cannot grow on carbonated beverages but may develop at the surface of uncarbonated ones containing air above the liquid. They may come from sugar, coloring materials or flavoring materials, from the air, or from bottles or closures.

SPICES AND OTHER CONDIMENTS

The dry spices are not normally subject to spoilage, although mold growth during their drying may give them a heavy load of mold spores. Chip dips flavored with vegetables or spices usually have much higher total, coliform, and mold counts than those flavored with cheese. As has been mentioned, treatment of the spices with propylene oxide greatly reduces their content of microorganisms. Other treatments to reduce the intial flora would include irradiation, steam, hot ethanol vapors, and acid treatments followed by neutralization. Spices can be purchased with guaranteed low numbers of organisms.

Prepared mustard can be spoiled by yeasts and by species of *Proteus* and *Bacillus,* usually with a gassy fermentation. Horseradish seldom spoils but on the contrary is bacteriostatic to bactericidal. The spoilage of vinegar is discussed in Chapter 22.

SALT

The three kinds of salt used in foods are (1) *solar salt* from the evaporation of surface salt water, (2) *mined* or *rock salt,* and (3) *welled salt* from salt dissolved from subterranean salt deposits. Solar salt contains halophiles, such as *Halobac-terium salinarium*. About three-fourths of the bacteria are *Bacillus* organisms, and the rest are mainly *Micrococcus** and *Sarcina*. Mined salt has been found to con-

TABLE 20-1
SOME REPORTS ON MISCELLANEOUS FOODS

Item	Comments	Reference
Cream-filled pastries	History of food-borne illnesses	Bryan (1975)
Health foods	Microbial comparison to traditional foods	Appledorf et al. (1973)
Barbecued foods	Public health implications	Todd and Pivnick (1972)
Spices and herbs	Microbiological quality	Seligmann and Frankblum (1974)
	Microbiological profile	Julseth and Deibel (1974)
	Microbiology	Powers et al. (1975)
Big game meat (Wyoming)	Microbiological quality	Smith et al. (1973)
Delicatessen foods	Bacteriological quality	Pace (1975)
		Harris et al. (1975)
Delicatessen salads	Microbiological quality	Fowler and Clark (1975)
Vended hamburgers	Microbiological quality	Mueller (1975)
Pecans	Salmonellae	Beuchat and Heaton (1975)
Tortillas, maize	Microflora	Capparelli and Mata (1975)
Mushrooms, fresh	Growth of *Clostridium botulinum*	Sugiyama and Yang (1975)
Coleslaw	Microbial shelf life	King et al. (1976)
Breaded fish	Microbiological quality	Baer et al. (1976)
Breaded onion rings	Microbiological quality	Wentz et al. (1984)
Soul food	Bacteriological populations	Stewart (1983)
Vegetable salads	Gram-negative isolates	Wright et al. (1976)
Salads, commercially prepared	Microbiological profile	Terry and Overcast (1976)
Salads, fresh	Microbiological survey	Fowler and Foster (1976)
Tofu	Microbiological quality	Rehberger et al. (1984)
Pasta products	Death kinetics of pathogens	Hsieh et al (1976)
Coconut products	Microbiological profile	Kajs et al. (1976)
		Kinderler (1984)
Meat loaf	Fate of contaminants	Maxcy (1976)
Dry soup mixes	Microbiological quality	Komarik et al. (1974)
Dry soup and sauces	*Clostridium perfringens*	Nakamura and Kelly (1968)
Cocoa powder	Microbial profile	Gabis et al. (1970)
Imitation cheese	*Clostridium botulinum*	Kautter et al. (1981)
Enteral nutrient solutions	Bacterial growth	Fagerman et al. (1984)
Precooked frozen foods	Microbiological quality	Peterson and Gunnerson (1974)
Frog legs	Salmonellae	Rao et al. (1978)
Natural mineral water	Microbiological quality	Schmidt-Lorenz (1976)
Instant coffee	Microbiological profile	Vanos and Bindschedler (1985)
Beef-soy blends	Microbial stability	Bell and Shelef (1978)
Beef-soy patties	Total and coliform counts	Craven and Mercuri (1977)
Soy-ground beef	Spoilage bacteria	Harrison et al. (1983)
Soy-protein extenders	Microbiological quality	Swartzentruber (1984)

tain about 70 percent *Micrococcus**, 20 percent coryneforms, and 4 percent *Bacillus;* putrefactive anaerobes also have been found. Wet salt used on fish averages about 10 to 1,000 organisms per gram. Most purified salt, however, adds few organisms to foods.

NUTMEATS

Nutmeats in the shell are usually sterile or nearly so. Shelled nuts to be used as ingredients of foods, e.g., in frozen desserts, may be contaminated with bacteria, yeasts, and molds. The test for coliform bacteria is used most often to indicate possible contamination with fecal matter during handling. Roasting and heating in oil or sugar solution reduce the load of microorganisms. Molds may produce mycotoxins on nuts, such as aflatoxin production in peanuts (see Chapter 2).

OTHER FOODS

The number of different food items displayed on a supermarket shelf is proof of the great diversity of commodity items, convenience foods, and prepared foods available. The microbiology of each of these is also varied. Add to this list the numerous foods which are prepared commercially and vended or distributed locally or regionally and it is evident that the microbial spoilage of each cannot be discussed. Table 20-1 provides an indication of the various miscellaneous foods which have been studied. This listing is surely not complete, but it represents a variety of items not covered in the chapters on various commodities.

BIBLIOGRAPHY

Anderson, E. E., W. B. Esselen, Jr., and A. R. Handleman. 1953. The effect of essential oils on the inhibition and thermal resistance of microorganisms in acid food products. Food Res. 18:40–47.

Appledorf, H., W. B. Wheeler, and J. A. Koburger. 1973. Health foods versus traditional foods: a comparison. J. Milk Food Technol. 36:242–244.

Appleman, M. D., E. P. Hess, and S. C. Rittenberg. 1949. An investigation of a mayonnaise spoilage. Food Technol. 3:201–203.

Baer, E. F., A. P. Duran, H. V. Leininger, R. B. Read, Jr., A. H. Schwag, and A. Swartzentruber. 1976. Microbiological quality of frozen breaded fish and shellfish products. Appl. Environ. Microbiol. 31:337–341.

Bain, N., W. Hodgkiss, and J. M. Shewan. 1958. The bacteriology of salt used in fish curing: the microbiology of fish and meat curing brines. II Int. Symp. Food Microbiol. Proc. pp. 1–11 (1957).

Bell, W. N., and L. A. Shelef. 1978. Availability and microbial stability of retail beef-soy blends. J. Food Sci. 43:315–318, 333.

Beuchat, L. R., and E. K. Heaton. 1975. *Salmonella* survival on pecans as influenced by processing and storage conditions. Appl. Microbiol. 29:795–801.

Byran, F. L. 1975. Public health aspects of cream-filled pastries: a review. J. Milk Food Technol. 39:289–296.

Capparelli, E., and L. Mata. 1975. Microflora of maize prepared as tortillas. Appl. Microbiol. 29:802–806.

Clayton, W. 1931, 1932. The bacteriology of common salt. Food Manuf. 6:133, 257; 7:76–77, 109–110, 172–173.

Connor, J. W. 1950. Mayonnaise spoilage. Can. Food Ind. 21:27.

Corran, J. W., and S. H. Edgar. 1933. Preservative action of spices and related compounds against yeast fermentation. J. Soc. Chem. Ind. 52:149–152T.

Craven, S. E., and A. J. Mercuri. 1977. Total aerobic and coliform counts in beef-soy and chicken-soy patties during refrigerated storage. J. Food Prot. 40:112–115.

Eagon, R. G., and C. R. Green. 1957. Effect of carbonated beverages on bacteria. Food Res. 22:687–688.

Fabian, F. W., and M. C. Wethington. 1950. Spoilage in salad and French dressing due to yeasts. Food Res. 15:135–137.

Fagerman, K. E., J. D. Paauw, M. A. McCamish, and R. E. Dean. 1984. Effects of time, temperature, and preservative on bacterial growth in enteral nutrient solutions. Am. J. Hosp. Pharm. 41:1122–1126.

Foter, M. J., and A. M. Gorlick. 1938. Inhibitory properties of horse-radish vapors. Food Res. 3:609–613.

Fowler, J. L., and W. S. Clark, Jr. 1975. Microbiology of delicatessen salads. J. Milk Food Technol. 38:146–149.

Fowler, J. L., and J. F. Foster. 1976. A microbiological survey of three fresh green salads: can guidelines be recommended for these foods? J. Milk Food Technol. 39:111–113.

Gabis, D. A., B. E. Langlois, and A. W. Rudnick. 1970. Microbiological examination of cocoa powder. Appl. Microbiol. 20:644–645.

Harmon, L. C., C. M. Stine, and G. C. Walker. 1962. Composition, physical properties and microbiological quality of chip-dips. J. Milk Food Technol. 25:7–11.

Harris, N. D., S. R. Martin, and L. Ellias. 1975. Bacteriological quality of selected delicatessen foods. J. Milk Food Technol. 38:759–761.

Harrison, M. A., F. A. Draughton, and C. C. Melton. 1983. Inhibition of spoilage of bacteria by acidification of soy-extended ground beef. J. Food Sci. 48:825–828.

Hsieh, F., K. Acott, and T. B. Labuza. 1976. Death kinetics of pathogens in a pasta product. J. Food Sci. 41:516–520.

Insalata, N. F. 1952. Balking algae in beverage water. Food Eng. 24(12):72–74, 197.

Insalata, N. F. 1956. These bacteria checks prevent beverage spoilage. Food Eng. 28(4):84–86.

Jacobs, M. B. 1959. Manufacture and analysis of carbonated beverages. Chemical Publishing Company, Inc., New York.

Jenson, L. B., and D. P. Grettie. 1937. Action of microorganisms on fats. Food Res. 2:97–120.

Julseth, R. M., and R. H. Deibel. 1974. Microbial profile of selected spices and herbs at import. J. Milk Food Technol. 37:414–420.

Kajs, T. M., R. Hagenmaier, C. Vanderzant, and K. F. Mattil. 1976. Microbiological evaluation of coconut and coconut products. J. Food Sci. 41:352–357.

Kauter, D. A., R. K. Lynt, T. Lilly, and H. M. Solomon. 1981. Evaluation of the botulism hazard from imitation cheeses. J. Food Sci. 46:749–750, 764.

Kinderler, J. 1984. Spoilage of dessicated coconut resulting from growth of xerophilic fungi. Food Micro. 1:23–28.

King, A. D., Jr., H. D. Michener, H. G. Bayne, and K. L. Mihara. 1976. Microbial studies on shelf life of cabbage and coleslaw. Appl. Environ. Microbiol. 31:404–407.

Komarik, S. L., D. K. Tressler, and L. Long. 1974. Food products formulary series. Volume 1. Meats, poultry, shellfish. AVI Publishing Co., Inc., Westport, Conn.

Lea, C. H. 1961. Some biological aspects of fat deterioration. Food Technol. 15(7):33–40.

Lehmann, D. L., and B. E. Byrd. 1953. A bacterium responsible for a musty odor and taste in root beer. Food Res. 18:76–78.

Maxcy, R. B. 1976. Fate of post-cooking microbial contaminants of some major menu items. J. Food Sci. 41:375–379.

Meyer, L. H. 1960. Food chemistry. Reinhold Publishing Corporation, New York.

Mueller, D. C. 1975. Microbiological safety and palatability of selected vended burgers. J. Milk Food Technol. 38:135–137.

Nakamura, M., and K. D. Kelly. 1968. *Clostridium perfringens* in dehydrated soups and sauces. J. Food Sci. 33:424–426.

Nicol, H. 1937. Watch your salt. Food Manuf. 12:111–113.

Pace, P. J. 1975. Bacteriological quality of delicatessen foods: are standards needed? J. Milk Food Technol. 38:347–353.

Pederson, C. S. 1930. Bacterial spoilage of a Thousand Island dressing. J. Bacteriol. 20:99–106.

Perigo, J. A., B. L. Gimbert, and T. E. Bashford. 1964. The effect of carbonation, benzoic acid and pH on the growth rate of a soft drink spoilage yeast as determined by a turbidostatic continuous culture apparatus. J. Appl. Bacteriol. 27:315–332.

Peterson, A. C., and R. E. Gunnerson. 1974. Microbiological critical control points in frozen foods. Food Technol. 28:37–44.

Powers, E. M., R. Lawyer, and Y. Masuoka. 1975. Microbiology of processed spices. J. Milk Food Technol. 38:683–687.

Rainbow, C., and A. H. Rose. 1963. Biochemistry of industrial microorganisms. Academic Press, Inc., New York.

Rao, N. M., S. C. Nandy, K. T. Joseph, and M. Santappa. 1978. Control of salmonella in frog legs by chemical and physical methods. Ind. J. Exp. Biol. 16:593–596.

Rehberger, T. G., L. A. Wilson, and B. A. Glatz. 1984. Microbiological quality of commercial tofu. J. Food Prot. 47:177–181.

Schmidt-Lorenz, W. 1976. Microbiological characteristics of natural mineral waters. Ann. Inst. Super. Sanit. 12:93–112.

Schultz, H. W. 1960. Food enzymes. AVI Publishing Co., Inc., Westport, Conn.

Seligmann, R., and H. Frankblum. 1974. Microbiological quality of barbecued chickens from commercial rotisseries. J. Milk Food Technol. 37:473–477.

Smith, F. C., R. A. Field, and J. C. Adams. 1973. Microbiology of Wyoming big game meat. J. Milk Food Technol. 37:129–133.

Smittle, R. B. 1977. Microbiology of mayonnaise and salad dressing: a review. J. Food Prot. 40:415–422.

Stewart, A. W. 1983. Effect of cooking on bacteriological population of "soul foods." J. Food Prot. 46:19–20.

Sugiyama, H., and K. H. Yang. 1975. Growth potential of *Clostridium botulinum* in fresh mushrooms packaged in semipermeable plastic film. Appl. Microbiol. 30:964–969.

Swartzentruber, A. H., A. H. Schwab, B. A. Wentz, A. P. Duran, and R. B. Read, Jr. 1984. Microbiological quality of biscuit dough, snack cakes, and soy protein meat extender. J. Food Prot. 47:467–470.

Terry, R. C., and W. W. Overcast. 1976. A microbiological profile of commercially prepared salads. J. Food Sci. 41:211–214.

Todd, E., and H. Pivnick. 1972. Public health problems associated with barbecued food. J. Milk Food Technol. 36:1–19.

Vakil, J. R., and J. V. Bhat. 1958. The microbiology of coconut oil. J. Univ. Bombay Sec. B 27(3):83–89.

Vanos, V., and O. Bindschedler. 1985. The microbiology of instant coffee. Food Micro. 2:187–197.

Vollrath, R. E., L. Walton, and C. C. Lindegren. 1937. Bactericidal properties of acrolein. Soc. Exp. Biol. Med. Proc. 36:55–58.

Wentz, B. A., A. P. Duran, A. Swartzentruber, A. S. Schwab, and R. B. Read, Jr. 1984. Microbiological quality of frozen breaded onion rings and tuna pot pies. J. Food Prot. 47:58–60.

Witter, L. D., J. M. Berry, and J. F. Folinazzo. 1958. The viability of *Escherichia coli* and a spoilage yeast in carbonated beverages. Food Res. 23:133–142.

Wright, C., S. D. Kominos, and R. B. Yee. 1976. *Enterobacteriaceae* and *Pseudomonas aeruginosa* recovered from vegetable salads. Appl. Environ. Microbiol. 31:453–454.

Wright, W. J., C. W. Bice, and J. M. Fogelberg. 1954. The effect of spices on yeast fermentation. Cereal Chem. 31:100–112.

PART FOUR

FOODS AND ENZYMES
PRODUCED BY
MICROORGANISMS

Microorganisms themselves may serve as food or feed; may be employed in the preparation of special nutrients, such as organic acids, flavor enhancers, and vitamins to be added to foods; may be used in the production of special foods by fermentation; or may serve as sources of enzyme mixtures or single enzymes for the treatment of foods during processing. The appropriate cultures for these various purposes must be maintained, usually in pure culture, in a stable yet active condition and must be built up to considerable volume for use as mass or bulk cultures for a particular process.

PRODUCTION OF CULTURES FOR FOOD FERMENTATIONS

Microorganisms necessary in food fermentation may be added as pure cultures or mixed cultures, or, in some instances, no cultures may be added if the desired microorganisms are known to be present in sufficient numbers in the original raw material. In the food fermentations discussed in Chapter 22 for the manufacture of sauerkraut, fermented pickles, and green olives and in the processing of cocoa, coffee, poi, and citron, the original raw product carries enough of the desired organisms, which will act in proper succession if favorable environmental conditions are provided and maintained. Therefore, the addition of pure or mixed cultures of the organisms responsible for the fermentations has not been found necessary, although in some of the fermentations, e.g., pickles and green olives, it is advantageous. On the other hand, controlled "starter" cultures, pure or mixed, usually are employed in the manufacture of certain dairy products, such as fermented milks, some kinds of butter, and most types of cheese, and in most of the other food fermentations discussed in Chapter 22, e.g., bread, malt beverages, wines, distilled liquors, and vinegar.

GENERAL PRINCIPLES OF CULTURE MAINTENANCE AND PREPARATION

Selection of Cultures

Cultures for food fermentations are selected primarily on the basis of their stability and their ability to produce desired products or changes efficiently. These cultures may be established ones obtained from other laboratories or may be selected after the testing of numerous strains. Stability is an important characteristic; yields and rates of changes must not be erratic. Some cultures may be improved by breeding, e.g., the sporogenous yeasts, but selection is the most commonly used method for the improvement of strains. Selection of cultures with desirable traits can be made from new strains isolated from the environment, from existing strains, or following mutation of strains by various means.

Refinement of plasmid transfer systems in the lactic acid bacteria will allow for gene cloning or gene amplification of a highly desirable trait such as lactic acid production. Since the gene responsible for lactose fermentation in some lactic streptococci is located on plasmids, the trait can be easily lost. Stabilizing these industrially important traits has been demonstrated to be possible. McKay and coworkers (Harlander, et al., 1984) have cloned the lac$^+$ genes of *S. lactis* and incorporated them into *S. sanguis*. The lac$^+$ genes, via a vector plasmid and transformation, were integrated into the chromosome of the host cell. As an integrated part of the chromosome, the lac$^+$ gene is much more stable than it is when it is plasmid-borne.

Maintenance of Activity of Cultures

Once a satisfactory culture has been obtained, it must be kept pure and active. Usually this objective is attained by periodic transfer of the culture into the proper culture medium, incubation until the culture reaches the maximal stationary phase of growth, and then storage at temperatures low enough to prevent further growth. Too frequent transfer of an unstable culture may lead to undesirable changes in its characteristics.

Stock cultures should be prepared for storage of cultures over long periods without transfer. Such cultures tend to remain stable and serve as a source of culture if the active culture deteriorates or is lost. Lyophilization (freeze drying) and freezing in liquid nitrogen (-196 C) are now frequently used to prepare stock cultures, although some use still is made of a paraffin-oil seal over ordinary tube cultures. Bacterial cultures have been preserved for months to years at room temperature on slants of agar in which 1 percent NaCl had been incorporated. A dry spore stock on sterilized soil can be used to preserve spores of bacteria or molds for long periods.

Maintenance of Purity of Cultures

To ensure the purity of cultures, they should be obtained periodically from a culture laboratory or be checked regularly for purity. Methods for testing a culture for purity vary with the type of culture being tested. Microscopic examination will indicate contamination only if the contaminant differs from the desired organism in appearance and is high in numbers. Another method is to plate the culture with an agar medium that will grow contaminants but not the desired organism. Tests may be made for the presence of substances not produced by the desired organism, e.g., for catalase in a culture of catalase-negative lactic acid bacteria as indicative of the presence of catalase-positive contaminants.

Preparation of Cultures

Mother culture is usually prepared daily from a previous mother culture and originally from the stock culture. These mother cultures can be used to inoculate a larger quantity of culture medium to produce the mass or bulk culture to be used in the fermentation process. Often, however, the fermentation is on such a large scale that several intermediate cultures of increasing size must be built up between the mother culture and the final bulk or mass culture. Culture makers attempt to produce and maintain a culture that (1) contains only the desired microorganism(s), (2) is uniform in microbial numbers, proportions (if a mixed culture), and activity from day to day, (3) is active in producing the products desired, and (4) has adequate resistance to unfavorable conditions if necessary, e.g., heat resistance, if it has to take heating in a cheese curd. They try to maintain uniformity by standardizing methods of preparation and sterilization of the culture medium, inoculation, and incubation temperature and time. The stage of growth to which they will grow the culture depends on the purpose for which it is to be used. If they wish prompt and rapid growth, they use a culture that is late in its logarithmic phase of growth. If they want more resistance to heat or other unfavorable conditions, they use a culture that has just entered the maximal stationary phase. The temperature of incubation usually is somewhere near the optimal temperature for the organism, although there are exceptions. Temperature and time of incubation often are adjusted so that the culture will be ready at the time it is needed. Otherwise, it may have to be cooled to stop further development.

Activity of Culture

The activity of a culture is judged by its rate of growth and production of products. It should be good if the mother or the intermediate culture is satisfactory and culture medium, incubation time, and temperature are optimal. Deterioration of cultures may result from improper handling and cultivation, frequent transfer over long periods in an inadequate culture medium, selection, variation or mutation, or attack of bacteria by a bacteriophage.

Mixed Cultures

Known mixtures of pure cultures sometimes are prepared, being grown together continuously or grown separately and mixed at the time of use. The so-called butter, or lactic, culture used in the dairy industry is an example of a mixture of several species of bacteria growing together and sometimes several strains of individual species. When different strains of the same species or different species are grown together, these organisms must be compatible, i.e., grow well together without any causing the elimination of others. The maintenance of the desired balance of kinds of organisms within these mixed cultures is difficult.

Unknown mixtures of organisms are present in starters used in some food products. Examples are the dough carried over from one lot of special French bread to a succeeding lot and the mixture of yeasts and bacteria carried from the surface smear of one Limburger cheese to the surface of another.

BACTERIAL CULTURES

Most of the bacterial cultures employed as starters for dairy products, sausage, and bread are pure or mixed cultures of lactic acid bacteria, exceptions being the propionic acid bacteria added to Swiss cheese. Acetic acid bacteria are used in vinegar making, and various bacteria are used for the manufacture of certain enzymes.

Lactic Acid Cultures

Although a few dairy plants still maintain their own cultures that they have carried successfully for years, most operators obtain new cultures periodically or use frozen, concentrated cultures prepared by commercial culture laboratories. The majority of commercially available cultures are now liquid-nitrogen-frozen culture concentrates prepared by growing the cultures in a suitable medium followed by harvesting and concentrating by centrifugation. The harvested cell pastes are standardized for activity and then packaged in pull-top cans and rapidly frozen in liquid nitrogen. Shipping, distribution, and storage of the frozen culture concentrates are feasible, and numerous advantages are evident. Acquiring such cultures eliminates the need for the maintenance and routine transfers involved in a company-maintained culture collection. Problems with contamination of the cultures during transfer and routine maintenance are eliminated. The use of the various strains of commercially available cultures can be rotated to provide a broader protection against bacteriophage infection. The numbers of cells are so high in many of these culture concentrate products that a 16-oz can (containing 11 oz of concentrate) can be used for direct inoculation of a cheese vat containing up to 5,000 lb of milk. This procedure would eliminate the older practice of preparing increasingly larger bulk-starter inocula over a succession of days. Preparation of enough bulk starter for a large cheese vat used to require several days of transferring to larger and larger volumes, all of which would have originated from the stock culture.

The most common dairy starter is the lactic starter, which ordinarily consists of a mixture of strains of *Streptococcus lactis* subsp. *lactis**, and *S. mesenteroides* subsp. *cremoris** for the production of lactic acid and *Leuconostoc** *cremoris* or *Streptococcus lactis* subsp. *diacetlactis** for the production of flavor and aroma. Several strains of lactic streptococci of different sensitivities to bacteriophage usually are included in the same culture concentrate as an insurance against trouble with phage.

Generally the lactic culture is incubated at 21.1 to 22.2 C, although 23.9 to 26.7 C has been employed in making starters for cheese. A culture is ripened to the desirable titratable acidity to suit the purpose for which the culture is to be used.

A mixed lactic culture is used in the manufacture of cultured buttermilk, yogurt, and several types of cheese. The aroma bacteria are especially important in flavor production in cultured buttermilk. The typical yogurt starter is a mixture of *Streptococcus thermophilus* and *Lactobacillus delbrueckii* subsp. *bulgaricus*. The transfer and handling of mixed cultures must take into account the temperature and length of incubation which will best maintain the desired mixed population and thereby prevent domination by one strain or species over another. The use of frozen concentrated cultures eliminates many of these concerns. In addition, cultures from commercial culture laboratories provide the benefit of purchasing previously determined and tested compatible strains.

As mentioned in Chapter 22, the "sour" used by the makers of rye bread is a mixture of various lactic acid bacteria ordinarily grown in mixed and impure culture in flour paste, dough, or other medium. It is claimed that *L. delbrueckii* subsp. *bulgaricus* must grow if enough acid is to be produced and that heterofermentative lactics are desirable from the standpoint of flavor production. Some breadmakers use pure cultures of *Streptococcus lactis* subsp. *lactis**, *Leuconostoc* spp., *Lactobacillus plantarum*, *L. casei*, *L. brevis*, *L. delbrueckii* subsp. *bulgaricus,* and *Streptococcus thermophilus* to inoculate bread. Other breadmakers also add yeasts.

Lactobacilli and *Pediococcus acidilactici* or *P. pentosaceus* cultures may be used as starters for summer, Thuringer, and similar fermented sausages. Broth cultures, dried cultures and frozen culture concentrates have been prepared.

Propionic Culture

Spray-dried or lypohilized cultures of *Propionibacterium freudenreichii* are added to milk used in the manufacture of Swiss cheese to improve the flavor and assist eye formation.

Cheese Smear Organisms

Most cheese makers inoculate the surfaces of smear-ripened cheese from previous cheeses, shelves, cloths, brine tank, hands, and other sources in the plant. The micrococci, *Brevibacterium linens,* and film yeasts important in the smear have been isolated and used in pure or mixed cultures to wash cheese surfaces, thereby inoculating them.

Acetic Acid Bacteria

Pure cultures of *Gluconobacter* or *Acetobacter* are not efficient in the production of acetic acid. Therefore, in vinegar making, impure mixed cultures are allowed to develop naturally, are added by means of raw vinegar from a previous run, or are transferred from a vinegar cask or generator.

YEAST CULTURES

Most yeasts of industrial importance are of the genus *Saccharomyces* and mostly of the species *S. cerevisiae*. These ascospore-forming yeasts are readily bred for desired characteristics. A yeast for a given purpose may be improved for that use but must also be guarded against possible undesirable changes.

Bakers' Yeast

Strains of *S. cerevisiae* used to manufacture bakers' yeast are usually single-cell isolates that have been selected especially for the purpose. They should give a good yield of cells in the mash or medium chosen for their cultivation, should be stable, should remain viable in the cake or dried form for a reasonably long period, and should produce carbon dioxide rapidly in the bread dough when used for leavening.

Like other cultures used on a large scale, this culture is built up from the original mother culture through several intermediate cultures of increasing size to the final "seed" culture. The cells from the seed-culture tank are concentrated into a "cream" by centrifugation, and this heavy suspension is added to the large volume of mash in which the yeast is to be grown, so that about 3 to 5 lb of yeast is added per 100 gal of medium.

The most commonly used medium for the buildup of cultures and the production of bakers' yeast is a cane or beet molasses–mineral-salts mash that contains molasses, nitrogen foods in the form of ammonium salts, urea, malt sprouts, etc., inorganic salts as phosphates and other mineral salts, and accessory growth substances in the form of extracts of vegetables, grain, or yeast, or small quantities of vitamin precursors or vitamins. The pH is adjusted to about 4.3 to 4.5, and the incubation temperature is around 30 C. During growth of the yeast the medium is aerated at a rapid rate, and molasses is added gradually to maintain the sugar level at about 0.5 to 1.5 percent. After four or five budding cycles, the yeast is centrifuged out in the form of a "cream," which is put through a filter press to remove excess liquid. The mass of yeasts is made into cakes of different sizes after incorporation of small amounts of vegetable oils.

Active dry yeast now is made by drying the yeast cells to less than 8 percent moisture. Cells so dried are grown especially for the purpose and are dried carefully at low temperatures so that most of the cells will survive and will retain for some months their ability to actively leaven dough.

Bakers' yeast also can be prepared from grain mashes, waste sulfite liquor from paper mills, wood hydrolyzate, and other materials.

Yeasts for Malt Beverages

Yeasts for malt beverages may be carried in pure culture in brewery laboratories or obtained when needed from specialized laboratories. The strain selected is one intended for the product to be made, a special bottom yeast for beer, usually a top yeast for ale but sometimes a bottom yeast, and a top yeast for stout and porter. The top yeasts used are strains of *Saccharomyces cerevisiae,* and the bottom yeast used is *S. uvarum (carlsbergensis).* When the yeast is started from a pure culture, it must be built up in wort from a laboratory culture to a final large seed or "pitching" culture. In practice, however, the pitching yeast is nearly always yeast recovered from a previous fermentation. The recovered yeast is concentrated and may or may not be washed. It is obvious that such a yeast culture will always be contaminated with other organisms, which ordinarily include bacteria and wild yeasts that build up during successive fermentations and recoveries. Fortunately, most of the contaminants, although able to grow in the yeast culture, are inhibited by the hops and low pH in the wort and do not damage the malt beverage appreciably. It is possible, however, for organisms causing "beer diseases" (see Chapter 22) to build up in the pitching yeast.

Wine Yeasts

For wine making, a special strain of *Saccharomyces cerevisiae* var. *ellipsoideus,* adapted to the making of the specific type of wine, is selected. Famous types are the Burgundy, Tokay, and champagne cultures so widely used. The cultures are grown and built up in volume in must (juice of the grape or other fruit) like that to be used in the main fermentation.

Distillers' Yeast

Distillers' yeast ordinarily is a high-alcohol-yielding strain of *S. cerevisiae* var. *ellipsoideus,* usually one adapted to growing in the medium or mash to be employed. The medium or mash would be malted grain, usually corn or rye for whiskey, molasses for rum, or juices or mashes of fruits for brandy. The liquors are distillates of the fermented mashes.

MOLD CULTURES

Stock cultures of molds usually are carried on slants of a suitable agar medium, e.g., malt-extract agar, and may be preserved in the spore state for long periods by lyophilization (freeze drying) or as soil stocks. There are a number of different ways of preparing spore or mycelial cultures for use on a plant scale. These include (1) surface growth on a liquid or agar medium in a flask or similar container, (2) surface growth on media in shallow layers in trays, (3) growth on loose, moistened wheat bran which may be acidified or may have liquid nutrient added, e.g., corn-steep liquor, (4) growth on previously sterilized and moistened bread or crackers, or (5) growth by the submerged method in an aerated liquid medium, usually resulting in pellets composed of mycelium, with or without spores. The mold spores are recovered in different ways, depending on the method of production. They may be washed or drawn from dry surfaces, may be left in dry material that is ground up or powdered, or for convenience in use may be incorporated in some dry powder, e.g., flour. The pellets, of course, are used as such.

Spores of *Penicillium roqueforti* for blue cheeses, Roquefort, Stilton, Gorgonzola, etc., usually are grown on cubes of sterilized, moistened, and usually acidified bread; whole wheat or bread of a special formula may be employed. After the sporulation of the mold is complete, bread and culture are dried, powdered, and packaged, commonly in cans.

P. camemberti spores are prepared by growing the mold on moistened sterile crackers. A spore suspension is prepared for the surface inoculation of the Camembert, Brie, or similar cheese.

Mold starters used as inoculum in industrial submerged fermentations usually are prepared in the form of pellets or masses of mycelium that are produced during submerged growth while the culture is being actively shaken. When surface growth is desired on liquid or agar medium or on bran, mold spores, produced by the methods listed previously, ordinarily serve as the inoculum.

The koji, or starter, for soy sauce, described in the next chapter, usually is a mixed culture carried over from a previous lot, although pure cultures of *Aspergillus oryzae,* together with a yeast and *Lactobacillus delbrueckii,* have been used. The mold culture is grown on cooked, sterilized rice.

BIBLIOGRAPHY

Amerine, M. A., H. W. Berg, and W. V. Cruess. 1972. The technology of wine making. AVI Publishing Co., Inc., Westport, Conn.

Chance, H. L. 1963. Salt: a preservative for bacterial cultures. J. Bacteriol. 85:719–720.

Christensen, V. W. 1975. New developments in cultures. 70th Annu. Meet. Am. Dairy Sci. Ass. Kans. State Univ.

Christensen, V. W. 1976. "Superstarts" direct set concentrated cultures for cheesemaking. Cheese Ind. Conf. August 1976.

Efstathiou, J. D., L. L. McKay, H. A. Morris, and E. A. Zottola. 1975. Growth and preservation parameters for preparation of a mixed species culture concentrate for cheese manufacture. J. Milk Food Technol. 38:444–448.

Foster, E. M. 1962. Symposium on lactic starter cultures. VI. Culture preservation. J. Dairy Sci. 45:1290–1298.

Foster, E. M., F. E. Nelson, M. L. Speck, R. N. Doetsch, and J. C. Olson, Jr. 1957. Dairy microbiology. Prentice-Hall, Inc., Englewood Cliffs, N.J.

Fry, R. M. 1954. The preservation of bacteria. In R. J. C. Harris (ed.), Biological applications of freezing and drying. Academic Press, Inc., New York.

Gibson, C. A., G. B. Landerkin, and P. M. Morse. 1966. Effects of additives on the survival of lactic streptococci in frozen storage. J. Appl. Microbiol. 14:665–669.

Gilliland, S. E. 1985. Bacterial starter cultures for foods. CRC Press, Inc., Boca Raton, Fla.

Gilliland, S. E., and M. L. Speck. 1974. Frozen concentrated cultures of lactic starter bacteria: a review. J. Milk Food Technol. 37:107–112.

Hales, M. W. 1963. The care of cultures. J. Dairy Sci. 46:1439–1440.

Harlander, S. K., L. L. McKay, and C. F. Schachtels. 1984. Molecular cloning of lactose-metabolizing genes from Streptococcus lactis. Appl. Environ. Microbiol. 48:347–351.

Hartsell, S. E. 1956. Maintenance of cultures under paraffin oil. Appl. Microbiol. 4:350–355.

Keogh, B. P. 1970. Survival and activity of frozen starter cultures for cheese manufacture. J. Appl. Microbiol. 19:928–931.

Lamprech, E. D., and E. M. Foster. 1963. The survival of starter organisms in concentrated suspensions. J. Appl. Bacteriol. 26(3):359–369.

McCoy, E. 1954. Selection and maintenance of cultures. In L. A. Underkofler and R. J. Hickey (eds.), Industrial fermentations. Chemical Publishing Company, Inc., New York.

Perlman, D., et al. 1955. Symposium on the maintenance of cultures of microorganisms. Bacteriol. Rev. 19:280–283.

Rose, A. H. (ed.). 1982. Fermented foods. Academic Press, Inc., New York.

Sellars, R. L. 1967. Lactic starter cultures. In H. J. Peppler (ed.), Microbial technology. Reinhold Publishing Corporation, New York.

Sellars, R. L., and F. J. Babel. 1970. Cultures for the manufacture of dairy products. Chr. Hansen's Laboratory, Inc., Milwaukee.

Simmons, J. C., and D. M. Graham. 1959. Maintenance of active lactic cultures by freezing as an alternative to daily transfer. J. Dairy Sci. 42:363–364.

Speck, M. L. (Convenor). 1962. Symposium on lactic starter cultures. J. Dairy Sci. 45:1262–1294.

Steel, K. J., and H. E. Ross. 1963. Survival of freeze dried bacterial cultures. J. Appl. Bacteriol. 26:370–375.

Tamine, A. Y. 1981. Microbiology of starter cultures. In R. K. Robinson (ed.), Dairy microbiology, vol. 2. Applied Science Publications, London.

Valles, E., and G. Mocquot. 1968. Préparation de suspensions concentrées et congelées de bactéries lactiques thermophiles destinées à la fromagerie. Lait. 48:631–643.

Wagman, J., and E. J. Weneck. 1963. Preservation of bacteria by circulating-gas freeze drying. Appl. Microbiol. 11:244–248.

Ziemba, J. U. 1970. Top-quality cultures made in unique plant. Food Eng. 42:68, 70, 73.

FOOD FERMENTATIONS

The lactic acid fermentation of cabbage, cucumbers, and green olives not only helps preserve the foods but also results in distinctive new food products. Many fermentations make new and desired products, and preservative effects are incidental. The fermentations may be by yeasts, bacteria, molds, or combinations of these organisms. In the first group of food products—bread, beer, wine, and distilled liquors—fermentation by yeasts is of primary importance. Yeasts and bacteria are involved in the manufacture of vinegar from sugar-bearing materials, and bacteria chiefly in the production of fermented milks. Molds are important in the preparation of some cheeses and Oriental foods.

BREAD

Microorganisms are useful in two chief ways in breadmaking: (1) They may produce gas to leaven, or raise, the dough, giving the bread the desired loose, porous texture, and (2) they may produce desirable flavoring substances. They also may function in the conditioning of the dough.

Leavening

Dough is usually leavened by bread yeasts (Chapter 21), which ferment the sugars in the dough and produce mainly carbon dioxide and alcohol. However, other actively gas-forming microorganisms, such as wild yeasts, coliform bacteria, saccharolytic *Clostridium* species, heterofermentative lactic acid bacte-

330

ria, and various naturally occurring mixtures of these organisms, have been used instead of bread yeasts for leavening. Leavening also may be accomplished by the direct incorporation of gas (CO_2) in the dough.

Leavening by Bread Yeasts   There is little or no growth during the first 2 hr after the yeast is added to the dough, but some growth in 2 to 4 hr, if that much time is allowed before baking, and then a decline in growth in 4 to 6 hr. Fermentation by the yeast begins as soon as the dough (or sponge) is mixed and continues until the temperature of the oven inactivates the yeast enzymes. The professional baker adds a considerable amount of yeast and has a comparatively short making time. Modern trends in home baking are toward the addition of an excess of yeasts so that the fermentation may be even shorter than it is in commercial practice. These short-time processes encourage little or no growth of yeast during the fermentation process. Older home methods involved the use of less yeast or less effective yeast and therefore resulted in a longer making time and some opportunity for yeast and bacterial growth. During the fermentation, "conditioning" of the dough takes place when the flour proteins (gluten) mature, i.e., become elastic and springy and therefore capable of retaining a maximal amount of the carbon dioxide produced by the yeasts. The conditioning results from action on the gluten by (1) proteolytic enzymes in the flour from the yeast, from the malt, or added otherwise and (2) the reduction in pH by the acids added and formed. Dough conditioners, sometimes called yeast foods, that are added include ammonium salts to stimulate the yeasts and various salts, e.g., $KBrO_3$, KIO_3, CaO_2, and $(NH_4)_2S_2O_8$, to improve dough characteristics.

Although the sugar in the flour plus that produced by the action of the flour amylase may be enough for the yeast fermentation, most formulas call for the addition of more sugar or of amylase-bearing malt. The rate of gas production by the yeasts is increased by adding (1) more yeast, (2) sugar or amylase-bearing malt, and (3) yeast food, within limits. It is decreased by (1) the addition of salt, (2) the addition of too much yeast food, and (3) the use of too high or too low temperatures. The main objectives of the baker during leavening are to have enough gas produced and to have the dough in such a condition that it will hold the gas at the right time.

In the sponge method of breadmaking, some of the ingredients are mixed at 23 to 24 C and allowed to ferment to the desired maturity. Then the rest of the ingredients are added and the fermentation is continued until the dough is in the desired condition. In the straight-dough method of making, all the ingredients are mixed at 26 to 28 C. The fermentation room, where the dough is held for most of the leavening process, is usually held at about 27 C.

Leavening by Other Microorganisms   Leavening can be accomplished by gas-forming organisms other than the bread yeasts. Breads can be leavened by dough carried over from a previous making, as for certain special breads and sourdough bread. Heterofermentative lactic acid bacteria and saccharolytic anaerobes can take part in the leavening. Salt-rising bread is leavened by "salt-rising yeast" as well as by microorganisms from the ingredients; it also may utilize bakers' yeast. In some cases a succession of organisms leaven, flavor, and modify dough, as in the production of soda crackers, where a 3- to 4-hr fermentation is followed by action by lactic acid bacteria. Soda-cracker sponge also may be fermented by added yeast and by bacteria that are present.

Leavening by Chemicals   Leavening of dough may be accomplished by chemical agents instead of by microorganisms, but the product cannot be called bread according to standards of identity which specify yeast leavening. Carbon dioxide gas, which may be incorporated directly into the dough, or baking powders, which are combinations of chemical compounds that release gas when mixed into the dough, may be employed for leavening. The addition of ammonium bicarbonate can be used since the heat of baking will result in the release of carbon dioxide and ammonium gas. Self-rising flour contains both the acid and basic components of baking powder, which react upon moistening.

Continuous Breadmaking

Continuous breadmaking processes usually involve growth and fermentation by the yeast in part of the ingredients to get a large yield of active yeast—or at least the addition of more yeast than usual—before the final dough is formed. Leavening may take place in the pans just before baking.

Flavor Production

Yeasts are reported to contribute to the flavor of bread through products released during the fermentation of sugars, although most workers believe that yeasts add little or no flavor, especially in bread made by the rapid methods now employed. Alcohol, acids, esters, and aldehydes are products that may add desirable flavors. Most experts maintain, however, that bacteria growing in the dough can contribute the most to flavor. Too little time is allowed in the usual industrial leavening and working process for the bacteria to grow enough to appreciably affect the flavor, but the longer time available during the older methods of making in the home permits enough bacterial growth for a considerable production of desirable flavors. Dough leavened by means of a previous lot of dough may receive a good inoculum of desirable flavor-producing bacteria in this way. Some special brands of bread made in this manner are famous for their characteristic flavors.

Most of the flavor in bakers' bread, then, comes from the ingredients and chemical reactions that occur, such as Maillard browning, during baking. If enough time is given previous to baking for the growth of bacteria, they may add to the flavor, as may the yeasts to a lesser extent. Flavoring substances so developed may include alcohol; diacetyl; aldehydes, acetoin, and isoalcohols; and lactic, acetic, and succinic acids and their esters.

The Baking Process

Although the interior of the loaf does not quite reach 100 C during baking, the heat serves to kill the yeasts, inactivate their enzymes and those of the flour and malt, expand the gas present, and set the structure of the loaf. Baking, besides producing the appearance of the loaf, also contributes desirable flavors. The heat also drives off most of the alcohol and other volatile substances formed by the yeasts but contributes substances such as furfural, pyruvic and other aldehydes, and other compounds that add to the flavor. The most important change in bread during baking is gelatinization of starch. "Set" of bread results from this process, in which gluten gives structural support in the dough, but starch supports the structure of baked bread.

Rye Bread

Rye bread may be made with or without a starter, or "sour." The old method of preparing sour depended on the bacteria naturally present in a mixture of rye flour and water. The mixture was allowed to ferment for 5 to 10 hr; then more flour and water were added and the fermentation was continued for an additional 5 to 6 hr; then this was repeated several times. Half of the sour thus produced was incorporated in the sponge or dough for the bread, and the rest was carried over to start a new sour. This sour was modified by some bakers by the addition of yeasts and of lactic acid bacteria from cultured buttermilk or Bulgarian buttermilk to a sour that was made anew daily. Obviously such sours lack uniformity.

Modern methods involve adding considerable amounts of cultures of acid-forming bacteria to the dough mass used as a sour and controlling the fermentation time (18 to 24 hr) and the incubation temperature (about 25 C). An excessively high incubation temperature, for example, 32 to 35 C, favors the growth of undesirable gas formers, such as coliform and butyric bacteria. Some bakers prefer to use low-temperature lactic acid bacteria, e.g., *Lactobacillus plantarum, L. brevis,* and *Leuconostoc mesenteroides**, whereas others use high-temperature lactics, such as *Lactobacillus bulgaricus** and *Streptococcus thermophilus* and adjust the incubation temperature accordingly. The growth of heterofermentative lactic acid bacteria is considered desirable. The starter imparts a desired tangy or sour flavor to the rye bread that is not given by the addition of lactic and acetic acids.

San Francisco Dough Bread

The leavening of this type of bread results from the action of *Torulopsis holmii,* the asporogenous form of *Saccharomyces exiguus.* The second principal organism involved, responsible for the acid development, has been identified as a heterofermentative lactobacillus, *Lactobacillus sanfrancisco.*

MALT BEVERAGES

Beer and ale are the principal malt beverages produced and consumed in this country and will be the ones discussed here. They are made of malt, hops, yeasts, water, and malt adjuncts. The malt is prepared from barley grains which have been germinated and dried and had the sprouts or germs removed. Hops are the dried flowers of the hop plant. The malt adjuncts are starch- or sugar-containing materials added in addition to the carbohydrates in the malt. Starch adjuncts include corn and corn products, rice, wheat, barley, sorghum grain, soybeans, cassava, potatoes, etc., with corn and rice used most frequently. Sweet adjuncts are materials such as sugars and sirups.

Brewing of Beer

The manufacture of beer will be outlined briefly as an example of the brewing process.

Malting In the preparation of malt, barley grains are soaked, or "steeped," at 10 to 15.6 C, germinated at 16 to 21 C for 5 to 7 days, and kiln-dried. Most of the sprouts or germs are removed, and the malt remains. The malt, a source of amylases and proteinases, is crushed before use.

Mashing The purpose of the mashing process is to make soluble as much as possible of the valuable portions of the malt and malt adjuncts and especially to cause hydrolysis of starches and other polysaccharides and of proteins and products of their hydrolysis. First, the main malt mash is prepared by mixing the ground malt with water at 38 to 50 C. To this are added the cooked, starchy malt adjuncts in water, which are at about 100 C after a boiling or cooking under steam pressure. This brings the temperature of the resulting cereal-malt mash to about 65 to 70 C, at which temperature saccharification (production of sugars from the starch) takes place within a short time. Then, the temperature is increased to about 75 C, which inactivates the enzymes. Insoluble materials that settle to the bottom of the container serve as a filter, so that the liquid that emerges, called **wort,** is clear. A special "lauter" tub may be used for this filtration. Rinsings from the filtering material are added to the wort. Next, hops are added to the wort to constitute the liquid from which the final wort is to be prepared for fermentation. Some of the mashing procedures and the mash itself may be substituted for in more advanced processes by using partially hydrolyzed sirups derived from corn or barley.

Boiling the Wort with Hops The liquid containing wort and hops is boiled for about 2.5 hr, after which it is filtered through the hop residues. In this way the hop solids and precipitated proteins are removed. The precipitate is washed with hot water to remove most of the soluble material, and the washings are added to the original filtrate. The resulting mash or wort is ready for fermentation.

Boiling the wort with hops has a number of purposes: (1) to concentrate it, (2) to practically sterilize it, (3) to inactivate enzymes, (4) to extract soluble substances from the hops, (5) to coagulate and precipitate proteins and other substances, (6) to caramelize the sugar slightly, and (7) to contribute antiseptic substances (chiefly the alpha resins humulone, cohumulone, and adhumulone) to the wort and the beer. These resins are effective against gram-positive bacteria. Extracted from the hops are the bitter acids and resins, which aid in flavor, stability, and head retention of the beer; essential oil, which adds a little flavor; and tannins, which are removed as much as possible, because they may be responsible for poor flavors and haziness in the beer. Recent developments include the use of concentrated hop extracts or vacuum-packed milled hops as a replacement for the dried, whole hop flower.

Fermentation A special beer yeast of the bottom type, a strain of *Saccharomyces carlsbergensis,* is used for the inoculation or "pitching" of the cooled wort. The pitching yeast ordinarily has been recovered from a previous fermentation. A fairly heavy inoculum, about 1 lb per barrel (31.5 gal) of beer, is employed. The wort temperature during the fermentation varies in different breweries but is usually in the range from 3.3 to 14 C. Some brewers maintain the temperature at about 3.3 to 4.4 C, while others start with a low temperature and raise it later. The fermentation is complete within 8 to 14 days, usually in 8 to 10 days.

During the fermentation, the yeast converts the sugar in the wort chiefly to alcohol and carbon dioxide, plus small amounts of glycerol and acetic acid. Proteins and fat derivatives yield small amounts of higher alcohols and acids, and organic acids and alcohols combine to form aromatic esters. As the carbon dioxide is evolved in increasing amounts, the foaming increases; later it decreases to none when the fermentation has concluded. At a later stage the bottom yeasts "break," i.e., flocculate and settle. Bacterial growth is not desired during the fermentation and subsequent aging of the beer.

Aging, or Maturing The young, or "green," beer is stored, or "lagered," in vats at about 0 C for from several weeks to several months, during which period precipitation of proteins, yeast, resin, and other undesirable substances takes place and the beer becomes clear and mellowed or matured. Esters and other compounds are produced to add to the taste and aroma, and the body changes from harsh to smooth.

Finishing After aging, the lager beer is carbonated to a CO_2 content of about 0.45 to 0.52 percent, mostly by means of gas collected during the fermentation. Then the beer is cooled, clarified, or filtered and packaged in bottles, cans, or barrels. The alcohol content is about 3.8 percent by weight. The beer for cans or smaller bottles is pasteurized briefly at about 60 to 61 C or filtered through membranes or other materials to remove all yeasts.

Continuous Processes   Continuous malting to shorten germination time of the barley involves application of aerated water to the grain as a finely divided spray after the barley has been wetted and washed. Continuous brewing employs nonstop mashing and boiling of wort as well as flow-through fermentation. The beer may be bottled without aging.

Microbiology   The procedures during the brewing process have a great influence on the ability of microorganisms to survive or grow. Little is known about the growth of organisms during malting, in the main malt mash, or in the cereal-malt mash, although growth must take place in the first two. Boiling the wort and hops for 2.5 hr, however, provides sufficient heat to destroy all but the most resistant bacterial spores, such as those of some *Bacillus* or *Clostridium* species, and the combined action of heat and hop antiseptics may destroy most of those and inhibit any survivors. The yeast used in pitching should be a pure culture (but usually is not) and hence should contribute no contaminating organisms. The wort is unfavorable to some organisms because of its low pH (3.7 to 4.5) and its content of antiseptics extracted from the hops. Then, too, temperatures are low during both fermentation and aging, and conditions are anaerobic. The alcohol produced also may be inhibitory to organisms.

Beer should hinder the growth of microorganisms because of its low pH, its content of antiseptics in the form of alcohol and hop extracts, (mainly resins or humulones), and its low temperature of storage. Also, conditions are anaerobic throughout its processing and storage, and much of the beer sold has been pasteurized or filtered.

Yet, despite all these reasons why beer should be free of spoilage organisms, it is subject not only to defects from physical and chemical causes but also to "diseases" caused by microorganisms. Since the microorganisms that are most important in causing diseases of beer are readily killed by temperatures below boiling, they must enter after the boiling of the wort with hops.

Beer Defects and "Diseases"

The term **defects** will be applied here to undesirable characteristics with causes that are not microbial, such as (1) turbidity due to unstable protein, protein-tannin complexes, starch, and resin, (2) off-flavors caused by poor ingredients or contact with metals, and (3) poor physical characteristics. This discussion will be limited to the troubles caused by microorganisms and therefore termed **beer infections** or **beer diseases.** The mash in the brewhouse may undergo butyric acid fermentation by *Clostridium* spp. or lactic acid fermentation by lactics if the mash is held too long at temperatures favoring these bacteria. Off-flavors so produced may carry over into the beer. It was pointed out in Chapter 21 that the pitching yeast ordinarily is contaminated with bacteria and wild yeasts and may be a source of spoilage organisms. Yeasts and bacteria produce turbidity when they grow in beer, and beer yeasts carried over from the fermentation may be responsible for cloudiness. Likewise, wild yeasts, e.g., *Saccharomyces pastorianus,* can cause cloudiness in beer. Yeasts can be inhibited or excluded by keeping out air, fermenting most of the sugar in the wort to produce a "dry" beer, using good cultures of beer yeasts, and sanitizing the plant adequately. Yeasts also may be responsible for off-tastes and off-odors. Thus, for example, bitterness may be caused by *S. pastorianus,* and an esterlike taste by *Hansenula anomala.* Most yeasts produce fruity odors, and some produce hydrogen sulfide from the hop extract in the beer. Yeasts able to utilize the dextrins in beer (e.g., *Saccharomyces diastaticus*) are potential spoilage organisms.

The bacteria causing beer diseases are mostly from the genera *Pediococcus, Lactobacillus, Flavobacterium,* and *Acetobacter.*

"Sarcina sickness," characterized by sourness, turbidity, and ropiness of beer, is caused by *Pediococcus cerevisiae.* Because the cocci often aggregate in fours or tetrads, they were first thought to be sarcinae.

Some lactobacilli, being tolerant to acid and hop antiseptics, can grow in beer. *Lactobacillus pastorianus** and *L. diastaticus** cause sourness and a silky turbidity. These bacteria produce lactic, acetic, and formic acids and alcohol and carbon dioxide from sugars, and are especially bad in top fermentations such as are used for ales.

Zymomonas anaerobium, when growing in beer, causes a silky turbidity and produces an odor reminiscent of hydrogen sulfide and apples. It forms carbon dioxide and alcohol. It is easily killed by heat and rarely occurs in pasteurized beer.

Obesumbacterium proteus is responsible for a parsniplike odor and taste in wort and in beer. It produces alcohol and acid and is not tolerant of a pH as low as 4.2. It has been found as a common contaminant of pitching yeast.

Species of *Acetobacter* and *Gluconobacter,* which are tolerant of acid and hop antiseptics, can cause sourness of wort or beer under aerobic conditions. Exposure to oxygen can occur in worts that are stored too long, in empty beer barrels, and in pitching yeast. A number of species can cause sourness; *Gluconobacter oxydans* subsp. *suboxydans** and *G. oxydans* subsp. *industrius** may produce ropiness; and *A. pasteurianus* has been blamed for turbidity and sourness.

Other incompletely described, unidentified bacteria have been blamed for beer diseases. *Micrococcus**, *Streptococcus,* and *Bacillus* species have been accused of causing trouble but in some instances probably merely were present. *Streptococcus mucilaginosus**, which probably is a pediococcus, has been reported to cause ropiness.

It should be reemphasized that all the yeasts and bacteria that cause infections or diseases in wort and beer are killed by boiling the wort and hops and must enter thereafter from equipment, the air, the water, or the pitching yeast and that aseptic and sanitary precautions will help prevent these troubles.

Other Malt Beverages and Beer Types

Variations in malt beverages or beer types are usually related to (1) alcohol content, (2) concentration of malt and hops used, (3) length of aging, (4) initial total solids (related to fermentable carbohydrate present and remaining after fermentation), and (5) temperature of fermentation.

Malt liquor may have a higher alcohol content than does regular beer.

Bock beer is a very dark beer with a high alcohol content. Brewing involves the addition of higher concentrations of malt and hops followed by longer aging.

Pilsener is a lager-type beer, light in color, containing little remaining fermentable carbohydrate.

Low-calorie, light, or **no-carbohydrate** beers are made from prehydrolyzed wort. Fungal enzymes (glucoamylases and amylases) are used to hydrolyze the dextrin to maltose and glucose, which can be completely fermented to alcohol; the net result is a lower concentration of remaining carbohydrate.

Ale usually is made with a top yeast, a strain of *Saccharomyces cerevisiae,* instead of the bottom yeast employed for beer, although a bottom yeast sometimes is used. The primary fermentation takes place at 12.2 to 24.4 C, a higher temperature than for beer, and therefore the fermentation is more rapid, taking 5 to 7 days. The top yeast forms clumps which collect carbon dioxide gas and are carried to the top of the wort. At intervals the yeast scum is skimmed off. More hops are used in ale than in beer, and some ales have a higher alcohol content. Ale usually is pale in color and tart in taste.

Weiss beer, porter, and **stout** are ales in that top yeasts are employed in their manufacture. Weiss beer is a light, tart ale made chiefly from wheat. Porter and stout are dark, heavy, sweet ales.

Related Beverages

Sake is a yellow rice beer or wine of Japanese origin with an alcohol content of about 14 to 17 percent. A starter, or koji, for sake is made by growing *Aspergillus oryzae* on a soaked and steamed rice mash until a maximal yield of enzymes is obtained. This koji contains amylases which cause the hydrolysis of rice starch to sugars available to yeasts plus other hydrolytic enzymes such as proteinases. The koji is mixed with more rice mash, starch is converted to sugar, and several species of yeast of the genus *Saccharomyces* carry out the alcoholic fermentation. The liquor filtered from the fermented mass after 10 to 14 days is the sake. **Sonti** is a rice beer or wine of India. The mold *Rhizopus sonti* and yeasts are active in the fermentation.

Pulque is a Latin-American beerlike beverage containing about 6 percent alcohol that results from a natural yeast fermentation of the juice of the agave, or century plant.

Ginger beer is a mildly alcoholic, acid beverage made by the fermentation of a sugar solution flavored with ginger. The starter is the "ginger-beer plant," in which a yeast, *Saccharomyces pyriformis,* and a capsulated bacterium, *Lac-*

tobacillus vermiformis*, are enclosed in the gelatinous capsular material of the lactobacillus.

WINES

Unless otherwise specified, the term **wine** is applied here to the product made by the alcoholic fermentation of grapes or grape juice by yeasts and a subsequent aging process. Wines, however, can be produced by the fermentation of the juices of fruits, berries, rhubarb, dandelions, honey, etc.

Grape Wine

Grape wines are for the most part either red or white. The red wines, fermented on the skins, contain the red pigment from the skins of purple or red varieties of grapes, whereas white wines are made from white grapes or the expressed juice of other grapes, fermented free of the skins. The manufacture of red wine will be outlined briefly as an example of the wine-making process.

Preparation of Juice   Grapes of a variety especially adapted to wine making are harvested at a stage when they have the desired sugar content. The concentration of sugar may range from 15 to 25 percent, depending on the grape variety and its degree of ripeness. They are stemmed and crushed by machine and then treated with sulfur dioxide (75 to 200 ppm) or potassium metabisulfite in equivalent amounts to inhibit the growth of undesirable competitors of the wine yeast.

Fermentation   A "natural inoculum" (yeast present on the grapes) or more commonly 2 to 5 percent of a special wine yeast, a strain of *Saccharomyces cerevisiae* var. *ellipsoideus*, is added to the crushed grapes, or **must.** At first the contents of the tank are mixed twice a day by punching the "cap" of floating skins, stems, etc., pumping juice over the skins, or mixing in some other way to aerate and hence encourage growth of the yeast and aid in the extraction of color from the skins (for red wines). Alternatively, the red pigments may be extracted from the skins by heat and added back to the juice. Later the mixing is discontinued, for anaerobic conditions are most favorable to the alcoholic fermentation. It is very important that the temperature be maintained within an optimal range, i.e., between 24 and 27 C for red wines, during the active fermentation, which takes about 3 to 5 days, and at 10 to 21 C for white wines (active fermentation takes 7 to 14 days). An excessively high temperature inhibits the wine yeasts and permits competing organisms, e.g., the lactobacilli, to grow and cause defects; too low a temperature slows action of the wine yeasts and permits wild yeasts, lactic acid bacteria, and other organisms to grow. Heat is liberated during the fermentation, and this, coupled with high atmospheric temperatures, may necessitate artificial cooling of the must.

After the primary or active fermentation has advanced sufficiently, the fermented juice is drawn off from the residues (pomace) and placed in a storage tank under a light pressure of carbon dioxide for the secondary fermentation for 7 to 11 days at about 21 to 29 C. Here the remaining sugar is fermented if a dry wine is desired. Clear wine is drawn off, or "racked," from the sediment at the bottom of the tank.

Storing and Aging   The wine may be flash-pasteurized before aging (but usually is not) to precipitate proteins. It is cooled, held for a few days, filtered, and transferred into wooden tanks (usually of white oak or redwood) or plastic-coated concrete tanks for aging. The tanks are filled completely and sealed to keep out air. Periodically the wine is racked from bottom sediment. Final aging may be in the bottle. Aging for months or years results in desirable changes in body and flavor of the wine, giving it the aroma or bouquet that should be one of its characteristics. Esters and alcohols are considered important contributors to bouquet and taste. During aging some fermentation of the malic acid of grape juice by lactobacilli or micrococci* (malolactic fermentation) may take place with the production of lactic acid and carbon dioxide and reduction in acidity.

After aging, the wine is filtered or otherwise clarified, barreled or bottled, and stored. Some wines are pasteurized after aging, usually in the bottle. The final alcohol content varies widely but usually is between 6 and 9 percent by weight or 8 and 13 percent by volume.

Volatile Acidity of Wines   A high content of volatile acid in wines is indicative of a faulty fermentation. In the United States the legal limit for volatile acid content is 0.14 g per 100 ml, expressed as acetic acid, for red wine and 0.12 g for white wine.

Microbiology   The grapes when crushed have a variety of microorganisms on their surfaces, including yeasts and bacteria. Not only is the surface flora of the grape present, but also an array of contaminants from the soil. To suppress these organisms the wine maker adds sulfur dioxide or sulfite or less commonly pasteurizes the must (expressed juice). During the primary fermentation the added wine yeast predominates. During early stages, growth of the yeast is favored by aeration of the must; later, anaerobic conditions favor the alcoholic fermentation by the yeasts, liberating carbon dioxide and ethyl alcohol, both of which help inhibit organisms other than the wine yeasts. The atmosphere of carbon dioxide above the wine during the secondary fermentation prevents the growth of aerobic contaminants, such as the acetic acid bacteria. The pasteurization that follows, although not for that purpose, reduces the numbers of microorganisms that later might cause spoilage ("diseases") of the wine. There should be little or no growth of organisms during the aging and storage of the wine, but organisms that can grow then may be introduced by contamination from the tanks, barrels, or bottles, and changes such as the malolactic fermentation may take place.

Kinds of Wine

No attempt will be made to list the scores of names applied to different types of wines. Instead a few general descriptive terms will be defined. Most wines are **still** wines—i.e., they retain none of the carbon dioxide produced during the fermentation—in contrast to **sparkling** wines, which contain considerable amounts. Other wines may be artificially **carbonated.**

Dry wines contain little or no unfermented sugar, as contrasted to **sweet** wines, which have sugar left or added. Wines usually contain from 11 to 16 percent alcohol by volume but may go as low as 7 percent. **Fortified** wines, however, to which distillate of wine called "wine spirits" or "brandy" has been added, contain about 19 to 21 percent of alcohol by volume. **Table** wines have a comparatively low content of alcohol and little or no sugar, while **dessert** wines are fortified, sweet wines.

French dry sherry is of interest because it is made from grapes which have a high sugar content as a result of being dried out by an infecting gray mold, *Botrytis cinerea;* they therefore yield a wine with a high content of alcohol. Spanish (Jerez) sherry supports the growth of a yeast film, presumably of one or more species of *Saccharomyces,* while the wine is being racked in partially filled barrels following the main fermentations. This yeast growth, or "flor," imparts a special bouquet and flavor to the wine.

Wine Defects and Microbial Spoilage

Like beer, wine has defects from nonmicrobial causes and spoilage caused by microorganisms. Defects include those due to metals or their salts, enzymes, and agents employed in clearing the wine. Iron, for example, may produce a sediment known variously as gray, black, blue, or ferric casse, and in white wine may be responsible for a white precipitate of iron phosphate termed white casse. Tin and copper and their salts have been blamed for cloudiness. White wines may be turned brown and red wines may have their color precipitated by peroxidase, an oxidizing enzyme of certain molds. Gelatin, used in clarifying wines, may cause cloudiness.

The microorganisms causing wine spoilage are chiefly wild yeasts, molds, and bacteria of the genera *Acetobacter, Lactobacillus, Leuconostoc,* and perhaps *Micrococcus** and *Pediococcus.*

Factors Affecting Growth of Microorganisms in Wine   Factors that are known to influence the susceptibility of wines to microbial spoilage are:

1 *Acidity or pH.* The lower the pH, the less likely there is to be spoilage. The minimal pH permitting the growth of microorganisms varies with the organism, the type of wine, and the alcoholic content. Molds, yeasts, and acetic acid bacteria would not be stopped by any pH normal to wines, but most lactic acid bacteria will tolerate acidity down to about pH 3.3 to 3.5, a pH lower than that of most wines (most California table wines have a pH of about 3.5 to 4.0).

2 *Sugar content.* Dry wines (about 0.1 percent or less of sugar), with their low sugar content, are rarely spoiled by bacteria, but 0.5 to 1.0 percent or more of sugar will favor spoilage.

3 *Concentration of alcohol.* Tolerance of alcohol varies with the spoilage organism. Thus acetic bacteria spoiling musts and wines are inhibited by over 14 to 15 percent of alcohol by volume, but deacidifying cocci are stopped by about 12 percent, *Leuconostoc* spp. by over 14 percent, heterofermentative lactobacilli by about 18 percent (except *Lactobacillus trichodes*,* which grows in fortified wines in over 20 percent of alcohol), and homofermentative lactobacilli by about 10 percent.

4 *Concentration of accessory growth substances.* Acetobacter species can make their own vitamins, but the lactic acid bacteria must have most of them provided. The chief source of these substances in wines is the wine yeast, which releases the accessory growth factors on autolysis. The more of these substances there are present, the greater the likelihood of spoilage by lactic acid bacteria.

5 *Concentration of tannins.* Tannins added with gelatin for clarification retard bacteria, but usually not enough are added to be of much practical importance as inhibitors.

6 *Amount of sulfur dioxide present.* The more sulfur dioxide added, the greater the retardation of the spoilage microorganisms. The 75 to 200 ppm customarily added to the must usually is adequate. Effectiveness depends upon the kind of organism to be suppressed and increases with a lowering of pH and sugar content.

7 *Temperature of storage.* Spoilage usually is most rapid at 20 to 35 C and slows as the temperature is dropped toward freezing.

8 *Availability of air.* Absence of air prevents the growth of aerobic organisms, such as molds, film yeasts, and *Acetobacter,* but the lactic acid bacteria grow well anaerobically.

Spoilage by Aerobic Microorganisms   Film yeasts, which can oxidize alcohol and organic acids, may grow on the surface of must and wines exposed to air, producing a heavy pellicle called "wine flowers." They should cause no trouble if the must is mixed periodically and if air is kept away from the wine.

In the presence of air the aerobic acetic acid bacteria, usually *Acetobacter aceti* or *Gluconobacter oxydans,* oxidize alcohol in must or wine to acetic acid, an undesirable process called **acetification.** They also may oxidize glucose in the must to gluconic acid and may give a "mousy" or "sweet-sour" taste to the must.

Molds, such as *Mucor, Penicillium, Aspergillus,* and others, may grow on plant walls, barrels, tanks, hose lines, and corks and may also grow on the grapes or on cold must. Molds are kept down by adequate cleansing of walls and equipment.

Spoilage by Facultative Microorganisms   Wild yeasts, which include all yeasts but the wine yeast added as starter, may bring about abnormal fermentations that result in low alcohol content, high volatile acidity, undesirable flavors, and cloudiness in the wine. These yeasts, which come chiefly from the grapes from which the must is prepared and usually are predominantly of the apiculate type, are suppressed or eliminated by use of an active starter of the wine yeast, sulfiting or pasteurization of the must before the fermentation, and control of the temperature of the must during the fermentation. Low temperatures, below 21.1 C, will favor some of the wild yeasts and slime-producing bacteria.

Lactic acid bacteria are the principal causes of the bacterial spoilage of must and wines. There has been some confusion in the application of names to the various types of bacterial spoilage of wines, probably because several different kinds of bacteria may be able to cause the same defect or because the same organism may cause different defects under different conditions. Probably the most commonly occurring is **tourne** (turned or soured) spoilage, in which acid is formed from sugars, glucose, and fructose in the wine, chiefly by heterofermentative *Lactobacillus* species, such as *L. brevis, L. hilgardii, L. trichodes** and perhaps *L. buchneri*. The growth of the lactobacilli produces silky cloudiness, increases lactic and acetic acid, yields carbon dioxide, sometimes gives "mousy" or other disagreeable flavors, and damages the color of the wine. When the fermentation of fructose results in the bitter product mannitol, the fermentation sometimes is termed "mannitic"; bitterness (**amertume**) also may result from the fermentation of the glycerol in the wine. Gassiness resulting from any cause, such as from the liberation of carbon dioxide by heterofermentative lactics, is called **pousse**. The homofermentative. *L. plantarum* forms mostly lactic acid from sugars in table wines, increasing the fixed acidity and giving a "mousy" flavor.

The acidity of the wine may be reduced by the spoilage bacteria through the oxidation of the malic, citric, and tartaric acids by *Acetobacter* (aerobic) or through fermentation of malic and tartaric acids by species of *Lactobacillus, Leuconostoc,* or *Pediococcus* or by other cocci.

Sliminess or ropiness of young white wines, accompanied by cloudiness and increased volatile acidity, has been blamed on *Leuconostoc* spp., *L. mesenteroides,* and *L. dextranicum*;* on micrococci*; and on lactobacilli. Addition of sucrose, when permitted, favors the production of dextran and therefore of sliminess by *Leuconostoc*.

Any bacteria or yeasts growing in wine are likely to cause an undesirable cloudiness, and any acetic bacteria or heterofermentative lactic growing in the wine may increase the volatile acidity to an extent that will make the product unsalable. Fermentation of sugars usually results in an increase in acidity, in fixed acid if the lactic is homofermentative, and in fixed and volatile acid if the organism is heterofermentative. Oxidation or fermentation of the organic acids of the grape results in a decrease in amounts of fixed acid. It should be reemphasized that the composition of the wine is important in determining its susceptibility to bacterial spoilage. Thus white wines of low alcohol content are more readily subject to sliminess and spoilage by cocci than are other wines; musts and table wines support the growth of *Lactobacillus hilgardii, L. brevis,* and *Leuconostoc mesenteroides;* while *Lactobacillus trichodes** is the only species known to spoil California dessert wines and does not grow in musts.

It is interesting to note that the formation of lactic acid from malic acid in very sour wines may improve their quality by reducing the acidity. Lactic acid is a weaker acid than malic, and only two molecules of lactic acid are formed from three of malic. Some bacteria can also form lactic acid from tartaric acid and glycerol in wine.

Other Wines

Wines from Other Fruits   Wines can be made from most kinds of fruits, including apples (**hard cider**), peaches, apricots, plums, pears (**perry**), cherries, berries, and many others. Berries and most other fruits (except wine grapes) contain insufficient sugar to make a good wine and must be "ameliorated" by the addition of sugar before the fermentation. Otherwise, the manufacture of the wine is similar to that of grape wine. The products may be dry, sweet, fortified, sparkling, or carbonated. Wines for consumption as such or for distillation to produce brandies may also be made from dried fruits such as raisins, dates, figs, and prunes.

The manufacture and diseases of apple wine or hard cider, prepared from juice expressed from apples, have received considerable attention. Much American hard cider is made locally from apples not especially suited to its manufacture and is fermented by the yeasts that happen to be present. Therefore, often only 4 to 6 percent alcohol is produced, there is a residue of sugar, and flavor and bouquet may be defective or lacking. British and French ciders and some industrially produced American hard ciders are made from apples that are high in sugars and in tannin. Manufacturing methods may include sulfiting, the addition of sugars and yeast food, and inoculation with a proved yeast culture. Heterofermentative lactobacilli have been reported to be active during cider making, fermenting malic and citric acids, sugars, and glycerol to produce carbon dioxide; lactic, acetic, propionic, and succinic acids; and mannitol.

Most of the sicknesses or diseases of hard cider are similar to those of grape wine: cloudiness, low alcohol content, and off-flavors caused by wild yeasts; cloudiness and bad flavors produced by lactobacilli; sliminess or ropiness due to bacteria; acetic acid production, etc. The low acidity and low nitrogen content of ciders encourage the growth of the spoilage organisms.

Wines from Other Agricultural Products   Theoretically any edible product that contains sufficient moisture, sugar, and other foods for yeasts can be used to make wine. Honey wine, or **mead,** is made from diluted honey to which minerals and nitrogenous food for the yeasts have been added. Dandelion wine is a homemade product made by alcoholic fermentation of a water extract of flowers of the dandelion to which sugar, flavoring substances, and yeast have been added.

DISTILLED LIQUORS

Distilled liquors or spirits of interest here are those produced by distillation of an alcoholically fermented product. **Rum** is the distillate from alcoholically fermented sugarcane juice, sirup, or molasses. **Whiskeys** are distilled from saccharified and fermented grain mashes, e.g., rye whiskey from rye mash, bourbon or corn whiskey from corn mash, wheat whiskey from wheat mash, etc. Rums and whiskeys are made from mashes fermented by special distillers' yeasts, strains of *Saccharomyces cerevisiae* var. *ellipsoideus,* which give high yields of alcohol. The grain mashes usually are acidified to favor the yeasts. The aging of the distilled liquors in charred oaken barrels or tuns is a chemical rather than a biological process. **Brandy** means the distillate from grape wine, unless a qualifying word is added, e.g., apple brandy (applejack), peach brandy, and apricot brandy.

There should be no problems of spoilage of distilled liquors by microorganisms.

VINEGAR

It was pointed out in Chapter 13 that the normal course of changes in fruit juices at ordinary temperatures is an alcoholic fermentation by yeasts, followed by oxidation of the alcohol to acetic acid by acetic acid bacteria. If enough acetic acid is produced, the product is vinegar. **Vinegar** is defined as a condiment made from sugary or starchy materials by an alcoholic fermentation followed by an acetous one. It must contain at least 4g of acetic acid per 100 ml (or 40 grain) to be legal vinegar.

Kinds of Vinegar

Vinegars may be classified on the basis of the materials from which they have been made: (1) those from the juices of fruits, e.g., apples, grapes, oranges, pears, berries, etc., (2) those from starchy vegetables, e.g., potatoes or sweet potatoes, whose starch must first be hydrolyzed to sugars, (3) those from malted cereals, such as barley, rye, wheat, and corn, (4) those from sugars, such as sirups, molasses, honey, maple skimmings, etc., and (5) those from spirits or alcohol, e.g., from waste alcoholic liquor (beer) from yeast manufacture or from dilute, denatured ethyl alcohol. Anything, in fact, that contains enough sugar or alcohol and is in no way objectionable as food may be used to make vinegar.

The vinegar usually derives its descriptive name from the material from which it was made: cider vinegar from apple juice, alegar from ale, malt vinegar from malted grains, spirit vinegar from alcohol, etc. In the United States most table vinegar is cider vinegar, and therefore the term vinegar by itself usually means cider vinegar. Vinegar from grapes (wine) is most popular in France, and vinegar from malt liquors (alegar) in the British Isles.

Fermentation

As has been indicated, the manufacture of vinegar from saccharine materials involves two steps: (1) the fermentation of sugar to ethyl alcohol and (2) the oxidation of alcohol to acetic acid. The first step is an anaerobic process carried out by yeasts, either those naturally present in the raw material or, preferably, added cultures of high-alcohol-producing strains of *Saccharomyces cerevisiae* var. *ellipsoideus*. A simplified equation for the process is:

$$C_6H_{12}O_6 \rightarrow 2CO_2 + 2C_2H_5OH$$
$$\text{glucose} \qquad\qquad \text{alcohol}$$

Actually a series of intermediate reactions takes place, and small amounts of other final products are produced, such as glycerol and acetic acid. Also, there are small amounts of other substances, produced from compounds other than sugar, including succinic acid and amyl alcohol.

The second step, oxidation of the alcohol to acetic acid, is an aerobic reaction carried out by the acetic acid bacteria:

$$C_2H_5OH + O_2 \rightarrow CH_3COOH + H_2O$$
$$\text{alcohol} \quad \text{oxygen} \quad \text{acetic acid} \quad \text{water}$$

Acetaldehyde is an intermediate compound in this reaction. Among the final products are small amounts of aldehydes, esters, acetoin, etc.

The eighth edition of Bergey's Manual suggested three groups of *Acetobacter* with a total of nine subspecies. The genus *Gluconobacter* contained species capable of oxidizing ethanol to acetic acid. Volume 2 of Bergey's Manual (1986) suggested a Family called *Acetobacteriaceae* with two genera, *Acetobacter* and *Gluconobacter*. The later species are differentiated from *Acetobacter* by their inability to oxidize acetic or lactic acid to carbon dioxide. *Acetobacter* is currently described as containing species which can oxidize acetic or lactic acid to carbon dioxide. Many "acetic acid bacteria" are now classified in the genus *Gluconobacter*. Although the majority of the vinegar fermentation "work" may be done by *Gluconobacter* sp., the cultures actually used commercially are not pure but rather are a mixture of strains that have been adapted to the fermentation.

Methods of Manufacture

The ways of making vinegar may be divided into the "slow" methods, such as the home, or "let-alone," method and the French, or Orleans, method, and "quick" methods, such as the generator process or the fogging procedure. In slow methods the alcoholic liquid is not moved during acetification, while in quick methods the alcoholic liquid is in motion. For the most part the slow methods utilize fermented fruit juices or malt liquors for acetic acid production, whereas the quick methods are applied mostly to the production of vinegar from spirits (alcohol). Fruit or malt liquors are well supplied with food for the vinegar bacteria, but to maintain active vinegar bacteria in generator methods using alcohol, denatured with ethyl acetate or vinegar, it must be supplemented with a "vinegar food," which is a combination of organic and inorganic compounds that varies with the compounder. Combinations of substances such as dibasic ammonium phosphate, urea, asparagine, peptones, yeast extract, glucose, malt, starch, dextrins, salts, and other substances have been reported in use.

Slow Methods   In the home, or let-alone, method, a fruit juice such as apple juice is allowed to undergo a spontaneous alcoholic fermentation, preferably to about 11 to 13 percent of alcohol, by yeasts originally present, after which a barrel is partially filled with the fermented juice and placed on its side with the bunghole upward and open. Then the alcoholic solution is allowed to undergo an acetic acid fermentation, called acetification, carried out by vinegar bacteria naturally present until vinegar is produced. A film of vinegar bacteria called "mother of vinegar" should grow on the surface of the liquid and oxidize the alcohol to acetic acid. Unfortunately, the yield may be low because of a poor yield of alcohol during the yeast fermentation, because of the absence of productive strains of vinegar bacteria, because of the oxidation of acetic acid by the vinegar bacteria if there is a shortage of alcohol, or because of the competitive growth of film yeasts and molds on the surface, which destroy alcohol and acids, and of undesirable bacteria in the liquid, which produce undesirable flavors. The process is very slow, and the product often is of inferior quality.

In contrast to the batch process just described, the Orleans, or French, method employed considerably in Europe is a continuous process, although both processes usually are carried out in barrels. In the Orleans process raw vinegar from a previous run is introduced to fill about one-fourth to one-third of the barrel and serves to introduce an inoculum of active vinegar bacteria and to acidify the added wine, hard cider, or malt liquor so as to inhibit competing microorganisms. Enough of the alcoholic liquor is added to the vinegar to fill about half the barrel, leaving an air space above that is open to the outside air through the bunghole at the top and a hole in each end of the barrel above the level of the liquid. These holes are protected by screening. The acetic acid bacteria growing in a film on top of the liquid carry out the oxidation of alcohol to acetic acid for weeks to months at about 21 to 29 C, after which part of the vinegar so formed is drawn off for bottling and is replaced in the barrel by an equal quantity of alcoholic liquor. This operation is repeated a number of times, so that the process in this way becomes more or less continuous. Vinegar of high quality can be produced by this rather slow process.

One difficulty in this method is the dropping of the gelatinous film of vinegar bacteria and the resulting retardation of acetification. To avoid this difficulty a raft or floating framework sometimes is provided to support the film. It is claimed that too heavy a bacterial film will result in reduced acetification.

Quick Methods   As has been indicated, quick methods of vinegar manufacture involve the movement of the alcoholic liquid during the process of acetification. Most commonly this liquid is trickled down over surfaces on which films of the vinegar bacteria have grown and to which a plentiful supply of air is provided.

The generator method is the one in common use at present. The simple generator is a cylindrical tank that comes in different sizes and usually is made of wood. The interior is divided into three parts: an upper section, where the alcoholic liquid is introduced; the large middle section, where the liquid is allowed to trickle down over beechwood shavings, corncobs, rattan shavings, charcoal, coke, pomace, or some other material that will give a large total surface yet not settle into a compact mass; and the bottom section, where the vinegar collects. The alcoholic liquid is fed in at the top through an automatic feed trough or a sprinkling device (sparger) and trickled down over the shavings or other material on which has developed a slimy growth of acetic acid bacteria, which oxidize the alcohol to acetic acid. Air enters through the false bottom of the middle section and, on becoming warm, rises, to be vented above. Since the oxidation process here releases considerable heat, it usually is necessary to control the temperature so that it does not rise much above 29 to 30 C. This can be done by using cooling coils, by adjusting the rate of feeding air and alcoholic liquid, and by cooling the alcoholic liquid before it enters the generator or by cooling the partially acetified liquid that is returned to the top from the bottom section of the tank for further action.

In starting a new generator, the slime of vinegar bacteria must be established before vinegar can be made. First, the middle section of the tank is filled with raw vinegar that contains active vinegar bacteria to inoculate the shavings with the desired bacteria, or this material is circulated through the generator. Then an alcoholic liquid, acidified with vinegar, is slowly trickled through the generator to build up bacterial growth on the shavings and then is recirculated. Some makers acidify all the alcoholic liquid with vinegar before introducing it into the generator or leave some vinegar to acidify the new lot of liquid.

The vinegar may be made by one run of the alcoholic liquid through the generator, or the vinegar collected at the bottom may be recirculated through the generator if insufficient acid has been produced at first or too much alcohol is left. Sometimes generators are operated in tandem, the liquid from the first tank going through a second or even a third generator.

The Frings generator (Figure 22-1) is a large, cylindrical, airtight tank equipped with a sparger (sprinkler) at the top, cooling coils about the lower part of the middle section containing the shavings, and facilities for the recirculation of the vinegar from the bottom collection chamber through the

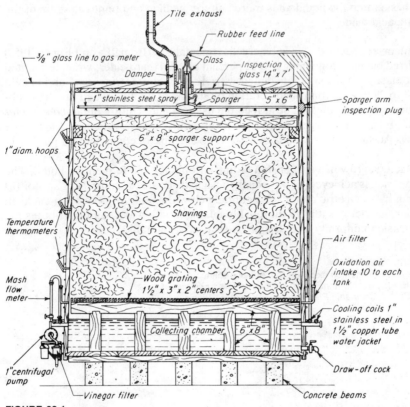

FIGURE 22-1
Diagram of a quick-method vinegar generator. (*Courtesy of Food Engineering.*)

system. Modern types of these generators are equipped with automatic controls for feeding the alcoholic liquid, for introducing filtered air, for controlling temperature, and for recirculating the liquid collected at the bottom. These generators give high yields of acetic acid and leave little residue of alcohol.

In the Mackin process, a fog or fine mist of a mixture of vinegar bacteria and nutrient alcohol solution is sprayed through jet nozzles into a chamber. The mist is kept in circulation by filtered air for a while and then is allowed to fall to the bottom for collection, to be cooled, reatomized, and returned to the chamber. This process is continued until oxidation of the alcohol is almost complete.

The dipping generator consists of a tank containing a basket filled with beechwood shavings that can be raised out of or lowered into dilute alcohol solution in the lower part of the tank. While the basket is out of the liquid, aeration permits rapid acetification by vinegar bacteria on the shavings, and lowering the basket into the liquid adds more culture medium and removes some of the acetic acid made.

Submerged Method   In submerged fermentation (Hromatka and Ebner, 1959) a stirred medium containing 8 to 12 percent alcohol (hard cider, wine, fermented malt mash, or spirits) is inoculated with *Acetobacter acetigenum** and is held at 24 to 29 C with controlled aeration by means of finely divided air. In a subsequent paper, Hromatka described the use of a pure culture of *Gluconobacter oxydans* in a submerged vinegar fermentation (Bergey's Manual, 1984). The Frings Acetator, shown in Figure 22-2, is an example of equipment for this method.

Bacteria grow in a suspension of fine air bubbles and fermenting liquid. The suspension is achieved by a specially designed aerator. It consists of a rotor (*a*) driven by an electric motor (*c*) mounted below the tank (*d*). The rotor sucks in the air, accelerates it after thoroughly mixing it with water, and distributes the suspension uniformly over the cross section of the tank.

FIGURE 22-2
Vinegar by submerged oxidation fermentation (Frings Acetator). (*By permission from Dr. H. Ebner and Food Engineering, Chilton Company, Philadelphia. Copyright© 1965.*)

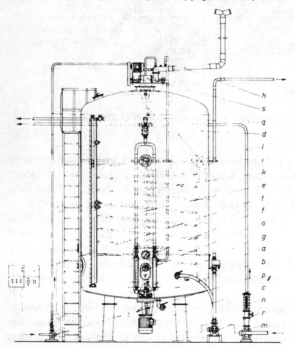

To ensure uniform distribution of the air bubbles, the self-priming rotor is surrounded by a stator (b). An air pipe (e) connected to the rotor leaves the inside of the tank near the top and continues in two branches outside of the tank. One branch leads to a rotameter (f), which measures the amount of air entering the tank at any minute. The other branch goes to a condensate cylinder (g) connected to the exhaust air pipe (h).

Four stabilizer boards (i) are fastened to the circumference of the inside of the tank. To these the stainless steel cooling coil (k) is fastened. Cooling water enters the coil through a pipe (l) coming from a pump (m) and a flowmeter (n). The pump is operated by a regulating thermometer (o) to maintain constant fermentation temperature. The charging pump (p), close to the charging vat, pumps the mash through the charging pipe (q). Entering the tank close to the center of the top, the mash flows directly into the rotor.

The discharging pump (r), near the Acetator, half empties the tank after the completion of each fermentation cycle. Attached to the top center of the tank is the defoamer (s), which destroys the foam mechanically (Morton generators do not have a defoamer). The liquid part of the foam is pumped back into the tank by the defoamer. Air leaves through the exhaust pipe. The controller (t) charges and discharges the generator.

Finishing

The composition of vinegar depends, of course, on the material from which it was made. Vinegars from fruits and malt liquors carry flavors characteristic of these materials. The method of manufacture also influences the character of the product. Vinegars made by slow methods are less harsh than those made by quick methods because of the aging undergone during the long time of preparation. Quickly made vinegars, when aged in tanks or barrels, improve in body, taste, and bouquet. Filtration and "fining," which is clarification by the settling out of added suspended materials, are employed to clarify the vinegar, which should be very clear. Most market vinegar now is pasteurized in bulk or in the bottles. Times and temperatures vary, but heating at 60 to 66 C for a few seconds is an example.

The strength of the vinegar is expressed in grains, that is, ten times the number of grams of acetic acid per 100 ml of vinegar. Thus 40-grain vinegar contains 4g of acetic acid per 100 ml of vinegar at 20 C.

Vinegar Defects and Diseases

As in wines, metals and their salts may cause cloudiness and discoloration of vinegar. Ferrous iron may be oxidized to ferric iron and combine with tannins, phosphates, or proteins to produce a haze. Cloudiness also may be caused by salts of tin or copper. Iron acting on tannin or oxidase activity may be responsible for the darkening of vinegar.

Microbial Defects   Defects caused by microorganisms may result in inferior materials from which the vinegar is made or in inferiority of the condiment itself. Wine and hard cider, for example, are subject to the troubles listed in the discussion of diseases of wine. *Lactobacillus* and *Leuconostoc* species in fruit juice not only may be responsible for off-flavors, e.g., the "mousy" taste, but also may produce enough acetic acid to interfere with the alcoholic fermentation by yeasts. Under anaerobic conditions butyric acid bacteria may produce their undesirable acid. These difficulties may be reduced by the addition of sulfur dioxide to the juices, but this chemical is inhibitory to the vinegar bacteria.

The defects of vinegar itself are confined for the most part to the production of excessive sliminess in the mass of vinegar bacteria and the destruction of acetic acid in the product. It has been mentioned that an especially heavy, thick, slimy film of bacteria in the slow process of vinegar manufacture reduces the rate of acetification. Excessive sliminess is much more harmful, however, in the generator process, for it interferes with aeration. Sliminess is favored by an alcoholic liquid that is a good culture medium, e.g., cider, wine, or a medium to which too much rich vinegar food has been added, but is not ordinarily troublesome in the acetification of a poor medium like that used in making vinegar from spirits (alcohol). Several species of vinegar bacteria can cause sliminess (cellulose), but *Acetobacter aceti* subsp. *xylinum** is probably the most important one.

Oxidation of acetic acid in vinegar to carbon dioxide and water can be brought about by the acetic acid bacteria themselves during the vinegar-making process if there is a shortage of alcohol or an excessive amount of aeration. Other organisms that can oxidize acetic acid under aerobic conditions are the film yeasts ("wine flowers"), molds, and algae.

FERMENTED VEGETABLES

The lactic acid fermentation of vegetables undoubtedly originated from the preserving effect on the product. The growth of lactic acid bacteria during vegetable fermentations results in (1) restriction of the growth of undesirable organisms and delay or prevention of the normal spoilage and (2) production of various unique flavors because of the accumulation of organic acids or by-products, giving a characteristic and distinct finished product.

A comparison of some of the various fermented vegetables is presented in Table 22-1. Note that reduced conditions (immersion) and the use of salt are common to all the fermentations listed. The reasons for these conditions will be explained in the discussion of sauerkraut fermentation.

Sauerkraut

The federal definition is as follows:

Sauerkraut is the clean, sound product, of characteristic flavor, obtained by full fermentation, chiefly lactic, of properly prepared and shredded cabbage in the presence

TABLE 22-1
A COMPARISON OF FERMENTED VEGETABLES

Commodity	Form used	Salt application	Conditions or modifications	Culture used	Resulting dominant lactic flora	Acid,%*	pH
Carrot	Whole, diced, shredded	Brine,† 2%	Immersion	Natural,‡ mixed lactic	Homofermentative	1.4	3.3
Celery	Sliced	Brine, $2\frac{1}{4}$%	Immersion	Natural	Homofermentative	1.2	3.5
Olive (green)§							
Old method	Whole	Brine, 5–8%	Immersion	Natural	Mixed	0.7–1.0	3.8
New method		Brine, 10%	Shorter lye and rinsing times, addition of lactic acid (3%)	L. plantarum	Mixed or homofermentative		3.8
Pickle	Whole						
Old method		Brine, 6–15%	Immersion	Natural	Mixed	0.6	3.8
New method		Brine, 6.6%	Chlorination, Na acetate (0.5%), N₂ purge	L. plantarum, P. cerevisiae*	Homofermentative		3.8
Sauerkraut	Shredded	Granular, $2\frac{1}{4}$%	Immersion	Natural	Mixed	1.7–2.5	3.5

*Expressed as lactic.
†After equilibration.
‡Natural, as found in plants.
§ Although olives are fruits, their fermentation resembles that of fermented vegetables.
Source: Summarized in Stamer (1973) from numerous references.

of not less than two percent nor more than three percent of salt. It contains, upon completion of the fermentation, not less than one and one-half percent of acid, expressed as lactic acid. Sauerkraut which has been rebrined in the process of canning or repacking contains not less than one percent of acid, expressed as lactic acid.

General Making Procedure   Closely filled, fully matured heads of a variety of cabbage preferred for kraut making are wilted for 1 or 2 days to bring the cabbage to a uniform temperature and to facilitate shredding. Spoiled spots and defective outer leaves are trimmed off, the heads are washed with pure water, and the core is drilled out and shredded to be added to the rest of the cabbage. The head is cut to shreds of desired size, usually fairly slim ones. Then 2.25 to 2.5 percent of salt by weight is mixed with the shredded cabbage before transfer to the vat or is added during the packing of the shreds into the vat. The first method is preferable because it results in more uniform salting, allows time for penetration of the salt into the cabbage, and makes the packing easier. After the shreds have been packed into the vat, they are tamped down and finally weighted down, so that a layer of expressed, brined juice stands on the surface. A covering of some kind should protect the surface from contamination with dirt or insects. The temperature during the lactic acid fermentation should be about 21 to 24 C. If the temperature is below 15.6 C, the fermentation will be slow and incomplete; if it is above 26 to 29 C, abnormal fermentations may result. During the fermentation, film yeasts or molds will grow on the surface of the liquor if the surface of the expressed juice is left uncovered. Formerly, these were skimmed off or their growth was prevented by covering the surface with mineral oil (or paraffin in small fermentors) after the evolution of gas had ceased or by filling containers completely. At present, plastic bags filled with water are placed on top of the fermenting cabbage to seal the surface and serve as a weight. When the desired acidity has been attained, the fermentation is stopped by heat treatment during canning or by low temperatures.

Composition of Cabbage   The composition of cabbage varies with the variety and the conditions during its growth. Especially significant in sauerkraut making is the sugar content because of its influence on the maximal acidity that can be produced by fermentation. Analyses have shown the sugar content to range from 2.9 to 6.4 percent in different lots of cabbage; the higher contents of sugar would permit the production of too much acidity if steps were not taken to stop the fermentation. The sugars are about 85 percent glucose and fructose and 15 percent sucrose.

Addition of Salt   Pederson and Ward (1949) have demonstrated that 2.25 to 2.5 percent of salt by weight should be added to the shredded cabbage to obtain kraut of the best quality and that this salt should be distributed evenly. The salt draws out the plant juices containing the sugars and other nutrients, helps control the flora of the fermentation (favoring the lactic acid bacteria), and has a dispersing effect on clumps of bacteria. Undesirable competitors of the lactics, e.g., proteolytic bacteria and aerobic and anaerobic sporeformers, are inhibited more by the salt than are the desired acid formers.

Washing the Heads Keipper et al. (1932) demonstrated that washing the cabbage heads not only reduces total numbers of microorganisms in the shredded cabbage, it also increases the percentage of desirable lactics in the flora remaining. In their experiments the lactics increased from 24 percent to 35 percent and the percentages of undesirable organisms such as chromogens, coliform bacteria, yeasts, and molds decreased.

Fermentation Anaerobic conditions develop rapidly in the salted, shredded cabbage and the surrounding juice, chiefly as the result of the removal of oxygen by the respiration of the plant cells but with some help from the bacteria. The juice contains the natural flora of the cabbage plus contaminants from soil and water. At first, different kinds of bacteria begin to grow, but the acid-forming types soon predominate. Prominent among the bacteria that attain appreciable numbers early in the fermentation are the coliform bacteria, e.g., *Enterobacter cloacae,* which produce gas and volatile acids, as well as some lactic acid. *Erwinia herbicola* also has been found early in the fermentation. These organisms must contribute some flavor. Soon, however, *Leuconostoc mesenteroides* bacteria begin to outgrow all other organisms and continue acid production up to 0.7 to 1.0 percent acid (as lactic acid). These streptococci, which appear in pairs or short chains, grow well at 18 to 21 C and are not inhibited but probably are even stimulated by 2.5 percent salt. They attack sugars to form lactic acid, acetic acid, ethanol, mannitol, dextran, esters, and carbon dioxide, which contribute to the flavor of good sauerkraut, as do the fatty acids produced by the lactic acid rods and cocci from the lipids of the cabbage. The volatile products inhibit yeasts, and the dextran and mannitol (having a bitter flavor) are available to the desired successor to the leuconostocs, *Lactobacillus plantarum,* but not to most competing organisms. *Streptococcus faecalis,* which may grow during the kraut fermentation, especially if the salt content is high (for example, 3.5 percent), produces chiefly lactic acid.

Next, non-gas-forming lactobacilli, chiefly of the species *Lactobacillus plantarum,* continue the production of acid and can raise the acidity to 1.5 to 2.0 percent. These bacteria produce chiefly lactic acid in their fermentation of the sugars. They also utilize the mannitol that had been produced by the *Leuconostoc* and thus remove the bitter flavor. *L. plantarum* completes the desired fermentation in the production of sauerkraut. Experience has shown that a final acidity of about 1.7 percent as lactic acid is most desirable. The fermentation can be stopped at this stage by canning or refrigerating the sauerkraut.

If enough sugar and mannitol remain after *L. plantarum* has finished its work, gas-forming lactobacilli, chiefly of the species *L. brevis,* can grow and continue acid production up to 2.4 percent, an acidity that is attained rarely, however, because of lack of sugar and mannitol. The gas-forming lactobacilli, producing the same products as the leuconostocs, give an undesirable, sharply acid flavor to the sauerkraut.

Good sauerkraut should be light-colored and crisp, with an acidity of about 1.7 percent and a clean, acid flavor. Small amounts of diacetyl are present to add a pleasant aroma and taste. According to Pederson (1931), the average finished kraut has a pH of 3.4 to 3.6, a lactic acid content of 1.25 percent, about 0.3 percent of acetic acid, and 0.58 percent ethyl alcohol. When 3.5 percent salt is used instead of the usual 2.25 percent, or when the temperature is 32 to 37 C instead of lower, *Pediococcus cerevisiae** may play a significant part in the fermentation but the kraut is likely to be inferior to that produced under normal conditions of salt content and temperature. Low salt, e.g., 1.0 percent, favors the heterofermentative *Leuconostoc mesenteroides* and *Lactobacillus brevis*.

Experiments have shown that it is not necessary or even advantageous to add starters of lactic acid bacteria in the making of sauerkraut.

Sauerkraut may be canned by filling the cans at 73.9 C, exhausting, sealing, and cooling.

Sauerkraut Defects and Spoilage Sauerkraut may be of inferior quality because of an abnormal fermentation. An excessively high temperature may inhibit the growth of *Leuconostoc* and consequently the flavor production by that organism and may permit the growth of *Pediococcus cerevisiae** and the development of undesirable flavors. An excessively low temperature may prevent adequate activity of the desired succession of lactic bacteria and encourage the growth of contaminants from the soil, e.g., *Enterobacter* and *Flavobacterium*. Too long a fermentation may favor the growth of the gas-forming *Lactobacillus brevis,* which yields a sharply acid flavor. Too much salt may encourage microorganisms other than the desired ones, e.g., *Pediococcus cerevisiae** and yeasts. Abnormal fermentation of cabbage may result in a cheeselike odor caused by propionic, butyric, caproic, and valeric acids, along with isobutyric and isovaleric acids.

Soft kraut may result from a faulty fermentation and from exposure to air or from excessive pressing or tamping.

Dark-brown or **black kraut** usually is due to oxidation during exposure to air and is caused by the combined action of plant enzymes and microorganisms. Destruction of acid by film yeasts and molds makes conditions favorable for proteolytic and pectolytic organisms to rot the kraut rapidly. Darkening is encouraged by uneven salting ("salt burn") and a high temperature. A brown color may result from iron in hoops and tannin from barrels.

Pink kraut often is caused by red, asporogenous yeasts in the presence of air and high salt and is found especially when the salt has been distributed unevenly. The development of pink color is favored by high temperature, dirty vats, low acidity, and iron salts. A light-pink color has been attributed to the pigments in some varieties of cabbage.

Slimy or **ropy kraut** is caused by encapsulated varieties of *Lactobacillus plantarum*. The product is edible but unsalable. The sliminess may disappear on longer holding and usually disappears during the cooking of the kraut.

Sauerkraut, then, is especially subject to spoilage at its surface, where it is exposed to air. There film yeasts and molds destroy the acidity, permitting other microorganisms to grow and causing softening, darkening, and bad flavors.

Pickles

Cucumber pickles may be prepared without fermentation or with partial or complete fermentation. Unfermented, partially fermented, or fully fermented cucumbers can be pasteurized to improve their keeping quality. Usually brined, acidified (naturally or artificially) cucumbers are heated so that the interior of the cucumbers will be maintained at 73.9 C for at least 15 min. Both heating and cooling should be fairly rapid. No attempt will be made here to describe different methods of pickle manufacture since they vary widely, and the discussion will be limited to pickles produced by fermentation. There are two chief types of fermented pickles—salt, or salt-stock pickles, and dill pickles. The salt pickles are prepared for use in making special products such as sour, sweet-sour, and mixed pickles and relishes.

Salt or Salt-Stock Pickles

In the preparation of fermented salt or salt-stock pickles immature cucumbers are washed, placed in barrels or tanks, and brined. Sometimes about 1 percent of glucose is added if the cucumbers are low in sugar, but some workers claim that the addition of sugar will favor the production of gassy pickles, or "bloaters."

Addition of Salt The rate of addition of salt and the total amount added are varied considerably by different makers. Two general methods of salting, the low-salt method and the high-salt method, are employed. In the low-salt method, a comparatively low amount of salt is added and the concentration is gradually increased until enough is present to stop any growth of bacteria. For example, a 30°-salometer (nearly 8 percent NaCl) brine may be added to the cucumbers along with 9 lb of salt per 100 lb of cucumbers. Some makers start with lower than 8 percent salt but risk off-fermentation or spoilage; 6 percent salt has been found to be the minimal concentration to hold down undesirable spore-forming bacteria. In the high-salt method the first brine is 40° salometer (about 10.5 percent salt), and 9 lb of salt is added per 100 lb of cucumbers.

The cucumbers are "keyed down" under a surface layer of brine, and the fermentation begins. In both methods, salt is added at weekly intervals to increase the salometer reading by about 3° salometer up to 60° (about 15.9 percent salt). In the low-salt method the increase is about 2° per week up to 50° and 1° per week up to 60° salometer. In warm climates the salt content of the brine may be increased more rapidly, and in cool climates a brine weaker than 30° salometer may be added initially.

The Traditional Fermentation   Only recently has a controlled fermentation of pickles with the inoculated homofermenters *L. plantarum* and *P. cerevisiae** been suggested. Before discussing this more recent advance, however, a description of the traditional pickle fermentation method will be given.

The traditional process usually takes 6 to 9 weeks for completion, depending on the salting method and temperature employed.

Any or all of a number of salt-tolerant species of bacteria may grow initially in the newly brined fresh cucumbers. In fact, there may be marked differences in the kinds of bacteria growing in different lots of cucumber brine, depending on the numbers and kinds introduced by the cucumbers or dirt left on them and by the water of the brine, the initial concentration of sodium chloride and the rate of increase in that concentration, and the temperature of the brined cucumbers. In general, the lower the salt concentration, the more kinds of bacteria will grow at the start, the faster the acid production, and the greater the total acidity produced. First to grow in most instances is a mixture of species of the genera *Pseudomonas* and *Flavobacterium,* types considered undesirable in that they would be classed as spoilage bacteria rather than acid formers. Likewise, *Bacillus* spp. are likely to come from soil on the cucumbers, and their growth would not be desired. In brines of low salt content, coliform bacteria (*Enterobacter*), *Leuconostoc mesenteroides, Streptococcus faecalis,* and *Pediococcus cerevisiae** may grow and form acid during the first few days of the fermentation, and in 15 percent brines unidentified gas-forming cocci may produce some acid. Later, *Lactobacillus brevis* may contribute to the acidity if the salt concentration is not too high. In most brines *L. plantarum* is the most important bacterium, developing acidity in both low- and high-salt brines. It begins to attain appreciable numbers several days after the start of the fermentation. As the salt concentration is increased from about 10 percent toward 15 percent, *L. plantarum* becomes decreasingly active. The total titratable acidity, as lactic acid, is about 0.6 to 0.8 percent on completion of the fermentation. Fermentations in which the heterofermentative lactics have been relatively effective generally yield pickles that are firm and have better density than those from homofermentative fermentations.

To complicate the fermentation further, yeasts may begin growth after some acid has been formed by the bacteria. These yeasts are of two general types, the film, or oxidative, yeasts, which grow on the surface of the brine and destroy lactic acid by oxidation, and the fermentative yeasts, which grow down in the brine and ferment sugars to alcohol and carbon dioxide. Film yeasts of the genera *Debaryomyces, Endomycopsis,* and *Candida* have been found. Various methods for the reduction or elimination of the scum of yeasts in the brine during the fermentation include daily agitation of the surface or the addition of mineral oil, sorbic acid, oil of mustard, or other substances. Pickle vats often are located out in the sunlight, which inhibits surface growth on the brine. In the order of frequency of occurrence the following genera of fermentative yeasts have been found in the brines: *Torulopsis, Brettanomyces, Zygosaccharomyces* (a subgenus of *Saccharomyces*), *Hansenula, Torulaspora,* and *Kloeckera.* Gas produced by these yeasts bubbles from the brine and may be responsible for bloated pickles.

A fermentation as variable, complicated, and unpredictable as that of brined cucumbers is difficult to summarize. Most of the acid normally is produced by *Lactobacillus plantarum* but also may be formed by *Leuconostoc mesenteroides, Lactobacillus brevis, Streptococcus faecalis, Pediococcus cerevisiae*,* and possibly coliform bacteria. Acid is destroyed by film yeasts. Gas may be produced by *Leuconostoc mesenteroides,* fermentative yeasts, and coliform bacteria.

When the cucumbers are first brined they are chalky-white and opaque in cross section, but during the fermentation and cure the color changes from the original bright-green to an olive- or yellowish-green and the flesh becomes increasingly translucent. Salt pickles in 15 percent salt brine can be kept for long periods if growth of film yeasts is prevented. They are too salty to be eaten and must be "freshened" by soaking before they are made into sour, sweet-sour, or mixed pickles, relishes, or other products.

The Controlled Fermentation   Numerous mishaps and problems can develop during the traditional fermentation by the indigenous cucumber flora, as will become evident in the section on pickle defects and spoilage. Years of research and experience by investigators at the U.S. Food Fermentation Laboratory, Southern Region, USDA, have resulted in a suggested procedure for the controlled fermentation of brined cucumbers (Etchells et al., 1973). Briefly, the process is designed to eliminate or at least minimize the usual defects of the traditional or natural fermentation. First the cucumbers are washed and sanitized (chlorine 80 ppm) in the vat. The chlorinated brine is then acidified with glacial acetic acid (6 ml per gallon). These two processes (chlorination and acidification) effectively suppress the growth of undesired bacteria during the initial salt addition and equilibration of the brine and cucumbers. Following a purge with nitrogen, sodium acetate is added (0.5 percent) to buffer the brine. This ensures effective utilization of all the fermentable carbohydrate present. About 10 to 24 hr following equilibration of the brine and cucumbers, they are inoculated with special cultures of *P. cerevisiae** and *L. plantarum.* During the active fermentation (10 to 14 days), nitrogen purges are repeated and additional salt is added to maintain 25° salometer (6.6 percent NaCl).

Dill Pickles

Dill pickles are so named because they are flavored by addition of dill herb in some form; usually spices are added as well, and to the kosher types, garlic or onion. Dill pickles may be unfermented or fermented or made from salt stock, but only the fermented types, "overnight" and "genuine" dill pickles, will be considered here.

The fermentation to produce dill pickles differs from that for salt stock in that a lower concentration of salt is employed than in salt stock and the brine usually is acidified with vinegar (acetic acid) at the start. The low salt content favors an increased rate and amount of acid production but adds to the risk of undesirable microbial changes. The flavoring materials, dill, spices, garlic, etc., do not markedly stimulate or inhibit the acid-forming bacteria, but they may be a source of considerable numbers of undesirable microorganisms and hence the cause of off-fermentations or spoilage of the pickles. Treated spices containing low numbers of microorganisms are now available.

Overnight Dill Pickles   Overnight dill pickles are prepared by a slow acid fermentation at a low temperature in a comparatively weak acidified brine. For example, one formula calls for a 20°-salometer brine (5.3 percent salt), 10 lb of cured dill weed, 1 lb of mixed spices, and 1 qt of 100-grain vinegar per barrel. The brined cucumbers are then held at about 3.3 C, where they undergo a slow lactic acid fermentation until 0.3 to 0.6 percent of acid has developed. The pickles must be kept cold, and they have a comparatively short keeping time because of the low content of salt and acid. A higher acidity can be obtained by permitting fermentation to take place before storage, but there is increased danger of off-fermentation or spoilage, and the green color is not retained as well as in the usual process.

Genuine Dill Pickles   In the manufacture of genuine dill pickles a brine containing about 7.5 to 8.5 percent salt (28 to 32° salometer) is added to the cucumbers, usually in a 45-gal barrel, so that the concentration of salt in the finished pickles will be about 3.5 to 4.5 percent. Dill and pickle spices also are added. Most makers add vinegar, e.g., 1 qt of 100-grain vinegar per barrel, to keep down abnormal fermentations. A temperature between 15 and 30 C is usually employed, with lower temperatures preferred.

Because of the comparatively low concentration of salt, miscellaneous soil bacteria first begin growing, but acid production probably is begun by bacteria such as *Leuconostoc mesenteroides, Streptococcus faecalis,* and *Pediococcus cerevisiae*,* and is continued by *Lactobacillus plantarum,* with possible help from *L. brevis.* The final acidity ranges from 1.0 to 1.5 percent as lactic acid.

Pickle Defects and Spoilage

Fermented pickles are subject to a number of defects or "diseases," most of which are caused by microorganisms. Shriveling results from the physical effect of too strong salt, sugar, or vinegar solutions. **Hollow pickles** grow that way, according to most authorities, and get worse if the cucumbers are allowed to stand for a while after harvesting and before fermenting. Other workers believe that improper conditions during fermentation, such as loose packing in the vat, insufficient weighting, too rapid a fermentation, and too strong or too weak a brine, cause hollow pickles.

Floaters, or **bloaters,** may result from hollow cucumbers or from gas being formed by yeasts, heterofermentative lactic acid bacteria, *L. plantarum,* or coliforms which can produce carbon dioxide. In addition carbon dioxide originating from the pickles can in some cases result in bloaters. This can be controlled by purging the brine with nitrogen to remove dissolved carbon dioxide. Floaters are favored by a thick skin that does not allow gas to diffuse out, by rapid gas production during fermentation, by high initial amounts of salt, by added acid, and by added sugar. Bloating is increased by factors that interfere with absorption of brine.

Slippery pickles occur when the cucumbers are exposed to the air, permitting the growth of encapsulated bacteria. Slipperiness also may be due to the broken scums of film yeasts that have grown on the surface of the brine and dropped onto the cucumbers. An early stage of softening gives a slippery surface to pickles.

Soft pickles are made so by pectolytic enzymes, mostly from molds and from cucumber flowers, which enter the fermentation vat. These molds are mostly in the genera *Penicillium, Fusarium, Ascochyta, Cladosporium,* and *Alternaria.* The first step in the degradation of the pectin of the cucumber may be the removal of methoxyl groups to form pectic acid by action of pectinesterase from brine yeasts and the cucumber and accessory parts. Pectin also may be converted to intermediate uronides by the polymethylgalacturonase produced by molds. Further hydrolysis to galacturonic acid is catalyzed by polygalacturonases from molds and from cucumber flowers and other parts. The cucumber flowers, which usually support a fairly heavy fungal population, are believed to be a main source of the pectolytic enzymes. Pectolytic bacteria of the genera *Bacillus* and *Aeromonas* and of the coliform group play only a minor role, if any, in pickle softening. Terminal hydrolyzing enzymes may be involved in the final degradation of the pectic substances. Molds on the cucumbers also can cause softening, as can enzymes of the cucumber or weak or strong acids. Deesterification of pectic substances by yeasts may hasten softening by polygalacturonase from other sources. Softening is favored by (1) an insufficient amount of salt and hence an abnormal fermentation, (2) too high a temperature, also affecting the acid production, (3) low acidity, either because not enough was formed or because it was destroyed by film yeasts or molds, (4) presence of air favoring the growth of film yeasts, molds, or pectin-fermenting bacteria, and (5) inclusion of many blossoms (usually with very small cucumbers), on which molds have grown and produced polygalacturonase, which causes softening.

Black pickles may owe their color to the formation of hydrogen sulfide by bacteria (or less commonly by chemical reaction) and combination with iron in the water to yield black ferrous sulfide. Therefore, water for pickles should have a low iron and gypsum ($CaSO_4$) content. The defect is favored by low acidity of the brines. Another cause of black pickles is the growth of black-pigmented *Bacillus nigrificans**, a variety of *Bacillus subtilis,* which is favored by (1) presence of an available carbohydrate like glucose, (2) a low level of available nitrogen, and (3) a neutral or slightly alkaline brine.

Ropy pickle brine, caused by various unidentified motile, gram-negative encapsulated rods, is favored by (1) low salt, (2) low acid, and (3) high temperature.

Green Olives

Although olives are fruits, rather than vegetables, they will be discussed here because their fermentation resembles that of the fermented vegetables just mentioned.

In the preparation of green olives, the fruits are harvested when fully developed but still green or straw-yellow; bruising is avoided to prevent defects in the product. In processing, they first are treated with and kept submerged in a 0.9 to 2.0% lye solution at about 15 to 21 C until the lye has penetrated one-half to three-quarters of the way toward the pit, and then they are washed several times (with as little exposure to air as is practicable to avoid darkening) to remove the lye. This treatment removes most but not all of the bitterness caused by the glucoside oleuropein. Next, the olives are barreled and covered with a salt brine, the concentration of which varies with the kind of olive. A 10 to 15% brine (40 to 50° salometer) is recommended for Manzanillo olives, resulting in a concentration of about 6 to 9 percent salt upon stabilization; the salt concentration is adjusted to and maintained at 7 to 8 percent salt throughout the fermentation. Sevillano olives, on the other hand, are started in brine with 5 to 6.25 percent salt (20 to 25° salometer) or less, resulting in a 2.5 to 4% brine, which is adjusted to 6 to 8 percent salt. Lost brine (leakage, evaporation, gas) is replaced promptly, and the olives are kept covered with brine at all times.

The lactic acid fermentation of the barreled olives may take as long as 6 to 10 months, the length of time depending on the atmospheric temperatures. Vaughn, Douglas, and Gililland (1943) have divided the normal fermentation into three stages: (1) the first stage, lasting 7 to 14 days, during which the brine is becoming stabilized, foods for microorganisms are being leached from the olives, and potential spoilage organisms, e.g., *Enterobacter* and *Pseudomonas,* and perhaps *Clostridium, Bacillus,* and yeasts, may grow until growth of *Leuconostoc mesenteroides* has well begun, (2) the intermediate stage, lasting 2 or 3 weeks, during which *Leuconostoc* becomes predominant in growth and acid production and *Lactobacillus plantarum* and *L. brevis* begin to grow and produce acid, and (3) the final stage, when these lactobacilli, especially *L. plantarum,* are predominant. Gas production by yeasts, coliforms, *Leuconostoc,* and the heterofermentative *L. brevis* and other lactobacilli takes place, especially during early stages of the fermentation. An average temperature of about 24 C favors a rapid fermentation. The final acidity usually is about 0.7 to 1.0 percent acid as lactic, and the final pH is 4.0 to 3.8 or lower. Sometimes, probably because of damage to the lactic acid bacteria by the lye treatment, the normal lactic fermentation is delayed or prevented. Olives may be low in sugar or have too much leached out during lye treatments and washing and therefore require the addition of glucose for the desired lactic fermentation to take place.

Recent advances in the fermentation of olives suggests the use of a 10% brine acidified with lactic acid (3 percent) to lower the pH and neutralize the residual lye. Heating olives before inoculation improves the fermentation. Recently a heat-sensitive bacterial inhibitor(s) has been isolated from green olives. Two products of hydrolysis of oleuropein, aglycone and elnolic acid, have an inhibitory action on a few lactic acid bacteria and on several other species (Fleming et al. 1973).

Olives that have been pitted and stuffed with brined pimento are barreled, brined, and allowed to stand for a month or so until the pimento flesh has been fermented.

The fermented green olives are sorted and graded and may be rebarreled and rebrined or washed, packed into glass jars or other containers under vacuum, and rebrined with a brine of about 28° salometer (7 percent salt). Edible lactic acid may be added to the final brine. They may be pasteurized in the container at about 60 C or brined at 79 to 82 C to improve their keeping quality.

Defects and Spoilage   Gassy spoilage of green olives usually is caused by coliform bacteria, especially *Enterobacter* spp. but sometimes by *Bacillus* spp. and *Clostridium* spp. Evidences of gas are blisterlike spots under the skin or fissures or gas pockets within the olives producing the defect termed "fisheye" and causing the olives to become "floaters." Gas-forming yeasts and heterofermentative lactics are less commonly responsible for gassy defects.

If conditions are not favorable for the normal lactic fermentation, an abnormal butyric fermentation by *Clostridium* spp. (e.g., *C. butyricum*) may result in bad odors and tastes. If the pH is above 4.2, a "sagy" off-odor and -taste, called "zapatera" spoilage, may develop, caused by species of *Clostridium* aided by propionic bacteria. The odor also has been described as from mildly cheesy (butyric) to foul and fecal (putrefactive).

Softening resulting from the destruction of pectic substances in the olive may have physical or chemical causes or may be caused by pectolytic coliform bacteria; by species of *Bacillus, Aeromonas,* or *Achromobacter*∗; by yeasts (*Rhodotorula*); or by molds (*Penicillium, Aspergillus,* etc.).

Raised white spots or pimples just under the epidermis of the olive, wrongly termed "yeast spots," are really colonies of *Lactobacillus plantarum* or *L. brevis.* Similar spots are sometimes found on fermented cucumber pickles.

Cloudiness of brine of glass-packed olives may be caused by microorganisms: (1) the lactics if fermentation of residual sugar resumes, (2) salt-tolerant bacteria, or (3) film yeasts or molds if air is available. Earlier, during the processing of the olives, surface growths of film yeasts may destroy lactic acid and produce undesirable odors and tastes that will carry over into the finished product.

Storage olives, i.e., those held for weeks to months in brines before processing, undergo a lactic acid fermentation and then, if exposed to air, may become subject to softening by pectinolytic action of an aerobic flora of film yeasts and molds developing on the surface. Most of the molds are in the genera *Fusarium* and *Penicillium*.

Ripe Olives

Olives for the production of ripe olives are picked when green to straw-colored, shipped in boxes or bins to the factory, and held before processing in the factory in a 5 to 10 percent brine. A lactic acid fermentation usually takes place while the olives are being held in the brine. After grading and sorting of the olives they are given the following "pickling" process: a first lye treatment with 0.5 to 2.0 percent lye to barely penetrate the skin; an aeration treatment with stirring or administration of compressed air to darken the skin; and more lye treatments, followed by further aeration. Finally the lye is allowed to penetrate to the pit, dehydrolyzing all the bitter glucoside oleuropein, and then the olives are leached with water to remove all the lye. Then comes stabilization of the ripe olives in a 2 to 3 percent brine for 2 or more days, during which fermentation may take place although it is not desired because it may lead to color defects. Ripe olives usually are canned in weak brine and are processed in the glass or tin container at about 115.6 C for 60 min.

Defects and Spoilage   Spoilage of ripe olives may take place while they are in the holding brine, with bleaching of the color and perhaps some softening. Coliform bacteria have been blamed for such defects, as well as for blistering or "fisheye" spoilage. Unless the temperature of the wash water is below 21 C or is in the range 49 to 60 C during the removal of lye from the olives, bacterial growth may take place with softening of the fruit. It has been demonstrated that pectolytic enzymes of *Bacillus subtilis* and *B. pumilus* can cause the defect.

Other Fermented Vegetables

Leafy vegetables such as spinach and chard and "greens" such as beet, mustard, and turnip may be prepared in a manner similar to that for making sauerkraut from cabbage. The addition of 2.5 percent by weight of dry salt causes moisture to be drawn from the vegetable and permits a lactic acid fermentation similar to that for sauerkraut. Lettuce kraut prepared in this way has been compared favorably with sauerkraut. Sauerrüben are made from unpeeled, shredded young turnips to which about 2.2 percent salt by weight is added. The salted turnips, packed in half-gallon fruit jars, are held at 21 to 24 C to undergo a lactic acid fermentation like that for sauerkraut.

Fermented green tomatoes may be prepared for incorporation in relishes and mixed pickles. The fermentation is similar to that for sauerkraut but slower, the same succession of bacteria being involved. The skins of the tomatoes may be punctured to hasten the process.

A number of Oriental fermented foods are made from vegetable products, and some of them will be discussed later.

FERMENTED DAIRY PRODUCTS

The numerous varieties of cheeses and fermented milks cannot be adequately covered in this book. We mention only briefly some of the fermented dairy products. The student should consult the references at the end of the chapter for a broader understanding and appreciation of the scope of the fermented-dairy-products industry. Fermented milks include cultured buttermilk, yogurt, Bulgarian buttermilk, acidophilus milk, kefir, kumiss, skyr, and taette as well as numerous others very similar to or identical with the ones listed. Cultured sour cream is a similar product. In all these fermented milks lactic acid bacteria carry on the main fermentation to produce lactic acid. Table 22-2 lists some of the cultures used in fermented dairy products.

Cultured buttermilk and sour cream employ the action of mixed cultures; one strain is usually responsible for the production of lactic acid, while another strain provides the aroma-forming bacteria. In both these products *Strepto-*

TABLE 22-2
CULTURES USED IN MAJOR FERMENTED DAIRY PRODUCTS

Culture	Culture function	Product use
Propionibacterium freudenreichii	Flavor and eye formation	Emmental (Swiss) cheese
Lactobacillus delbrueckii subsp. *bulgaricus,* *L. lactis,* *L. helveticus*	Acid and flavor	Bulgarian buttermilk, yogurt, kumiss, and Emmental (Swiss) and Italian cheese
L. brevis		Kefir
L. acidophilus	Acid	Acidophilus buttermilk
Streptococcus thermophilus	Acid	Emmental, Cheddar, and Italian cheese and yogurt
S. lactis subsp. *diacetylactis**	Acid and flavor	Sour cream, ripened cream butter, cheese, buttermilk, and starter cultures
S. lactis subsp. *lactis**	Acid	Cultured buttermilk, sour cream, cottage cheese, all types of cheese, domestic and foreign, and starter cultures
Leuconostoc cremoris	Flavor	Cultured buttermilk, sour cream, cottage cheese, ripened cream butter, and starter cultures
S. faecium, *S. faecalis*	Acid and flavor	Soft Italian, Cheddar, and some Swiss cheeses

coccus lactis subsp. *cremoris** or *S. lactis* subsp. *lactus** could be used to produce the acidity (0.7 to 0.9 percent as lactic acid), and *Leuconostoc mesenteroides* subsp. *cremoris* or *Streptococcus lactis* subsp. *diacetylactis* as the flavor- or aroma-forming strain to produce diacetyl, the characteristic flavor compound of buttermilk.

Bulgarian buttermilk is made with a pure culture of *Lactobacillus delbrueckii* subsp. *bulgaricus,* while yogurt employs a mixed culture of *Streptococcus thermophilus* and *L. delbrueckii* subsp. *bulgaricus.* The starter for kefir is kefir grains, which are aggregates of a mixture of microorganisms, chiefly *Lactobacillus brevis* and several yeasts. In addition to acid, a small amount of alcohol, 0.5 to 1.0 percent is produced, and enough carbon dioxide to carbonate the drink if it is kept tightly sealed during fermentation. Kumiss, ordinarily made from mare's milk, results from fermentation by a mixture of lactics and yeasts carried over from a previous lot. Acidophilus milk, prepared for its therapeutic properties for intestinal disorders, utilizes a pure culture of *Lactobacillus acidophilus* grown in milk that has been sterilized or nearly sterilized. Recently, the addition of large numbers (a frozen concentrate) of *L. acidophilus* has been used to make a nonfermented "sweet acidophilus" milk. Taette is a ropy buttermilk made with a ropy variety of *Streptococcus lactis* subsp. *lactis**, and skyr is a semisolid fermented milk in which chiefly *S. thermophilus* and *L. delbrueckii* subsp. *bulgaricus* have been active.

The acidity of the fermented milks is sufficient to prevent spoilage by proteolytic or other bacteria that are not acid-tolerant. Chilling is necessary to stop acid formation by the starter bacteria at the desired stage and packaging and sealing to avoid mold growth.

A lactic acid fermentation is involved in making most kinds of cheese. Unripened cheeses, such as cottage cheese and cream cheese, are made by starters similar to those used for cultured buttermilk. They must be chilled and kept cold until consumed and have a comparatively short keeping time. Ripened cheeses have an initial acid fermentation by lactic acid bacteria followed by action of their enzymes and those of other microorganisms; in some cheeses there is the additional action of rennet, and in certain Italian cheeses the action of added animal lipases. The chief compounds contributing to the flavor of ripened cheeses are salt, lactic acid, fatty acids, amino acids, and carbonyl compounds (e.g., aldehydes and ketones). The soft, ripened cheeses, such as Limburger, are more perishable than the harder cheeses, e.g., Cheddar and Swiss, but all completely cured cheeses require storage at chilling temperatures to aid in their preservation. Cheeses with hard rinds, such as natural Cheddar and Swiss, are protected by these rinds to some extent from drying and spoilage. Chilling also is necessary for most kinds of cheese, as well as packaging for perishable cheeses and cut pieces of larger, more stable cheeses. Packaging is done to minimize losses of moisture and penetration of oxygen, which otherwise would permit growth of molds.

In general, the curing or ripening processes do not greatly improve the keeping quality, although losses in moisture occur during the aging of long-cured hard cheeses and a protective rind forms on most of them. The chemical products formed during ripening have little preservative effect for the most part, although fatty acids repress the anaerobes; in fact, most cheeses become more alkaline as they age and hence more susceptible to spoilage by bacteria. The propionate formed in the ripening of good Swiss cheese delays the growth of most molds on the cheese, and the surface "smear" of organisms on surface-ripened cheeses such as brick or Limburger may produce products that are inhibitory to other organisms.

SPOILAGE AND DEFECTS OF FERMENTED DAIRY PRODUCTS

Fermented milks and cheese depend on a desired fermentation or succession of fermentations for their manufacture. Therefore, any abnormality in these fermentations will affect the quality of the product and may even spoil it. The finished product, too, may be subject to spoilage by microorganisms.

Fermented Milks

In the manufacture of most fermented milks a starter is added to pasteurized milk, which is incubated until the desired acidity is attained. The chief product of the fermentation is lactic acid, but lesser amounts of flavoring substances may be produced or added. If the starter bacteria are inactive, other bacteria may grow and damage the curd and the flavor. Proteolytic bacteria, which ordinarily cannot compete with the lactics, may cause a poor curd and off-flavors. Coliform bacteria and lactose-fermenting yeasts should not be present but may enter from equipment and other sources to produce bad flavors and gas. The finished product is susceptible to spoilage by molds from air or equipment if air is available at the surface.

Cheese

Defects of cheese may have mechanical or biological causes, but only the latter will be discussed. The types of spoilage can be divided into those developing during the manufacture and ripening of cured cheese and those occurring in the finished product.

Spoilage during Manufacture   During the manufacture of most types of cheese or while the cheese is draining, a lactic acid fermentation is encouraged. If the lactics are ineffective or contamination with other microorganisms is unduly heavy, abnormal changes may take place that affect the quality of the cheese adversely. In cheese made from raw milk the gas-forming organisms may be producing off-flavors as well as gas holes in the curd. Lactose-fermenting yeasts, although not commonly present in appreciable numbers, also can cause gassiness. Spore-forming gas producers, especially species of *Clos-*

tridium, can cause trouble in either raw-milk or pasteurized-milk cheese if the lactic starter bacteria are not functioning properly; less commonly, the aerobacilli*, spore-forming species of *Bacillus* such as *B. polymyxa,* may produce gas and other defects. These sporeformers also can cause defects in ripening cheese.

Other bacteria may compete with the starter organisms with results that do not become evident until during the curing process, where body and flavor may be affected. Thus acid-proteolytic bacteria may produce a bitter flavor, or *Leuconostoc* spp. may cause holes or openness in Cheddar cheese from pasteurized milk.

Cottage cheese especially is subject to spoilage during storage before consumption. If the starter bacteria produce insufficient acid or yield it too slowly, a usable curd will not result or the cheese will be inferior because of the growth of undesirable organisms. Proteolysis, gas production, sliminess, and off-flavors may ruin the product. Cheese with too low an acidity because of the addition of cream or the failure of the starter often is made gelatinous or slimy by soil or water bacteria such as *Pseudomonas, P. fragi,* and *Alcaligenes metalcaligenes*.*

Spoilage during Ripening   During ripening or curing, cheeses normally undergo physical and chemical changes resulting from the action of enzymes released from the autolyzed cells of bacteria that grew during manufacture and from the action of microorganisms that increase during the ripening period. The growth of organisms other than the desired ones results in inferior or, in extreme cases, even worthless cheese because of alterations in texture, body, general appearance, or flavor. The most important kinds of spoilage differ enough, however, with the kind of cheese concerned to discourage generalization. Most kinds may be subject to "late gas," usually caused by heterofermentative lactic acid bacteria, or by lactate-fermenting *Clostridium* spp. but possibly by bacilli, propionic bacteria, or heterofermentative lactics. Gas holes, or eyes, are desirable in Swiss and related cheeses but not to any extent in other varieties. Especially bad in Swiss and similar cheeses is the cracking or splitting of the cheese by gas or the production of too many, too small, or misshapen eyes. Gas formation by the sporeformers is accompanied by the production of undesirable flavors, e.g., butyric acid from the anaerobes.

Bitterness may be caused by certain lactic streptococci; the proteolytic bacteria, e.g., the acid-proteolytic types; coliforms; micrococci*; various other bacteria; and (rarely) yeasts, which usually give a sweet, fruity, or yeasty flavor.

Putrefaction may occur locally or generally in cheese where insufficient acidity has been produced by the lactics or the acid has been destroyed by a lactate fermenter, e.g., *Clostridium tyrobutyricum.* Putrefactive anaerobes, such as *C. sporogenes* or *C. lentoputrescens*,* may be involved.

Discolorations of the ripening cheese may result from the action of microorganisms on compounds produced during curing or on added coloring material, such as the annatto used in Cheddar cheese, or may result from the development of pigmented colonies or organisms on or in the cheese. Blue, green, or black discoloration may be produced by the reaction of hydrogen sulfide produced by organisms with metals or metallic salts. Bacterially formed sulfhydryl groups give a pink to muddy appearance to annatto. Reddish-brown to grayish-brown colors sometimes result from the oxidation of tyrosine by bacteria growing in soft cheeses. Rusty spots of Cheddar and similar cheese are caused by colonies of *Lactobacillus plantarum* var. *rudensis** or *L. brevis* var. *rudensis**, while yellow, pink, or brown spots in Swiss cheese, mostly on the surface of the eyes, are colonies of pigmented species of *Propionibacterium*.

Spoilage of the Finished Cheese　In general, the perishability of cured cheeses increases with their moisture content. Therefore, soft cheeses such as Limburger and Brie are most perishable, and hard cheeses such as Cheddar and Swiss are the most stable. Most feared among the spoilage organisms are the molds that tend to grow on the cheese surfaces and into cracks or trier holes. Even cheeses that depend partly on a specific mold for ripening may be demaged by other molds. Most natural cheeses have rinds that serve as some protection to the anaerobic interior but usually are not dry enough to prevent mold growth. The acidity of the cheese is no deterrent to growth, and the storage temperature is not too low for such growth. Most molds grow in colored colonies on the surface or in crevices, without much penetration into the cheese, but some kinds produce actual rots. Products produced by molds, such as mycotoxins and antibiotics, can migrate into the cheese. Not only are discolorations evident, but off-flavors are produced locally. Among the molds that grow on cheese surfaces are the following:

1　*Oospora (Geotrichum)* spp. *Oospora (Geotrichum) lactis,* called the **dairy mold,** grows on soft cheeses and during ripening sometimes suppresses other molds as well as surface-ripening bacteria. The curd gradually becomes liquefied under the felt. *O. rubrum* and *O. crustacea* produce a red coloration, and *O. aurianticum* forms orange to red spots. *O. caseovorans* causes "cheese cancer" of Swiss and similar cheeses. Bumps of growth become filled with a white, chalky mass.

2　*Cladosporium* spp. The mycelium and spores of these molds are dark or smoky and give dark colors to the cheese. Most common is *C. herbarum,* characterized by dark-green to black colors. Other species cause green, brown, or black discolorations.

3　*Penicillium* spp. *P. puberulum* and other green-spored species grow in cracks, crevices, and trier holes of Cheddar and related cheeses to give a green coloration because of their spores. They may act on annatto to cause mottling and discoloration. *P. casei* causes yellowish-brown spots on the rind, and *P. aurantio-virens* discolors Camembert cheese.

4　*Monilia* spp. *M. nigra* produces penetrating black spots on the rind of hard cheeses. Species of many other genera may discolor cheeses and give off-flavors, e.g., the genera *Scopulariopsis, Aspergillus, Mucor,* and *Alternaria*.

If the surface is sufficiently moist, yeasts may form colored colonies or areas, and film yeasts may pave the way for the yellow to red growth of *Brevi-*

bacterium linens. The latter is desired in some surface-ripened cheeses but not in others.

TEA, COFFEE, CACAO, VANILLA, CITRON

Tea

Tea can be classified as (1) fermented, or black, (2) unfermented, or green, and (3) semifermented, or oolong. The experts agree that the "fermentation" of tea leaves is the result of the activity of enzymes of the leaves rather than of microorganisms present, although action of microorganisms may harm the flavor and reduce the quality of black tea. Molds of the genera *Aspergillus, Penicillium,* and *Rhizopus* have been reported to cause spoilage.

Coffee

The two chief methods of curing coffee are (1) the dry method, in which the berries or "cherries" are spread out and air-dried in the sun or artificially, and (2) the wet, or washed-coffee, method, in which the berries, after removal of outer skin, are soaked in water. The removal of pulpy material in either method is accomplished primarily by pectinolytic bacteria, mostly coliforms, although pectinolytic bacilli and fungi may be present. This is followed by an acid fermentation by lactic acid bacteria such as *Leuconostoc mesenteroides, Lactobacillus brevis* and *L. plantarum*, and *Streptococcus faecalis*. The acids produced may be degraded by oxidizing organisms. After the pulp and its residues have been washed away, the beans are dried and hulled.

There are patents on the fermentation of coffee beans by certain kinds of bacteria before the roasting process to improve the taste and aroma of the roasted product. Also, a pectinolytic enzyme derived from molds has been utilized in a method for removal of the pulpy layer from the beans, thus avoiding the production of off-flavored coffee that sometimes results from the uncontrolled natural fermentation.

Deterioration of the released coffee beans can occur during drying if this procedure is too prolonged.

Cacao

Cacao, or cocoa beans (seeds), when taken from the pod are covered with a slimy or fruity pulp, which is removed by means of a fermentation process. The pulp-covered seeds are placed in piles, in pits, or in a "sweating box," where the beans are covered with banana or plantain leaves. During the 3 to 13 days of fermentation the beans are stirred and turned to aerate them and keep down the temperature. The fermentation has the following purposes: (1) to remove the adhering pulp from the bean, (2) to kill the embryo in the seed, and (3) to give aroma, flavor, and color to the bean. Here again it is difficult to say how much is accomplished by the plant enzymes and how much by the growing microorganisms. According to some reports the fermentation is in several stages: (1) the fermentation of sugars in the pulp to ethanol and carbon dioxide by a variety of yeasts, especially *Candida krusei* and apiculate yeasts, and to acid by lactic acid bacteria, (2) the oxidation of the ethanol to acetic acid by acetic bacteria, (3) chemical changes brought about by the heat of the fermentation, where the temperatures may rise to 44 to 50 C, and by plant enzymes, and (4) further chemical changes during curing or drying of the beans. Molds and actinomycetes can cause spoilage of the beans during curing.

Citron

Halved citron fruits are held for 6 to 7 weeks in seawater or a 5 to 10 percent brine. It has been reported that yeasts improve the aroma by esterification of the essence of citron and that alcoholic fermentation by yeasts followed by an acetic acid fermentation combine to improve the flavor, color, and texture of citron. A yeast, *Saccharomyces citri medicae,* and a bacterium, *Bacillus citri*,* have been found to predominate during the fermentation.

ORIENTAL FERMENTED FOODS

Most of the Oriental fermented foods mentioned below have molds involved in their preparation. In the starter, termed **koji** by the Japanese and **chou** by the Chinese, molds serve as sources of hydrolytic enzymes, such as amylases to hydrolyze the starch in the grains, proteinases, lipases, and many others. For the most part the starters are mixtures of molds, yeasts, and bacteria, but for a few products pure cultures have been employed.

Soy Sauce

The chief Oriental fermented food imported into the United States and also made here is soy sauce, a brown, salty, tangy sauce used on dishes such as chop suey or as a constituent of other sauces. The methods of preparation of the starter and of manufacture of soy sauce have many variations and may result in different types of products.

The Starter The starters (koji or chou) may be mixed cultures carried over from previous lots or pure cultures grown separately. The substrate on which the starter is grown varies, although most often it is an autoclaved mixture of soybeans, cracked wheat, and wheat bran; a mixture of wheat bran and soybean flour; or rice. This moistened material is inoculated with spores of *Aspergillus oryzae* (*A. soyae*), spread in small boxes or trays, and held at 25 to 30 C until the mold growth on the surfaces of the mash is judged to have attained a maximal content of enzymes (usually after about 3 days). A flora of lactic acid bacteria, streptococci and lactobacilli, also develops in the koji and produces lactic acid, and some growth of *Bacillus* spp. takes place. The starter may be used at once as it is, may be dried and used later, or may be dried and extracted and the extract used.

Manufacture of Soy Sauce The mash may consist of autoclaved soybeans or defatted, chemically hydrolyzed soybeans, roasted and crushed wheat, and steamed wheat bran. The mash is inoculated with the koji and incubated in trays for 3 days at about 30 C. Then it is soaked with sterile, 24 percent sodium chloride brine (sometimes the koji is mixed directly with an equal amount of saline water). The brined mash is held for from 2.5 months to a year or longer, depending on the temperature.

Fermentation The proteinases, amylases, and other enzymes of the koji continue to act throughout the holding period. There are three stages in the curing: (1) lactic acid fermentation by lactic acid bacteria from the koji, followed by more acid production by *Pediococcus halophilus,* (2) alcoholic fermentation by yeasts, such as *Saccharomyces rouxii* and *Zygosaccharomyces soyae,* and (3) completion of the fermentation and aging.

The various microorganisms important in the making of soy sauce may be added in pure culture or may come from previous lots of koji and from the ingredients. The chief organisms are *Aspergillus soyae (oryzae),* the most important organism, which grows in the koji to yield proteinases, amylases, and other enzymes for soy-sauce brewing and contributes aromas and flavors; lactic acid bacteria, e.g., *Lactobacillus delbrueckii,* which makes the koji acid enough to prevent spoilage and acidifies the mash; *Bacillus subtilis* and other bacilli, which grow in the koji to improve flavor and make the soy sauce less turbid; *Pediococcus halophilus,* which increases the acid in the mash, thereby stimulating the yeasts, contributing to essential aromas and flavors, decreasing color intensity, and reducing the activity of the mold proteinases; and *Hansenula* spp., *Saccharomyces rouxii,* and other yeasts, which produce alcohol and help the flavor.

Tamari Sauce This is a Japanese sauce, similar to soy sauce, made by a short fermentation process from a soybean mash to which rice may have been added. A different mold, *Aspergillus tamarii,* is the principal mold involved in the manufacture of tamari sauce.

Miso

The koji for **miso** is a culture of *Aspergillus oryzae* grown at about 35 C on a steamed polished-rice mash in shallow trays until the grains are completely covered but the mold has not sporulated. The koji is mixed with a mash of crushed, steamed soybeans, salt is added, and the fermentation is allowed to proceed for a week at 28 C and then for two months at 35 C, after which the mixture is ripened for several weeks at room temperature. Involved in the main fermentation are the enzymes of the koji, yeasts (*Saccharomyces rouxii* and *Zygosaccharomyces* spp.), lactic acid bacteria, and bacilli. The final product is ground into a paste to be used in combination with other foods.

Tempeh

In the manufacture of **tempeh,** an Indonesian food, soybeans are soaked overnight at 25 C, the seed coats are removed, and the beans, split into halves, are boiled in water for 20 min, dried on mats, cooled, and inoculated with a previous lot of tempeh or with mold spores of species of *Rhizopus* (*R. stolonifer, R. oryzae, R. oligosporus,* or *R. arrhizus*). The mash is packed into a plastic container or a hollow tube or is rolled in banana leaves. It then is incubated at about 32 C for 20 hr until there is good growth of mycelium but little sporulation. The product is sliced thin (Figure 22-3), dipped into salt water, and fried in vegetable fat to a golden brown.

Ang-khak

Ang-khak, or Chinese red rice, is produced by growth of *Monascus purpureus* on autoclaved rice and is used for coloring and flavoring fish and other food products.

FIGURE 22-3
A tempeh cake. (*Photography Division, USDA.*)

Natto

In the manufacture of **natto,** boiled soybeans are wrapped in rice straw and fermented for 1 or 2 days. The package becomes slimy on the outside. *Bacillus natto*,* probably identical with *Bacillus subtilis,* grows in natto, releasing trypsinlike enzymes that are supposed to be important in the ripening process.

Soybean cheese

Soybean cheese, **tou-fu-ju**, or **tofu,** is a Chinese fermented food made by soaking soybeans, grinding them to a paste, and then filtering them through linen. The protein in the filtrate is curdled by means of a magnesium or calcium salt, after which the curd is pressed into blocks. The blocks, arranged on trays, are held in a fermentation chamber for a month at about 14 C, during which period white molds, probably *Mucor* spp., develop. Final ripening takes place in brine or in a special wine.

Minchin

Fermented **minchin** is made from wheat gluten from which the starch has been removed. The moist, raw gluten is placed in a closed jar and allowed to ferment for 2 to 3 weeks, after which it is salted. A typical specimen was found to contain seven species of molds, nine of bacteria, and three of yeasts. The final product is cut into strips to be boiled, baked, or fried.

Idli

Idli, a fermented food of India, is made from rice and black gram mungo in equal parts. The ingredients are washed and soaked separately, ground, mixed, and finally allowed to ferment overnight. When the batter has risen enough, it is cooked by steaming and served hot. *Leuconostoc mesenteroides* grows first in the batter, leavening it, and is followed by *Streptococcus faecalis* and finally *Pediococcus cerevisiae*,* all of which contribute to the acidity.

Fermented Fish

The Japanese prepare a fermented fish by cutting it into strips, cooking it, and then encouraging fermentation by molds, chiefly species of *Aspergillus*. The strips then are dried. The Chinese have a fermented fish product preserved in **lao-chao,** a fermented rice product. Molds and yeasts are involved in the fermentation of the steamed rice, and some alcohol is produced.

Preserved Eggs

Pidan, or the Chinese preserved egg, is made from duck eggs coated with a slurry of soda, burned straw, salt, and slaked lime and covered with rice husks.

The eggs then are kept in sealed clay jars for a month or longer. An assortment of bacteria grow in the egg, but coliform bacteria and species of *Bacillus* apparently are predominant.

Poi

Poi, although Hawaiian rather than Oriental, will be mentioned here. In the preparation of poi, the corms (bulblike, fleshy stems) of the taro plant are steamed at 70 to 100 C for 2 to 3 hr, cooled, washed, peeled, trimmed and scraped, and then finely ground. This ground mass, after being mixed with water to attain a desired consistency, is fresh poi that is ready for consumption. The sour or fermented poi is prepared by the incubation of barrels or other containers of fresh poi at room temperatures for at least 1 day and at most not more than 6 days. During the first 6 hr of the fermentation, the poi swells or puffs slightly and the color changes. During this period a mixture of soil and water microorganisms are prominent, organisms such as coliforms, *Pseudomonas* spp., chromogenic bacteria, and yeasts. Between 6 hr and 4 days the flora consists predominantly of acid-forming bacteria, among which are *Lactobacillus pastorianus*, L. delbrueckii, L. brevis, Streptococcus lactis* subsp. *lactis,* and *S. kefir (Leuconostoc).* These lactic acid bacteria carry on the main fermentation‚in the poi, although during the latter part of the process, yeasts, film yeasts, and the mold *Geotrichum candidum* increase in numbers and probably contribute pleasing fruity odors and tastes (bouquet). The fermentation products are chiefly lactic, acetic, and formic acids, alcohol, and carbon dioxide. Abnormal fermentations are likely to be of the butyric acid type.

BIBLIOGRAPHY

General

Gray, W. D. 1973. The use of fungi as food and in processing, pt. II. CRC Press, Cleveland.

Hesseltine, C. W. 1965. A millennium of fungi food and fermentation. Mycologia. 57: 149–197.

Miller, B. M., and W. Litsky. 1976. Industrial microbiology. McGraw-Hill Book Company, New York.

Pederson, C. S. 1971. Microbiology of food fermentations. AVI Publishing Co., Inc., Westport, Conn.

Reed, G. 1982. Prescott and Dunn's industrial microbiology. 4th ed. AVI Publishing Co., Inc., Westport, Conn.

Reed, G. R., and H. J. Peppler. 1973. Yeast technology. 3d ed. AVI Publishing Co., Inc., Westport, Conn.

Rose, A. H. 1961. Industrial microbiology. Butterworth & Co. (Publishers), Ltd., London.

Rose, A. H. (ed). 1982. Economic microbiology. Volume 7. Fermented foods. Academic Press, Inc., New York.

Steinkraus, K. H. 1983. Handbook of indigenous fermented foods. Marcel Dekker, Inc., New York.

Underkofler, L. A., and R. J. Hickey (eds.). 1954. Industrial fermentations. Chemical Publishing Company, Inc., New York.

Weiser, H. H., G. J. Mountney, and W. A. Gould. 1971. Practical food microbiology. AVI Publishing Co., Inc., Westport, Conn.

Breads

Amos, A. J. 1942. Microbiology and baking. Chem. Ind. 61:117–119.

Biltcliffe, D. O. 1971. Active dried baker's yeast. I. Systems involved in the fermentation of mono- and disaccharides. J. Food Technol. 6:423–432.

Biltcliffe, D. O. 1972. Active dried baker's yeast. II. Factors involved in the fermentation of flour. J. Food Technol. 7:63–77.

Food Engineering Staff. 1962. Bread-dough process. Food Eng. 34(2):51.

Fortmann, K. L. 1967. New developments in continuous dough making. Baker's Dig. 41:114–118.

Kline, L., and T. F. Sugihara. 1971. Microorganisms of the San Francisco sour dough bread process. II. Isolation and characterization of undescribed bacterial species responsible for the souring activity. Appl. Microbiol. 21:459–465.

Matz, S. A. 1972. Bakery technology and engineering. AVI Publishing Co., Inc., Westport, Conn.

Micka, J. 1955. Bacterial aspects of soda cracker fermentation. Cereal Chem. 32:125–131.

Ng, H. 1972. Factors affecting organic acid production by sour dough (San Francisco) bacteria. Appl. Microbiol. 23:1153–1159.

Oura, E., H. Suomalainen, and R. Viskari. 1982. Breadmaking. In A. H. Rose (ed.), Fermented foods. Volume 7. Academic Press, Inc., New York.

Pomeranz, Y., and J. A. Shellenberger. 1971. Bread science and technology. AVI Publishing Co., Inc., Westport, Conn.

Schulz, A. 1952. The microbiology of sour dough. Baker's Dig. 26(5):27–29, 37.

Sugihara, T. F., L. Kline, and M. W. Miller. 1971. Microorganisms of the San Francisco sour dough bread process. I. Yeasts responsible for the leavening action. Appl. Microbiol. 21:456–458.

Sultan, W. J. 1969. Practical baking. 2d ed. AVI Publishing Co., Inc., Westport, Conn.

Alcoholic Beverages

Amerine, M. A. 1964. Wine. Sci. Am. August, pp. 169–179.

Amerine, M. A. 1972. Quality control in the California wine industry. J. Milk Food Technol. 35:373–378.

Amerine, M. A., H. W. Berg, and W. V. Cruess. 1972. Technology of wine making. 3d ed. AVI Publishing Co., Inc., Westport, Conn.

Asai, T. 1968. Acetic acid bacteria. Classification and biochemical activities. University Park Press, Baltimore.

Berger, D. G. 1972. Quality control in the brewing industry. J. Milk Food Technol. 35: 719–725.

Broderick, H. M. 1977. The practical brewer: a manual for the brewing industry. 2d ed. Master Brewers Assoc. of the Americas, Madison, Wisc.

Carr, J. G. 1962. The microbiology of wines and ciders. Rep. Prog. Appl. Chem. 47: 645–657.

Cruess, W. V. 1947. The principles and practice of wine making. AVI Publishing Co., Inc., Westport, Conn.

Dadd, M. J. S., and P. A. Martin. 1973. The Genus *Zymomonas:* a review. J. Inst. Brew. 79:386–391.

Gini, B., and R. H. Vaughn. 1962. Characteristics of some bacteria associated with the spoilage of California dessert wines. Am. J. Enol. Viticult. 13:20–31.

Haas, G. J. 1960*a*. Microbial control methods in the brewery. Academic Press, Inc., New York.

Haas, G. J. 1960*b*. Microbial control methods in the brewery. Appl. Microbiol. 2:113–162.

H ⸱row, R. M. 1963. Biological considerations of brewery water supplies. Brewers Dig. δ(8):39–45.

Hardwick, W. A. 1973. Recent advances in brewing technology. *In* Fermented Foods, 8th Ann. Symp. N.Y. State Agr. Exp. Stn. Spec. Rep. 16, April 1974.

Hoggan, J. 1963*a*. Recent developments in brewing technology. Food Manuf. 38:308–314, 331.

Hoggan, J. 1963*b*. Brewing, malting, and allied processes. Rep. Prog. Appl. Chem. 48: 524–532.

Joe, A. M., and K. M. Shahani. 1975. Grapes and wine technology: grapes to wine. J. Milk Food Technol. 38:237–243.

Joslyn, M. A., and M. W. Turbovsky. 1954. Commercial production of table and dessert wines, Volume I, chap. 7. *In* L. A. Underkofler and R. J. Hickey (eds.), Industrial fermentations. Chemical Publishing Company, Inc., New York.

Kleyn, J., and J. Hough. 1971. The microbiology of brewing. Annu. Rev. Microbiol. 25:583–608.

Kodama, K., and K. Yoshizawa. 1977. Sake. *In* A. H. Rose (ed.), Economic Microbiology. Volume 1. Academic Press, Inc., New York.

Rice, A. C. 1973. Yeast fermentation in wine technology. 8th Annu. Symp. N.Y. State Agr. Exp. Stn. Spec. Rep. 16, April 1974.

Rose, A. H. 1977. Alcoholic beverages. Academic Press, Inc., New York.

Samuel, O. C. 1963. Continuous brewhouse operation. Food Proc. 24(9):60–63.

Shimwell, J. L. 1960. The beer acetic acid bacteria. Brewers Dig. 25(7):38–40.

Vaughn, R. H. 1955. Bacterial spoilage of wines with special reference to California conditions. Adv. Food Res. 6:67–108.

Webb, A. D. (ed.). 1974. Chemistry of wine making. Adv. Chem. Ser. 137. American Chemical Society, Washington.

Wiles, A. E. 1961. The wild yeasts: a review. Brewers Dig. 36(1):40–46.

Windisch, S. 1962. Microbiological problems in brewing. Brewers Dig. 37(2):47–51.

Vinegar

Allgeier, R. J., and F. M. Hildebrandt. 1960. Newer developments in vinegar manufacture. Adv. Appl. Microbiol. 2:163–182.

Asai, T. 1970. Acetic acid bacteria. University Park Press, Baltimore.

Carr, J. G., and J. L. Shimwell. 1961. Acetic acid bacteria. 1941–1961: a critical review. Antonie van Leuwenhoek. J. Microbiol. Serol. 27:386–400.

Conner, H. A., and R. J. Allgeier. 1976. Vinegar: its history and development. Adv. Appl. Microbiol. 20:81–133.

Hromatka, O., and H. Ebner. 1959. Vinegar by submerged oxidative fermentation. Ind. Eng. Chem. 51:1279–1280.

Fermented Vegetables

Bates, R. D. 1970. Lactic acid fermentation of outer celery petioles. J. Food Sci. 35: 476–479.

Etchells, J. L., J. A. Bell, H. P. Fleming, R. E. Kelling, and R. L. Thompson. 1973. Pickle Pak Sci. 3:4–14.

Etchells, J. L., A. F. Borg, and T. A. Bell. 1968. Bloater formation by gas-forming lactic acid bacteria in cucumber fermentations. Appl. Microbiol. 16:1029–1035.

Etchells, J. L., A. F. Borg, I. D. Kittel, T. A. Bell, and H. P. Fleming. 1966. Pure culture fermentation of green olives. Appl. Microbiol. 14:1027–1041.

Etchells, J. L., R. N. Costilow, T. E. Anderson, and T. A. Bell. 1964. Pure culture fermentation of brined cucumbers. Appl. Microbiol. 12:523–535.

Etchells, J. L., H. P. Fleming, and T. A. Bell. 1973. Factors influencing the growth of lactic acid bacteria during fermentation of brined cucumbers. In J. G. Carr et al. (eds.), Lactic acid bacteria in beverages and foods. Academic Press, Inc., New York, 1975.

Etchells, J. L., H. P. Fleming, L. H. Hontz, T. A. Bell, and R. J. Monroe. 1975. Factors influencing bloater formation in brined cucumbers during controlled fermentation. J. Food Sci. 40:569–575.

Etchells, J. L., and I. D. Jones. 1943a. Bacteriological changes in cucumber fermentation. Food Ind. 15(2):54–56.

Etchells, J. L., and I. D. Jones. 1943b. Commercial brine preservation of vegetables. Fruit Prod. J. 22:242–246, 251, 253.

Fabian, F. W., and L. J. Wickerham. 1935. Experimental work on cucumber fermentation (dills). VIII. Mich. State Coll. Agr. Exp. Stn. Bull. 146.

Fleming, H. P., and J. L. Etchells. 1967. Occurrence of an inhibitor of lactic acid bacteria in green olives. Appl. Microbiol. 15:1178–1184.

Fleming, H. P., J. L. Etchells, R. L. Thompson, and T. A. Bell. 1975. Purging of CO_2 from cucumber brines to reduce bloater damage. J. Food Sci. 40:1304–1310.

Fleming, H. P., R. F. McFeeters, and M. A. Daeschel. 1985. The lactobacilli, pedococci, and leuconostocs: vegetable products. In S. E. Gilliland (ed.), Bacterial starter cultures for foods. CRC Press, Inc., Boca Raton, Fla.

Fleming, H. P., R. L. Thompson, T. A. Bell, and L. H. Hontz. 1978 Controlled fermentation of sliced cucumbers. J. Food Sci. 43:888–891.

Fleming, H. P., R. L. Thompson, J. L. Etchells, R. E. Kelling, and T. A. Bell. 1973. Bloater formation in brined cucumbers fermented by *Lactobacillus plantarum*. J. Food Sci. 38:499–503.

Fleming, H. P., W. M. Walter, Jr., and J. L. Etchells. 1969. Isolation of a bacterial inhibitor from green olives. Appl. Microbiol. 18:856–860.

Fleming, H. P., W. M. Walter, Jr., and J. L. Etchells. 1973. Antimicrobial properties of oleuropein and products of its hydrolysis from green olives. Appl. Microbiol. 26:777–782.

Fulde, R. C., and F. W. Fabian. 1953. The influence of gram-negative bacteria on the sauerkraut fermentation. Food Technol. 7:486–488.

Keipper, C. H., W. H. Peterson, E. B. Fred, and W. E. Vaughn. 1932. Sauerkraut from pretreated cabbage. Ind. Eng. Chem. 24:884–889.

Pederson, C.S. 1931. Sauerkraut. N.Y. State Agr. Exp. Stn. Bull. 595

Pederson, C. S., and M. N. Albury. 1953. Factors affecting the bacterial flora in fermenting vegetables. Food Res. 18:290–300.

Pederson, C. S., and M. N. Albury. 1954. The influence of salt and temperature on the microflora of sauerkraut fermentation. Food Technol. 8:1–5.

Pederson, C. S., and L. Ward. 1949. Effect of salt on the bacteriological and chemical changes in fermenting cucumbers. N.Y. State Agr. Exp. Stn. Bull. 288.

Splittstoesser, D. F., and W. P. Wettergreen. 1964. The significance of coliforms in frozen vegetables. Food Technol. 18:392–394.

Splittstoesser, D. F., W. P. Wettergreen, and C. S. Pederson. 1961. Control of microorganisms during preparation of vegetables for freezing. I. Green beans. II. Peas and corn. Food Technol. 15:329–331; 332–334.

Stamer, J. R. 1973. Recent developments in the fermentation of sauerkraut. *In* J. G. Carr et al. (eds.), Lactic acid bacteria in beverages and food. Academic Press, Inc., New York. 1975.

Stamer, J. R., B. O. Stoyla, and B. A. Dunckel. 1971. Growth rates and fermentation patterns of lactic acid bacteria associated with sauerkraut fermentation. J. Milk Food Technol. 34:521–525.

Vaughn, R. H. 1954. Lactic acid fermentation of cucumbers, sauerkraut and olives, Volume II, chap. 11. *In* L. A. Underkofler and R. J. Hickey (eds.), Industrial fermentations. Chemical Publishing Co., Inc., New York.

Vaughn, R. H. 1973. Lactic acid fermentation of olives with special reference to California conditions. *In* J. G. Carr et al. (eds.), Lactic acid bacteria in beverages and food. 1975. Academic Press, Inc., New York.

Vaughn, R. H., H. C. Douglas, and J. R. Gililland. 1943. Production of Spanish-type green olives. Calif. Agr. Exp. Stn. Bull. 678.

Walter, W. M., Jr., H. P. Fleming, and J. L. Etchells. 1973. Preparation of antimicrobial compounds by hydrolysis of oleuropein from green olives. Appl. Microbiol. 26:773–776.

Fermented Dairy Products

Collins, E. B. 1972. Biosynthesis of flavor compounds by microorganisms. J. Dairy Sci. 55:1022–1028.

Foster, E. M., F. E. Nelson, M. L. Speck, R. D. Doetsch, and J. C. Olson, Jr. 1957. Dairy microbiology. Prentice-Hall, Inc., Englewood Cliffs, N.J.

Gilliland, S. E. 1972. Flavor intensification with concentrated cultures. J. Dairy Sci. 55:1028–1031.

Gilliland, S. E. (ed.). 1985. Bacterial starter cultures for foods. CRC Press, Inc., Boca Raton, Fla.

Harper, W. J. 1959. Chemistry of cheese flavors. J. Dairy Sci. 42:207–213.

Hettinga, D. H., and G. W. Reinbold. 1972a. The propionic acid bacteria: a review. I. Growth. J. Milk Food Technol. 35:295–302.

Hettinga, D. H., and G. W. Reinbold. 1972b. The propionic acid bacteria: a review. II. Metabolism. J. Milk Food Technol. 35:358–373.

Hettinga, D. H., and G. W. Reinbold. 1972c. The propionic acid bacteria: a review. III. Miscellaneous metabolic activities. J. Milk Food Technol. 35:436–448.

Hettinga, D. H., and G. W. Reinbold. 1975. Split defect of Swiss cheese. II. Effect of low temperatures on the metabolic activity of *Propionibacterium*. J. Milk Food Technol. 38:31–35.

Hettinga, D. H., G. W. Reinbold, and E. R. Vedamuthu. 1974. Split defect of Swiss cheese. I. Effect of strain of *Propionibacterium* and wrapping material. J. Milk Food Technol. 37:322–328.

Jensen, J. P., G. W. Reinbold, C. J. Washam, and E. R. Vedamuthu. 1975a. Role of enterococci in cheddar cheese: proteolytic activity and lactic acid development. J. Milk Food Technol. 38:3–8.

Jensen, J. P., G. W. Reinbold, C. J. Washam, and E. R. Vedamuthu. 1975b. Role of enterococci in cheddar cheese: free fatty acid appearance and citric acid utilization. J. Milk Food Technol. 38:78–84.

Jensen, J. P., G. W. Reinbold, C. J. Washam, and E. R. Vedamuthu. 1975c. Role of enterococci in cheddar cheese: organoleptic considerations. J. Milk Food Technol. 38:142–146.

Kosikowski, F. V. 1973. New developments in milk and cheese fermentation processes. 8th Ann. Symp. N.Y. State Agr. Exp. Stn., Spec. Rep. 16, April 1974.

Langsrud, T., and G. W. Reinbold. 1973a. Flavor development and microbiology of Swiss cheese: a review. I. Milk quality and treatments. J. Milk Food Technol. 36:487–491.

Langsrud, T., and G. W. Reinbold. 1973b. Flavor development and microbiology of Swiss cheese: a review. II. Starters, manufacturing processes and procedures. J. Milk Food Technol. 36:531–543.

Langsrud, T., and G. W. Reinbold. 1973c. Flavor development and microbiology of Swiss cheese: a review. III. Ripening and flavor production. J. Milk Food Technol. 36:593–610.

Langsrud, T., and G. W. Reinbold. 1974. Flavor development and microbiology of Swiss cheese: a review. IV. Defects. J. Milk Food Technol. 37:26–42.

Law, A. B. 1982. Cheeses. *In* A. H. Rose (ed.), Fermented foods. Volume 7. Academic Press, Inc., New York.

Marth, E. H. 1963. Microbiological and chemical aspects of Cheddar cheese ripening: a review. J. Dairy Sci. 46:869–890.

Marth, E. H. 1982. Cheese. *In* G. Reed (ed.), Prescott and Dunn's industrial microbiology. AVI Publishing Co., Inc. Westport, Conn.

Price, W. V., and M. G. Bush. 1974a. The process cheese industry in the United States: a review. I. Industrial growth and problems. J. Milk Food Technol. 37:135–153.

Price, W. V., and M. G. Bush. 1974b. The process cheese industry in the United States: a review. II. Research and development. J. Milk Food Technol. 37:179–199.

Sandine, W. E., C. Daly, and P. R. Elliker. 1973. Causes and control of culture-related flavor defects in cultured dairy products. J. Dairy Sci. 55:1031–1039.

Sandine, W. E., P. C. Radich, and P. R. Elliker. 1972. Ecology of the lactic streptococci. J. Milk Food Technol. 35:176–185.

Speck, M. L. 1972. Control of food-borne pathogens by starter cultures. J. Dairy Sci. 55:1019–1023.

Vedamuthu, E. R. 1982. Fermented milks. *In* A. H. Rose (ed.), Fermented foods. Volume 7. Academic Press, Inc., New York.

Others

Allen, O. N., and E. K. Allen. 1933. The manufacture of poi from taro in Hawaii. Hawaii Agr. Exp. Stn. Bull. 70.

Camargo, R. de, J. Leme, Jr., and A. F. Martinelli. 1963. General observations on the microflora of fermenting cocoa beans (*Theobroma cacao*) in Bahia (Brazil). Food Technol. 17:1328–1330.

Djien, K. S., and C. W. Hesseltine. 1961. Indonesian fermented foods. Soybean Dig. November, pp. 14–15.

Domercq, Simone. 1957. Étude et classification des levures de vin de la Gironde. Annu. Inst. Natl. Rech. Agron. Ser. E Annu. Technol. Agr. 6:5–58.

Fell, G. 1961. Étude sur la fermentation malolactique du vin et les possibilités de la provoquer par ensemencement. Landw. Jahrb. Schweiz. 10:249–264.

Hesseltine, C. W. 1961. Research at Northern Regional Research Laboratory on fermented foods. Proceedings of the Conference on Soybean Products for Protein in Human Foods. USDA Agr. Res. Serv.

Hesseltine, C. W., M. Smith, and H. L. Wang. 1967. New fermented cereal products. Dev. Ind. Microbiol. 8:179–195.

Hoynak, S., T. S. Polansky, and R. W. Stone. 1941. Microbiological studies of cacao fermentation. Food Res. 6:471–479.

Mukherjee, S. K., M. N. Albury, C. S. Pederson, A. G. van Veen, and K. H. Steinkraus. 1965. Role of *Leuconostoc mesenteroides* in leavening the batter of idli, a fermented food of India. Appl. Microbiol. 13:227–231.

Palo, M. A., L. Vidal-Adeva, and L. M. Maceda. 1962. A study of ang-kak and its production. Philipp. J. Sci. 89:1–22.

Pederson, C. S., and R. S. Breed. 1946. Fermentation of coffee. Food Res. 11:99–106.

Martinelli, A. F., and C. W. Hesseltine. 1964. Tempeh fermentation: package and tray fermentations. Food Technol. 18:761–765.

Rusmin, S., and S. D. Ko. 1974. Rice-grown *Rhizopus oligosporus* inoculum for tempeh fermentation. Appl. Microbiol. 28:347–350.

Sakaguchi, K. 1959. Studies on the activities of bacteria in soy sauce brewing. V. The effects of *Aspergillus soyae, Pediococcus soyae, Bacillus subtilis* and *Saccharomyces rouxii* in purely cultured soy sauce brewing. Rep. Noda Inst. Sci. Res. 3:23–29.

Steinkraus, K. H. 1974. Research on traditional oriental and Indian fermented foods. 8th Annu. Symp. N.Y. State Agr. Exp. Stn., Spec. Rep. 16. April 1974.

Steinkraus, K. H., Y. B. Hwa, J. P. Van Buren, M. I. Provvidenti, and D. B. Hand. 1960. Studies on tempeh: an Indonesian fermentation soybean food. Food Res. 25:777–788.

Steinkraus, K. H., J. P. Van Buren, L. R. Hackler, and D. B. Hand. 1965. Pilot-plant process for the production of dehydrated tempeh. Food Technol. 19:63–69.

Van Veen, A. G. 1965. Fermented and dried seafood products in Southeast Asia. *In* Fish as food, chap. 8. Academic Press, Inc., New York.

Wang, H. L., L. Kraidej, and C. W. Hesseltine. 1974. Lactic acid fermentation of soybean milk. J. Milk Food Technol. 37:71–74.

Wang, H. L., E. W. Swain, and C. W. Hesseltine. 1975. Mass production of *Rhizopus oligosporus* spores. J. Food Sci. 40:168–170.

Yokotsuka, T. 1960. Aroma and flavor of Japanese soy sauce. Adv. Food Res. 10:75–134.

CHAPTER

FOODS AND ENZYMES FROM MICROORGANISMS

Microorganisms may serve as food for human beings or feed for animals, as a source of enzymes to be used in the processing of foods, or as manufacturers of products to be added to foods.

MICROORGANISMS AS FOOD: SINGLE-CELL PROTEIN

Although a number of kinds of microorganisms have been recommended for human consumption, including yeasts, molds, and algae, to date only yeasts have been used as food to any extent and then under unusual conditions. During World War II, when there were shortages in proteins and vitamins in the diet, the Germans produced yeasts and a mold (*Geotrichum candidum*) in some quantity for food. After the war the British established a plant in Jamaica for the production of food yeast. Food- and feed-yeast plants are reported in operation now in Germany, Switzerland, Finland, the Union of South Africa, Jamaica, Formosa, and the United States. Production is of special interest to areas having plentiful supplies of cheap carbohydrate and shortages of proteins and vitamins. In the past most of the yeast used in the United States for feed and pharmaceuticals was recovered by brewers and distillers after alcoholic fermentation, but now increasing quantities of yeast are being grown directly for such purposes. Organisms may be termed **primary** when grown directly for the purpose in mind and **secondary** when they are recovered as a by-product of a fermentation.

382

Secondary yeasts recovered as a by-product of an alcoholic fermentation are strains of brewers' yeasts, *Saccharomyces cerevisiae* or *S. carlsbergensis,* or of distillers' yeasts, *S. cerevisiae* var. *ellipsoideus.* Brewers' yeast is debittered by washing with caustic soda solution and water, adjusted to pH 5.5 to 5.7 with phosphoric acid, salted, and dried, usually on a drum dryer. Before drying it may be fortified with thiamine, riboflavin, and niacin. A type of primary yeast may be produced by growing harvested yeast cells from breweries or distilleries for a few generations in a molasses or similar medium. The consumption of "yeast cakes" containing viable cells may actually result in the yeast scavenging vitamins. A better nutritional supplement would be a "dead" product such as yeast single-cell protein.

Single-cell protein (SCP) is a term generally accepted to mean the microbial cells (primary) grown and harvested for animal or human food. Apparently the names bacterial, algal, or microbial protein are less appealing than single-cell protein. Research on SCP has been stimulated by a concern over the eventual food crisis or food shortage that will occur if the world's population is not controlled. Many scientists believe that the use of microbial fermentations and the development of an industry to produce and supply SCP are possible solutions to meet a shortage of protein if and when the amount of protein produced or obtained by agriculture and fishing becomes insufficient. Students requiring further information should begin with the references at the end of this chapter.

The more obvious advantages of the use of SCP include (1) the possibility of using a nonhuman food for the substrate of SCP production, (2) the inherent high protein content of microorganisms—on a dried-weight basis, protein content might approach 60 to 70 percent of the cell, (3) the rapid increase in cells (protein) because of the extremely short generation times, and (4) lack of dependence of the SCP production process on climatic conditions. Table 23-1 summarizes many of the SCP processes currently in use or being considered. Many of these processes are designed to produce an SCP for use in animal feeds (feed grade) and some for human food (food grade).

Microorganisms Used

As shown in Table 23-1 various yeasts, bacteria, fungi, and algae are possible agents for SCP production. Two algae, *Scenedesmus acutus* (267-3A) and *Spirulina maxima,* have been used in culture ponds or basins. Their use may be somewhat limited in two ways: (1) geographically, since they require warm temperatures and plenty of sunlight in addition to carbon dioxide, and (2) nutritionally, since the cell wall is undigestible. *S. maxima* is being grown on a commercial basis in Lake Texcoco in Mexico. Possibly useful bacteria include species of *Pseudomonas* (used in the United Kingdom, and by the Chinese Petroleum Corp., Taiwan, processes), *Alcaligenes* spp. (utilize H_2 and CO_2), and *Cellulomonas* spp. (will break down cellulosic material). Bacteria are capable of growth on a wide variety of substrates, have a short generation time, and are high in protein content. Their use is somewhat limited by (1) poor public acceptance of bacteria as food, (2) small size and difficulty of harvesting, and (3) high content of nucleic acid on a dried-weight basis (see following section). Yeasts are probably the most widely accepted and used microorganisms for

TABLE 23-1
SOME SCP PROCESSES

Type	Company	Plant location	Substrate	Type of organism	Plant size, thousands of tons per year
Feed grade	British Petroleum	U.K.	n-Paraffin	Yeast	4
	Chinese Petroleum	Taiwan	n-Paraffin	Yeast	1
	Dai Nippon	Japan	n-Paraffin	Yeast	?
	ICI	U.K.	Methanol	Bacteria	1
	Kanegafuchi	Japan	n-Paraffin	Yeast	5
	Kohjin	Japan	?	Yeast	2.4
	Kyowa Hakko	Japan	n-Paraffin	Yeast	1.5
	Milbrew	U.S.	Whey, beer wort	Yeast	10
	Shell	Holland	Methane	Bacteria	1
	Svenska-Socker	Sweden	Potato starch	Yeast	2
	British Petroleum	France	Gas oil	Yeast	20
	United Paper Mills	Finland	Sulfite waste	Yeast	10
	USSR	USSR	?	Yeast	20
	British Petroleum	Italy	n-Paraffin	Yeast	100
	Liquichimica	Italy	n-Paraffin	Yeast	100
	LSU-Bechtel		Cellulose waste	Bacteria	
	Tate & Lyle		Citric acid waste	Fungi	
	ICAITI	Guatemala	Coffee waste	Fungi	
	IFP		CO_2, sunlight	Algae	
	General Electric		Feed-lot waste	Bacteria	
	Mitsubishi		Methanol	Yeast	
	Finnish Pulp and Paper		Paper-pulp waste	Fungi	
Food grade	AMOCO	U.S.	Ethanol	Yeast	7.5
	Boise Cascade	U.S.	Sulfite waste	Yeast	6
	St. Regis Paper	U.S.	Sulfite waste	Yeast	5
	Slovnaft-Kojetin	Czechoslovakia	Ethanol	Yeast	1
	Exxon-Nestlé		Ethanol	Bacteria	
	Dai Nippon		Molasses	Yeast	
	RHM-Dupont		Starch	Fungi	
	Kraft Co.		Whey	Yeast	
	Anheuser-Busch	U.S.	Beer wort	Yeast	5
	Yeast Products, Inc.	U.S.	Beer wort	Yeast	

Source: Miller and Litsky (1976) and other sources.

SCP production. These include strains of *Candida utilis* (torula yeast), which grows rapidly, utilizes pentose as well as hexose sugars, and synthesizes its accessory foods for growth from simple compounds, making possible its production from raw materials that are comparatively poor culture media. This is in contrast to *S. cerevisiae,* which utilizes only hexose sugar and otherwise is more fastidious in its growth requirements. Two special varieties of *Candida utilis* have been used, *C. utilis* var. *major,* which has larger cells than the original strain, and *C. utilis* var. *thermophila,* a high-temperature strain which can be grown at 36 to 39 C rather than at 32 to 34 C. *C. arborea (Monilia candida), C. pulcherrima,* and other yeasts also have been employed. A lactose fermenting yeast is required if yeast is to be grown in whey. *Candida lipolytica* strains are used for processes using alkanes and gas oil as substrates. Yeasts in general have several advantages over bacteria and algae including (1) better public acceptance, (2) lower content of nucleic acid, (3) easier harvesting because of size and concentration, and (4) growth in substrates of low pH.

Other studies on SCP production have used the yeasts *Rhodotorula* and *Saccharomyces* and the fungi *Aspergillus, Penicillium,* and *Fusarium.*

Raw Materials Used as Substrates

Materials that have been employed include (1) molasses from sugar manufacture or hydrolysis of starch, (2) spent sulfite liquor, which is a waste product of the sulfite-pulping process in the paper industry, (3) the acid hydrolyzate of wood, (4) agricultural wastes, e.g., whey from the dairy industry, hydrolyzed starchy foods, e.g., grains and cull potatoes, and fruit wastes, e.g., fruit juice or citrus-peel hydrolyzate, (5) methane, (6) methanol and ethanol, as a carbon source for yeast, (7) paraffin or alkanes, (8) gas oil, the petroleum fraction between lubricating oil and diesel fuel, and (9) combustion gas, a source of carbon dioxide for algal cultures.

Conditions for Growth and Production

Since numerous processes are being used or experimented with, this discussion will be limited to the use of yeasts in commonly utilized raw materials. For the most part, yeasts are produced by a continuous process which requires (1) establishment of active yeast growth in the fermentor, (2) feeding of carbohydrates and sources of nitrogen, phosphorus, and potassium at increasing rates until a maximal level of yeast growth is maintained continuously, (3) application of optimal aeration and agitation, and (4) withdrawal of liquor (beer) containing the yeast cells at rates and volumes equaling the additions of fresh medium.

Optimal conditions for yeast production vary with the yeast employed and the raw material used. Aeration should be considerable but at an optimal level; too little encourages alcohol production rather than growth, and too much favors increased respiration and heat production and hence lowered yields of the yeast cells. The optimal temperature depends on the yeast strain. The pH should be kept on the acid side, usually between 4.5 and 6.0. The concentration of fermentable sugar is maintained at a level no higher than that necessary for a good yield of cells. The amounts and kinds of inorganic nutrients to be added depend on the substrate. Cane- or beet-sugar molasses, for example, usually is high in potassium and fairly well supplied with available phosphorus and nitrogen, but spent sulfite liquor is deficient in all three of these elements, which are needed in relatively large amounts. Nitrogen usually is added in the form of ammonia or ammonium salts.

Yields are 45 percent or more of dry yeast on the basis of the sugar fed. The yeast cells are centrifuged from the medium, washed, concentrated, and dried. All food yeasts are killed before use.

Special pretreatments are required before some of the raw materials can be used to grow yeast. Most of the sulfur dioxide must be removed from the spent sulfite liquor by steam stripping or by aeration and treatment with lime. The treated liquor remains selective enough to favor the yeasts over competing organisms so that troubles with contamination are negligible throughout a long period of continuous yeast production. Wood hydrolyzate similarly requires pretreatment.

Nutritive Value and Use of SCP

Nutritive value varies with the microorganism used. Protein digestibility values, expressed as a percentage, range from 65 to 96 for the various cultures tested. Protein efficiency ratio (PER) values range from 0.6 to 2.6. The method of harvesting, drying, and processing has an effect on the nutritive value of the finished product. Food yeast is high in protein and in most of the B complex vitamins but may be deficient in methionine and perhaps cysteine. Also, the thiamine content may be lower than in secondary yeast, and there is a deficiency of vitamin B_{12}. Furnished by food yeast in varying amounts are thiamine, riboflavin, biotin, niacin, pantothenic acid, pyridoxine, choline, streptogenin, glutathione, and perhaps folic acid and p-aminobenzoic acid.

The United Nations Protein Advisory Group has summarized the major concerns over the use of SCP for human beings as follows: (1) high concentration of nucleic acids (6 to 11 percent) elevating serum uric acid levels and resulting in kidney stone formation or gout, (2) possible skin reactions from consuming foreign proteins, (3) possible carryover of carcinogenic factors from the diverse substrates, and (4) possible gastrointestinal reactions resulting in nausea and vomiting.

FATS FROM MICROORGANISMS

Fats (more properly lipids) are synthesized in appreciable amounts by certain yeasts, yeastlike organisms, and molds, but production in this manner has been employed only during periods of emergency, e.g., a state of war, when cheaper and more easily available animal and plant lipids were not available in sufficient quantity.

Organisms Used

Among the yeasts, *Candida pulcherrima, Torulopsis lipofera, Saccharomyces cerevisiae,* and *Rhodotorula glutinis* have been studied for their fat production, and the first was used for this purpose in Germany and Sweden during World War II. The yeastlike *Trichosporon pullulans* was used by the Germans during World War I, as were special strains of the mold *Geotrichum candidum.*

Raw Materials

Media for fat production should in general have a high carbon-to-nitrogen ratio, a good supply of phosphates, and for most organisms a pH on the acid side. In fat production by *Trichosporon pullulans,* good growth first is obtained in a mash with a high ratio of nitrogen to carbon, and fat production is carried out in a medium with a high ratio of carbon to nitrogen. Molasses, cellulose waste, hydrolyzed wood, and spent sulfite liquor are among the sources of carbohydrate employed. Nitrogen can be in the form of ammonium salts, urea, urine, yeast water, molasses slop, or extracts of grains. Salts to be added include potassium chloride, monopotassium phosphate, and magnesium sulfate. Addition of small amounts of alcohol or sodium acetate increases yields of lipids. The choice of a yeast will depend on its ability to utilize both pentoses and hexoses or only the latter. *Geotrichum candidum* is able to utilize the lactose in whey, to which some additional nitrogenous food and salts may be added.

Production of Fat

Since all the previously mentioned organisms grow best under aerobic conditions, their growth for fat production has been in thin layers on trays or other flat areas when *Trichosporon pullulans* or a mold was employed and in well-aerated tanks when yeasts were grown submerged. The optimal temperature varies with the organism employed, ranging from 15 to 20 C for *T. pullulans* to 25 to 30 C or slightly higher for molds and yeasts. A fairly long period is required for maximal fat production by most of the organisms mentioned. *T. pullulans,* for example, requires 2 to 3 days to attain growth and 6 to 8 days more for maximal yields of lipids. Fields of lipids vary widely with the organisms and with methods of production. Recovery of lipids is by extraction with solvents, with or without autolysis.

PRODUCTION OF AMINO ACIDS

Commercial fermentation processes for the production of glutamate have developed rapidly since the recognition of monosodium glutamate (MSG) as an important flavor-accentuating food ingredient. Annual production of glutamate approaches 200,000 tons. The strains of *Corynebacterium, Arthrobacter, Brevibacterium,* or *Micrococcus glutamicus (Corynebacterium glutamicus)* used lack α-ketoglutarate dehydrogenase, an enzyme in the Krebs cycle responsible for the conversion of α-ketoglutarate to succinyl-CoA. Glutamate accumulates because the ketoglutarate in the presence of ammonia is shunted to glutamate via transamination. The commercial fermentation of lysine is also a large industry. Many commodities, particularly cereal products, are low in this essential amino acid. Its use in the food industry has been mainly for the fortification of products low in lysine. Other fermentations have been developed for aspartic acid, threonine, isoleucine, phenylalanine, proline, tryptophan, valine, homoserine, ornithine, leucine, arginine, histidine, and tyrosine.

PRODUCTION OF OTHER SUBSTANCES ADDED TO FOODS

Microorganisms may be employed to produce dextran, xanthan, lactic and citric acids, and perhaps other substances added to foods.

Dextran and Xanthan

Dextran, a gummy polysaccharide, is a neutral glucan made by *Leuconostoc mesenteroides* from a molasses or refined-sucrose medium; it serves as a stabilizer for sugar sirups, ice cream, and confections and as a plasma extender. Commercial production from sucrose or a sucrose-rich medium is possible with cell-free filtrates since the enzyme responsible for the polymerization is extracellular. Xanthan is a polyionic hydropolysaccharide made by *Xanthomonas campestris* when grown in a glucose-based medium. Xanthan has many possible uses in the food industry, particularly as a stabilizer. Xanthan differs from dextran in that it is not hydrolyzed or degraded by human beings or animals and is excreted intact.

Lactic Acid

For the most part, lactic acid is produced industrially by homofermentative lactic acid bacteria or bacteria resembling them. A simplified equation for the production of lactic acid from glucose by such organisms is

$$C_6H_{12}O_6 \xrightarrow[\text{bacteria}]{\text{lactic acid}} 2CH_3CHOH\ COOH$$
$$\text{glucose} \qquad\qquad\qquad \text{lactic acid}$$

Actually a series of steps is involved, and small amounts of other products are produced. It has been estimated that edible lactic acid makes up about half of the commercial acid produced by fermentation.

Microorganisms Used The microorganism used depends on the raw material to be fermented. *Lactobacillus delbrueckii* was most often employed in the past for lactic acid production from glucose, maltose, or sucrose, although increasing use is being made of a flat sour bacterium such as *Bacillus coagulans*. *Lactobacillus delbrueckii* subsp. *bulgaricus* has been selected for making lactic acid from whey. The pentose-fermenting *L. pentosus* (*L. plantarum*) is recommended for use in spent sulfite liquors, and *L. brevis* (*L. pentoaceticus*) for hydrolyzed corncobs, cottonseed hulls, etc. Molds, e.g., *Rhizopus oryzae,* have been used experimentally to produce lactic acid from a glucose-salts medium.

Raw Materials It is advantageous in the manufacture of lactic acid by fermentation to start with a relatively simple medium or mash in order to facilitate the recovery of the product. When glucose, sucrose, or maltose is the carbohydrate fermented, as with a molasses or a starch hydrolyzate mash, *Lactobacillus delbrueckii* or a flat sour bacillus usually is employed. Nitrogenous food, minerals, and various growth factors required by the bacteria may be added in the form of malt sprouts, corn-steep liquor, milk, etc. Similar addition must be made to spent sulfite liquor for the growth of *L. plantarum.* The production of lactic acid from whey by *L. delbrueckii* subsp. *bulgaricus* also has been carried out on an industrial scale. Other raw materials that have been suggested are cull fruits, Jerusalem artichokes, molasses, beet juice, hydrolyzed starchy materials, e.g., potatoes or grains, and hydrolyzed corncobs, corn stalks, cottonseed hulls, and straw.

Production of Lactic Acid The heat-processed mash is held at a temperature favorable to the organism with which it is inoculated: about 45 C for *L. delbrueckii,* 45 to 50 C for *L. delbrueckii* subsp. *bulgaricus* or *Bacillus coagulans,* and 30 C for *L. plantarum.* The optimal sugar content of the mash will vary from 5 to 20 percent, depending on the raw material and the fermenting organism. Anaerobic conditions are maintained in the mash. The pH is kept slightly on the acid side, the lactic acid being neutralized as formed by the periodic addition of calcium hydroxide or calcium carbonate during the several days of the fermentation. The calcium lactate may be crystallized as such or converted to lactic acid by the addition of sulfuric acid. The edible grade of lactic acid requires considerably more refining than does the technical grade.

Uses of Edible Lactic Acid In the food industries, lactic acid is used to acidify jams, jellies, confectionery, sherbets, soft drinks, extracts, and other products. It is added to brines for pickles and olives and to horseradish and fish to aid in preservation. Its addition makes milk more digestible for infants. Calcium lactate is an ingredient of some baking powders.

Citric Acid

In the United States most citric acid is produced by fermentation.

Organisms Used *Aspergillus niger* is the principal mold used in citric acid production, although various other molds are known to be able to make the acid and many have been tried experimentally: molds such as *A. clavatus, A. wentii, Penicillium luteum, P. citrinum, Mucor pyriformis,* and others. Apparently different strains of *A. niger* are preferred for surface methods of citric acid production than for methods involving submerged growth. A simplified theoretical equation for the production of citric acid from glucose is

$$\underset{\text{glucose}}{C_6H_{12}O_6} + 1\tfrac{1}{2}O_2 \rightarrow \underset{\text{citric acid}}{C_6H_8O_7} + 2H_2O$$

A series of intermediate steps is involved, and other products are produced.

Raw Materials Most citric acid is made from molasses, with beet molasses preferred over cane. Cane blackstrap and cane invert molasses also have been tried, as well as solutions of glucose or sucrose plus sources of nitrogen and minerals. The source of nitrogen usually is some simple compound such as ammonium salts or urea. The concentration of mineral ions is very important in obtaining good yields, especially levels of iron, zinc, and manganese. A slight deficiency in nitrogenous food and phosphate also favors production. Factors that tend to reduce the formation of mycelium below the maximum therefore appear to increase the yield of citric acid. Conditions favoring citric acid production tend to suppress the formation of oxalic acid.

Production of Citric Acid The older method of citric acid manufacture was by means of surface growth; the mold mycelium was cultured on shallow layers of medium in trays or similar containers. Modern methods involve the submerged growth of the mycelium. It should be noted again that the strain of mold selected and the medium for production differ with the method of cultivation of the mold. Most methods utilize a sugar concentration between 14 and 20 percent, a fairly low pH that is more acid for the surface method, and a temperature of about 25 to 30 C and a fermentation period of 7 to 10 days for the surface method and a shorter time for the submerged method.

Uses of Citric Acid In the food industries, citric acid is added to flavoring extracts, soft drinks, and candies. It has been added to fish to adjust the pH to about 5.0 to aid in its preservation, to artichokes to enable the processor to utilize a milder heat treatment in their canning than would otherwise be possible, to crabmeat to prevent discoloration, as a synergist with antioxidants for oils, and as a dip for sliced peaches to delay browning. A large portion of the citric acid produced is used for medicinal purposes.

PRODUCTION OF ENZYMES

The protein biocatalysts, called **enzymes**, used by living cells are responsible for numerous metabolic processes of the cell. The use of microbial enzymes, although only recently understood, has been going on for centuries. Since microorganisms are responsible for the fermentations of beer, wine, bread, cheese, and various vegetables, all these processes are examples of cell-mediated conversions or applications of enzymes.

Current technology makes it possible to isolate, purify, and even immobilize (bind to a fixed support) the specific enzyme needed for a desired function. Several enzymes used in the food and fermentation industries and their respective sources are presented in Table 23-2, accompanied by a discussion of several of the more important groups of enzymes.

Amylases

The amylases, which hydrolyze the starches, are classified in various ways, depending on how they act on the starch molecules. Starch is composed of two glucans, the linear amylose, containing D-glucose units joined by α-1,4 linkages, and the branched amylopectin, containing in addition 1,6 linkages at the branching points. The amylases include α-**amylase**, which randomly hydrolyzes the α-1,4-glucoside linkages of amylose or amylopectin but not the 1,6-glucosidic linkages of amylopectin; β-**amylase**, which splits only the second α-1,4-glucoside linkage from the nonreducing chain ends, detaching one molecule of maltose at a time from the chain and finally leaving limit dextrins; and **amyloglucosidase**,

TABLE 23-2
MICROBIAL ENZYMES, SOURCE, AND USE

Enzyme	Source	Industry	Application
Amylase	*Aspergillus niger*	Baking	Flour supplement
	A. oryzae	Brewing	Mashing
	Bacillus subtilis	Food	Precooked foods
	Rhizopus spp.,	Food	Sirup manufacture
	Mucor rouxii		
Cellulase	*A. niger,*	Food	Preparation of liquid-coffee
	Trichoderma viride		concentrates
Dextransucrase	*Leuconostoc*	Food	Dextran for various uses
	mesenteroides		
Glucose oxidase	*A. niger*	Food	Glucose removal from egg solids
Invertase	*Saccharomyces*	Food	Artificial honey, prevents granulation
	cerevisiae		in soft-center candies
Lactase	*S. fragilis*	Dairy	Hydrolysis of lactose
Lipase	*A. niger,*	Dairy	Flavors in cheese
	Mucor spp.,		
	Rhizopus spp.		
Pectinase	*A. niger,*	Food	Clarification of wine and fruit juices
	Penicillium spp.,		
	Rhizopus spp.		
Protease	*A. oryzae*	Brewing	Prevents chill haze in beer
(proteinase)	*B. subtilis,*	Baking	Bread
		Food	Meat tenderizer
	Mucor spp.,		
	Rhizopus spp.		
Renninlike	*M. miehei,*	Food	Curdling of milk for cheese
enzymes	*M. pusillus*		

Source: Condensed from Porter (1974) and Underkofler (1976).

which hydrolyzes both 1,6- and 1,4-glucoside linkages to produce glucose without intermediate dextrins and maltose. **Maltase** or α-**glucosidase** (not an amylase) hydrolyzes maltose to glucose. Much of the amylase used in industry is provided by grain malt, which contains amylases in varying proportions. Increasing amounts of amylase are being produced, however, from molds and bacteria, and they may yield primarily one kind of amylase or a mixture of amylases.

From Molds Molds are used as sources of amylases as well as of other hydrolytic enzymes, the species and strain of mold being selected especially for the purpose. *Rhizopus delemar, Mucor rouxii,* and related species have been employed in the Amylo process, in which a starchy grain mash is saccharified by amylases produced by the mold growing on it. This process has been applied principally to the preparation of mashes for alcoholic fermentation by yeasts. For the production of preparations rich in amylases, *Aspergillus oryzae* has been used most, although *A. niger* has been recommended for submerged methods of production. The preparation of koji, the *A. oryzae* starter for soy sauce that is rich in amylases as well as other hydrolytic enzymes, was described in Chapter 22.

Moistened, steamed wheat or rice bran is used for the production of amylases from *A. oryzae* by the tray method, in which the mold is grown on thin layers of the medium in trays, or the drum method, in which the bran is tossed loosely in a rotating drum. A maximal yield is obtained by the tray method in 40 to 48 hr at about 30 C in an atmosphere with a high humidity and adequate ventilation. The amylases are extracted from the mycelium and may be purified by precipitation and washing or may be concentrated as desired. Other hydrolytic enzymes also are present in such preparations.

From Bacteria *Bacillus subtilis* has been the principal bacterium used for the production of amylases, although other species of bacteria are known to yield these enzymes. Most bacteria produce more α-amylase than β-amylase. Production may be by the surface-growth method on shallow layers of mash in trays or by the submerged method.

Various culture media or mashes have been recommended for the production of amylases by means of *B. subtilis,* ranging from a complex medium such as thin stillage, a by-product of alcohol production from grains, to a simpler medium consisting of soluble or hydrolyzed starch, ammonium salts, and buffers. Another mash utilizes hydrolyzed soybean cake, peanut cake, or casein as a source of nitrogen, hydrolyzed starch for energy, and various mineral salts. Also, wheat bran has been used in a bran-salts medium. Incubation temperatures from 25 to 37 C and times of from 2 to 6 days have been employed in the tray method, and 24 to 48 hr at 30 to 40 C in the submerged method.

Bacterial amylase may be purified and concentrated by dialysis, condensation, and fractional precipitation.

Uses of Amylases   In the food industries, fungal amylases have been employed to remove starch from fruit extracts, e.g., in the production of pectin from apple pomace; to clarify starch turbidities in wines, beer, and fruit juices; to convert acid-modified starches to sweet sirups; to substitute for malt in breadmaking in aiding leavening and improving dough consistency and hence gas retention (proteinases also are involved); and to saccharify starch in mashes for alcoholic fermentation. Bacterial amylase, chiefly the alpha type, has been used in brewing to produce dextrins of low fermentability and also to clarify the beer and in the manufacture of corn sirup and chocolate sirup to prevent thickening by dextrinizing the starch present.

Invertase

Invertase catalyzes the hydrolysis of sucrose to glucose and fructose. The invertase of yeasts is a fructosidase in that it attacks the fructose end of the sucrose molecule, in contrast to the glucosidase of molds, which attacks the glucose end. Industrially, invertase is produced mainly by growth of special strains of *Saccharomyces cerevisiae* (bottom type) in a medium that contains sucrose, an ammonium salt, and phosphate buffer and other minerals and is adjusted to about pH 4.5. Incubation is for about 8 hr at 28 to 30 C. For recovery of the invertase the yeast cells are filtered off, compressed, plasmolyzed, and autolyzed. The invertase extracted from the cells may be dried with sugar or held in a sucrose sirup, or the enzyme may be purified by dialysis, ultrafiltration, adsorption, and elution. Most commercial preparations of invertase are not highly purified.

Uses   Invertase is used in the confectionery industry to make invert sugar for the preparation of liqueurs and ice creams in which the crystallization of sugars from high concentrations is to be avoided. In soft-center, chocolate-coated candies, e.g., Maraschino cherries, invertase incorporated in the centers softens the fondant after it has been coated with chocolate. Invertase is added to sucrose sirups to hydrolyze that sugar and in this way to prevent crystallization on standing. It also has been used in the manufacture of artificial honey.

Pectolytic Enzymes

Pectin, which is methylated polygalacturonic acid, is important in food industries because of its ability to form gels with sugar and acid. In jellies this characteristic is desirable, but it is not desirable in fruit juices. Most authorities agree that chiefly two enzymes are involved in the hydrolysis of pectin: **pectinesterase**, to hydrolyze the pectin to methanol and polygalacturonic acid (pectic acid), and **polygalacturonase**, to hydrolyze the polygalacturonic acid to monogalacturonic acid. Further hydrolysis would yield sugars and other products.

The mixture of pectolytic enzymes sometimes is called **pectinase** (pectase, pectinols, or filtragols), a term which will be used here for a mixture of pectolytic enzymes such as is produced by microorganisms. Pectinase is yielded by a number of molds and by various bacteria, including the clostridia involved in retting. Only the fungal type of pectinase is produced industrially to any extent, and this from molds such as species of *Aspergillus, Penicillium,* and other genera. The mycelium is developed on a medium containing pectin or a pectinlike compound; a nitrogen source, such as plant, yeast, or malt extract, ammonia, peptone, etc.; and mineral salts. The mycelium is harvested, macerated, and extracted, and the crude enzyme mixture thus obtained may be precipitated and concentrated.

Uses   Pectinases from extracts of plant materials or from fungi are used in the food industries for the clarification of fruit juices, wines, vinegars, sirups, and jellies that may contain suspended pectic material. Treatment of fruit juices with pectinase helps prevent jelling of the juices upon concentration. The addition of pectinase to crushed fruit, e.g., grapes, aids in the expression of the juice and results in wines that clarify readily. Partial deesterification by means of pectinesterase to yield modified pectins which set slowly is employed in the manufacture of candy jellies of high sugar content.

Proteolytic Enzymes

The proteolytic enzymes, or **proteases,** include the **proteinases,** which catalyze the hydrolysis of the protein molecule into large fragments, and the **peptidases,** which hydrolyze these polypeptide fragments as far down as amino acids. The proteolytic enzyme preparations from microorganisms are proteases, i.e., mixtures of proteinases and peptidases. Proteases also are prepared from plant or animal sources. Papain, for example, from the papaya fruit, is injected into meat animals before slaughter, so that the meat will be tenderized by the enzyme during cooking.

From Bacteria   For the most part, bacterial protease is prepared from cultures of *Bacillus subtilis,* although many other bacteria yield proteases. A high-yielding strain is selected, special culture media are employed, and temperature and degree of aeration are adjusted to favor the production of protease over that of amylase. The medium or mash has a fairly high content of carbohydrate (2 to 6 percent), as well as of protein, and also contains mineral salts. Incubation is for 3 to 5 days at about 37 C with adequate ventilation. The filtrate from the culture is concentrated, and the enzymes are used in this form, purified further, or absorbed onto some inert material, such as sawdust. The enzyme mixture also contains varying amounts of amylases.

From Molds   Protease preparations from molds also contain other enzymes. Thus the koji for soy sauce or the Taka-Diastase for pharmaceutical purposes contains a variety of enzymes. It is possible, however, to select strains of molds that give high yields of proteases and comparatively low yields of other enzymes. The mold also can be chosen for its ability to produce proteases which are active under acid conditions or active under alkaline conditions. The methods of preparation of mold proteases are similar to those for the production of amylases. *Aspergillus oryzae* is a good source of proteases, although other molds have been recommended. Many different media have been suggested, including those containing wheat bran, soybean cake, alfalfa meal, middlings, yeast, and other materials. Recovery of the enzyme is by extraction, concentration, and precipitation, as for other hydrolytic enzymes.

Uses The proteases from microorganisms are used primarily for their proteinase activity. Bacterial proteases have been applied to the digestion of fish livers to liberate fish oil, to the tenderization of meat, and to the clarification and maturing of malt beverages. Fungal proteases are active in the manufacture of soy sauce and other Oriental mold-fermented foods and may be added to bread dough, where, along with amylase, they help improve the consistency of the dough. They also may be used for chill-proofing beer and ale by removal of protein haze (the fungal tannase present also may be helpful), for the tenderization of meats, for thinning egg white so that it can be filtered before drying, and for the hydrolysis of the gelatinous protein material in fish waste and press water to facilitate concentration and drying.

Glucose Oxidase

Glucose oxidase is produced by the submerged growth of *Aspergillus niger* or another mold. It is used to remove glucose from egg white or whole eggs to facilitate drying, prevent deterioration, and improve the whipping properties (of the reconstituted dried whites). It has been employed also to extend the shelf life of canned soft drinks by retarding the pickup of iron and the fading of color. Oxidation of the glucose by glucose oxidase forms gluconic acid and hydrogen peroxide, the latter then being decomposed by the catalase in the same preparation. A combination of glucose oxidase and catalase is used to remove small residues of oxygen in packaged foods.

Other Enzymes

Cellulase, catalyzing the hydrolysis of cellulose to cellulodextrins and glucose, has been recommended for producing more fermentable sugar in brewers' mashes, clarifying orange and lemon juices and concentrates, and tenderizing green beans. Microbial **lipase** removes fat from yolk residues in dried egg albumen, assists mold spores in production of blue-cheese flavor in spreads, and adds to the flavor of milk chocolate. **Dextransucrase** increases viscosity by production of dextran in sucrose-containing foods. Flavor-producing enzymes, both from raw foods and from microorganisms, are receiving special attention. **Lactase** from *Saccharomyces fragilis* may find use in hydrolysis of the lactose in whey to glucose and galactose, which are less laxative sugars. **Catalase**, the enzyme that converts hydrogen peroxide to water and oxygen is commercially prepared from *Aspergillus niger, Penicillium vitale,* and *Micrococcus lysodelilaticus.* Catalase is used in many applications where the removal of hydrogen peroxide is desired, for example, in cake baking, irradiated foods, and hydrogen peroxide sterilization. **Glucose isomerase** converts glucose to fructose and is used in the corn milling industry. Commercially, *Streptomyces* or *Bacillus coagulans* is used. Undoubtedly more kinds of enzymes could be added to those mentioned.

BIBLIOGRAPHY

Anderson, R. F., H. T. Huang, S. Singer, and M. H. Rogoff. 1966. The biochemistry of glutamic acid fermentation. Symp. Microb. Prod. Amino Acids. Dev. Ind. Microbiol. 7:7–15.

Anonymous. 1964. What you can do with enzymes. Food Eng. 36(5):80–81.

Anonymous. 1966. Symp. Microb. Prod. Amino Acids. Dev. Ind. Microbiol. 7:7–58.

Barton, R. R., and C. E. Land, Jr. 1961. How latest enzymes sharpen your process control. Food Eng. 33(9):85–88.

Cooney, C. L., C. Rha, and S. R. Tannenbaum. 1980. Single-cell protein: engineering, economics, and utilization in foods. Adv. Food Res. 26:1–52.

Davis, P. 1974. Single cell protein. Academic Press, Inc., New York.

Hankin, L., and D. C. Sands. 1974. Selecting lysine-excreting mutants of lactobacilli for use in food and feed enrichment. Appl. Microbiol. 28:523–524.

Humphrey, A. E. 1974. Current developments in fermentation. Chem. Eng. December. 89–112.

Jeanes, A. 1974. Extracellular microbial polysaccharides. Food Technol. 28:34, 36, 38, 40.

Jones, J. G. W. (ed.). 1973. The biological efficiency of protein production. Cambridge University Press, New York.

Joslyn, M. A. 1962. The chemistry of protopectin: a critical review of historical data and recent developments. Adv. Food Res. 11:1–107.

Lipinsky, E. S., and J. H. Litchfield. 1974. Single-cell protein in perspective. Food Technol. 28:16, 18, 20, 22, 24, 40.

Litchfield, J. H. 1977. Single-cell proteins. Food Technol. 31:175–179.

Mateles, R. I., and S. R. Tannenbaum (eds.). 1968. Single-cell protein. The M.I.T. Press, Cambridge, Mass.

Miller, B. M., and W. Litsky. 1976. Industrial microbiology. McGraw-Hill Book Company, New York.

Perlman, D. 1970. Some prospects for the fermentation industries. Wallerstein Lab. Commun. 33:165–175.

Porter, J. R. 1974. Microbiology and the food and energy crisis. Am. Soc. Microbiol. News. 40:813–825.

Prescott, S. C., and C. G. Dunn. 1959. Industrial microbiology. 3d ed. McGraw-Hill Book Company, New York.

Reed, G. (ed). 1982. Prescott and Dunn's industrial microbiology. AVI Publishing Co., Inc., Westport, Conn.

Rose, A. H. 1961. Industrial microbiology. Butterworth & Co. (Publishers), Ltd., London.

Sardinas, J. L. 1972. Microbial rennets. Adv. Appl. Microbiol. 11:39–66.

Schultz, H. W. 1960. Food enzymes. AVI Publishing Co., Inc., Westport, Conn.

Shacklady, C. A. 1972. Yeasts grown on hydrocarbons as new sources of protein. World Rev. Nutr. Diet. 14:154–179.

Tannenbaum, S. R., and D. I. C. Wang (eds.). 1975. Single-cell protein. Volume 2. M.I.T. Press, Cambridge, Mass.

Umbarger, H. E., and B. D. Davis. 1962. Pathways of amino acid biosynthesis. *In* I. C. Gunsalus and R. Y. Stanier (eds.), The Bacteria. Volume III. Academic Press, Inc., New York.

Underkofler, L. A. 1976. Microbial enzymes. *In* B. M. Miller and W. Litsky, Industrial microbiology, chap. 7. McGraw-Hill Book Company, New York.

Waslien, C. I. 1976. Unusual sources of proteins for man. CRC Crit. Rev. Food Sci. Nutr. 6:77–151.

Zaborsky, O. R. 1973. Immobilized enzymes. CRC Press, Cleveland, Ohio.

PART FIVE

FOODS IN RELATION TO DISEASE

Every food microbiologist should know how disease can be spread by foods and how such transmission can be prevented. Of special interest are the contemporary agents of food-borne illness, including their habitat, source in foods, foods frequently involved, mechanism of pathogenicity, and means of control.

FOOD-BORNE ILLNESS: BACTERIAL

Gastrointestinal disturbances resulting from the ingestion of food can have a variety of causes, e.g., overeating; allergies; nutritional deficiencies; actual poisoning by chemicals, toxic plants, or animals; toxins produced by bacteria; infestation by animal parasites; and infection by microorganisms. These illnesses often are grouped together because they have rather similar symptoms at times and sometimes are mistaken for each other. This chapter will discuss food-borne diseases of which the etiologic agents are bacteria.

FOOD-BORNE DISEASES

Ordinarily, the term "food poisoning," as applied to diseases caused by microorganisms, is used very loosely to include both illnesses caused by the ingestion of toxins elaborated by the organisms and those resulting from infection of the host through the intestinal tract. A further classification of food-borne diseases is shown in Figure 24-1. Here, all food-borne diseases are subdivided into poisonings and infections. Food poisonings can be the result of either chemical poisoning or the ingestion of a toxicant (intoxication). The toxicant might be found naturally in certain plants or animals (see Chapter 25) or be a toxic metabolic product excreted by a microorganism. A **bacterial food intoxication** therefore refers to food-borne illnesses caused by the presence of a bacterial toxin formed in the food. A **bacterial food infection** refers to food-borne illnesses caused by the entrance of bacteria into the body through ingestion of contam-

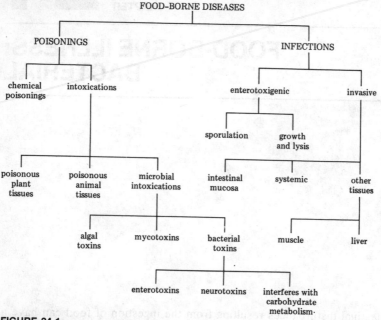

FIGURE 24-1
A classification of food-borne diseases. (*Adapted from Bryan, F. L. 1976. Diseases transmitted by foods. DHEW Pub. No. (CDC) 76–8237, Center for Disease Control, Atlanta, Ga.*)

inated foods and the reaction of the body to their presence or to their metabolites.

According to this classification, there are two chief kinds of food intoxications caused by bacteria (see Figure 24-2): (1) botulism, caused by the presence in food of toxin produced by *Clostridium botulinum,* and (2) staphylococcal intoxication, caused by a toxin in the food from *Staphylococcus aureus.*

Food infections listed in Figure 24-2 can be divided into two types: (1) those in which the food does not ordinarily support growth of the pathogens but merely carries them, i.e., pathogens such as those causing tuberculosis, diphtheria, the dysenteries, typhoid fever, brucellosis, cholera, infectious hepatitis, Q fever, etc., and (2) those in which the food can serve as a culture medium for growth of the pathogens to numbers that will increase the likelihood of infection of the consumer of the food; these include *Salmonella* spp., *Vibrio parahaemolyticus,* and enteropathogenic *Escherichia coli.* Outbreaks of food infections of the second type are likely to be more explosive than outbreaks caused by other intestinal pathogens.

Some workers suggest that *Clostridium perfringens* food-borne illness and *Bacillus cereus* gastroenteritis should be listed as food intoxications rather than food infections since toxin *might be* released by *B. cereus* as a result of autolysis of the cells in the food or by *C. perfringens* during sporulation in the food. If the toxins were released in the food, they would be better classified as food intoxications. However, as is discussed in the following sections, a large number of viable cells must be consumed in both cases, which implies the release of toxin in vivo rather than in the food. The controversial status of these two food-borne illnesses is recognized. Additionally, the whole categorization into food infections and food intoxications is not as straightforward as it once was. *S. aureus* produces an enterotoxin in the food and is frequently referred to as the classical food intoxication. However, several gram-positive bacteria, including *S. aureus, C. perfringens,* and *B. cereus,* can colonize the intestinal mucosa and be responsible for chronic diarrhea. Also, the pathogenicity of *Salmonella* is thought to be due to an enterotoxin and perhaps a cytotoxin. Therefore, these terms should be used cautiously.

Table 24-1 shows the number of outbreaks and cases during a 4-year period in the United States from several bacterial agents. These figures probably represent only a fraction of the outbreaks and cases that really occurred during each period. Since many people do not consult a physician about some diarrheal illnesses, health departments and normal surveillance channels would not be

FIGURE 24-2
Examples of bacteria responsible for food-borne intoxications and infections.

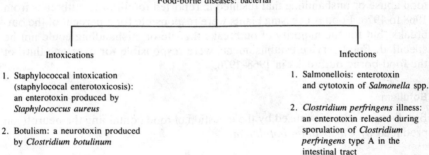

Food-borne diseases: bacterial

Intoxications

1. Staphylococcal intoxication (staphylococal enterotoxicosis): an enterotoxin produced by *Staphylococcus aureus*

2. Botulism: a neurotoxin produced by *Clostridium botulinum*

Infections

1. Salmonellois: enterotoxin and cytotoxin of *Salmonella* spp.

2. *Clostridium perfringens* illness: an enterotoxin released during sporulation of *Clostridium perfringens* type A in the intestinal tract

3. *Bacillus cereus* gastroenteritis: an exoenterotoxin released during lysis of *Bacillus cereus* in the intestinal tract

4. *Enteropathogenic Escherichia coli* infection: Several serotypes of *E. coli*, some invasive and some enterotoxigenic

5. Others (see Table 24–8): Yersiniosis Shigellosis *Vibrio parahaemolyticus*

TABLE 24-1
SOME FOOD-BORNE ILLNESSES REPORTED IN THE UNITED STATES, 1978–1982

Disease	1978	1979	1980	1981	1982
Staphylococcal intoxication	—	2,391(34)	944(27)	2,934(44)	669(28)
Clostridium perfringens gastroenteritis	617(9)*	1,110(2)	1,463(25)	1,162(28)	1,189(22)
Salmonellosis	1,921(45)	2,794(44)	2,381(39)	2,456(66)	2,056(55)
Botulism	58(12)	9(7)	18(14)	22(11)	30(21)
Bacillus cereus gastroenteritis	248(6)	—	187(9)	74(8)	200(8)
Shigellosis	159(4)	356(7)	1,184(11)	351(9)	116(4)
Vibrio parahaemolyticus gastroenteritis	86(2)	14(2)	12(4)	13(2)	39(3)
Escherichia coli gastroenteritis	35(1)	—	500(1)	—	47(2)

* Number of cases followed by number of outbreaks in parentheses.
Source: Center for Disease Control, U.S. Department of Health, Education and Welfare, Foodborne Outbreak Annual Summaries.

aware of the incident, and therefore it would not be reported and tabulated. The majority of outbreaks and cases were attributed to staphylococcal intoxication, salmonellosis, and *Clostridium perfringens* gastroenteritis.

Despite the efforts of many agencies, industries, and people, outbreaks continue to occur. Table 24-2 summarizes data regarding the location or site of food abuse or mishandling that resulted in reported food-borne outbreaks from 1968 to 1976. Food processing plants were responsible for 5 percent of the outbreaks, but for the majority of outbreaks the site of mishandling could not be specified. Food service establishments were responsible for over one-third of the food-borne outbreaks in 1968–1976.

Botulism

Botulism is a disease caused by the ingestion of food containing the neurotoxin produced by *Clostridium botulinum.*

TABLE 24-2
PLACES WHERE FOODS WERE MISHANDLED
1968–1976

Place	Number	Percent
Food service establishments	1,283	39
Homes	504	15
Food processing plants	163	5
Unknown or unspecified	1,354	41
Total	3,304	100

Source: Center for Disease Control, U.S. Department of Health, Education and Welfare, Foodborne Outbreak Annual Summaries.

The Organism   This rod-shaped soil bacterium is saprophytic, spore form-ing, gas forming, and anaerobic. Seven types are distinguished on the basis of the serological specificity of their toxins; the predominant (or only) toxin from these types is designated by the same capital letter.

Type A is the one commonly causing human botulism in the western part of the United States. It is more toxic than type B.

Type B is found more often than type A in most soils of the world and is less toxic to human beings.

Type C causes botulism of fowls, cattle, mink, and other animals but not of human beings so far as is known.

Type D is associated with forage poisoning of cattle in the Union of South Africa.

Type E, which is toxic for humans, has been obtained chiefly from fish and fish products.

Type F, which except for its toxin is similar to types A and B, has been isolated in Denmark and produces human botulism.

Type G has been isolated from the soil in Argentina but has not been impli-cated in human botulism.

Not all types produce a single toxin. For example, some type C strains pro-duce predominately C_1 toxin with smaller amounts of D and C_2, or only C_2. Type D strains produce predominately D toxin with lesser amounts of C_1 and C_2 toxins.

Type A strains and most cultures of type B are proteolytic and are putre-factive enough to give an obnoxious odor to proteinaceous foods, but some strains of type B and those of type E are not. Even the first two types fail to give marked indications of putrefaction in low-protein foods such as string beans and corn, although they produce toxin. The organism ferments carbohydrates with gas production, but sometimes this is not evident either.

Separation of the various strains of *C. botulinum* solely on the basis of toxin types results in very heterogeneous groups. For this reason, *C. botulinum* strains frequently are divided into three general groups, based on cultural and physi-ological characters, as follows:

Group I includes all type A strains (proteolytic) and the proteolytic strains of B and F.

Group II includes all type E strains (nonproteolytic) and the nonproteolytic strains of B and F.

Group III includes types C and D; they are nonproteolytic and share a com-mon metabolic pattern.

Growth and Toxin Production   Toxin production by *C. botulinum* depends on the ability of the cells to grow in a food and to autolyze there, for the types A, B, E, and F toxins apparently are synthesized as large, comparatively in-active proteins which become fully toxic after some hydrolysis. Therefore, the factors that influence spore germination, growth, and hence toxin production are of special interest. These factors include the composition of the food or medium, especially its nutritive properties (e.g., glucose or maltose is known to be essential for toxin production), moisture content, pH, O-R potential, and salt content, and the temperature and time of storage of the food. It is the combination of these factors that determines whether growth can take place and the rate and extent of that growth. Thus the nutritive properties of the food are likely to determine the minimal pH or temperature and the maximal concentration of sodium chloride for growth and toxin production. Results will differ with the serological type of organism and the particular strain.

Although foods are known to differ as culture media for *C. botulinum,* much of the evidence is empirical. Most of the studies have been on toxin production in various foods. Meats, fish, and low- or medium-acid canned foods have been shown to support toxin production and to differ in the potency of the toxin formed. Even good culture media may differ in the relative potency of the toxin formed in them. It has been reported, for instance, that media containing milk or casein, glucose or maltose, and corn-steep liquor yield more potent type A toxin than other media and that potencies of toxin from the following canned foods are, in descending order, corn>peas>string beans>spinach. Dissolved tin from cans has been shown to inhibit growth and toxin production in canned vegetables. Experiments on dehydrated meat have shown that toxin was produced more slowly when the moisture content was 40 percent than when it was 60 percent and that reduction to 30 percent prevented toxin production.

The concentrations of sodium chloride necessary to prevent growth and toxin production in foods depend on the composition of the food and the temperature. The presence of sodium nitrate in sausage or of disodium phosphate in cheese spread reduces the level of sodium chloride necessary to prevent toxin production. More salt is needed at a higher temperature, such as 37 C, than at a lower one, say, 15 C. Under favorable conditions for growth 8 percent or more of salt is needed to inhibit *C. botulinum.*

A pH near neutrality favors *C. botulinum.* The minimal pH at which growth and toxin production will take place depends on the kind of food and the temperature. A pH of 4.5 or lower will prevent toxin production in most foods, but the lowest pH for spore germination is considerably higher. Minimal pH values reported are 4.87 for vegetative cells and 5.01 for spore germination in a veal infusion broth, 4.8 to 5.0 in bread, and 4.8 in pineapple-rice pudding. A maximal pH of 8.89 was found for vegetative growth. *C. botulinum* has been found growing and producing toxin, however, in foods that normally are too acid for it, when other microorganisms also were growing in the food and presumably raising the pH locally or generally.

There have been outbreaks of botulism from inadequately heat-processed canned high-acid foods (pH less than 4.5) including tomatoes, tomato juice, and blackberries. Possible explanations for these outbreaks have included (1) growth of other organisms which could raise the pH of a food so that *C. botulinum* could grow, (2) growth of *C. botulinum* followed by growth of other organisms which lowered the pH of a food that originally had a pH higher than 4.5, and (3) variation or stratification of the pH in an acidulated product to permit growth of *C. botulinum*. Tanaka (1982) has reported toxin production in media at a pH lower than 4.6.

Temperature is an important factor in determining whether toxin production will take place and what the rate of production will be. Vegetative growth will take place at a lower temperature than the minimum for spore germination. Different strains of *C. botulinum* types A and B vary in their temperature requirements. A few strains have been reported able to grow at 10 to 11 C, but about 15 C has been claimed to be the lowest temperature for germination of spores. The maximal temperature for growth is about 48 C for these types and about 45 C for type E. Type E organisms produce gas and toxin within 31 to 45 days at temperatures as low as 3.3 C.

The optimal temperature for toxin production and growth of the proteolytic strains is about 35 C, while 26 to 28 C is usually given for the optimal temperature for the nonproteolytic strains. Obviously, the slower the rate of toxin production, the longer it will take to obtain appreciable amounts. Interesting work (Lund et al., 1985) has begun to describe the interactions between pH, O-R, and temperature in regard to growth and toxin production.

The toxin   The toxin of *C. botulinum,* a protein that has been purified and crystallized, is so powerful that only a tiny amount is sufficient to cause death. It is absorbed mostly in the small intestine and paralyzes the involuntary muscles of the body. An important characteristic is its comparative thermolability. The heat treatment necessary to destroy it depends on the type of organism producing the toxin and the medium in which it is heated. In the laboratory, heat treatments of 5 to 6 min at 80 C will inactivate type A toxin, while 15 min at 90 C will inactivate type B toxin. This should not imply that the thorough cooking of a highly suspect food would be a worthwhile risk. As previously stated, the growth of *C. botulinum* in some foods results in such a foul, rancid odor that they would be rejected. Meats and proteinaceous, low-acid vegetables develop an especially obnoxious odor. More acid foods, however, and those low in proteins may become just as toxic without much evidence of putrefaction. Moreover, the nonproteolytic strains of *C. botulinum* give less evidence of spoilage than do the proteolytic ones. Also, gas production is not always evident and therefore is not a reliable indication of spoilage by this organism. Certainly it is advisable to reject all foods, raw or canned, that give evidence of spoilage and to reject canned foods that exhibit any pressure in the container.

The toxin can be destroyed in cheese by 7.3 Mrad of gamma rays and in broth by 4.9 Mrad. The toxin has been known to persist in foods for long periods, especially when storage has been at low temperatures. It is unstable at pH values above 6.8.

The nonproteolytic strains produce toxins which are not fully activated, and the addition of trypsin will result in a greater maximum potential for toxicity.

As has been indicated, the seven toxins (A to G) are antigenic, causing the production of antitoxin specific for a given toxin type injected. Toxoids have been prepared for some of the types for the active immunization of researchers who might be exposed to accidental poisoning by the toxin of botulism.

Toxicity and Bacteriophages   It is not uncommon to isolate nontoxigenic colonies from a known toxigenic strain of *C. botulinum*. Recent studies on the relationship between toxigenicity (ability to produce the toxin) and temperate bacteriophages (intracellular, integrated phage nucleic acid) have suggested that the bacterial genome may not be responsible for the production of the toxin but is coded for by the genome of an incorporated temperate bacteriophage. This would explain the occasional loss of toxigenicity by some strains. Experimentally, types C and D can be "cured" of their temperate bacteriophage and become nontoxigenic. Types A, B, and F have been "cured" of bacteriophages also but have remained toxigenic. Apparently, there also exist bacteriophages for *C. botulinum* which impart toxigenesis. Also, one strain may harbor more than one temperate bacteriophage (multiple infection), and this may account for the fact that some strains produce more than one type of toxin, as mentioned previously.

Heat Resistance of Spores   Compared with the spores of most other *Clostridium* species, those of some of the putrefactive anaerobes, including *C. botulinum*, have a comparatively high resistance to heat. The heat treatment necessary to destroy all the spores in a food depends on the kind of food, the type and strain of *C. botulinum*, the medium in which the spores were formed, the temperature at which they were produced, the age of the spores, and the numbers of spores present. The reader should refer to Chapter 6 for a discussion of the factors that influence the heat resistance of spores. Esty and Meyer (1922) have recommended the following heat treatments to destroy all spores of *C. botulinum* in a food:

Temperature, C	Time, min
100	360
105	120
110	36
115	12
120	4

In general, spores of organisms of types C, D, and E are less heat-resistant than those of types A and B, type E spores being inactivated in 15 min at 80 C.

Types A and B spores have D_{121C} values of 0.21 min while the D_{100C} value for type E has been reported to be 0.003 to 0.017 min. A comparison of type C spores has shown that marine strains are more heat-resistant than are terrestrial strains (D_{104C} of 0.4 to 0.9 min for the former and $D_{104\ C}$ of 0.02 to 0.08 for the latter).

Distribution of Spores   The habitat of *C. botulinum* is believed to be the soil, for spores have been found in both cultivated and virgin soils all over the world. Tests have shown that type A spores are found more in western soils in this country and type B spores elsewhere. Plant crops may become contaminated from the soil, and intestinal contents and hence manure of animals after consumption of such plants. Type E spores are found in soil, in sea and lake mud, and in fish, primarily in their intestinal tracts.

Incidence of Botulism   Fortunately, botulism occurs only rarely, but it always receives much attention because of the high mortality. The case fatality rate has declined. For example, between 1970 and 1973 it was about 23 percent, but between 1899 and 1949 the case fatality rate in the United States was above 60 percent. An examination of the 688 reported outbreaks of botulism from 1899 to 1973 revealed that 23.1 percent were caused by type A, 6.3 percent by type B, and 3.2 percent by type E. In the majority of outbreaks, 67.3 percent, the type was not determined. The number of outbreaks in which the type is not determined has decreased in recent years; e.g., from 1970 and 1973 only 19.0 percent of outbreaks went untyped.

Foods Involved   In the United States, inadequately processed home-canned foods are most often the cause of botulism (Table 24-3); in Europe the main

TABLE 24-3
OUTBREAKS OF FOOD-BORNE BOTULISM ATTRIBUTED TO
COMMERCIALLY PROCESSED OR HOME-PROCESSED FOODS,
1889–1973

Year	Source of food			
	Home-processed	Commercially processed	Unknown	Total
1889	1	0	0	1
1900–1909	1	1	0	2
1910–1919	48	14	8	70
1920–1929	77	26	13	116
1930–1939	135	6	13	154
1940–1949	120	1	13	134
1950–1959	50	2	51	103
1960–1969	42	10	26	78
1970–1973	21*	2	7	30
Total	495	62	131	688

* Includes one outbreak in which the vehicle was canned by the owner of a restaurant and sold to his customers.
Source: Center for Disease Control (1974).

causes are preserved meats and fish. Commercially processed foods have accounted for less than 10 percent of the outbreaks (Table 24-3), while home-processed foods were responsible for 72 percent of the outbreaks.

Of the home-canned foods, those most often responsible for botulism have been string beans, sweet corn, beets, asparagus, spinach, and chard, but each of many other kinds of food has been responsible for one or several outbreaks (fifty kinds of canned fruits and vegetables have been involved between 1899 and 1947). Table 24-4 lists home-canned foods responsible for six or more outbreaks of botulism in the United States from 1899 to 1947. In general, the low- and medium-acid canned foods are most often incriminated, but there have been exceptional instances of poisoning from acid foods, such as tomatoes, apricots, pears, and peaches. These acid foods had been grossly underprocessed, and the underprocessing had permitted the growth of other microorganisms to aid growth and toxin production by *C. botulinum*.

Table 24-5 summarizes the various foods implicated in all reported outbreaks (1899–1973), both commercial and home-processed, and the toxin types involved. Vegetables were implicated in 56 percent of these outbreaks.

Investigators have shown that spores of *C. botulinum* will survive long storage periods in raw and precooked frozen foods and can grow and produce toxin if these foods are held long enough at a high enough temperature after thawing. Similarly, temperature abuse of foods that may support the growth of *C. botulinum* and that may be contaminated must be avoided.

The Disease   People are so susceptible to botulism that if appreciable amounts of toxin are present, everyone who eats the food becomes ill and consumption of very small pieces of food, a pod of a string bean or a few peas, can cause illness and death. The typical symptoms of botulism usually appear within 12 to 36 hr, although a longer or shorter time may be required. The earliest symptoms usually are an acute digestive disturbance followed by nausea and vomiting and possibly diarrhea, together with fatigue, dizziness, and a headache. Later there is constipation. Double vision may be evident early, and dif-

TABLE 24-4
HOME-CANNED FOODS CAUSING SIX OR MORE OUTBREAKS OF BOTULISM,
1899–1947 (UNITED STATES)

Food	Number of outbreaks	Food	Number of outbreaks
String beans	94	Beet greens	9
Corn	46	Chili peppers	9
Beets	22	Beans	7
Asparagus	21	Tomatoes	7
Spinach and chard	12	Mushrooms	6
Peas	10	Sausages	9
Figs	10	Fish	10

TABLE 24-5
FOOD PRODUCTS CAUSING BOTULISM OUTBREAKS,* 1899–1973

Food	Botulinum toxin type					
	A	B	E	F	A and B	Total
Vegetables	115	31	1	—	2	149
Fish and fish products	11	4	25	—	—	40
Fruits	22	7	—	—	—	29
Condiments†	17	5	—	—	—	22
Beef‡	6	1	—	1	—	8
Milk and milk products	3	2	—	—	—	5
Pork	2	1	—	—	—	3
Poultry	2	2	—	—	—	4
Other§	8	3	3	—	—	14
Total	186	56	29	1	2	274

* Includes only outbreaks in which the toxin type was determined.
† Includes outbreaks traced to tomato relish, chili peppers, chili sauce, and salad dressing.
‡ Includes one outbreak of type F in venison and one outbreak of type A in mutton.
§ Includes outbreaks traced to vichyssoise, spaghetti sauce, and corn and chicken mash.
Source: Center For Disease Control (1974).

ficulty in swallowing and speaking may be noted. Patients may complain of dryness of the mouth and constriction of the throat, and the tongue may become swollen and coated. The temperature of the victim is normal or subnormal. Involuntary muscles become paralyzed, paralysis spreads to the respiratory system and heart, and death usually results from respiratory failure. Symptoms are similar for types A, B, and E poisoning, although nausea, vomiting, and urinary retention usually are more severe with type E toxin. In fatal cases, death usually comes within 3 to 6 days after the poisonous food has been ingested, but the period may be shorter or longer.

The only known method for the successful treatment of botulism is the administration of antitoxin. Unfortunately, this injection usually is not successful if made after the symptoms of botulism have appeared, but it should always be used at the earliest possible moment since it may prove helpful. Other treatments include artificial respiration, keeping the patient quiet, maintaining the fluid balance in the body, and, perhaps, elimination treatments.

Conditions Necessary for an Outbreak The following conditions are necessary for an outbreak of botulism: (1) presence of spores of *C. botulinum* of type A, B, or E in the food being canned or being processed in some other way, (2) a food in which the spores can germinate and the clostridia can grow and produce toxin, (3) survival of the spores of the organism, e.g., because of inadequate heating in canning or inadequate processing otherwise, (4) environmental conditions after processing that will permit germination of the spores and growth and toxin production by the organism, (5) insufficient cooking of the food to inactivate the toxin, and (6) ingestion of the toxin-bearing food.

Prevention of Outbreaks   The methods and precautions for the prevention of botulism that have been mentioned in the preceding discussion include (1) use of approved heat processes for canned foods, (2) rejection of all gassy (swollen) or otherwise spoiled canned foods, (3) refusal even to taste a doubtful food, (4) avoidance of foods that have been cooked, held, and not well reheated, and (5) boiling of a suspected food for at least 15 min. To this list might be added avoidance of raw or precooked foods that have been frozen, thawed, and held at room temperatures. To prevent botulism from smoked fish it has been recommended that (1) good sanitation be maintained throughout production and handling, (2) during smoking or thereafter the fish be heated to at least 82 C for 30 min in the coldest part, (3) the fish be frozen immediately after packaging and kept frozen, and (4) all packages be marked "Perishable—Keep Frozen."

Infant Botulism

In the late 1970s infant botulism became recognized as a distinct disease. Several hundred cases have been confirmed since that time. The disease is different from food-borne botulism in that the toxin appears to be released in vivo following growth of the organism in the intestine. Many of the infants involved have had predisposed constipation. Clinical symptoms include weakness, lack of sucking, loss of head control, and diminished gag reflex. Infection of infant mice with *C. botulinum* spores results in toxin production in the intestines of about 50 percent of the mice. Adult mice apparently cannot be infected this way. However, an infection can be established in adult germ-free mice. These observations and the fact that many human infants have constipation before the infection suggest the importance of a normal microbial flora.

The number of cases reported each year has increased significantly since the early 1970s and is now normally higher than the number of cases of food-borne botulism (Figure 24-3).

Staphylococcus Food Intoxication

One of the most commonly occurring food poisonings is caused by the ingestion of the enterotoxin formed in food during growth of certain strains of *Staph-*

FIGURE 24-3
Reported cases of botulism per year in the United States. (*A*) Food-borne. Sixteen outbreaks (19 cases) of food-borne botulism were reported for 1984. Two of these outbreaks involved four individuals and were associated with eating fermented foods. Type E toxin was implicated. Type A toxin was associated with thirteen of the remaining cases. Type B toxin was associated with one case, and for the other case a toxin type was not determined. (*B*) Infant botulism. Of the ninety-nine infant botulism cases reported in 1984, slightly more than half (fifty-six) were in females. The age range for all patients was 3 to 37 weeks. Type A toxin was found in forty-two (42 percent) of the cases, type B toxin in fifty-six (57 percent), and both type A and type B toxins in one. (*Center for Disease Control, Annual Summaries for 1984, 1986.*)

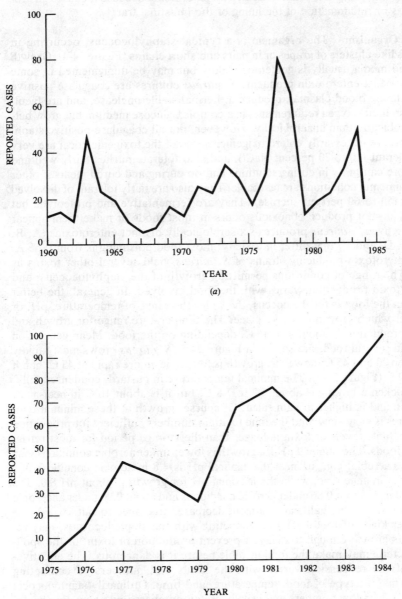

YEAR

(a)

YEAR

(b)

ylococcus aureus. The toxin is termed an **enterotoxin** because it causes gastro-enteritis or inflammation of the lining of the intestinal tract.

The Organism The organism is a typical staphylococcus, occurring in masses like clusters of grapes or in pairs and short chains (Figure 24-4). Growth on solid media usually is golden or yellow but may be unpigmented in some strains. Most enterotoxin-producing *S. aureus* cultures are coagulase-positive (coagulating blood plasma), produce a thermal stable nuclease, and are facul-tative in their oxygen requirements in a complex glucose medium but grow bet-ter aerobically than anaerobically. However, not all coagulase-positive staph-ylococci are necessarily enterotoxigenic. Some of the toxigenic cocci are very salt-tolerant (10 to 20 percent NaCl), and also tolerate nitrites fairly well and therefore can grow in curing solutions and on curing and cured meats if other environmental conditions are favorable. They also are fairly tolerant of dissolved sugars (50 to 60 percent sucrose). They are fermentative and proteolytic but usually do not produce obnoxious odors in most foods or make them appear unattractive. *S. aureus* produces six serologically distinct enterotoxins (A, B, C_1, C_2, D, and E) that differ in toxicity; most food poisoning is from type A. The enterotoxin-producing strains of *S. aureus* yield several other toxins as well. The range of conditions permitting growth of the staphylococcus, and hence toxin production, varies with the food involved. In general, the better medium the food is for the coccus, the wider the range of temperature, pH, or a_w over which growth can take place. The temperature range for growth and toxin production is about 4 to 46 C, depending on the food. Mean generation times in several foods are shown in Figure 24-5. *S. aureus* grows most rapidly between 20 and 45 C; however, growth is four times more rapid at 45 C than it is at 20 C (Figure 24-5). The minimal temperature in custard, condensed milk, and chicken à la king is about 6.7 to 7.8 C, but it is about 10 C in beef-heart infusion and is higher in ham salad. Of course, growth at these minimal tem-peratures is very slow, and the time to attain numbers sufficient for production of detectable levels of toxin is longer than the storage period for most refrig-erated foods. The minimal pH for growth is lower under aerobic conditions than under anaerobic; e.g., in meat the minimal pH is 4.8 in aerobic conditions and about 5.5 in anaerobic, while the maximal pH for growth is about pH 8.0. The minimal a_w is about 0.86 under aerobic conditions and about 0.90 under anaerobic conditions. A sublethal heat treatment decreases tolerance to salt.

Other kinds of food bacteria, competing with the staphylococcus, may re-press its growth enough to delay or prevent production of toxin, or the spoil-age bacteria may make the food inedible before it is dangerous. The effective-ness of the repression varies with the kinds and numbers of competing organisms, the type of food, temperature, and time. Ordinarily staphylococci enter foods in low numbers and usually are outnumbered by competing bacte-ria in raw foods. This competition may not occur, however, in heated foods, and unrestrained growth of staphylococci may ensue.

A million staphylococci per milliliter or gram of perishable foods will be in-activated by 66 C maintained for at least 12 min or by 60 C at 78 to 83 min.

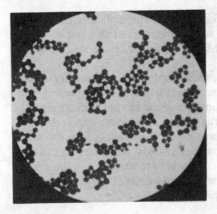

FIGURE 24-4
Photomicrograph of *Staphylococcus aureus*.
(*From J. Nowack.*)

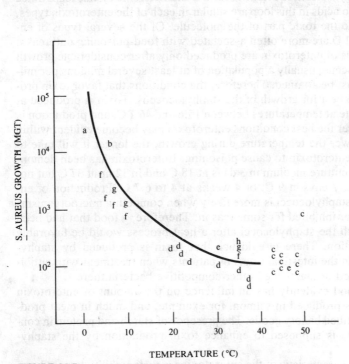

FIGURE 24-5
Mean generation times (MGT) of *Staphylococcus aureus* in (A) raw ground beef, (B) fresh raw eggs, (C) roast beef, (D) skim, whole, and raw milk, (E) barbequed chicken, (F) egg custard, (G) chicken à la king, and (H) ham salad. Regression coefficient, r =0.89. (*From Rivituso and Synder, 1980.*)

Heat resistance varies somewhat with the food and the strain of staphylococcus. D values at 60 C in custard are about 7.7 to 7.8 min, and in chicken à la king about 5.2 to 5.4 min. About 0.37 to 0.48 Mrad of gamma rays on moist foods will kill most of the staphylococci.

The sources from which the food-poisoning staphylococci enter foods are for the most part human or animal. The nasal passages of many persons are laden with these organisms, which are a common cause of sinus infections. Also, boils and infected wounds may be sources. The human skin apparently is a source of these bacteria only when they have come from nasal passages or local infections. Staphylococci are becoming increasingly important in causing mastitis in cows, and some of these cocci can form enterotoxin in milk or milk products. Ordinarily, air is a relatively unimportant source of the cocci, except when they are being introduced there from human sources.

The Enterotoxin   The staphylococcal enterotoxins are simple proteins with molecular weights between 26,000 and 30,000. The single polypeptide chains are cross-linked by a disulfide bridge to form a characteristic **cystine loop**. Since many of the amino acids in this loop are similar in each of the enterotoxin types, it is thought to be the toxic part of the molecule. Of the several types of enterotoxins, A and D are more often associated with food-poisoning outbreaks. Appreciable levels of enterotoxin are produced only after considerable growth of the staphylococcus; usually a population of at least several millions per milliliter or gram must be attained. Therefore, the conditions that favor toxin production are those best for growth of the staphylococcus. Toxin is produced at an appreciable rate at temperatures between 15.6 and 46.1 C, and production is best at 40 C. Under the best conditions enterotoxin may become evident within 4 to 6 hr. The lower the temperature during growth, the longer it will take to produce enough enterotoxin to cause poisoning. Enterotoxin has been demonstrated in a good culture medium in 3 days at 18 C and in 12 hr at 37 C but not in 3 days at 15 C, 7 days at 9 C, or 4 weeks at 4 to 6.7 C. Production of enterotoxin by the staphylococci is more likely when competing microorganisms are absent, few, or inhibited for some reason. Therefore, a food that had been contaminated with the staphylococci after a heat process would be favorable for toxin production. There is evidence that toxin is produced by staphylococci growing in the intestinal tracts of patients when treatment with antibiotics has destroyed or inactivated other competitive bacteria there.

The type of food evidently has an influence on the amount of enterotoxin produced; little is produced in salmon, for example, and much in meat products and custard-filled bakery goods. The presence of starch and protein in considerable amounts is supposed to enhance toxin production by the staphylococci.

An important characteristic of the enterotoxins is their stability toward heat. Interpretation of data on heat inactivation of enterotoxin should include a consideration of the assay procedure employed. A discussion on the thermal stability of the enterotoxins is further complicated by (1) variation in the initial concentration of each type in foods, (2) the medium in which heated, and (3) the temperature of heating; some observations suggest greater thermal inactivation at lower temperatures than at higher temperatures. This has been explained by a low-temperature aggregation phenomenon. Additionally, low-temperature heat-inactivated enterotoxin can undergo reactivation in some foods. In general the heat treatments of pasteurization (72 C for 15 sec) and ultrahigh-temperature heating (143.3 C for 9 sec) would not be sufficient to inactivate the enterotoxins. Some of the characteristics of thermal inactivation are presented in Table 24-6. The effect of concentration and suspending medium is evident. Type B enterotoxin is the most heat-resistant, as indicated by the higher z value (Table 24-6). The normal cooking of foods will not destroy the toxin formed therein before the heat process. Such foods might cause poisoning, although no live staphylococci could be demonstrated.

Incidence of the Disease   Reported cases in the United States are presented in Table 24-1. There probably are no reliable figures on the numbers of cases of staphylococcus poisoning in the United States or in any of the states for any given period. The poisoning usually is not reported or publicized unless the outbreak is fairly large, as at a picnic, large dinner, or convention. It is known, however, that a large percentage of all cases reported as food poisoning or food infection actually are staphylococcus poisoning and that many of us encounter this illness during our lifetime.

Foods Involved   Of the many kinds of food that have been involved in causing staphylococcus food poisoning, custard- and cream-filled bakery goods, ham, and poultry have caused the most outbreaks. About 75 percent of all staphylococcal food-poisoning outbreaks occur because of inadequate cooling of foods. Other foods incriminated include other meats and meat products, fish and fish products, milk and milk products, cream sauces, salads, puddings, custards, pies, and salad dressings. The fillings in bakery goods usually are good culture media in which the staphylococci can grow during the time that these foods are held at room temperatures. Toxin production has even been reported in imitation cream filling. Tongue and mildly cured, rapidly cured, tenderized, or precooked hams, although perishable, are often held without adequate refrigeration, as had been done without difficulty with the old-style country-cured hams. If contaminated leftover turkey, or other fowl, along with the gravy and dressing, is kept out of the refrigerator, it may cause poisoning. Foods that ordinarily are too acid for good growth of the staphylococci may have this acidity reduced by added ingredients, such as eggs or cream, and then become dangerous. Growth and toxin production by staphylococci may take place in the steam tables in cafeterias and restaurants and in food-vending machines that keep foods heated for extended periods if temperatures and times are not properly controlled.

The Disease   Individuals differ in their susceptibility to staphylococcus poisoning, so that of a group of people eating food containing toxin some may become very ill and a lucky few may be affected little or not at all. The incu-

TABLE 24-6
THERMAL INACTIVATION CHARACTERISTICS OF STAPHYLOCOCCAL ENTEROTOXINS

Type of entero-toxin	Assay system used	Sensitivity or amount injected or fed	Initial toxin concen-tration, µg/ml	Heating medium*	Heating temp., F	F_{250}, min	z value, F
A	Monkey feeding	47.25 µg	7	Distilled water	212–250	8	46
A	Cat; intravenous injection	2.3 µg	7	Distilled water	212–250	11	48
B	Serological; double diffusion tube	0.7 µg/ml	30	0.04 M veronal buffer, pH 7.2	204–259	19–16.4	55–58
	Cat; intravenous injection	2.0 µg	30	0.04 M veronal buffer, pH 7.2	240	32.5	
A	Serological; single diffusion tube	1 µg/ml	21	0.04 M veronal buffer, pH 7.2	212–250	22	50
B	Serological single diffusion tube	1 µg/ml	10–100	0.04 M veronal buffer, pH 7.2	250–320	62	52
					320	2.8	

* Dialyzed growth material dissolved in listed solvent.
Source: Summarized from various workers by Tatini (1976).

bation period (time between consumption of the food and appearance of the first symptoms) for this kind of poisoning usually is brief, 2 or 4 hr (ranging from 1 to 7 hr), differing in this respect from the other common food poisonings and infections, which usually have longer incubation periods.

The most common human symptoms are salivation, then nausea, vomiting, retching, abdominal cramping of varying severity, and diarrhea. Blood and mucus may be found in stools and vomitus in severe cases. Headache, muscular cramping, sweating, chills, prostration, weak pulse, shock, and shallow respiration may occur. Usually a subnormal body temperature is found rather than fever. The duration is brief, usually only a day or two, and recovery ordinarily is uneventful and complete. The mortality is extremely low. For the most part no treatment is given, except in extreme cases, when saline solutions may be given parenterally to restore the salt balance and counteract dehydration.

Outbreaks of food poisoning often are attributed to staphylococci on the basis of the type of food involved, the short incubation period, and perhaps the demonstration of the presence of staphylococci in the food. An actual diagnosis of the poisoning would depend, however, on isolation of staphylococci and demonstration that these produce enterotoxin or isolation and detection of the enterotoxin.

Conditions Necessary for an Outbreak   The following conditions are necessary for an outbreak of staphylococcus food poisoning: (1) The food must contain enterotoxin-producing staphylococci, (2) the food must be a good culture medium for growth and toxin production by the staphylococci, (3) the temperature must be favorable to growth of the cocci, and enough time must be allowed for production of enterotoxin, and (4) the enterotoxin-bearing food must be ingested.

Prevention of Outbreaks   The means of prevention of outbreaks of staphylococcus food poisoning include (1) prevention of contamination of the food with the staphylococci, (2) prevention of the growth of the staphylococci, and (3) killing staphylococci in foods. Contamination of foods can be reduced by general methods of sanitation, by using ingredients free from the cocci, e.g., pasteurized rather than raw milk, and by keeping employees away from foods when these workers have staphylococcal infections in the form of colds, boils, carbuncles, etc. Growth of the cocci can be prevented by adequate refrigeration of foods and, in some instances, by adjustment to a more acid pH. Also the addition of a bacteriostatic substance, such as serine or an antibiotic, has been suggested. Some foods may be pasteurized to kill the staphylococci before exposure of the foods to ordinary temperatures, e.g., pasteurization of custard-filled puffs and éclairs for 30 min at 190.6 to 218.3 C oven temperature.

Salmonellosis

Salmonellosis may result following the ingestion of viable cells of a member of the genus *Salmonella*. It is the most frequently occurring bacterial food infection and in some years it is the most frequently occurring bacterial food-borne illness (Table 24-1). In addition to the typical food-poisoning salmonellosis syndrome, two other disease syndromes can result following consumption of salmonella, and they are compared in Table 24-7. Classification of the genus *Salmonella* is confusing, and the naming of organisms does not follow the usual rules of nomenclature. Historically, the names given to isolated salmonellae were related to their pathogenicity in people or animals—for example, *S. typhimurium,* responsible for typhoid in mice, and *S. typhi,* responsible for human typhoid. This approach gave way to naming based on the site or location of first isolation in human infections, for example, *S. london, S. panama,* and *S. stanleyville. Salmonella* isolates are currently identified using the Kauffman-White scheme, a serological procedure in which organisms can be represented by the numbers and letters of the different antigenic sites: O (somatic), Vi (capsular), and H (flagellar). This scheme only identifies antigens of diagnostic importance and does not provide a complete antigenic record of an isolate. The term **serovar** is used to distinguish strains of different antigenic complements. Further subdivision can be made to **biovars,** i.e., different sugar fermentation patterns shown by members of the same serovar. This detail is helpful in epidemiological investigations because serovars and biovars can be used as "markers" to trace the actual route of an outbreak to its source. There are currently over a thousand known serovars.

The *Salmonella* infections that are called food poisoning may be caused by any of a large number of serovars (Table 24-7). Usually the infecting bacterium has grown in the food to attain high numbers, increasing the likelihood of infection and often resulting in outbreaks in families or larger groups. By contrast, other intestinal pathogens, such as organisms causing the dysenteries and typhoid and paratyphoid fevers, usually have a longer incubation period before symptoms and, except under epidemic conditions, occur in only scattered cases.

The Organism   The salmonellae are gram-negative non-spore-forming rods that ferment glucose, usually with gas, but usually do not ferment lactose or sucrose. Like other bacteria, they will grow over a wider range of temperature, pH, and a_w in a good culture medium rather than in a poor one. For example, minimal temperatures for growth in foods range from 6.7 to 7.8 C in chicken à la king to over 10 C in custard and ham salad. Their maximal temperature is about 45.6 C. They grow well at room temperatures, but their optimum is about 37 C. Mean generation times in several foods are presented in Figure 24-6. The pH range for growth is 4.1 to 9.0, growing in low-acid foods; salad at pH 5.5 to 5.7 has been found unfavorable for growth. The lowest a_w for growth varies with the food but is about 0.93 to 0.95. The species and strains of *Salmonella* differ, too, in heat resistance and in the effect of environmental factors on growth. Depending on the food and the serotype, the $D_{60\,C}$ values range from 0.06 to 11.3 min. Recommendations for thermal destruction of sal-

TABLE 24-7
THE SALMONELLOSIS SYNDROMES IN HUMANS

Disease	Etiologic agent	Nature of organism	Incubation period, signs, and symptoms	Source, reservoir, and epidemiology
Salmonellosis	*Salmonella choleraesuis, enteritidis, typhimurium, heidelberg, derby, java, infantis, enteritidis, montevideo, etc.*	Has O (somatic) and two phases of H (flagellar) antigens, over 2,000 known serovars, but only about 50 occur commonly	5–72 hr, commonly 12–36 hr; diarrhea, abdominal pain, chills, fever, vomiting, dehydration, prostration, anorexia, headache, malaise; duration of several days; enteritis or local infection may also occur	Feces of infected domestic or wild animals and human beings; infants, aged, and malnourished persons and those with concomitant diseases are more susceptible; carrier state usually lasts a few days to a few weeks, but sometimes for months
Typhoid fever (enteric fever)	*Salmonella typhi*	Similar to other salmonellae but adapted to human host; has VI (capsular) antigens as well as O and H antigens	7–28 days, mean 14 days; in food outbreaks may be in shortest incubation range; septicemia and lymphoid tissue involvement; malaise, headache, high continued fever, cough, anorexia, nausea, vomiting, constipation, slow pulse rate, tender and distended abdomen, enlarged spleen, nosebleed, rose spots on chest and trunk, perspiration, chills, delirium, dulled sensorium, diarrhea, bleeding from bowel; relapses occur; slow convalescence of 1 to 8 weeks	Feces and urine of infected persons; carriers are important in transmission; some are long-term carriers; water also is involved in transmission
Paratyphoid fever (enteric fever)	*Salmonella enteritidis,* paratyphi A, paratyphi B, paratyphi C, sendai	Similar to other salmonellae but more or less adapted to human host	1–15 days; bloodstream infection; headache, continued fever, profuse perspiration, nausea, vomiting, abdominal pain, enlarged spleen, diarrhea, sometimes rose spots; milder and shorter duration (1–3 weeks) than typhoid	Feces and urine of infected persons; carriers important in transmission

Source: Adapted from: Bryan, F. L. 1982. Diseases transmitted by foods. DHEW No. (CDC) 76–8237. Center for Disease Control, Atlanta, Ga.

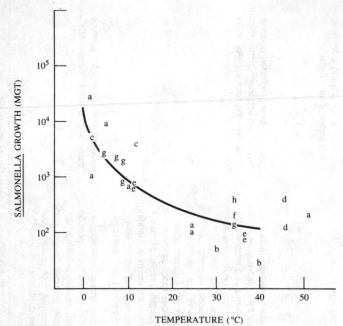

FIGURE 24-6
Mean generation times (MGT) of *Salmonella* in (*A*) raw ground beef,
(*B*) barbequed chicken, (*C*) bacon, (*D*) roast beef, (*E*) milk, (*F*) egg
custard, (*G*) chicken à la king, and (*H*) ham salad. Regression coefficient, $r = 0.66$. (*From Rivituso and Synder, 1981.*)

monellae in perishable foods are similar to those for staphylococci, namely,
heating to 66 C and holding all parts at that temperature for at least 12 min (or
78 to 83 min at 60 C). F_{140} values (minutes at 140 F necessary to reduce an
inoculum to an undetectable level) found for two species were 78 and 19 min,
respectively, in custard, and 81.5 and 3.1 min in chicken à la king. These results illustrate how the required heat treatment differs with the species of *Salmonella* and the food heated.

The likelihood of infection by consumption of a food containing salmonellae
depends on the resistance of the consumer, the infectiveness of the particular
strain of *Salmonella,* and the number of organisms ingested. Less infective species such as *S. pullorum* must be ingested in hundreds of millions or in billions
to bring about infection, but considerably fewer (about a million) organisms of
more infective·species, e.g., *S. enteritidis,* usually would be sufficient. Salmonellae apparently can attain considerable numbers in foods without causing detectable alterations in appearance, odor, or even taste. Of course, the more of
any of these pathogens the food contains, the greater the likelihood of infection on the person who eats the food and the shorter the incubation time.

Sources of Salmonella   Human beings and animals are directly or indirectly the source of the contamination of foods with salmonellae. The organisms may come from actual cases of the disease or from carriers. Most frequently isolated serovars, such as *S. typhimurium* and others (see Table 24-7) cause human gastroenteritis, but any of many other types may be responsible. The organisms also may come from cats, dogs, swine, and cattle, but more important sources for foods are poultry and their eggs and rodents. Chickens, turkeys, ducks, and geese may be infected with any of a large number of types of *Salmonella,* which are then found in the fecal matter, in eggs from the hens, and in the flesh of the dressed fowl. About one-third of all the food products involved in *Salmonella* outbreaks are meat and poultry products. Considerable attention has been given to shell eggs and to liquid, frozen, and dried eggs as sources of *Salmonella.* Infected rodents, rats and mice, may contaminate unprotected foods with their feces and thus spread *Salmonella* bacteria. Flies may play an important role in the spread of *Salmonella,* especially from contaminated fecal matter to foods. Roaches apparently also can spread the disease.

Changes in processing, packaging, and compounding of foods and feeds in recent years have resulted in an apparent increase in salmonellosis from these products. Salmonellae have been introduced by the incorporation of cracked and dried eggs in baked goods, candy, ice cream, and convenience foods such as cake and cookie mixes. The compounding of new food products may make possible the growth of salmonellae or other food-poisoning organisms, introduced by means of an ingredient in which they had been unable to grow, or these organisms may be in a product when sold and become able to grow in this food as it is modified for use. Large-scale handling of foods, as by commissaries or institutions, tends to increase the spread of trouble, and food vending machines add to the risk, as do precooked foods.

Feeds, especially those from meat or fish by-products, may carry salmonellae to poultry or meat animals. Even pet feeds have been known to transmit salmonellae to domestic animals, from which children have been infected.

Incidence of the Disease   Numbers of reported human cases of salmonellosis (other than typhoid and paratyphoid fever) in the United States during recent years are given in Table 24-1 and Figure 24-7. Like most food-poisoning syndromes, the reported number of cases probably represents only a small percentage of the number of cases actually occurring.

Food Involved   A large variety of foods are involved in causing outbreaks of *Salmonella* infections. Most commonly incriminated are various kinds of meats, poultry and products from them, especially if they are held unrefrigerated for long periods. Fresh meats may carry *Salmonella* bacteria that caused disease in the slaughtered animals or may be contaminated by handlers. Meat products, such as meat pies, hash, sausages, cured meats (ham, bacon, and tongue), sandwiches, and chili, often are allowed to stand at room temperatures, permitting the growth of salmonellae. Poultry and its dressing and gravy should not give trouble if properly handled and cooked but often are mishandled, as

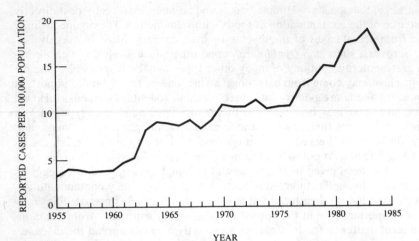

YEAR

FIGURE 24-7
Reported cases of salmonellosis by year in the United States, 1955–1984. A slight decrease in reported cases of human salmonellosis was noted in 1984. This decrease most likely represents annual variation rather than a reversal of the secular trend toward increasing rates of salmonellosis in the United States. This steady increase in reported rates is thought to reflect increasing incidence of the disease rather than more efficient reporting. (*Centers for Disease Control, Annual Summaries for 1984, 1986.*)

are fish and other seafood and products from them. Milk and milk products, including fresh milk, fermented milks, ice cream, and cheese, have caused infections. Since eggs may carry the salmonellae, foods made with eggs and not sufficiently cooked or pasteurized may carry live organisms, e.g., pastries filled with cream or custard, cream cakes, baked Alaska, and eggnog.

The Disease   As with other infectious diseases, individuals differ in their susceptibility to *Salmonella* infections, but in general morbidity is high in any outbreak. As has been stated, the susceptibility of humans varies with the species and strain of the organism and the total numbers of bacteria ingested.

A longer incubation period usually distinguishes salmonellosis from staphylococcus poisoning: usually 12 to 36 hr for the former and about 2 to 4 hr for the latter. Shorter (as little as 5 hr) or longer (up to 72 hr) incubation periods may occur in some cases of *Salmonella* infections.

The principal symptoms of a *Salmonella* gastrointestinal infection are nausea, vomiting, abdominal pain, and diarrhea that usually appear suddenly. This may be preceded by a headache and chills. Other evidences of the disease are watery, greenish foul-smelling stools, prostration, muscular weakness, faintness, usually a moderate fever, restlessness, twitching, and drowsiness. The mortality is low, being less than 1 percent. The severity and duration vary not only with the amount of food eaten and hence the numbers of *Salmonella* bacteria ingested but also with the individual. Intensity may vary from slight discomfort and diarrhea to death in 2 to 6 days. Usually the symptoms persist for 2 to 3 days, followed by uncomplicated recovery, but they may linger for weeks or months. About 0.2 to 5 percent of the patients may become carriers of the *Salmonella* organism.

The laboratory diagnosis of the disease is difficult unless *Salmonella* can be isolated from the suspected food and from the stools of individuals. Often, however, the incriminated foods are no longer available, and the organisms disappear from the intestinal tract.

Conditions Necessary for an Outbreak   The following conditions are necessary for an outbreak of a food-borne *Salmonella* gastrointestinal infection: (1) The food must contain or become contaminated with the *Salmonella* bacteria, (2) these bacteria must be there in considerable numbers, either because of contamination or more often because of growth; these high numbers mean that the food must be a good culture medium, the temperature must be favorable, and enough time must be allowed for appreciable growth, and (3) the viable organisms must be ingested.

Prevention of Outbreaks   Three main principles are involved in the prevention of outbreaks of food-borne *Salmonella* infections: (1) avoidance of contamination of the food with salmonellae from sources such as diseased human beings and animals and carriers and ingredients carrying the organisms, e.g., contaminated eggs, (2) destruction of the organisms in foods by heat (or other means) when possible, as by cooking or pasteurization, paying special attention to held-over foods, and (3) prevention of the growth of *Salmonella* in foods by adequate refrigeration or by other means. In the prevention of contamination, care and cleanliness in food handling and preparation are important. The food handlers should be healthy (and not be carriers) and clean. Rats and other vermin and insects should be kept away from the food. Ingredients used in foods should be free of salmonellae, if possible. Of course foods should not be allowed to stand at room temperature for any length of time, but if this happens, thorough cooking will destroy the *Salmonella* organisms (but not staphylococcus enterotoxin). Warmed-over leftovers, held without refrigeration, often support the growth of *Salmonella,* as may canned foods that have been contaminated and held after the cans were opened. Inspection of animals and meats at packing houses may remove some *Salmonella*-infected meats but is not in itself a successful method for the prevention of human salmonellosis.

Clostridium perfringens Gastroenteritis

First reported in the United States in 1945, *Clostridium perfringens* gastroenteritis is being detected and reported more frequently than formerly, although it probably is no more prevalent (Table 24-1).

The Organism   The bacterium causing this illness is *C. perfringens (welchii),* type A, a gram-positive, nonmotile, anaerobic, spore-forming rod. Maximal temperature for growth is about 55 C, and optimal temperature is about 43 to 47 C. Growth is restricted at 15 to 20 C. Mean generation times in several foods are illustrated in Figure 24-8. The organism will not grow below pH 5.0 or above pH 9.0. It is inhibited by 5 percent NaCl ($a_w = 0.97$), *and some strains are held back by 2.5 percent sodium nitrate.*

The spores of food-poisoning strains differ considerably in their heat resistance; $D_{90 \ C} = 0.015$ to 8.71 min.

Foods Involved   The spores have been found in part of the samples of most raw foods examined as well as in soil, sewage, and animal feces. Most commonly involved are meats that have been cooked, allowed to cool slowly, and then held for some time before consumption. Meat and poultry products account for about three-quarters of outbreaks attributed to *C. perfringens*. Fish paste and cold chicken also have been incriminated.

Since the spores are fairly common in raw foods and are heat-resistant, their presence in many foods may be unavoidable. Cooking of foods will destroy the vegetative cells and the spores of some strains; however, germination and out growth of surviving spores are possible in cooked foods which have been in-

FIGURE 24-8
Mean generation times (MGT) of *Clostridium perfringenes* in (A) fresh chicken, (B) rolled beef strips, (C) barbequed chicken, (D) raw ground beef, (E) cooked ground beef, (F) turkey rolls, (G) ground beef casseroles, (H) roast beef, (I) cooked meat, (J) turkey rice soup, and (K) mashed potatoes. Regression coefficient, $r = 0.71$. (*From Rivituso and Synder, 1981.*)

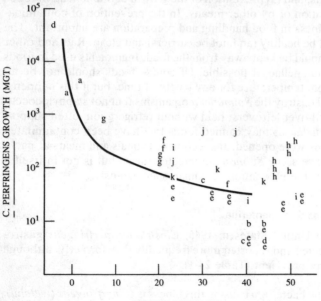

adequately refrigerated. A typical outbreak might involve a large cut of roasted meat. The oven cooking would not kill all the spores but might create favorable reduced conditions. Following cooking and in the absence of proper cooling, the spores of *C. perfringens* germinate and their numbers increase. The presence of a large number of *C. perfringens* in a cooked food is indicative of mishandling.

The Disease   The symptoms, which appear usually in 8 to 24 hr (median 12 hr) following ingestion include acute abdominal pain, diarrhea, and gas; fever, nausea, and vomiting are rare. Most outbreaks suggest that the ingestion of millions of viable cells of *C. perfringens* per gram of food are required for symptoms to occur. A toxin (enterotoxin) is released in the gut during sporulation of the cells and results in excessive fluid accumulation in the intestinal lumen. The enterotoxin is relatively heat-sensitive, being inactivated at 60 C for 10 min.

Conditions Necessary for an Outbreak   The following conditions are necessary for an outbreak of *C. perfringens* gastrointestinal infection: (1) The food contains or becomes contaminated with *C. perfringens*, (2) usually the food is cooked and reduced conditions develop, (3) the food is inadequately cooled, and favorable temperatures and enough time are allowed for appreciable growth, (4) the food is consumed without reheating so that large numbers of viable cells are ingested, and (5) the cells sporulate in vivo and elaborate the enterotoxin.

Prevention of Outbreaks   Means of prevention of outbreaks of *C. perfringens* food infection include (1) adequate and rapid cooling of cooked meats and other foods, (2) holding hot foods above 60 C, (3) reheating of leftover foods, and (4) good personal hygiene.

Vibrio parahaemolyticus Infection and Other Vibrios

Outbreaks of *V. parahaemolyticus* gastroenteritis have received considerable attention in Japan, where it is one of the most commonly occurring food-poisoning syndromes. In recent years, this organism has been responsible for several food-borne outbreaks in the United States (Table 24-1).

V. parahaemolyticus is a gram-negative straight or curved motile rod. It is a halophile (requiring 1 to 3 percent NaCl) and will grow in 7.0 percent NaCl. Optimal temperature for growth is 35 to 37 C, but it will grow over a range of 10 to 44 C. Growth is inhibited below pH 5.0 and above pH 11.0. *V. parahaemolyticus* has been isolated from many seafoods, including oysters, shrimp, and blue crabs. The organism can readily be killed by proper cooking of the seafood. Most outbreaks in this country occur because raw or uncooked seafood is allowed to contaminate and reinoculate cooked seafood. Holding recontaminated cooked seafood at too high temperatures permits rapid growth and a subsequent high population of *V. parahaemolyticus*. If the food is not reheated, signs and symptoms will result. Some of the characteristics of *V. para*

TABLE 24-8
CHARACTERISTICS OF SOME FOOD-BORNE ILLNESSES

Disease	Etiologic agent	Incubation period, signs, and symptoms	Foods involved	Control measures
Vibrio parahaemolyticus infection	*V. parahaemolyticus*	2–48 hr, usually 12 hr; abdominal pain, diarrhea (watery stools containing blood and mucus), usually nausea and vomiting, mild fever, chills, headache, prostration; recovery within 2–5 days	Raw foods of marine origin; saltwater fish, shellfish, crustacea, and fish products	Cook foods thoroughly; chill foods rapidly in small quantities; prevent cross contamination from saltwater fish; sanitize equipment; avoid using seawater for rinsing foods to be eaten raw or for cleaning
Enteropathogenic *Escherichia coli* infection	*E. coli;* both enterotoxigenic and invasive strains cause illness	8–24 hr, mean 11 hr (invasive type); 8–44 hr, mean 26 hr (enterotoxigenic type); invasive illness: fever, chills, headache, myalgia, abdominal cramps, profuse, watery diarrhea, similar to shigellosis; enterotoxigenic illness: diarrhea (rice-water stools), vomiting, dehydration, shock; similar to cholera	Coffee substitute, salmon(?), cheese	Chill foods rapidly in small quantities; cook foods thoroughly; practice personal hygiene; prepare foods in sanitary manner; protect and treat water; dispose of sewage in sanitary manner
Bacillus cereus gastroenteritis	Diarrheal, syndrome, diarrheagenic toxin	8–16 hr or 1.5–5 hr; nausea, abdominal cramps, watery diarrhea, some vomiting	Custards, cereal products, puddings, sauces, meat loaf	Chill foods rapidly in small quantities; hold hot foods at 65 C or above; practice personal hygiene; process and prepare food in sanitary manner; reheat leftover foods to 71.1 C
	Emetic syndrome, emetic toxin	Incubation period 1–6 hr, 2–5 most common, with nausea and vomiting predominant, similar to staphylococcal intoxication); short duration, 1 day or less	Fried rice, mashed potatoes, vegetable sprouts	

Disease	Causative agent	Symptoms and incubation period	Foods usually involved	Prevention
Shigellosis (bacillary dysentery)	Shigella sonnei, S. flexneri, S. dysenteriae, S. boydii	1–7 days, usually less than 4 days; extremely variable, mild to severe symptoms: abdominal cramps, fever, chills, diarrhea, watery stools (frequently containing blood, mucus, or pus), tenesmus, headache, lassitude, prostration, nausea, dehydration	Moist, mixed foods; milk, beans, potato, tuna, shrimp, turkey, and macaroni salads; apple cider; and poi	Practice personal hygiene; chill foods rapidly in small quantities; prepare food in sanitary manner; cook foods thoroughly; protect and treat water; dispose of sewage in sanitary manner; control flies
Yersiniosis	Yersinia pseudotuberculosis, Y. enterocolitica	24–36 hr and longer; abdominal pain suggesting acute appendicitis, fever, headache, malaise, anorexia, diarrhea, vomiting, nausea, chills, pharyngitis, leukocytosis, erythema nodosum	Pork and other meats, raw milk, or any contaminated raw or leftover food	Cook foods thoroughly; protect foods from contamination; control rodents
Arizona infection	Arizona hinshawii	2–46 hr, usually 24 hr; abdominal pain, diarrhea, nausea, chills, headache, weakness, fever, lasts a few days	Turkey, chicken, cream-filled pastry, ice cream, custard containing eggs	Chill foods rapidly in small quantities; cook foods thoroughly; prevent fecal contamination; avoid cross contamination from raw to cooked foods; sanitize equipment; reheat leftover foods thoroughly
Beta-hemolytic streptococcal infections (scarlet fever, septic sore throat)	Streptococcus pyogenes	1–3 days; sore and red throat, pain in swallowing, tonsillitis, high fever, headache, nausea, vomiting, malaise, rhinorrhea; occasionally a rash occurs	Milk, ice cream, eggs, steamed lobster, potato salad, egg salad, custard, and pudding; foods usually contain eggs or milk	Chill foods rapidly in small quantities; practice personal hygiene; cook foods thoroughly; pasteurize milk, exclude workers with respiratory illness or skin lesions

Source: Adapted from Bryan, F. L. 1982. Diseases transmitted by foods. DHEW No. (CDC) 76-8237. Center for Disease Control, Atlanta, Ga.

Vibrio cholerae serovar O group 1 is responsible for epidemic or Asiatic cholera. Cholera is an extremely serious worldwide, usually water-borne disease. A limited number of outbreaks in the continental United States have been identified as being transmitted by seafoods. Other serovars, not O1, do not represent the same health threat as does *Vibrio cholerae* O1 but can be responsible for intestinal infection or gastroenteritis. These *Vibrio cholerae* strains, which closely resemble O1, are referred to as nonagglutinable (NAG) vibrios because they do not react or agglutinate in the anti-O1 serum. Several surveys conducted in the Chesapeake Bay and along the gulf states suggest that both O1 and and non-O1 *Vibrio cholerae* are fairly common in estuary water. Food-borne outbreaks of *Vibrio cholerae* and non-O1 strains have been associated with the consumption of oysters.

Vibrio vulnificus can also be isolated from seafoods and seawater. The organism is highly invasive, releasing both a hemolysin and a cytotoxin, and can result in primary septicemia in humans.

Enteropathogenic *Escherichia coli*

E. coli is generally regarded as part of the normal flora of the human intestinal tract and that of many animals. Several nursery epidemics in the 1940s implicated *E. coli* in diarrheal disease in infants. Serotypes of *E. coli* which have been implicated in human diarrheal diseases or food-poisoning outbreaks have been designated enteropathogenic *E. coli* (EEC). The human disease syndromes resulting from the ingestion of EEC have been divided into two main groups. The first group consists of strains which produce an enterotoxin and result in a choleralike or enterotoxigenic illness in humans (see Table 24-8). These enterotoxigenic strains usually produce two enterotoxins, a heat-stable (ST) and a heat-labile (LT) toxin, and are thought to be responsible for infantile diarrheal diseases and traveler's diarrhea. To experience the enterotoxigenic illnesses, EEC serotypes capable of elaborating the enterotoxins must be ingested, followed by colonization in the upper small intestine and production of the enterotoxins. The enterotoxins apparently mediate a net movement of water into the intestinal lumen. This fluid accumulation occurs without any gross macroscopic change in the intestinal epithelium and in the absence of penetration or invasion by the bacteria.

The second major group consists of invasive strains which produce a cytotoxin and result in the invasive illness, colitis, or dysenterylike syndrome. These serotypes are nonenterotoxigenic, grow in the colon, and invade or penetrate the epithelial cells of colonic mucosa, resulting in the signs and symptoms outlined in Table 24-8.

A large infective dose of EEC is required for either the enterotoxigenic or invasive illness to occur. Therefore, foods must be highly contaminated or inadequately preserved or refrigerated to allow for prolific growth. The optimal temperature for growth is 37 C, with a temperature range for growth of 10 to 40 C. The optimal pH for growth is 7.0 to 7.5, with the minimum at pH 4.0 and the maximum at pH 8.5. The organism is relatively heat sensitive and can readily be destroyed at pasteurization temperatures and by the proper cooking of foods. Table 24-8 lists some of the foods implicated in EEC outbreaks and some methods of prevention. In addition to the above strains, there is a group referred to as hemorrhagic *E. coli*. These strains can result in illness in humans as manifested by bloody diarrhea and severe abdominal pain.

Bacillus cereus

Reports of outbreaks of *B. cereus* food gastroenteritis are quite uncommon in the United States; however, many European countries report frequent implication of this organism in food-borne illness. *B. cereus* is a gram-positive, aerobic, spore-forming rod. Its optimal temperature for growth is 30 C, with a minimal temperature for growth at 10 C and a maximum of 49 C. The pH range for growth is 4.9 to 9.3. *B. cereus* spores have reported D values (heat resistance) of $D_{100 \, C}$ of 2.7 to 3.1 min in skim milk and $D_{100 \, C}$ of 8 min in phosphate buffer (pH 7.0). Numerous surveys on foods and ingredients have indicated a high percentage of samples containing *B. cereus*. It is undoubtedly widely distributed in nature and our food supply.

Extremely large numbers (10^8 per gram) of viable cells of *B. cereus* must be ingested to develop signs and symptoms (Table 24-8) of the syndrome. Two syndromes are recognized: the diarrheal syndrome and the emetic syndrome. Some of the characteristics of *B. cereus* gastroenteritis are presented in Table 24-8.

Shigellosis

Food-borne outbreaks of shigellosis have been reported in the United States, but most incidents of shigellosis involve contaminated water.

Optimal temperature for growth is 37 C, with a temperature range of 10 to 40 C. The organisms tolerate salt concentrations of 5 to 6 percent and are relatively heat sensitive. Pathogenicity involves the release of a lipopolysaccharide endotoxin which affects the intestinal mucosa. Some of the characteristics of this food-borne illness are presented in Table 24-8, and numbers of cases are shown in Figure 24-9.

Yersinia enterocolitica

Yersinia enterocolitica is a small rod-shaped bacteria that can cause gastrointestinal illness in humans. It has been isolated from the intestinal tracts and feces of many animals, including cats, pigs, dogs, deer, raccoons, and horses. The pig appears to be the main reservoir for the strains causing infection in humans. *Y. enterocolitica* has been isolated from many foods, including beef, pork, liquid eggs, soft cheese, raw milk, pasteurized milk, fish, raw oysters, shrimps, crabs, chocolate milk, turkey, chow mein, powdered milk, and tofu.

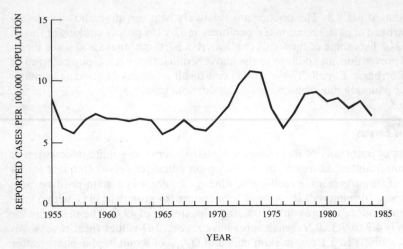

FIGURE 24-9
Reported cases of shigellosis by year in the United States, 1955–1984. For 1984, 17, 371 cases of shigellosis were reported in the United States. Approximately 70 percent of the *Shigella* isolates reported to the CDC each year are *Shigella sonnei*, with *Shigella flexneri* accounting for a large percentage of the rest. (*Centers for Disease Control, Annual Summaries for 1984, 1986.*)

Some strains are known as environmental or noninvasive types and are not known to cause illness in humans. The invasive or virulent strains of *Y. enterocolitica* are responsible for gastroenteritis in humans.

The usual symptoms, including severe abdominal pain, fever, and diarrhea, occur 24 to 36 hr after consumption of the product. Occasionally, the incubation time may be considerably longer. The abdominal discomfort is quite specific and usually manifests itself as a sharp pain in the lower right quadrant of the abdomen. For this reason it has frequently been described as pseudoappendicitis. In one outbreak sixteen children had appendectomies.

Although the organism has been isolated from many foods, there have been relatively few food-borne outbreaks attributed to *Y. enterocolitica*. The isolation from pasteurized milk is probably the result of postpasteurization contamination, since even the most heat-resistant strains are reported to be killed by pasteurization. The unique characteristic of the organism is its ability to grow at commercial refrigeration temperatures, i.e., less than 5 C.

A closely related organism, *Y. pseudotuberculosis,* has also been implicated as an etiological agent in human illness. Both *Y. enterocolitica* and *Y. pseudotuberculosis* are currently classified as members of the family Enterobacteriaceae.

Campylobacter

The heat-tolerant *Campylobacter,* i.e., *C. jejuni* and *C. coli,* are the strains most frequently associated with acute gastroenteritis in humans. The term "heat-tolerant" is a misnomer since it refers to growth at 42 C and not to any degree of heat tolerance or heat resistance; actually, these strains are inactivated at temperatures above 45 to 50 C. Their most distinguishing characteristics are absence of growth below 25 C, sensitivity to air (21 percent O_2), resistance to cephalothin, a generation or doubling time of about 1 hr at optimum temperature (42 C), sensitivity to drying, sensitivity to acid conditions, and being a poor competitor in mixed populations because of an inability to utilize carbohydrates. It is therefore very unlikely that they can grow to large populations in foods held at or below room temperature.

C. jejuni is associated with warm-blooded animals, and many animals and animal by-products used for human and animal feeds are contaminated with the organism. Various strains have been isolated from chicken carcasses and feces, swine carcasses and feces, sheep carcasses and feces, turkeys, pork sausages, various red meats, and ground beef.

Many researchers have suggested that *C. jejuni* and *C. coli* are a major cause of a large number of cases of bacterial enteritis worldwide. Limited specific outbreaks have been reported; the products incriminated include raw milk, raw clams, undercooked chicken, contaminated pasteurized milk, cake icing, raw hamburger, and barbecued chicken. However, campylobacters are isolated from the feces of patients experiencing gastroenteritis at a greater rate than are salmonellae. For this reason it is suspected that the actual number of cases is much higher than the number reported.

Little is known about the actual mechanism of pathogenicity in humans; however, at least some strains produce a heat-labile enterotoxin. The organism is also invasive. Furthermore, it is thought that the organism is highly virulent since the actual numbers in foods are quite low.

Symptoms include abdominal pain, cramps, diarrhea, headache, fever, and occasionally bloody stools. The incubation time is usually 2 to 3 days but may be as long as 7 to 10 days.

Pasteurization of milk or the proper cooking of foods prior to consumption would eliminate many outbreaks. Since *Campylobacter* are widespread in foods of animal origin care must be taken to avoid cross contamination from raw meats to cooked items.

Plesiomonas shigelloides

Plesiomonas shigelloides is a facultatively anaerobic gram-negative rod. Most strains are motile by polar flagella and can grow on minimal media containing ammonium salts as the nitrogen source and glucose as the carbon source. The organism can be pathogenic in humans, causing disturbances of the intestinal tract. Diarrhea in various degrees of severity is the major symptom. The organism has been isolated from the aquatic environment, fish, oysters, and crabs and from mammals such as cats, dogs, zoo animals, goats, sheep, and monkeys.

P. shigelloides has been implicated in several food-borne outbreaks involving oysters, crabs, and fish. The organism can be isolated from the feces of individuals with no apparent symptoms. However, it is thought that *P. shigelloides* is an opportunistic pathogen and not a normal member of the human intestinal flora. Miller and Koburger (1986) examined forty environmental isolates of *P. shigelloides* and noted that all strains grew at pH 4.5 and 8.5. Fifty-eight percent of the isolates grew at pH 4.0, 22 percent grew at 8 C, and 25 percent grew at 45 C. All the isolates were inactivated by heating at 60 C for 30 min. Additionally, all the isolates grew in 3% sodium chloride, and some strains even grew in 5% sodium chloride. All the isolates were inactivated by heating at 60 C for 30 min.

Listeria monocytogenes

Listeria monocytogens is a gram-positive, motile, short rod capable of growth at 4 C. In cattle, it can result in abortion and mastitis, and the infected animals will shed the organism in the milk. Other infected animals, including sheep and chickens, can serve as a source of the organism in the food supply. *L. monocytogenes* has been isolated from water, milk, silage, sewage, and the feces of many animals, including humans.

The first cases of human listeriosis were reported in 1929. Human infections usually manifest themselves as an infection in a pregnant woman, a fetus, or a newborn infant. In adults, the disease occurs most frequently in immuno-compromised individuals and is characterized as septicemia, meningitis, or meningoencephalitis.

Major food-borne outbreaks have been reported in various countries. Table 24-9 outlines three outbreaks in the United States. The contaminated coleslaw had been made from cabbage which had been fertilized with sheep manure. Several of the sheep had experienced ovine listerosis. Following harvesting, the cabbage was held in cold storage; this prolonged low-temperature condition probably enriched for *L. monocytogenes*.

Like many gram-positive organisms, it is capable of persisting in the soil, and the use of manure containing listeria may represent a significant concern when applied to cropland, particularly when the products are fruits or vegetables which may not undergo additional heat treatments.

TABLE 24-9
THREE OUTBREAKS OF *LISTERIA MONOCYTOGENES* IN THE UNITED STATES

Date	Location	Food vehicle	Cases	Fatality rate,%
1981	Nova Scotia	Coleslaw	34 P* 7 A	44
1983	Massachusetts	Milk†	7 P 42 A‡	29
1985	Los Angeles County	Soft cheese§	93 P 49 A	33

* A = adult; P = perinatal.
† Pasteurized.
‡ Most were immunocompromised.
§ Mexican-style.

The presence of *L. monocytogenes* in pasteurized milk raised considerable concern about the adequacy of milk pasteurization. At least two reports (Bradshaw et al., 1985; Donnelly and Briggs, 1986) have suggested that proper pasteurization of milk will eliminate the organism. It is proposed that the contamination of milk is a postpasteurization problem. In 1986 the FDA concentrated on surveillance for the organism in the dairy processing plant environment and in finished products. *L. monocytogenes* and *L. inocula* were obtained from many environmental sources and from some finished products. At this time, no major studies on the thermal resistance of listeria in naturally infected cows have been published, although there has been an indication that the organism may survive the minimum times and temperatures established for milk HTST pasteurization, i.e., 161 F for 15 sec. The psychrotrophic growth characteristics of this organism suggest that contamination of a refrigerated food could represent a significant health hazard.

Aeromonas hydrophilia

A. hydrophilia is a gram-negative motile rod with an optimum temperature of 28 C. It may be pathogenic for frogs, fish, and mammals including humans (Krieg, 1984). The organism has rarely been incriminated in food-borne outbreaks in the United States; however, it is a newly recognized pathogen that may cause food-borne diarrhea. It is ubiquitous in water and has been reported to be the cause of outbreaks in other countries.

Other Bacterial Food-borne Infections

Streptococcus faecalis and closely related species have been blamed for food illnesses, and since no enterotoxin could be demonstrated, the organisms were presumed but not proved to cause an infection. Foods reported to be involved in a limited number of outbreaks included barbecued beef, beef croquettes, Vienna sausage, ham bologna, turkey dressing, turkey à la king, Albanian and other cheeses, charlotte russe, and evaporated milk. Enterococci were isolated from most of these foods. The incubation period has been given as from 2 to 18 hr, and the symptoms as nausea, vomiting, and diarrhea. Formerly it was thought that only certain strains caused poisoning, but most authorities now maintain that all the accused organisms are innocuous. Volunteers have been fed massive doses of the organisms, including some supposedly incriminated in food-poisoning outbreaks, and also their products without any resulting enteritis.

For other organisms proof of implication in food-borne outbreaks is more substantial, e.g., *Arizona hinshawii* and *Streptococcus pyogenes*. The disease syndromes resulting from the ingestion of these bacteria are summarized in Table 24-8.

The food infections just discussed have been those involving bacteria able to grow in foods and hence to increase the dosage of the pathogen delivered to the person eating the food. Pathogenic organisms unable to grow in the food as it ordinarily is handled may be carried by it, the food in this instance serving merely as an inactive carrier of the disease organisms, much as a doorknob, handkerchief, bus strap, drinking cup, or other forms would serve that purpose. Most of the diseases so transmitted are intestinal or respiratory. Some of the intestinal diseases so transported are typhoid and paratyphoid fevers, bacillary and amebic dysenteries, and cholera. Disease organisms from the throat and respiratory tract are those causing tuberculosis, scarlet fever, diphtheria, and other diseases. Also reportedly spread by foods are brucellosis, tularemia, Q fever, scarlet fever, septic sore throat, and infectious hepatitis.

Foods may be contaminated with disease organisms from food handlers, food utensils (eating, drinking, and kitchen), air, soil, water (e.g., oysters), the animal from which meat or milk came, and vermin such as flies, roaches, and rodents. Especially likely to be important are the people who handle foods after pasteurization, cooking, or other processing, e.g., cooks and helpers in the kitchen; waiters in the eating place; preparers and salespersons of unwrapped foods such as bulk candies, ice cream sandwiches and cones, baked goods, hot dogs, and hamburgers; and vendors of frozen desserts from counter freezers or other bulk sources.

Foods consumed raw, of course, are possible sources of pathogens. Thus, fresh fruits or vegetables may carry pathogens from a diseased handler to a healthy consumer, although few instances of such a transfer have been proved. Where night soil is used as fertilizer, there is a great risk of the presence of intestinal pathogens on the surface of fresh salad greens. Depending on the heat treatment administered, the cooking of foods may or may not destroy all pathogens present. Usually all on the surface will be killed, but not always those in the interior. Instances have been reported where even comparatively non-heat-resistant pathogens have survived cooking and caused an outbreak of disease.

The principle to be applied in the prevention of food-borne infections is to prevent the transfer of the pathogen from its source to the food, preferably by elimination of that source, but this objective is not always readily attained. Contamination from vermin can be prevented by their eradication; use of night soil for fertilizing soil for growing plant foods to be consumed raw can be prohibited; fruits or vegetables to be eaten raw can be washed thoroughly with water or with chlorine solution; shellfish from polluted waters can be rejected; and milk from diseased cows can be refused. However, meat animals or fod handlers that are diseased or are carriers are not always easy to detect. Methods for the detection of disease or disease organisms are for the most part laborious, difficult, and not always reliable; usually the tests are impractical to apply to meat animals at the packing plant and cannot be applied to food handlers as often as desirable. Of course, food handlers should not be permitted to work while they are ill or recovering, but they may be only mildly ill or be carriers and therefore may be allowed to work while giving off pathogens.

Many municipalities have ordinances which state that no person who is affected with any disease in a communicable form or is a carrier of such disease shall work in any eating or drinking establishment or be hired there, but the difficulty lies in enforcement of the ordinances. In most plants where foods are handled and processed, however, any check on the health of the workers is at present primarily the responsibility of the employer.

BIBLIOGRAPHY

Alouf, F. E., F. J. Fehrenbach, J. H. Freer, and J. Jeljaszemicz. 1984. Bacterial protein toxins. Academic Press, Inc., New York.

Angelotti, R., M. J. Foter, and K. H. Lewis. 1960. Time-temperature effects on salmonellae and staphylococci in foods. II. Behavior at warm holding temperatures; thermal-death-time studies. U.S. Dept. of Health, Education, and Welfare, Robert A. Taft Sanit. Eng. Cent. Tech. Rep. F60-5.

Angelotti, R., E. Wilson, M. J. Foter, and K. H. Lewis. 1959. Time-temperature effects on salmonellae and staphylococci in foods. I. Behavior in broth cultures and refrigerated foods. U.S. Dept. of Health, Education, and Welfare, Robert A. Taft Sanit. Eng. Cent. Tech. Rep. F59-2.

Anonymous. 1965. Government agencies step up surveillance of *Salmonella* in foods. Food Proc. 26(3):21–23.

Bergdoll, M. S., and R. N. Robbins. 1973. Characterization of types of staphyloccal enterotoxins. J. Milk Food Technol. 36:610–615.

Bowmer, E. J. 1965. Salmonellae in food: a review. J. Milk Food Technol. 28:74–86.

Bradshaw, J. G., J. T. Peeler, J. J. Corwin, J. M. Hunt, J. T. Tierney, E. P. Larkin, and R. M. Twedt. 1985. Thermal resistance of *Listeria monocytogenes* in milk. J. Food Prot. 48:743–745.

Bryan, F. L. 1968. What the sanitarian should know about staphylococci and salmonellae in non-dairy products. I. Staphylococci. J. Milk Food Technol. 31:110–116.

Bryan, F. L. 1968. What the sanitarian should know about staphylococci and salmonellae in non-dairy products. II. Salmonellae. J. Milk Food Technol. 31:131–140.

Bryan, F. L. 1969. What the sanitarian should know about *Clostridium perfringens* food-borne illness. J. Milk Food Technol. 32:383–389.

Bryan, F. L. 1972a. Emerging foodborne diseases. I. Their surveillance and epidemiology. J. Milk Food Technol. 35:618–625.

Bryan, F. L. 1972b. Emerging foodborne diseases. II. Factors that contribute to outbreaks and their control. J. Milk Food Technol. 35:632–638.

Bryan, F. L. 1974. Microbiological food hazards today: based on epidemiological information. Food. Technol. 28:52–66.

Bryan, F. L. 1982. Diseases transmitted by foods: a classification and summary. 2d ed. Center for Disease Control, Atlanta, Ga.

Buchanan, R. E., and N. E. Gibbons (eds.). 1974. Bergey's manual of determinative bacteriology, 8th ed. The Williams & Wilkins Company, Baltimore.

Center for Disease Control. 1974. Botulism in the United States, 1899–1973: handbook for epidemiologists, clinicians, and laboratory workers. Atlanta, Ga., June 1974.

Center for Disease Control. 1976. Diseases transmitted by foods: a classification and summary. U.S. Dept. Health, Education, and Welfare Publ. (CDC) 76-8237, Atlanta, Ga.

Chordash, R. A., and N. N. Potter. 1976. Stability of staphylococcal enterotoxin A to selected conditions encountered in foods. J. Food Sci. 41:906–910.

Committee on Salmonella. 1969. An evaluation of the salmonella problem. Natl. Acad. Sci. Publ. 1683. Washington.

Deibel, R. H., and J. H. Silliker. 1963. Food-poisoning potential of the enterococci. J. Bacteriol. 85:827–832.

Donnelly, C. W., and E. H. Briggs. 1986. Psychrotrophic growth and thermal inactivation of *Listeria monocytogenes* as a function of milk composition. J. Food Prot. 49: 994–998, 1002.

Edwards, P. R., M. A. Fife, and C. H. Ramsey. 1959. Studies on the *Arizona* group of *Enterobacteriaceae*. Bacteriol. Rev. 23:155–174.

Esty, J. R., and K. F. Meyer. 1922. The heat resistance of spores of *Bacillus botulinus* and allied anaerobes. J. Infect. Dis. 31:650–659.

Foster, E. M. 1965. Food-borne illnesses: minor problem or hidden epidemic? Food Proc. 26(2):56–58, 108.

Fujino, T., G. Sakaguchi, R. Sakazaki, and Y. Takeda. (eds). 1974. International symposium on *Vibrio parahaemolyticus*. Saiko Publishing Co., Ltd., Tokyo.

Georgala, D. L., and A. Hurst. 1963. The survival of food poisoning bacteria in frozen foods. J. Appl. Bacteriol. 26:346–358.

Goepfert, J. M., W. M. Spira, and H. U. Kim. 1972. *Bacillus cereus:* Food poisoning organism: a review. J. Milk Food Technol. 35:213–227.

Greenwood, M. H., and W. L. Hooper. 1985. *Yersinia* spp. in foods and related environments. Food Microbiol. 2:263–269.

Hall, H. E., and R. Angelotti. 1965. *Clostridium perfringens* in meat and meat products. Appl. Microbiol. 13:352–357.

Hariharan, H., and W. R. Mitchell. 1976. Observations on bacteriophages of *Clostridium botulinum* type C isolates from different sources and the role of certain phages in toxigenicity. Appl. Envir. Microbiol. 32:145–158.

Hauge, S. 1955. Food poisoning caused by aerobic spore-forming bacilli. J. Appl. Bacteriol. 18:591–595.

Hauschild, A. H. W. 1971. *Clostridium perfringens* enterotoxin. J. Milk Food Technol. 34:596–599.

Hobbs, B. C. 1965. *Clostridium welchii* as a food poisoning organism. J. Appl. Bacteriol. 28:74–82.

Krieg, N. R. (ed.). 1984. Bergey's Manual of systematic bacteriology. Volume 1. The Williams & Wilkins Company, Baltimore.

Lewis, K. H., and K. Cassel, Jr. (eds.). 1964. Botulism. U.S. Department of Health, Education, and Welfare, Public Health Serv. Pub. 999-FP-1.

Lund, B. M., G. W. Wyatt, and A. F. Graham. 1985. The combined effect of low temperature and low pH on survival of, and growth and toxin formation from, spores of *Clostridium botulinum*. Food Microbiol. 2:135–145.

Miller, M. L., and J. A. Koburger. 1986. Tolerance of *Pleasiomonas shigelloides* to pH, sodium chloride and temperature. J. Food Prot. 49:877–879.

Minor, T., and E. H. Marth. 1976. Staphylococci and their significance in foods. American Elsevier Publishing Company, New York.

Miwatani, T., and Y. Takeda. 1976. *Vibrio parahaemolyticus:* a causative bacterium of food poisoning. Saikon Publishing Co., Ltd., Tokyo.

Rechcigel, M. J. 1983. Handbook of foodborne diseases of biological origin. CRC Press, Boca Raton, Fla.

Reichert, C. A., and D. Y. C. Fung. 1976. Thermal inactivation and subsequent reactivation of staphylococcal enterotoxin B in selected liquid foods. J. Milk Food Technol. 39:516–520.

Riemann, H. (ed.). 1969. Food-borne infections and intoxications. Academic Press, Inc., New York.

Riemann, H. 1973. Botulinum food poisoning. J. Inst. Can. Sci. Technol. Aliment. 6: 111–125.

Rivituso, C. P., and O. P. Synder. 1981. Bacterial growth at food service operating temperatures. J. Food Prot. 44:770–775.

Roberts, T. A., and M. Ingram. 1965. The resistance of spores of *Clostridium botulinum* type E to heat and radiation. J. Appl. Bacteriol. 28:125–138.

Sack, R. B. 1975. Human diarrheal disease caused by enterotoxigenic *Escherichia coli*. Annu. Rev. Microbiol. 29:333–353.

Sadler, W. W., and R. E. Corstvet. 1965. Second survey of market poultry for *Salmonella* infection. Appl. Microbiol. 13:348–351.

Segner, W. P., and C. F. Schmidt. 1971. Heat resistance of marine and terrestrial strains of *Clostridium botulinum* type C. Appl. Microbiol. 22:1030–1034.

Slanetz, L. W., C. O. Chichester, A. R. Gaufin, and Z. J. Ordal (eds.). 1963. Microbiological quality of foods. Academic Press, Inc., New York.

Sojka, W. J. 1973. Enteropathogenic *Escherichia coli* in man and farm animals. Can. Inst. Food Sci. Technol. 6:52–63.

Smith, L. D. S. 1972. Factors involved in the isolation of *Clostridium perfringens*. J. Milk Food Technol. 35:71–76.

Strong, D. H., E. M. Foster, and C. L. Duncan. 1970. Influence of water activity on the growth of *Clostridium perfringens*. Appl. Microbiol. 19:980–987.

Tanaka, N. 1982. Toxin production by *Clostridium botulinum* in media at pH lower than 4.6. J. Food Prot. 45:234–237.

Tatini, S. R. 1973. Review of influence of food environments on growth of *Staphylococcus aureus* and production of various enterotoxins. J. Milk Food Technol. 36: 559–563.

Tatini, S. R. 1976. Thermal stability of enterotoxins in food. J. Milk Food Technol. 39:432–438.

U.S. Department of Health, Education, and Welfare, Public Health Service. 1965. Proc. Natl. Conf. Salmonellosis. Public Health Serv. Publ. 1262.

U.S. Department of Health, Education, and Welfare, Communicable Disease Center. 1965. *Salmonella* surveillance; Annual Summary 1964.

U.S. Department of Health and Human Services, Food and Drug Administration. 1984. Proceedings of the Second National Conference for Food Protection. Washington, D.C.

Wilson, E., R. S. Paffenbarger, Jr., M. J. Foter, and K. H. Lewis. 1961. Prevalence of salmonellae in meat and poultry products. J. Infect. Dis. 109:166–171.

FOOD-BORNE POISONINGS, INFECTIONS, AND INTOXICATIONS: NONBACTERIAL

Some food-borne disease outbreaks are not caused by bacteria or their toxins but result from mycotoxins, viruses, rickettsias, parasitic worms, or protozoa or from the consumption of food contaminated with toxic substances. The implication in human health is not clearly understood for the mycotoxins or for many of the viruses, but their incidence and the nature of their action in animals justify their discussion.

MYCOTOXINS

Mycotoxins are fungal metabolites. Some are highly toxic to many animals and potentially toxic to human beings. Recent concern is related to their carcinogenic properties and their presence in many food items.

Fungi and Human Beings

The fungi include the molds, yeasts, mildews, blights, rusts, and mushrooms. Many fungi are useful. Some are edible, e.g., mushrooms and single-cell protein from yeast. Others are widely used in industrial and food fermentations; e.g., *Aspergillus oryzae* is used in the production of soy sauce, miso, and sake, and molds take part in the ripening of certain cheese. The metabolite of *Penicillium chrysogenum,* penicillin, has contributed immensely to human well-being. Some mushrooms are harmful or poisonous to humans, but in contrast, molds have generally been regarded as harmless. Many fungi can be isolated from plants, including *Alternaria, Rhizopus, Fusarium, Cladosporium, Helminthosporium,* and *Chaetomium.* The two predominant genera of fungi in stored products are probably *Penicillium* and *Aspergillus,* members of which produce mycotoxins.

The syndrome resulting from the ingestion of toxin in a mold-contaminated food is referred to as **mycotoxicosis.** Historically, the first documented case of mycotoxicosis attributed to a fungus-containing food was that of rye ergot. *Claviceps purpurea* parasitizes rye and other grains and elaborates many lysergic acid derivatives which are responsible for the syndrome. Consumption of the grain or flour made from it over a period of time can result in gangrenous ergotism. Outbreaks of ergotism were quite common during the Middle Ages. More recent outbreaks of ergotism have been reported in the Soviet Union (1926–1927), England (1928), and France (1951); however, there has not been a major outbreak in the United States since 1925 (Gray, 1970).

Aflatoxin

In 1960, 100,000 turkey poults died suddenly in England. This was followed by the reported death of 14,000 ducklings and nine outbreaks of disease in calves (Gray, 1970). A common factor in each of these episodes was the use of Brazilian peanut meal as part of the animal feed. *Aspergillus flavus* was isolated from the meal, and subsequently a toxic metabolite, or toxin, was isolated and identified. The resulting *A. flavus* toxin was called **aflatoxin.** The attention and research associated with these outbreaks have greatly stimulated an interest in, and concern for, the presence of aflatoxins and other mycotoxins in foods for human consumption.

Aflatoxins are produced by certain strains of *Aspergillus flavus* and *A. parasiticus* and others (Table 25-1). Just because a fungus is identified as *A. flavus* or *A. parasiticus* does not mean it will produce aflatoxin. Actually, there is some confusion in the literature regarding *A. flavus.* The genus *Aspergillus* is divided into morphologically distinguishable groups, one of which is the *A. flavus* group, containing the species *A. flavus* and *A. parasiticus.* The number and types of aflatoxins produced vary with the strain. For example, *A. flavus* Link strains produce B_1 and its related metabolites, while *A. parasiticus* Speare produces both B_1 and G_1 and the related metabolites. Both species will grow on a wide variety of substrates over a mesophilic range of temperatures. Optimal conditions for the production of aflatoxin would be an a_w of 0.85 and a temperature of 25 to 40 C.

Chemistry The two major metabolites or aflatoxins have been designated B_1 and G_1 because they fluoresce blue (B_1) and green (G_1) when exposed to long-wave ultraviolet light. Aflatoxins B_2 and G_2 are the dihydroderivatives of B_1 and G_1 (Figure 25-1). Other closely related aflatoxins include B_2a, G_2a, and GM_1. Aflatoxins M_1, M_2, and P_1 are the hydroxylated derivatives of B_1 and B_2 which are excreted in the urine, feces, and milk as metabolic products of B_1

TABLE 25-1
MYCOTOXINS THAT MAY BE SIGNIFICANT IN FOODS

Mycotoxin	Some molds producing the toxin	Foods or feeds isolated from	Animals affected	
			Toxic to	Carcinogenic to
Aflatoxins	Aspergillus flavus, A. parasiticus, some Penicillium	Barley, corn, cottonseed, millet, oats, peanuts, peanut meal, peanut butter, rice, soybeans, wheat, spaghetti, cassava, cottonseed meal, cowpeas, sorghum, peas, sesame, soybean meal, sweet potatoes	(B₁) quail, cats, chickens, pheasants, salmon, rabbits, monkeys, dogs, hamsters, turkeys, mink, cattle, guinea pigs	(B₁) trout, rats, sheep, mice, ducklings
Patulin	Penicillium expansum, P. claviforme, P. patulum, P. melinii, P. leucopus, P. urticae, P. equinum, P. cyclopium, Aspergillus clavatus, A. giganteus, A. terreus	Apple sap, apple cider, apple juice	Mice, rats, cats, rabbits, quail, guppies, brine shrimp	Mice
Ochratoxin A	Aspergillus ostianus, A. petrakii, A. alliaceus, A. sclerotiorum, A. sulphureus, A. melleus, Penicillium cyclopium, P. purpurescens, P. commune, P. viridicatum	Corn, wheat, barley, white beans, peanuts, dough, bread, hen's eggs	Rats, chicks, ducklings, trout	Rats, trout, chicks
Luteoskyrin	Penicillium islandicum	Mold, rice flour	Mice	Mice
Sterigmatocystin	Aspergillus regulosus, A. nidulans, A. versicolor, Penicillium luteum	Wheat, oats	Mice, monkeys, rats	Rats
Penicillic acid	Penicillium puberulum, P. cyclopium, P. marteusii, P. thomii, P. suavolens, P. madriti, P. baarneuse, Aspergillus quercinus, A. sulphureus, A. ochraceus, A. mellens	Dried beans, tobacco	Rats	Rats
Alimentary toxic aleukia (ATA)	Species of Cladosporium, Penicillium, Fusarium, Mucor, Alternaria	Grain	Human beings	
Roquefortine	Penicillium roqueforti	Blue cheese, Roquefort cheese, Stilton cheese	Mice	

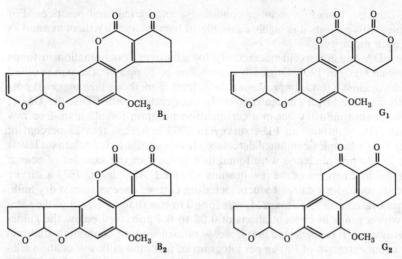

FIGURE 25-1
Structure of four aflatoxins. (*From W. D. Gray, The Use of Fungi as Food and in Food Processing, The Chemical Rubber Co., 1970. Used by permission of The Chemical Rubber Co.*)

and B_2 following their consumption by mammals. They are all highly oxygenated heterocyclic compounds.

Toxicity   Aflatoxin B_1, the most toxic of the aflatoxins, is toxic to various animals, as summarized in Table 25-1. Many of the other aflatoxins have been shown to be toxic or carcinogenic to different species of fish, mammals, and poultry.

When cows eat feed containing aflatoxin, aflatoxin M_1 and M_2 is excreted in the milk. Although M_1 and M_2 are less toxic than the parent compounds B_1 and B_2, M_1 retains its toxic and carcinogenic ability in many animals. M_1 has also been detected in the urine of Philippine women who had consumed peanut butter containing aflatoxin.

Significance in Foods   Since the discovery (or at least the identification) of the aflatoxins in the early 1960s numerous surveys have been conducted on the detection of the aflatoxins in foods (Table 25-1). Many commodities will support the growth of toxigenic strains if inoculated, including various dairy products, bakery products, fruit juices, cereals, and forage crops.

In most cases, the growth of a toxigenic strain and the elaboration of aflatoxin occurs following harvesting or formulation of the product. Peanuts, cottonseeds, and corn, however, differ significantly in that these products are susceptible to fungal invasion, growth, and mycotoxin production before harvesting. The contamination and potential for aflatoxin production in these crops is related to insect damage, humidity, weather conditions, and agricultural practices. For example, with peanuts it is highly desirable to harvest and dry them as soon as they reach maturity.

The FDA began surveillance activity for aflatoxin contamination in foods and animal feeds in 1963. Originally a guideline of 20 ppb of aflatoxin resulted in action against a food. Improvement in detection methods now makes it possible to measure lower concentrations. In cooperation with FDA, the USDA and the peanut industry began a certification program for aflatoxin-free raw peanuts. The results of an FDA survey in 1973 indicated that 25 percent of peanut butter samples contained detectable levels of aflatoxin. Aflatoxin levels above the 20 ppb guideline were found in 4 percent of the samples of peanut butter and in 2 percent of the raw peanuts sampled. Also during 1973 a survey was made on various dairy products including cottage cheese, nonfat dry milk, and evaporated milk. Aflatoxin M_1 was found in less than 1 percent of the samples, with a range in concentrations of 0.05 to 0.4 ppb, well below the guideline. However, it is suggested that if a cow consumes feed containing aflatoxin B_1 at a concentration of 100 μg per kilogram of feed, the milk will contain aflatoxin M_1 at a concentration of 1 μg per liter. Therefore, only about 1.0 percent of the amount consumed finds its way into the milk. The elimination of aflatoxins in dairy products is really a problem of keeping the aflatoxins out of the animal feed.

International efforts to monitor and control the aflatoxin levels in foods resulted in the establishment of a 30 ppb guideline (FAO/WHO/UNICEF, Protein Advisory Board). This guideline had as its basis a no-effect level in monkeys with a safety factor of 50 (Van Walbeek, 1973). Peanut products and cottonseed products are imported by many countries, and the value of peanut flour as a good protein source for malnourished populations is recognized. However, considering all available data on aflatoxins, it is now suggested that peanut flour not be depended on as a protein source for feeding malnourished infants.

Patulin

First isolated and described as an antibiotic, patulin is structurally synonymous with expansin, penicidin, claviformin, clavatin, clavacin, mycoin C, and gigantic acid. Several molds have been reported to produce patulin, as shown in Table 25-1.

Chemistry   Patulin in the pure state is a white crystal with a melting point of 110.5 C and a molecular weight of 154. It is an unsaturated lactone (Figure 25-2) with the chemical name of 4-hydroxy-4H-furo[3, 2c]pyran-2(6H)-one. It is sensitive to SO_2 and is unstable in alkali but stable in acid.

Toxicity   Originally isolated as an antibiotic, it is effective against many bacterial species. Concentrations as low as 0.1 percent completely inhibit *E. coli*

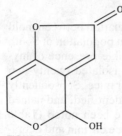

FIGURE 25-2
Structure of patulin.

and *S. aureus*. It also exhibits strong fungistatic activity and is toxic to seeds and seedlings of higher plants including sugar beets, corn, wheat, peas, tomato, cucumber, and flax.

Oral and intravenous injections of patulin in concentrations of 0.3 to 2.5 mg per gram of body weight are fatal to mice and rats. Pathological changes included edema of the brain, hemorrhaging of the lungs, and capillary damage of the liver, spleen, and kidney. Carcinogenic and mutagenic properties of patulin have been observed in mice at sublethal doses. Since many other animals are known to be sensitive to patulin, it is considered a potential human carcinogen (Scott and Bullerman, 1975).

Significance in Foods   Many patulin-producing strains have been isolated from food and animal feeds. The presence of patulin has been detected in apple cider and apple juice. Its occurrence in apple products may be related to the fact that over 60 percent of sampled rotted apples have yielded patulin-producing strains of *Penicillium expansum*. In most other products patulin-producing molds represent only a small percentage of the total isolates. Another explanation for the inability to detect patulin chemically in foodstuffs which support good growth of patulin-producing fungi might be the observed inhibitory effect of several food compounds on patulin. For example, peptone, glycine, methionine, *p*-aminobenzoic acid, asparagine, sodium sulfate, sodium thiosulfate, and casein hydrolyzate have an inhibitory action on patulin. It is possible, therefore, that some foods which will support patulin-producing fungi do not constitute a problem because of their inherent composition. Of additional interest to the food microbiologist is that several patulin-producing fungi when grown on a synthetic medium will elaborate patulin at refrigeration temperatures. The resistance of patulin to heat also has been noted. This mycotoxin resists boiling; e.g., it is stable at 100 C for 15 min.

The carcinogenic property of patulin in animals, the isolation of patulin-producing fungi from several foodstuffs, its inactivation in some foods, the potential for toxin production at refrigeration temperatures, and its stability to heat suggest that patulin will be the subject of further study and concern in the food industry.

Ochratoxin

Published work on the aflatoxins and suggestions of a correlation between mold metabolites and a high incidence of liver cancer in the Bantu population of South Africa provided the impetus for investigation of the possible presence of mycotoxins in the cereal grains of that region. Scott (1965) isolated twenty-two fungi (seven species) which were toxic to ducklings, rats, or mice. Subsequently a toxic metabolite of *Aspergillus ochraceus* was isolated, identified, and named ochratoxin A. Other ochratoxin A–producing molds have been noted (Table 25-1). Some strains of *P. viridicatum* and *P. palitans* produce citrinin and ochratoxin A. There is some speculation that these two mycotoxins can act synergistically in animals to result in nephrotoxicity.

Chemistry   Ochratoxin A is structurally a chlorinated isocoumarin derivative with an amide bond to phenylalanine. A dechloro analog of this compound has also been isolated and named ochratoxin B. In addition, there are other minor components including a methyl and ethyl ester of A and B and 4-hydroxyochratoxin A. Ochratoxin A fluoresces green under ultraviolet light, and ochratoxin B fluoresces blue.

Toxicity   Ochratoxin A is toxic to ducklings, rats, chicks, trout, and other animals. It is about one-third as toxic as aflatoxin B_1 to rats. The other derivatives or analogs are all equally toxic or less toxic than ochratoxin A. They have been shown to produce lesions in the kidneys of rats and lesions in trout and chicks. Citrinin also has a pathological effect on the kidneys of animals. Mold nephrosis, a disease in pigs, has occurred at high rates when the animals were fed grain which had been harvested wet. There is speculation that molds producing ochratoxin A and citrinin are responsible for this syndrome. If these mycotoxin-producing molds are isolated and grown on synthetic media, citrinin is produced. Consumption of the citrinin by rats, rabbits, guinea pigs, and pigs results in kidney damage similar to that observed in pigs with mold nephrosis (Van Walbeek, 1973). A moldy alfalfa-grass mixture was considered to be responsible for a high abortion rate in dairy cows (Still et al., 1971). Although ochratoxin A was not isolated, an ochratoxin-producing *Aspergillus* strain was identified.

Significance in Foods   In addition to their unknown effect on human beings, the ochratoxins are of interest in foods for at least three reasons: (1) They are toxic to some animals, (2) some are very heat resistant, e.g., prolonged autoclaving does not destroy ochratoxin A when heated in oatmeal (Trenk et al., 1971), (3) many ochratoxin- and citrinin-producing fungi are capable of growth and mycotoxin production at temperatures below 10 C, and (4) ochratoxins have been isolated from numerous foods.

Luteoskyrin

Penicillium islandicum produces two metabolites, luteoskyrin and cyclochlorotine, which are hepatotoxic to some animals. Although luteoskyrin is not as carcinogenic as aflatoxin B_1, mice seem to be more sensitive to luteoskyrin than to aflatoxin B_1. There are no known acute human intoxications attributed to luteoskyrin or cyclochlorotine.

Sterigmatocystin

Structurally similar to aflatoxin, sterigmatocystin has a carcinogenic potency probably between one-tenth and one-hundredth of that of aflatoxin.

Penicillic Acid

Several molds have been reported to produce penicillic acid, and its carcinogenic ability has been noted. Many commodities, including oats, wheat, rice, corn, and barley, support the growth of penicillic acid–producing strains.

Alimentary Toxic Aleukia (ATA)

Outbreaks of this mycotoxicosis have occurred in the Soviet Union, where between 1942 and 1947 casualties approached 1,000 per 10,000 population in certain regions. The syndrome in humans is caused by the toxic metabolites fusariogenin, epicladosporic acid, and fagicladosporic acid. ATA is not a problem if grain is harvested and stored properly. Previous outbreaks have all resulted from the consumption of overwintered grain, i.e., grain that has been allowed to remain in the fields during the winter and harvested late.

Roquefortine

A toxic substance has recently been detected in commercial blue cheese from several countries. Heavily molded portions of the cheese contain higher concentrations than the white portions, suggesting that *Penicillium roqueforti* may be producing a mycotoxin during curing of Roquefort cheese (blue cheese). The toxic factor, tentatively named roquefortine, acts as a neurotoxin when injected into mice and leads to convulsive seizures.

Implications

The above list of mycotoxins is far from complete. Since the isolation and characterization of the aflatoxins, much information has been published on a large number of diverse toxic metabolities of fungal origin.

There is little question that many fungi produce and elaborate toxic metabolites. Of major concern is their carcinogenic property. This topic has been excellently reviewed by Enomoto and Saito (1972). Most of the studies on the toxicological and carcinogenic effects of the mycotoxins have, of course, been made with experimental animals, with limited or nonexisting data on human beings. Therefore, clinical evidence and the effects of mycotoxins on people is essentially not known. Studies with human tissue cells for determination of human susceptibility to mycotoxins is now possible and should prove to be a valuable research tool. The possible wide range of effects and susceptibility to carcinogens may make it impossible ever to establish safe dose levels of the mycotoxins in human foods.

The abundance of surveys and field and storage studies has definitely established the presence of many of the mycotoxins in our food supply. The actual impact on human health and its long-term implications are still being established.

VIRUSES

Some common characteristics of viruses are that they are (1) ultramicroscopic in size, varying from 10 to 450 nm, (2) able to pass through most bacterial filters (i.e., 0.22 μm), (3) cultivatable only on a susceptible host cell line, (4) incapable of reproduction without a host, and (5) able to infect people, animals, plants, or bacteria; however, they have a very specific target host. Viruses consist of a core of nucleic acid, either deoxyribonucleic acid (DNA) or ribonucleic acid (RNA), and a protein coat. They actually exist in two different states, the intracellular state and the extracellular state. When the virus particle invades a susceptible host cell (the intracellular state), the nucleic acid core and the protein coat separate. There are two possible responses of the viral nucleic acid in the host cell. In most instances the viral nucleic acid serves as the template to direct the host cell's machinery to synthesize new virus particles. In this way viruses multiply and destroy host cells. Sometimes, however, a stable relationship between the host nucleic acid and the viral nucleic acid is established, and new virus particles are not produced; instead the viral nucleic acid is replicated when the host cell's nucleic acid is replicated.

Classification

Arbitrary and convenient forms for the classification of viruses include subdivisions based on (1) the host in which the virus multiplies, (2) the types of tissue or organs of primary infection, and (3) the mode of transmission. More recent taxonomical approaches include consideration of (1) the nucleic acid present, i.e., RNA or DNA, (2) symmetry, (3) presence or absence of an envelope, (4) diameter of the helical nucleocapsids, and (5) base sequence of the nucleic acid.

Numerous viral infections may result in the death of animals or the destruction of plants. This consequence could be considered a reduction of potential foods available for humans. In addition, many of the animal viruses can cause disease in humans, e.g., encephalitis, hepatitis, measles, mumps, rabies, smallpox, and yellow fever. Those associated with food-borne outbreaks will be discussed subsequently. Many of the enteroviruses, including the coxsackie viruses and ECHO viruses, may result in human gastroenteritis. Since many cases of food-borne human gastroenteritis are not caused by bacteria ("nonbacterial acute gastroenteritis"), it is widely believed that viruses may be responsible for, or implicated in, these outbreaks of food-borne diseases in humans. Several viruses implicated in food-borne outbreaks, their mode of transmission, and measures to prevent their spread are summarized in Table 25-2. Further clarification of possible relationships is hampered by the lack of practical laboratory methodology for detection and isolation of viruses from foods.

Infectious Hepatitis

The hepatitis virus enters a person through the oral route normally as a result of fecal contamination of water or food. The incubation time (onset of symptoms) is long (see Table 25-2) but eventually may result in serious liver complications. There are many documented food-borne outbreaks in people; perhaps the classic outbreak was described by Mason and McLean (1962), who identified the source as oysters harvested from polluted waters. Oysters and clams are able to concentrate the numbers of bacteria or viruses during their normal feeding, which is to filter and remove particles from the water. The infectious hepatitis virus has been shown to be stable during refrigerated storage of oysters. The problem is of further concern since many oysters are eaten raw. Cliver (1967) summarized reports over a 20-year period involving 3,000 cases of food-borne infectious hepatitis and noted that in addition to shellfish, raw milk, potato salad, sandwiches, and cold meat cuts also were implicated.

Poliomyelitis

There are a limited number of reported food-borne outbreaks of polio. Cliver (1967) noted ten such outbreaks between 1914 and 1949. Milk (both pasteurized and raw) was implicated in eight of the ten outbreaks, and lemonade and a cream-filled pastry in the remaining two. The implication of pasteurized milk (two outbreaks) is noteworthy since the heat required for pasteurization should inactivate the polio virus. It was assumed either that the milk was improperly pasteurized or that it was contaminated following processing.

Other Viruses

The virus responsible for foot and mouth disease in cattle can be transmitted to people in foods. Two viral diseases of poultry, ornithosis and Newcastle disease, have been implicated in human ailments. Workers in poultry processing plants have been known to contract an eye infection, possibly as a result of the splashing of water containing the Newcastle virus. The ornithosis virus produces a respiratory infection in man. Other viruses which are considered good

TABLE 25-2
VIRUSES IMPLICATED IN FOOD-BORNE OUTBREAKS

Illness	Causative agent	Foods usually involved	Other modes of transmission	Incubation period	Signs and symptoms	Measures to prevent spread by food
Poliomyelitis*	Poliovirus types I, II, III	Milk; possibly other beverages and prepared foods	Case or carrier; contaminated water	5–35 days	Fever; vomiting; headache; pain in muscle groups; paralysis	Personal cleanliness; adequate heating of foods; disinfection of water; prevention of contact of flies with foods
Infectious hepatitis*	Infectious hepatitis virus (or viruses)	Milk and other beverages; shellfish (raw oysters and clams); specific foods served as part of a meal, such as potato salad	Case or carrier; contaminated water	10–50 days, mean 25 days	Jaundice in approximately one-half of cases; loss of appetite, gastrointestinal disturbance	Cooking of shellfish; checking personnel handling food; adequate heating of milk and foods; adequate heating or disinfection of water; cleanliness of food handlers
Acute nonbacterial gastroenteritis*	Coxsackie and ECHO viruses; viral agents as yet unidentified	Possibly food-borne, but as yet this mode of transmission is unestablished	Case or carrier	27–60 hr (average)	Fever; constitutional symptoms; headache; abdominal pain, vomiting, and diarrhea	Probably the same as for poliomyelitis

*Usually not food-borne.
Source: From International Association of Milk, Food, and Environmental Sanitarians, Inc., Procedure for the Investigation of Foodborne Disease Outbreaks, 2d ed., 1966.

candidates for food-borne transmission are enteroviruses including coxsackie and ECHO viruses.

At least eighty individuals became ill following the consumption of coleslaw in a 1976 outbreak which was attributed to ECHO virus 4. One of the most frequently involved virus in recent years has been the "Norwalk" virus or Norwalk-like agents. Shellfish is the common vehicle for this viral diarrheal syndrome. In 1982 viral agents (hepatitis A and Norwalk virus) accounted for 21 outbreaks and 5,325 cases. Norwalk gastroenteritis was involved in two large outbreaks, one of over 3,000 cases (frosting on bakery items) and one of over 2,000 cases (coleslaw).

Significance in Foods

In addition to the known food-borne viral outbreaks there are many suspected viral implicated food-borne disease outbreaks. The lack of methodology and susceptible host cell lines complicates viral surveys of foods. It is not unreasonable to assume that the enteroviruses (intestinal viruses) can enter our food supply as readily and as frequently as the enteric bacteria, since they can be isolated from feces as readily as the coliforms and the enteric pathogens. They follow the same oral-fecal route of contamination and dissemination. Although the resistance to heat and the persistence during storage vary considerably between viruses, some do have a greater resistance than vegetative bacteria. Details of some specific viruses in regard to effects of processing and storage can be found in several of the references cited at the end of this chapter.

RICKETTSIAS

The rickettsias may be considered degenerative bacteria since they represent a form of life closely resembling bacteria except that they cannot be cultivated outside of living cells. Like the viruses, they are obligate parasites. The mode of transmission of rickettsias to people is quite variable, but at some point in their normal life cycle rickettsias are associated with fleas, lice, or ticks. Therefore, many of the major human rickettsial diseases are contracted by bites from these bloodsucking arthropods. Epidemic typhus, rickettsial pox, Rocky Mountain spotted fever, and Q fever are examples of human rickettsial diseases.

Cows infected with the rickettsia of Q fever, *Coxiella burnetii,* are of public health concern, since the organism can be excreted in milk in large quantities and result in human infections. At one time the pasteurization times and temperatures for milk (61.7 C for 30 min) were based on the complete destruction of *Mycobacterium tuberculosis.* When it was shown that *C. burnetii* was able to survive these conditions, the pasteurization temperature was raised to 62.8 C (30 min) to ensure its destruction in milk.

FOOD-BORNE PARASITES

Although no attempt will be made to discuss in any detail the numerous parasitic round- or flatworms, protozoa, and flukes occasionally encountered in foods, it is important for the food microbiologist to be aware of their existence. A summary of common parasites is presented in Table 25-3. A comprehensive listing of possible parasites transmitted in foods can be found in Table 25-4.

Trichinosis

Trichinosis, although caused by a nematode worm, *Trichinella spiralis,* usually is discussed along with bacterial food poisoning and infection because all have similar symptoms and all are food-borne. Most human trichinosis results from the consumption of raw or incompletely cooked pork containing the encysted larvae. The larvae are released into the intestinal tract during digestion and invade the mucous membranes of the first parts of the small intestine, where they develop into adults. The fertilized females give birth to numerous larvae, which travel through the blood vessels and lymphatics to skeletal muscle tissue, where they encyst. The worm goes through a similar cycle in hogs, rats, and other hosts, e.g., mice, rabbits, cats, dogs, and bears. Recent trends in the number of cases of trichinosis reported in the United States are illustrated in Figure 25-3.

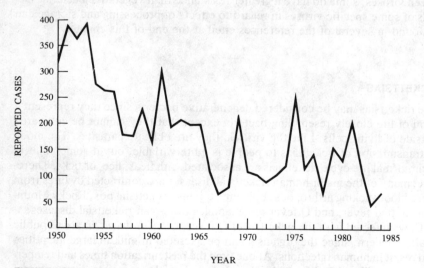

FIGURE 25-3
Reported cases of trichinosis in the United States, 1950–1984. In 1984, sixty-eight cases of trichinosis were reported. Pork was incriminated in fifty-three cases (82 percent), and bear meat in six (9 percent). Sausage was the most frequently implicated form of pork (43 percent). One death was attributed to trichinosis, the first reported since 1981. (*Centers for Disease Control, Annual Summaries for 1984, 1986.*)

TABLE 25-3
IMPORTANT PARASITIC INFECTIONS TRANSMITTED BY FOODS

Illness	Causative agent	Foods usually involved	Incubation period	Signs and symptoms	Measures to prevent spread by food
Anisakiasis	*Anisakis* spp. (a nematode)	Raw or insufficiently cooked fish	Several days	Irritation of throat and digestive tract	Cook fish thoroughly
Amebic dysentery (amebiasis)	*Endamoeba histolytica*	Water contaminated with sewage; moist food contaminated with human feces	Several days to 4 weeks	Diarrhea of varying severity; fatalities not uncommon	Protect water supplies; cleanliness in food preparation; ensure proper disposal of human excreta
Beef tapeworm (taeniasis saginata)	*Taenia saginata*	Raw or insufficiently cooked beef containing live larvae	Several weeks	Abdominal pain, hungry feeling, vague discomfort	Use meat processed under veterinary inspection; cook beef thoroughly
Fish tapeworm (diphyllobothriasis)	*Diphyllobothrium latum*	Raw or insufficiently cooked fish containing live larvae	3–6 weeks	Usually none; anemia in heavy infections	Cook fish thoroughly; avoid eating raw smoked fish
Pork tapeworm (taeniasis solium)	*Taenia solium*	Raw or insufficiently cooked pork containing live larvae	Several weeks	Varies from a mild chronic, digestive disorder to severe malaise with encephalitis; may be fatal	Use meat processed under veterinary inspection; cook pork thoroughly
Trichinosis	*Trichinella-spiralis*	Raw or insufficiently cooked pork and pork products; whale, seal, bear, or walrus meat containing live larvae	Usually 9 days but may vary from 2 to 28 days; in heavy infections 24 hr	Nausea, vomiting, diarrhea, muscular pains, fever, labored breathing, swelling of eyelids; occasionally fatal	Cook pork and pork products thoroughly; freeze pork at −15 C for 30 days, or at −23 C for 20 days, or −29 C for 12 days; cook garbage fed to swine; eliminate rats from hog lots

Source: Chiefly from International Association of Milk, Food, and Environmental Sanitarians, Inc., *Procedure for the Investigation of Foodborne Disease Outbreaks,* 2d ed., 1966

TABLE 25-4
ENDOPARASITES TRANSMISSABLE THROUGH FOODS

Parasites	Potential patho-genicity	Method of infection
Protozoa		
Entamoeba histolytica	+	Food and drink contaminated with cysts
Entamoeba coli	−	Food and drink contaminated with cysts
Endolimax nana	−	Food and drink contaminated with cysts
Iodamoeba butschlii	−	Food and drink contaminated with cysts
Dientamoeba fragilis	+	Food and drink contaminated with tropho-zoites
Retortamonas intestinalis	−	Food and drink contaminated with cysts
Retortamonas sinensis	+	Food and drink contaminated with cysts
Chilomastix mesnili	−	Food and drink contaminated with cysts
Enteromonas hominis	−	Food and drink contaminated with cysts
Enteromonas hervei	−	Probably via food and drink contaminated with cysts
Trichomonas hominis	−	Food and drink contaminated with tropho-zoites
Trichomonas tenax	−	Food and drink contaminated with tropho-zoites
Giardia lamblia	+	Food and drink contaminated with cysts
Isospora belli	+	Food and drink contaminated with cysts
Isospora natalensis	+	Food and drink contaminated with cysts
Balantidium coli	+	Food and drink contaminated with cysts
Sarcocystis ssp.	+	Red meat containing cysts
Toxoplasma gondii	+	Meats and milk contaminated with cysts
Nematoda		
Trichinellaspiralis	+	Meats containing larvae
Trichuris trichiura	+	Food and drink contaminated with eggs
Capillaria hepatica	+	Food and drink contaminated with eggs
Capillaria philippinensis	+	Ingestion of fish harboring larvae
Dioctophymae renale	+	Ingestion of fish harboring larvae
Rhabditis sp.	−	Contaminated drink; molluscs
Syngamus laryngeus	−	Food and drink contaminated with larvae
Trichostrongylus sp.	+	Vegetables contaminated with larvae
Haemonchus contortus	+	Vegetables contaminated with larvae
Enterobius vermicularis	+	Food and drink contaminated with eggs
Syphacia obvelatea	−	Food and drink contaminated with eggs
Ascaris lumbricoides	+	Food and drink contaminated with eggs
Toxocara cati	+	Food and drink contaminated with eggs
Toxocara canis	+	Food and drink contaminated with eggs
Gnathostoma spinigerum	+	Fish and frog legs containing larvae
Echinocephalus sp.	+	Oysters containing larvae
Phocanema decipiens	+	Fish containing larvae
Anisakis spp.	+	Fish containing larvae
Porrocaecum sp.	+	Fish containing larvae
Contracaecum sp.	+	Fish containing larvae
Angiostrongylus cantonensis	+	Vegetables contaminated with larvae or small molluscs harboring larvae; prawns and other paratenic hosts

TABLE 25-4 (Continued)

Parasites	Potential pathogenicity	Method of infection
Nematoda (Continued)		
Angiostrongylus costaricensis	+	Vegetables contaminated with slugs harboring larvae
Cestoda		
Spirometra sp. larvae	+	Water containing procercoid infected Cyclops sp.
Diphyllobothrium latum	+	Fish harboring plerocercoids
Diplogonoporus grandis	+	Fish harboring plerocercoids
Digramma brauni	−	Fish harboring plerocercoids
Ligula intestinalis	−	Fish harboring plerocercoids
Braunia jasseyensis	−	Probably fish harboring plerocercoids
Taenia solium	+	Pork containing cysticerci
Taeniarhynchus saginatus (=Taenia saginata	+	Beef containing cysticerci
Multiceps multiceps (larva)	+	Food and drink contaminated with eggs
Multiceps serialis (larva)	+	Food and drink contaminated with eggs
Echinococcus granulosus (larva)	+	Food and drink contaminated with eggs
Echinococcus multilocularis (larva)	+	Food and drink contaminated with eggs
Echinococcus vogeli (larva)	+	Food and drink contaminated with eggs
Hymenolepis nana	+	Food contaminated with eggs
Hymenolepis diminuta	+	Food contaminated with cysticercoid infected beetles
Trematoda		
Watsonius watsoni	+	Vegetables contaminated with metacercariae
Gastrodiscoides hominis	+	Vegetables contaminated with metacercariae
Fasciola hepatica	+	Vegetables contaminated with metacercariae
Fasciola gigantica	+	Vegetables contaminated with metacercariae
Fasciolopsis buski	+	Vegetables contaminated with metacercariae
Echinostoma spp.	+	Molluscs harboring metacercariae
Himasthla muehlensis	+	Clams harboring metacercariae
Echinochasmus perfoliatus	+	Fish harboring metacercariae
Opisthorchis felineus	+	Fish harboring metacercariae
Clonorchis sinensis	+	Fish harboring metacercariae
Heterophyes heterophyes	+	Fish harboring metacercariae
Metagonimus yokagawai	+	Fish harboring metacercariae
Metagonimus minutus	+	Fish harboring metacercariae
Centrocestus armatus	+	Fish harboring metacercariae
Centrocestus formosanus	+	Fish and frog legs harboring metacercariae
Haplorchis pumilio	+	Fish and frog legs harboring metacercariae

TABLE 25-4 *(Continued)*

Parasites	Potential pathogenicity	Method of infection
Trematoda *(Continued)*		
Haplorchis microrchia	+	Fish harboring metacercariae
Haplorchis yokogawai	+	Fish and shrimp harboring metacercariae
Haplorchis taichui	+	Fish harboring metacercariae
Diorchitrema formosanum	+	Fish harboring metacercariae
Diorchitrema amplicaecale	+	Fish harboring metacercariae
Diorchitrema pseudocirratum	+	Fish harboring metacercariae
Nanophyetus salmincola	+	Fish harboring metacercariae
Paragonimus westermani	+	Crabs and other crustacea harboring metacercariae
Isoparorchis hypselobagri	–	Fish harboring metacercariae
Alaria americana	+	Frog legs harboring mesocercariae

Source: Speck (1984).

Symptoms   The incubation period between ingestion of the pork and the first symptoms varies widely, being reported to be as short as a day or two and as long as several weeks. The first symptoms, which may be confused with food poisoning, appear when the larvae, freshly released from their cysts in the ingested and digested pork, invade the mucosa. Symptoms may include nausea, vomiting, diarrhea, profuse sweating, colic, and loss of appetite and may continue for days. Later symptoms, resulting from the migration of the newborn larvae to the muscles and their encystment there, are mostly related to muscular soreness and swelling and would not be confused with food poisoning. Death may follow in severe cases.

Diagnosis   Diagnosis often is based primarily on symptoms since other methods of diagnosis are difficult. The suspected food may be examined for encysted larvae, but they usually are hard to find, as are adult worms in stools of patients. Muscle strips from the patient may be examined for cysts, or intradermal and precipitin tests may be positive several weeks after the first symptoms have appeared.

Prevention   The chief method for the prevention of trichinosis is the treatment of pork (or other meat) to ensure the destruction of any trichinae that may be present. This can be accomplished by (1) the thorough cooking of all pork so that every part reaches at least 58.3 C, (2) quick freezing or storage at −15 C or lower for not less than 20 days, (3) treatment with 20,000 rep of ionizing rays, or (4) processing sausage or similar pork products according to recommended schedules of salting, drying, smoking, and refrigeration as formulated originally by the former Bureau of Animal Industry of the USDA. Directions for drying specify 1 part of salt per 30 parts of meat and holding in the drying room for over 20 days at 7.2 C or above. Smoking should be for 40 hr or more in the drying room at 7.2 C or above.

Inspection of animals and meats for trichinae at the packing plant is laborious and not always successful, although formerly practiced. Some attempt has been made to reduce the incidence of trichinosis in swine by control of rats and by cooking garbage fed to hogs.

SEAFOOD TOXICANTS

Shellfish Poisoning

Many shellfish become toxic to humans as a result of feeding on toxic algae, particularly the dinoflagellates, including *Gonyaulax catenella* and *G. tamareusis*. Symptoms include numbness of lips, fingertips, and tongue shortly after consumption of the shellfish. Death can result within 2 to 12 hr as a result of eventual respiratory paralysis.

Ciguatera Poisoning

Numerous species of fish have been implicated in ciguatera poisoning; however, the fish do not produce the poison but acquire it as a consequence of feeding on smaller fish which may have been fed on toxic plankton, plants, or algae. Isolated incidences of fish poisonous to humans have been shown to be a result of the fish feeding on the toxic alga *Lyngbya majuscula*.

Scombroid Fish Poisoning

This poisoning is thought to be caused by the ingestion of histamine, formed in the fish product as a result of bacterial degradation. The name comes from a certain group of fish, i.e., the scombroid fishes (tuna, mackerel, skipjack, and bonito). Symptoms include nausea, facial flushing, vomiting, labial edema, oral burning sensation, and itching of the skin. Bacteria such as *Proteus morganii* and *Klebsiella pneumoniae* are thought to be involved.

POISONING BY CHEMICALS

Poisoning by consumption of chemicals is rather uncommon and usually is characterized by appearance of the symptoms within a short time after the poisonous food is eaten. Antimony, arsenic, cadmium, chlorinated hydrocarbons, copper, cyanide, fluoride, nicotinic acid, lead, and zinc in foods have been blamed for food poisoning. Poisonous chemicals may enter foods from utensils, e.g., from cadmium-plated ware or cheap enameled ware containing antimony. The insecticide sodium fluoride has been accidentally added to food in place of baking powder, flour, dry milk, or starch. Lead and arsenic residues from fruit sprays may be on the surfaces of fruits but usually in harmless amounts, especially after washing. Often the source of poison is wrongly attributed to food; methyl chloride poisoning from a leaking mechanical refrigerator, for example, or poisoning from materials that are hazards in some industries has been mistaken for food poisoning.

BIBLIOGRAPHY

Berg, G. 1964. The food vehicle in virus transmission. Health Lab. Sci. 1:51–59.

Berg, G. 1965. Transmission of viruses by the water route. Interscience Publishers (a division of John Wiley & Sons, Inc.), New York.

Blackwell, J. H., D. O. Cliver, J. J. Callis, N. D. Heidelbaugh, E. P. Larkin, P. D. McKercher, and D. W. Thayer. 1985. Foodborne viruses: their importance and need for research. J Food Prot. 48:717–723.

Bryan, F. L. 1972a. Emerging foodborne diseases. I. Their surveillance and epidemology. J. Milk Food Technol. 35:618–625.

Bryan, F. L. 1972b. Emerging foodborne diseases. II. Factors that contribute to outbreaks and their control. J. Milk Food Technol. 35:632–639.

Campbell, T. C., and L. Stoloff. 1974. Implication of mycotoxins for human health. J. Agr. Food Chem. 22(6):1006–1015.

Carlin, A. F., C. Mott, D. Cash, and W. Zimmerman. 1969. Destruction of trichina larvae in cooked pork roasts. J. Food Sci. 34:210–212.

Centers for Disease Control. 1984. Morbidity and Mortality Annual Summary 1984. U.S. Department of Health and Human Services, Public Health Service, Atlanta, Ga.

Chitwood, M. B. 1969. Systematics and biology of some parasitic nematodes. Chem. Zool. 3:223–244.

Ciegler, A., S. Kadis, and S. J. Ajl. 1971. Microbial toxins. Volume VI. Fungal toxins. Academic Press, Inc., New York.

Cliver, D. O. 1967. Food associated viruses. Health Lab. Sci. 34:213–221.

Cliver, D. O., and J. Grindrod. 1969. Surveillance methods for viruses in foods. J. Milk Food Technol. 32:421–426.

Cliver, D. O., and J. E. Herrmann. 1973. Enterovirus persistence in sausage and ground beef. J. Milk Food Technol. 36:426–429.

Cliver, D. O., K. D. Kostenbader, Jr., and M. R. Vallenas. 1970. Stability of viruses in low moisture foods. J. Milk Food Technol. 33:484–491.

Enomoto, M., and M. Saito. 1972. Carcinogens produced by fungi. Annu. Rev. Microbiol. 26:279–306.

Fenner, F., B. R. McAuslan, C. A. Mimms, J. Sambrook, and D. O. White. 1974. The biology of animal viruses, 2d ed. Academic Press, Inc., New York.

Frobisher, M., R. D. Hinsdill, K. T. Crabtree, and C. R. Goodheart. 1974. Fundamentals of microbiology. W. B. Saunders Company, Philadelphia.

Fugate, K. J., D. O. Cliver, and M. T. Hatch. 1975. Enteroviruses and potential bacterial indicators in Gulf Coast oyster. J. Milk Food Technol. 38:100–105.

Gammon, D. L., J. D. Kemp, J. M. Edney, W. Y. Varney. 1968. Salt, moisture and aging time effects on the viability of *Trichinella spiralis* in pork hams and shoulders. J. Food Sci. 33:417–419.

Gill, T. A., J. W. Thompson, and S. Gould. 1985. Thermal resistance of paralytic shellfish poison in soft-shell clams. J. Food Prot. 48:659–663.

Goldblatt, L. A. (ed.). 1969. Aflatoxin: scientific background, control, and implications. Academic Press, Inc., New York.

Graham, H. D. (ed.). 1968. The safety of foods. AVI Publishing Co., Inc., Westport, Conn.

Gray, W. D. 1970. The use of fungi as food and in food processing, pp. 85–113. CRC Press, Cleveland, Ohio.

Hedstrom, C. E., and E. Lycke. 1964. An experimental study of oysters as virus carriers. Am. J. Hyg. 79:134–142.

Horsfall, F. L., and I. Tamm (eds.). 1965. Viral and rickettsial infections of man. J. B. Lippincott Company, Philadelphia.

Jackson, G. J. 1975. The "new disease" status of human anisakiasis and North American cases: a review, J. Milk Food Technol. 38:769–773.

Jacobs, L. 1962. Parasites in food. In J. C. Ayres, A. A. Kraft, H. Walker, and H. Synder (eds.), Chemical and biological hazards in foods. Iowa State Univ. Press, Ames.

Konowalchuk, J., and J. I. Speirs. 1974. Recovery of coxsackievirus B5 from stored lettuce. J. Milk Food Technol. 37:133–135.

Konowalchuk, J., and J. I. Speirs. 1975. Survival of enteric viruses on fresh vegetables. J. Milk Food Technol. 38:469–473.

Little, M. D., and J. MacPhail, 1972. Anisakid larvae from the throat of a woman in New York. Am. J. Trop. Med. Hyg. 22:609–612.

Marth, E. H. 1967. Aflatoxins and other mycotoxins in agricultural products. J. Milk Food Technol. 30:192–198.

Mason, J. O., and W. R. McLean. 1962. Infectious hepatitis traced to the consumption of raw oysters: an epidemiologic study. Am. J. Hyg. 75:90–111.

Mateles, R. I., and G. N. Wogan. 1967. Biochemistry of some foodborne microbial toxins. The M.I.T. Press, Cambridge, Mass.

Miyake, M., and M. Saito. 1965. Liver injury and liver tumors induced by toxins of *Penicillium islandicum* Sopp growing on yellowed rice. In G. N. Wogan (ed.), Mycotoxins in foodstuffs. The M.I.T. Press, Cambridge, Mass.

Myers, B. J. 1970. Nematodes transmitted to man by fish and aquatic animals. J. Wildlife Dis. 6:266–271.

Myers, B. J. 1975. The nematodes that cause anisakiasis. J. Milk Food Technol. 38:774–782.

National Academy of Sciences. 1973. Toxicants occurring naturally in foods. Committee on Food Protection, Washington.

Potter, N. N. 1973. Viruses in foods. J. Milk Food Technol. 36:307–310.

Rechcigel, M. J. 1983. Handbook of foodborne disease of biological origin. CRC Press, Boca Raton, Fla.

Scott, de B. 1965. Toxigenic fungi isolated from cereal and legume products. Mycopath. Mycol. Appl. 25:213–221.

Scott, W. T., and L. B. Bullerman. 1975. Patulin: a mycotoxin of potential concern in foods. J. Milk Food Technol. 38:695–705.

Speck, M. L. (ed.). 1984. Compendium of methods for the microbiological examination of foods, 2d ed. American Public Health Association, Washington, D.C.

Spencer, F. M., and L. S. Monroe. 1975. The color atlas of intestinal parasites. Charles C. Thomas, Publisher, Springfield, Ill.

Still, P. E., A. W. Macklin, W. E. Ribelin, and E. B. Smalley. 1971. Relationship of ochratoxin A to fetal death in laboratory and domestic animals. Nature. 234:563–569.

Strock, N. R., and N. N. Potter. 1972. Survival of poliovirus and ECHO virus during simulated commercial egg pasteurization treatments. J. Milk Food Technol. 35:247–252.

Sullivan, R., R. M. Marnell, E. P. Larkin, and R. B. Read, Jr. 1975. Inactivation of poliovirus 1 and coxsackievirus B-2 in broiled hamburgers. J. Milk Food Technol. 38:473–476.

Trenk, H. W., M. E. Butz, and F. S. Chu. 1971. Production of ochratoxins in different cereal products by *Aspergillus ochraceus*. Appl. Microbiol. 21:1032–1036.

United States Department of Health and Human Services, Food and Drug Administration. 1984. Proceedings of the Second National Conference for Food Protection. Washington, D.C.

Van Walbeek, W. 1973. Fungal toxins in foods. Can. Inst. Food Sci. Technol. J. 6(2): 96–104.

Withers, N. 1982. Ciguatera fish poisoning. Am. Rev. Med. 33:97–111.

Wogan, G. N. (ed.). 1965. Mycotoxins in foodstuffs. The M.I.T. Press, Cambridge, Mass.

INVESTIGATION OF FOOD-BORNE DISEASE OUTBREAKS

A manual entitled Procedures to Investigate Foodborne Illness has been written by the Committee on Communicable Diseases Affecting Man in the International Association of Milk, Food, and Environmental Sanitarians and has been published and recommended by that association (1976). Much of the discussion to follow is based on the contents of this manual, to which the reader is referred for a more complete discussion of the subject, for typical report forms to be employed, and for details that must be omitted from a textbook discussion.

Several publications available from the U.S. Department of Health, Education, and Welfare, Public Health Service, and the Center for Disease Control (CDC) are also excellent sources of additional information. Morbidity and Mortality Weekly Report is a weekly summary of diseases (including food-borne disease outbreaks) occurring in the United States. Specific data on numbers of cases and outbreaks in a given year can be found in the CDC Foodborne Outbreaks Annual Summary. A very complete listing of diseases transmitted by foods, including the etiologic agents, the nature of the organisms, incubation periods, signs and symptoms, source or reservoir, epidemiology, foods involved, and control measures can be found in Center for Disease Control (1976a).

FOOD-BORNE DISEASES

Food-borne diseases include those resulting from consumption of any solid food or of milk, water, or other beverage. The more important diseases and their causes have been mentioned in Chapter 25: staphylococcus intoxication, caused by *Staphylococcus aureus;* botulism, by *Clostridium botulinum; C. perfringens* gastroenteritis, salmonellosis, including typhoid and paratyphoid fevers, by *Salmonella* serovars; bacillary dysenteries, by *Shigella* species; and diseases from *Bacillus cereus, Yersinia enterocolitica, Campylobacter jejuni, E. coli, Vibrio parahaemolyticus, Listeria monocytogenes,* and others. These microorganisms or evidences of their presence and growth are sought by the investigators of outbreaks of food-borne diseases. Other food-borne infections are brucellosis, diphtheria, scarlet fever, septic sore throat, tuberculosis, infectious hepatitis, and tularemia. Various nonbacterial parasitic infections, and poisoning by chemicals, plants, and animals and by ionizing radiations may be encountered.

OBJECTIVES OF INVESTIGATION

From the public health viewpoint the main purposes of the investigation of an outbreak of food-borne disease are to determine how the foodstuff became contaminated and if growth of a toxigenic or infectious organism was involved, to find how such growth could take place so that measures can be taken to prevent a repetition of the same set of conditions. This requires the location and identification of the causative agent, establishment of the means of transmission, demonstration of the opportunity for growth of the pathogen, and, in instances of infections, proof that the pathogen has infected the victims. Prompt investigation also may help limit the spread of the outbreak and sometimes be of assistance to physicians treating the victims. Publicity given an outbreak and the explanation of its cause may be helpful in educating and warning the public and therefore in avoiding future outbreaks.

PERSONNEL INVOLVED IN INVESTIGATION

The organization of the team to investigate an outbreak of food-borne disease varies with the public health department concerned, but this team will consist ordinarily of a person in charge, a field group, and a laboratory group. The field group interviews persons, both ill and healthy, who consumed the suspected foods, physicians and nurses who are treating the victims, and personnel at the place of exposure to the disease; collects samples of suspected foods and transmits them to the laboratory; collects specimens from patients or food handlers when such sampling is indicated; inspects the premises where the foods were stored, prepared, and served; ascertains where suspected foods were purchased and the conditions there; and fills out appropriate reports on these activities, to be made available to the person in charge and to the laboratory staff. The laboratory group makes such microbiological and chemical tests as are indicated by the reports of the field group and the nature of the suspected food and records its findings on appropriate report blanks. The person in charge or a qualified epidemiologist then can interpret the data from all sources to determine the cause and the source of the disease outbreak. The manual cited at the beginning of this chapter states that, at times, cooperation may be needed between the epidemiologist, the health officer, physicians, nurses, veterinarians, sanitarians, sanitary engineers, laboratory technicians, and statisticians in an investigation.

MATERIALS AND EQUIPMENT REQUIRED

The equipment and supplies needed to equip a field kit to take food samples and transmit them to the laboratory include sterile containers and sampling devices for sampling, a thermometer, an alcohol lamp, sterile swabs in diluent, sterile wrapping paper, tape for sealing samples, sterile paper towels, ice, an insulated chest for conveying samples, and forms for recording data. The laboratory should be prepared, of course, to conduct the necessary microbiological and chemical tests and record results. Prepared materials would include sterile glassware, water blanks, appropriate culture media, test solutions, serological materials and equipment, and hypodermic syringes and needles, as well as experimental animals. If possible, the laboratory staff should be warned far enough ahead to be ready for the samples and specimens on their arrival. Specific examples of food sampling techniques can be found in Speck (1984).

THE FIELD INVESTIGATION

Prompt reporting of an outbreak to the health department is most important if the investigation is to be successful, yet the information often is delayed. Reports usually come from physicians, hospitals, news agencies, or even rumors. Promptness in initiating the investigation also is important because samples or specimens may be available for only a short time, information obtained promptly is usually more reliable than delayed reports, and additional cases in the outbreak may be prevented.

Gathering Information

A complete inspection is made immediately of the place or places where the suspected meal, meals, or beverages were prepared and consumed, and the results are recorded on appropriate forms. Information sought includes the menu for the meal or meals, the source and method of preparation of each item of food on the menu, methods of storage of perishable foods, sources of purchase of foods served, and health of employees serving or preparing foods and their health history. Observations are made on infections on exposed surfaces of the bodies of employees and on the sanitary condition of the establishment.

Theoretically, all persons present at the time the questionable meal was eaten, including those who prepared, served, or ate the meal, and physicians treating victims should be interviewed. Actually, it usually is not practicable to interview all victims of a large outbreak. Geidt (1957) has suggested that in outbreaks where no more than 20 persons are involved, an attempt should be made to question all of them; if about 50 persons were involved, about half of them should be questioned, including proportionate numbers of those who became ill and those who did not; and about 25 percent of a total of 100 or more persons should be interviewed. The information obtained may be recorded on a form such as that entitled "Case History Questionnaire" in the previously mentioned manual, where there is a place to record age and sex, whether the individual partook of the suspected meal and if so the exact time, whether he or she became ill and if so the incubation time and symptoms, and which of the list of the foods and beverages served were consumed. The case histories are then summarized on a second form, and by means of these data the suspected food is located.

Collection of Food Samples

Samples of all leftover foods and beverages served at the suspected meal or meals should be taken aseptically, and samples of perishable foods should be refrigerated immediately and kept cold in transit to the laboratory. Samples of food should be taken aseptically by means of sterilized sampling devices into sterile containers. Entire packages of foods in small, unopened containers may be taken when available. It is essential to label each sample to give information as to the type of food, the place and time of sampling, the reason for its collection, the organism or chemical suspected, and any other pertinent information. Each sample must be sealed, both inner and outer container, with the date and time of sealing and the name of the person who collected and sealed the sample written on the tape. All the information available at the time of sampling (see preceding section) should accompany the samples, and the reasons for suspecting one or more of the foods should be given.

Unfortunately, the food samples sought often are no longer available, such as food scraps from plates on which the food was served or samples from serving containers. Then the collector of samples must settle for what he or she can get—rinsings, garbage, or food handled in the same manner as the suspected food. If a canned food is involved, part of the used can of food is first choice, but only a sample from the same lot may be available. Brand and lot number should be obtained from the can of the commercially canned food, and the method of canning and heating of the home-canned food should be ascertained. Food samples should be taken, labeled, and sealed in the presence of witnesses if legal action is likely.

Collection of Specimens from Human Sources

Specimens may be obtained from patients with food illnesses or from food handlers, sometimes for the purpose of finding the causative organism of the outbreak but more often to ascertain the ultimate source of the pathogen that entered the food. The type of specimen to be taken will depend, of course, on the illness concerned. Cultures from the nose or throat or from skin lesions of food handlers are made to test for staphylococci able to produce enterotoxin. Fecal samples are used to test for organisms, e.g., *Salmonella* and *Shigella* spp., capable of causing enteric infections; the tests might be to find carriers among food handlers or to identify the cause of illness in patients. Blood specimens from patients may be used for serological tests for the identification and typing of certain pathogens, e.g., *Salmonella* spp. Vomitus may be tested when chemical poisoning is suspected. A complete listing of suggested specimens to be analyzed as indicated by predominant symptoms and incubation periods can be found in Table 26-1.

LABORATORY TESTING

The procedure to be followed in testing the samples of food or specimens from human sources upon receipt in the laboratory will depend on the type of food and the information available about the outbreak of food illness. A suggested guide for testing foods incriminated as a vechicle in food-borne illness is outlined in Table 26-2. The more complete that information is, the better the laboratory can select the type of examination to be used. Especially helpful will be reliable information on the symptoms of those made ill and the incubation period (see Chapter 24 and 25).

The first act in most laboratories is to make a microscopic examination of a preparation of the food stained by the Gram method. The smear is made from liquid or from the sediment from homogenized, centrifuged food. The microscopic examination may give a clue to the causative organism and may indicate the numbers in the original food if the sample has been properly refrigerated. The methods of testing for the various causes of important food-borne illnesses is beyond the scope of this text. Recommended procedures can be found in Speck (1984) and in the FDA's Bacterological Analytical Manual.

INTERPRETATION AND APPLICATION OF RESULTS

The results of the field and laboratory investigations, if complete, can lead to incrimination of the guilty food and location and elimination of the ultimate source of the cause of the food-borne disease outbreak. For reasons previously indicated, data often are incomplete, and circumstantial evidence may have to be substituted for actual proof.

When an outbreak is small, as within a family, the location of the food responsible for the illness may be fairly simple. Table 26-3 summarizes a simplified report on such an outbreak. Chocolate éclairs obviously are the food to be suspected, and because of the nature of the food and the short incubation $(2\frac{1}{2}$ to 4 hr), staphylococcus intoxication is probable. The source of the staphylo-

TABLE 26-1
GUIDE FOR LABORATORY TESTS INDICATED BY CERTAIN SYMPTOMS AND INCUBATION PERIODS

Incubation periods	Predominant symptoms	Specimens to analyze	Organism, toxin, or toxic substances
Upper gastrointestinal tract symptoms (nausea, vomiting) occur first or predominate			
Less than 1 hr	Nausea, vomiting, unusual taste, burning of mouth	Vomitus, urine, blood, stool	Metallic chemicals*
1–2 hr	Nausea, vomiting, cyanosis, headache, dizziness, dyspnea, trembling, weakness, loss of consciousness	Blood	Nitrites†
1–6 hr, mean 2–4 hr	Nausea, vomiting, retching, diarrhea, abdominal pain, prostration	Vomitus, stool	Staphylococcus aureus and its enterotoxins
8–16 hr (2–4 hr rarely)	Vomiting, abdominal cramps, diarrhea, nausea	Vomitus, stool	Bacillus cereus
6–24 hr	Nausea, vomiting, diarrhea, thirst, dilation of pupils, collapse, coma	Urine, blood	Amanita mushrooms‡
Sore throat and respiratory symptoms			
12–72 hr	Sore throat, fever, nausea, vomiting, rhinorrhea, sometimes a rash	Throat swab	Streptococcus pyogenes
2–5 days	Inflamed throat and nose, spreading grayish exudate, fever, chills, sore throat, malaise, difficulty in swallowing, edema of cervical lymph node	Throat swabs, blood	Corynebacterium diphtheriae
Lower gastrointestinal tract symptoms (abdominal cramps, diarrhea) occur first or predominate			
8–22 hr, mean 10–12 hr	Abdominal cramps, diarrhea, putrefactive diarrhea associated with C. perfringens	Stool	Clostridium perfringens, Bacillus cereus, Streptococcus faecalis, S. faecium

Incubation period	Symptoms	Specimen	Agent
12–74 hr, mean 18–36 hr	Abdominal cramps, diarrhea, vomiting, fever, chills, malaise	Stool	*Salmonella* (including *S. arizonae*), *Shigella*, enteropathogenic *Escherichia coli*, other Enterobacteriaceae, *Yersinia enterocolitica*, *Pseudomonas aeruginosa*(?), *Aeromonas hydrophila*, *Plesiomonas shigelloides*, *Campylobacter jejuni*, *Vibrio cholerae* (01 and non-01), *V. parahaemolyticus*
3–5 days	Diarrhea, fever, vomiting, abdominal pain, respiratory symptoms	Stool	Enteric viruses
1–6 weeks	Mucoid diarrhea (fatty stools), abdominal pain, weight loss	Stool	*Giardia lamblia*
1–several weeks, mean 3 to 4 weeks	Abdominal pain, diarrhea, constipation, headache, drowsiness, ulcers, variable—often asymptomatic	Stool	*Entamoeba histolytica*
3–6 months	Nervousness, insomnia, hunger pains, anorexia, weight loss, abdominal pain, sometimes gastroenteritis	Stool	*Taenia saginata, T. solium*
Neurological symptoms (visual disturbances, vertigo, tingling, paralysis)			
Less than 1 hr	Tingling and numbness, giddiness, staggering, drowsiness, tightness of throat, incoherent speech, respiratory paralysis	Blood, urine, fat biopsy	Shellfish toxin
	Gastroenteritis, nervousness, blurred vision, chest pain, cyanosis, twitching, convulsions	Urine	Organic phosphate insecticides
	Excessive salivation, perspiration, gastroenteritis, irregular pulse, pupils constricted, asthmatic breathing		Muscaria-type mushrooms
	Tingling and numbness, dizziness, pallor, gastroenteritis, hemorrhage, desquamation of skin, eyes fixed, loss of reflexes, twitching, paralysis		Tetraodon toxin (puffer fish poisoning)

*Consider chemical tests for such substances as zinc, copper, lead, cadmium, arsenic, antimony
†Test for discoloration of blood.
‡Identify mushroom species eaten; test urine and blood for evidence of renal damage (SGOT, SGPT enzyme tests).

TABLE 26-1 (Continued)
GUIDE FOR LABORATORY TESTS INDICATED BY CERTAIN SYMPTOMS AND INCUBATION PERIODS

Incubation periods	Predominant symptoms	Specimens to analyze	Organism, toxin, or toxic substances
1–6 hr	Tingling and numbness, gastroenteritis, dizziness, dry mouth, muscular aches, dilated eyes, blurred vision, paralysis		Ciguatera toxin
	Nausea, vomiting, tingling, dizziness, weakness, anorexia, weight loss, confusion	Blood, urine, stool, gastric washings	Chlorinated hydrocarbons (insecticides)
12–72 hr	Vertigo; double or blurred vision; loss of reflex to light; difficulty in swallowing, speaking, and breathing; dry mouth; weakness; respiratory paralysis	Blood, stool	*Clostridium botulinum* and its neurotoxins
More than 72 hr	Numbness, weakness of legs, spastic paralysis, impairment of vision, blindness, coma	Urine, blood, stool, hair	Organic mercury
	Gastroenteritis, leg pain, ungainly high-stepping gait, foot and wrist drop		Triorthocresyl phosphate
Allergic symptoms (facial flushing, itching)			
Less than 1 hr	Headache, dizziness, nausea, vomiting, peppery taste, burning of throat, facial swelling and flushing, stomach pain, itching of skin	Vomitus	Histamine§
	Numbness around mouth, tingling sensation, flushing, dizziness, headache, nausea		Monosodium glutamate (Chinese restaurant syndrome)
	Flushing, sensation of warmth, itching, abdominal pain, blood, puffing of face and knees		Nicotinic acid
Generalized infection symptoms (fever, chills, malaise, prostration, aches, swollen lymph nodes)			
4–28 days, mean 9 days	Gastroenteritis, fever, edema about eyes, perspiration, muscular pain, chills, prostration, labored breathing	Muscle biopsy	*Trichinella spiralis*

Incubation period	Symptoms	Specimens	Causative agent
7–28 days, mean 14 days	Malaise, headache, fever, cough, nausea, vomiting, constipation, abdominal pain, chills, rose spots, bloody stools	Stool, blood	*Salmonella typhi*
10–13 days	Fever, headache, myalgia, rash	Lymph node biopsy, blood	*Toxoplasma gondii*
10–50 days, mean 25–30 days	Fever, malaise, lassitude, anorexia, nausea, abdominal pain, jaundice	Urine, blood	Etiological agent not yet isolated, probably viral
Varying periods (depends on specific illness)	Fever, chills, head- or joint ache, prostration, malaise, swollen lymph nodes, and other specific symptoms of disease in question	Blood, stool, urine, sputum, lymph node, gastric washings (one of more, depending on organism)	*Bacillus anthracis, Brucella melitensis, B. abortus, B. suis, Coxiella burnetii, Francisella tularensis, Listeria monocytogenes, Mycobacterium tuberculosis, Mycobacterium* spp., *Pasteurella multocida, Streptobacillus moniliformis, Campylobacter jejuni*

§Scrombroid poisoning should be considered. Examine foods for *Proteus* species or other organisms capable of decarboxylating histidine into histamine and for histamine.
Source: Speck (1984).

TABLE 26-2
GUIDE FOR TEST OF FOODS ALLEGED, SUSPECTED, OR EPIDEMIOLOGICALLY
INCRIMINATED AS VEHICLES OF FOOD-BORNE ILLNESS

Food	Organism, toxin, or toxic substance
Soft drinks, fruit juices, and concentrates (in metallic containers or vending machines)	Tests for chemicals such as copper, zinc, cadmium, lead, antimony, tin
Canned foods	*Clostridium botulinum* and its neurotoxins
Cereals, rice, foods containing cornstarch	*Bacillus cereus,* mycotoxins
Cream-filled baked goods	*Staphylococcus aureus* and its enterotoxins, *Salmonella* spp.
Confectionery products	*Salmonella* spp.
Egg and egg products	*Salmonella* spp.
Molluscan shellfish	*Vibrio parahaemolyticus,* shellfish toxin (Saxotoxin), *V. cholerae,* hepatitis A virus (epidemiological implication only)
Raw fruits and vegetables	Parasites, *Shigella* spp.
Mixed vegetable, meat, poultry, fish salads	*Staphylococcus aureus* and its enterotoxins, *Salmonella* spp., beta-hemolytic streptococci. *Shigella* spp., enteropathogenic *Escherichia coli*
Meat and poultry, and mixed foods containing meat and poultry	*Salmonella* spp., *Clostridium perfringens, Staphylococcus aureus* and its enterotoxins, *Taenia* spp.
Ham	*Staphylococcus aureus* and its enterotoxins, *Trichinella spiralis*
Fermented meats	*Staphylococcus aureus* and its enterotoxins
Fish	*Vibrio parahaemolyticus,* histamine (*Proteus* spp.), fish poisons, *V. cholerae* (01 and non-01), *V. vulnificus,* anisakine nematodes, *Aeromonas hydrophilia, Plesiomonas shigelloides, Diphyllobothrium* spp. tapeworms
Crustaceans	*Vibrio parahaemolyticus,* fish poisons, *V. cholerae* (01 and non-01) *V. vulnificus, Aeromonas hydrophilia, Plesiomonas shigelloides*
Cheese	*Staphylococcus aureus* and its enterotoxins, *Brucella* spp., enteropathogenic *Escherichia coli*
Dry milk	*Salmonella* spp., *Staphylococcus aureus* and its enterotoxins
Raw milk	*Campylobacter jejuni, Brucella* spp., *Salmonella* spp., *Coxiella brunetii*

Source: Speck (1984)

cocci would be sought among the food handlers at the bakery from which the éclairs came.

When the number of persons involved in an outbreak is fairly large, it is difficult to obtain complete and accurate data. Not all the persons may be available for interviewing, not all persons are equally susceptible to food illnesses, and people are forgetful about just what they ate. An aid to finding the offending food is a comparison of the percentage of persons who ate each food without becoming ill with the percentage of those who became ill. A complete tabulation includes data on the group of persons who ate each of the foods served,

TABLE 26-3

SUMMARY OF DATA ON A FOOD-BORNE DISEASE OUTBREAK WITHIN A FAMILY

Name	Age, years	Time of first symptoms, hr*	Ham-burger	Gravy	Pota-toes	Fruit salad	Chocolate éclairs	Fresh peas	Milk	Coffee	Canned cherries
			Foods consumed								
Jones, John	35	3	✔	✔	✔	✔	✔	✔		✔	✔
Jones, Mary	33	$2\frac{1}{2}$	✔	✔	✔	✔	✔	✔		✔	✔
Jones, Wm.	4			✔	✔			✔	✔		
Jones, Ruth	8	4	✔	✔	✔	✔	✔	✔	✔		✔
Jones, Mabel	63		✔	✔	✔	✔		✔		✔	✔

*Nausea, vomiting, abdominal cramping, diarrhea.

on the group of persons who did not eat each of the foods, and for each food the percentage of persons consuming this food who became ill. The highest percentage of ill persons should be in the group which ate the offending food, a markedly higher percentage of ill persons than for any of the other foods consumed. The lowest percentage of ill persons should be in the group that did not eat the offending food. Statistical analyses are useful in determining the food responsible for a large outbreak. Final conclusions in regard to the food involved are drawn only after the laboratory results also are considered.

As has been mentioned, the likelihood that an outbreak will come to the attention of local, state, or federal agencies varies considerably and depends to a great extent on the cooperation of the attending physician (if one is consulted) and the general awareness of the public. Usually local health department officials are responsible for most of the epidemiological investigations and the completion of initial reports. This information is forwarded to state health departments and reported on standardized CDC reporting forms and sent to the CDC. In some instances, e.g., a botulism outbreak, the CDC will work closely with the initial investigation or be asked to conduct it. Consideration of data for confirmation of outbreaks is based on clinical, laboratory and epidemiological criteria, as presented in Table 26-4. Only outbreaks in which sufficient data are available to satisfy these criteria are reported as a confirmed outbreak.

As has been indicated, one of the main purposes of the investigation is to locate the source of the agent causing the food illness so that this source can be eliminated and future outbreaks prevented. The location of the source also usually requires an analysis of both field and laboratory data.

The completely successful investigation of an outbreak of food-borne disease finds the food responsible for the transmission of the disease, identifies the causative agent, finds the source of contamination of the food with the agent, and eliminates that source.

PREVENTIVE MEASURES

Means of prevention of food-borne outbreaks of some of the more important intoxications and infections have been discussed in Chapters 24 and 25. The general principles are:

1 To keep foods as free as possible from contamination with pathogenic agents by selection of uncontaminated foods, by adequate pasteurization or other heat processing, by keeping away pathogen-bearing vermin, by avoiding contamination from infected food handlers or carriers, and by generally good sanitary practice throughout the handling, preparation, and serving of foods.

2 To eliminate opportunities for the growth of pathogens, toxigenic or infectious, in foods by adjustment of the composition, by prompt consumption after preparation, and by adequate refrigeration of perishable foods if they must be held for any considerable time. Keeping foods warm for long periods is especially to be avoided.

TABLE 26-4
CRITERIA TO BE SATISFIED BEFORE LISTING AN OUTBREAK AS CONFIRMED

Etiological agent	Clinical syndrome	Laboratory and/or epidemiological criteria
Bacillus cereus	Incubation period 2–16 hr Gastrointestinal syndrome	Isolation of $\cdot10^5$ organisms per gram in epidemiologically incriminated food or Isolation of organism from stools of ill person
Clostridium botulinum	Incubation 2 hr –8 days (usually 12 –48 hr) Clinical syndrome compatible with botulism (see CDC Botulism Manual)	Detection of botulinal toxin in human sera, feces, or food or Isolation of *C. botulinum* organism from epidemiologically incriminated food or stools or Food epidemiologically incriminated
Clostridium perfringens	Incubation period 9–15 hr Lower-intestinal syndrome: majority of cases with diarrhea but little vomiting or fever	Organisms of same serotype in epidemiologically incriminated food and stool of ill individuals or Isolation of organisms with same serotype in stool of most ill individuals and not in stool or controls or $\cdot10^5$ organisms per gram in epidemiologically incriminated food provided specimen properly handled
Escherichia coli	Incubation period 6–36 hr Gastrointestinal syndrome: majority of cases with diarrhea	Demonstration of organisms of same serotype in epidemiologically incriminated food and stool of ill individuals and not in stool of controls or Isolation of $\cdot10^5$ per gram organisms or same serotype in implicated food or Isolation of organism of same serotype from stool of most ill individuals, and if possible, organisms should be tested for enterotoxigenicity and invasiveness by special laboratory techniques

TABLE 26-4
CRITERIA TO BE SATISFIED BEFORE LISTING AN OUTBREAK AS CONFIRMED (*Continued*)

Etiological agent	Clinical syndrome	Laboratory and/or epidemiological criteria
Salmonella	Incubation period 6–48 hr Gastrointestinal syndrome: majority of cases with diarrhea	Isolation of *Salmonella* from epidemiologically implicated food or Isolation of *Salmonella* from stools of ill individuals
Shigella	Incubation period 12–50 hr Gastrointestinal syndrome: majority of cases with diarrhea	Isolation of *Shigella* from epidemiologically implicated food or Isolation of *Shigella* from stools of ill individuals
Staphylococcus aureus	Incubation period 30 min–8 hr (usually 2–4 hr) Gastrointestinal syndrome: majority of cases with vomiting	Detection of enterotoxin in epidemiologically implicated food or Organisms with same phage type in stools or vomitus of ill individuals and, when possible, implicated food and/or skin or nose of food handler or Isolation of ·10⁵ organisms per gram in epidemiologically implicated food
Vibrio parahaemolyticus	Incubation period 15–24 hr Gastrointestinal syndrome: majority of cases with diarrhea	Isolation of ·10⁵ organisms from epidemiologically implicated food (usually seafood) or Isolation of Kanagawa-positive organisms of same serotype from stool of ill individuals

Source: Condensed from Center For Disease Control (1976b).

3 To reject suspected foods.

4 To educate the public better concerning the causes and prevention of food-borne illnesses and the dangers involved.

BIBLIOGRAPHY

Center for Disease Control. 1976*a*. Diseases transmitted by foods: a classification and summary. U.S. Dept. of Health, Education, and Welfare Publ. (CDC) 76-8237. Atlanta.

Center for Disease Control. 1976*b*. Foodborne and waterborne disease outbreaks annual summary 1975. U.S. Dept. of Health, Education, and Welfare Publ. (CDC) 76-8185, Atlanta.

Geidt, W. R. 1957. The field application of the "suggested procedures for the investigation of foodborne disease outbreaks." J. Milk Food Technol. 10:39–43.

International Association of Milk, Food, and Environmental Sanitarians, Inc. 1976. Procedures to investigate foodborne illness, Ames, Iowa.

Reimann, H. (ed.). 1969. Foodborne infections and intoxications. Academic Press, Inc., New York.

Speck, M. L. (ed.). 1984. Compendium of methods for the microbiological examination of foods, 2d ed. American Public Health Association, Washington, D.C.

PART SIX

FOOD SANITATION, CONTROL, AND INSPECTION

Food sanitation, control, and inspection have been considered primarily from the microbiological standpoint.

MICROBIOLOGY IN FOOD SANITATION

The food-industry sanitarian is concerned with aseptic practices in the preparation, processing, and packaging of the food products of a plant (or plants), the general cleanliness and sanitation of plant and premises, and the health of employees. Specific duties in connection with the food products may involve quality control and storage of raw products; the provision of a good water supply; prevention of the contamination of the foods at all stages during processing from equipment, personnel, and vermin; and supervision of packaging and warehousing of finished products. The supervision of cleanliness and sanitation of plant and premises includes not only the maintenance of clean and well-sanitized surfaces of all equipment touching the foods but also generally good housekeeping in and about the plant and adequate treatment and disposal of wastes. Duties affecting the health of the employees include provision of a potable water supply, supervision of matters of personal hygiene, regulation of sanitary facilities in the plant and in plant-operated housing units, and contact with sanitary aspects of plant lighting, heating, and ventilation. The sanitarian may also participate in training employees in sanitary practices. Only bacteriological aspects of plant sanitation will be discussed here. For other facets of the problem the reader is referred to the references at the end of this chapter.

For the most part, sanitarians concern themselves chiefly with general aspects of sanitation, making inspections, consulting with personnel responsible for details of sanitation and executives directing such work, and training personnel in sanitation. They may or may not be connected with a plant laboratory.

BACTERIOLOGY OF WATER SUPPLIES

The water for drinking purposes and for plant use may be from the same source or from different sources.

Drinking Water

The water that the employees drink must meet public health standards when tested by methods recommended in the latest edition of Standard Methods for the Examination of Water and Wastewater (American Public Health Association, 1985). Coliform bacteria must not be present at levels indicating contamination of the water by sewage. Total plate counts of the water sometimes are made to indicate when trouble may be incipient so that such trouble can be forestalled.

Plant Water

All water that comes into contact with foods should meet the bacteriological standards for drinking water, and preferably all fresh water at the plant should be that good. But this water also should be satisfactory from a bacteriological standpoint for use with the particular food being processed. A water supply may be adjudged potable yet be unsatisfactory for use with a food. Thus, for example, water containing appreciable numbers of psychrotrophs of the genera *Pseudomonas* or *Alcaligenes* might be unsatisfactory without treatment in a dairy plant making butter or cottage cheese. The slimy growth of iron bacteria in water supplies often leads to trouble in the food plant.

More likely to be important is the chemical composition of the water, which must be suited to the use to be made of it. Thus hard water is undesirable in pea canning and in brewing; iron and manganese are bad in beet canning and in brewing; excessive organic matter may lead to off-flavors, etc.

Of special interest in canning factories is the bacteriology of the water in which the cans of processed foods are cooled after their heat treatment. If this water contains microorganisms able to spoil the food, it can enter defective cans through minute leaks and increase the percentage of cans of food spoiling during storage. Many canneries routinely chlorinate the cooling water to reduce or eliminate this problem.

The shortage of water in many food plants has necessitated reuse of part of the water, and microorganisms may build up in such reused water. Water employed for the final rinse of a food must be fresh and potable, but after use it may be returned for soaking, first wash, or fluming, preferably after treatment with chlorine, chlorine dioxide, or a similar germicide.

In-plant or continuous chlorination beyond the break point (the point where the chlorine demand has been satisfied) to a residual of 5 to 7 ppm of chlorine is employed for continuous application to areas and equipment where slime bacteria may be a problem, e.g., conveyors or belts, can coolers, product washers, and flumes. The chlorinated water may be applied as a spray, or parts of equipment may be immersed. When operations cease, chlorinated water may be applied to fillers, peelers, dicers, and similar equipment. Contaminated or polluted water lines are held filled with chlorinated water containing 50 to 100 ppm of chlorine for 12 to 48 hr, the strength of chlorine and length of time depending on the extent of pollution (Table 27-1).

Ice used in contact with foods should meet the bacteriological requirements for potable water. Much work has been done on the incorporation of bacteriostatic or bactericidal chemicals in water and in ice to aid in food preservation. It has been noted previously that a chlortetracycline or oxytetracycline dip for dressed poultry had been approved, but approval was later revoked; however, these antibiotics may be incorporated in ice to be applied to fish and other seafood.

SEWAGE AND WASTE TREATMENT AND DISPOSAL

The food sanitarian is concerned directly or indirectly with the adequate treatment and disposal of wastes from the industry. Solid and concentrated wastes ordinarily are kept separate from the watery wastes and may be used directly for food, feed, fertilizer, or other purpose; may first be concentrated, dried, or fermented (e.g., pea-vine silage); or may be carted away to available land as unusable waste. Care is taken to keep out of the waste waters as much wasted liquid or solid food material as possible by taking precautions to avoid introduction into the watery wastes of drip, leakage, overflow, spillage, large residues in containers, foam, frozen-on food, and food dust during the handling and processing of the food. It is recommended that sewage of human origin be kept separate from other plant waters because of the possible presence of human intestinal pathogens and the necessity for a guarantee of their removal or

TABLE 27-1
SUGGESTED CONCENTRATIONS
OF CHLORINE FOR VARIOUS PURPOSES
IN FOOD PROCESSING PLANTS

	ppm*
Drinking water	0.2
Process water	0–0.5
Cleaning	10–20
Sanitizing	100–250
Rinse water	1.0–5.0
Cooling (can)	0.5–10.0
Conveying water	0.5–5.0
Belt sprays	1.5–3.0
Hydrocooling meat	5.0–200
Fish thawing	5.0–10.0

* As total residual chlorine.
Source: Troller (1983).

destruction. Such sewage may be turned into a municipal system, if one is available, for adequate treatment and disposal or may be treated separately at the food plant. Other food-plant wastes should not contain human pathogens.

Wastes from food plants ordinarily contain a variety of organic compounds, which range from simple and readily oxidizable kinds to those which are complex and difficult to decompose. The strength of the sewage or food waste containing organic matter is expressed in terms of **biochemical oxygen demand (BOD)**, which is the quantity of oxygen used by aerobic microorganisms and reducing compounds in the stabilization of decomposable matter during a selected time at a certain temperature. A period of 5 days at 20 C is generally used, and results are expressed as 5-day BOD. The BOD is determined by dilution of a measured quantity of waste with water that has been saturated with oxygen and incubation of the mixture at 20 C, along with a control of dilution water alone. After 5 days, the residual oxygen in both control and test sample is measured by titration. The difference represents the oxygen-consuming capacity of the waste and is calculated to be expressed as parts per million of oxygen taken up by the waste. The strength of the waste in terms of pounds of BOD is calculated as follows:

$$\frac{\text{ppm 5-day BOD} \times \text{gallons of waste} \times 8.34}{1,000,000} = \text{pounds BOD}$$

This value can be converted to population equivalent (PE) by assuming that the domestic sewage of one person is equivalent to one-sixth of a pound of BOD per day.

Whenever appreciable amounts of wastes high in oxidizable organic matter (high BOD) are emptied into natural waters, such as streams, ponds, or lakes, the 7 to 8 ppm of free oxygen normally present in the waters is used up soon by oxidation processes carried out by aerobic or facultative microorganisms. When the oxygen drops below 3 ppm, the fish either leave or die, and when anaerobic conditions have been attained, hydrolysis, putrefaction, and fermentation by microorganisms will follow, with the result that the body of water will become malodorous and cloudy and hence unsuited for recreational use and unfit for drinking and for use in the food plant. Wastes from a food plant to be emptied into a body of water must either be so greatly diluted by that water as to be innocuous or must be treated first to reduce the oxidizable compounds to a harmless level. Even the effluent from an efficiently operated sewage treatment system will encourage the growth of algae and higher aquatic plants in the water and make it less attractive for recreational purposes.

Preliminary treatments of food-plant wastes by chemical means may be employed, but most systems of treatment and disposal depend on (1) screening out of large particles, (2) floating off of fatty and other floating materials, (3) sedimentation of as much of the remaining solids as practicable, (4) hydrolysis, fermentation, and putrefaction of complex organic compounds, and finally (5) oxidation of the remaining solids in the water to a point where they can enter a municipal sewage treatment and disposal system, a plant disposal system, a lake or stream, or soil. The completeness of oxidation required will depend on the disposal to be made. Thus less oxidation might be required for feeding to a municipal system or for irrigating soil than for entering a stream or lake.

Chemical Treatment

In chemical pretreatments, a chemical or mixture of chemicals is added to the sewage or waste so as to cause formation of a flocculent precipitate, which, in settling, carries with it much of the suspended and colloidal material, including bacteria. The effluent then is run into a body of water, onto soil, or into a biological treatment system. The chemicals commonly used are soluble aluminum or iron salts, such as alum or ferrous sulfate, plus lime, giving a flocculent precipitate of aluminum or ferric hydroxide. Disposal of the sludge (settlings) so obtained may be difficult.

Biological Treatment and Disposal

The general biological methods for waste disposal and/or treatment include (1) **dilution**, by running waste waters into a large body of water, (2) **irrigation**, in which waste waters are sprayed onto fields of open-textured soil, (3) **lagooning**, by running the waste waters into shallow artificial ponds (with or without other treatments), (4) use of **trickling filters**, made of crushed rock, coke, filter tile, etc., (5) use of the **activated-sludge** method, in which waste water is inoculated heavily with sludge from a previous run and is actively aerated in tanks, and (6) use of **anaerobic tanks** of various kinds, where settling, hydrolysis, putrefaction, and fermentation take place, usually to be followed by some aerobic treatment.

The dilution method seldom is practicable because a sufficiently large or rapidly moving volume of water rarely is available or because the location is such that sewage decomposition cannot proceed without objections from nearby populations. Irrigation is increasing in popularity and is especially adaptable to use by plants located in rural areas and near open-textured soil. Lagooning has been used especially for seasonal wastes, as from canning factories. The wastes are decomposed slowly in these shallow ponds or lagoons until the liquid part can be run into a stream or other body of water during the rainy season or time of melting snow, when there is a good volume of water. Usually, sodium nitrate is added to reduce obnoxious odors. Sometimes the liquid is pumped from and returned to a lagoon, or it may be pumped from one lagoon to another in a series of lagoons. Trickling filters and activated sludge systems are probably the most effective of the systems listed, but they are expensive to run and require supervision by an expert. Anaerobic tanks yield an effluent that needs further treatment and should be either turned into a municipal system or given an aerobic treatment.

Types of Food Wastes

An extended discussion of the nature and composition of wastes from the different food industries cannot be given here. It should be noted, however, that each type of waste has a characteristic BOD that may be high, low, or intermediate and that each presents its own problems of treatment and disposal. Dairy wastes, for example, are usually high in protein and lactose and contain many microorganisms. Such wastes, if not already acid, will turn acid if kept under anaerobic conditions and then will be more difficult to treat. Some wastes may be acid originally, e.g., wastes from fruit canneries. Malthouse, brewery, distillery, sweet-corn cannery, and corn-products plant wastes are high in carbohydrates and likely to become acid under anaerobic conditions. Wastes high in proteins, e.g., pea- or fish-cannery and packing-plant wastes, are likely to putrefy under anaerobic conditions. Other wastes may contain antiseptic chemicals, such as the sulfite in waste sulfite liquors from paper mills, and therefore may be difficult to decompose by means of microorganisms. Ranges of 5-day BOD values reported for wastes from various types of food-processing plants are shown in Table 27-2. Most industry-related wastes have been the subject of extensive research on waste utilization.

MICROBIOLOGY OF THE FOOD PRODUCT

To reduce contamination with microorganisms to a minimum and obtain good keeping quality of the product, the raw materials are examined; the equipment contacting the food is adequately cleaned, sanitized, and tested; the preserving process is checked; and packaging and storage are supervised.

The Ingredients

The raw product is inspected and tested for quality, but this does not necessarily involve bacteriological laboratory testing in all instances. Some of the ingredients of some products may contain numbers and kinds of microorgan-

TABLE 27-2
RANGE OF 5-DAY BOD VALUES FOR WASTES FROM VARIOUS
FOOD PROCESSING PLANTS

Source of waste	5-day BOD, ppm	Source of waste	5-day BOD, ppm
Dairy plants	500–2,000	String bean cannery	160–600
Meat-packing plants	Up to 2,500	Lima bean cannery	190–450
Poultry plants	300–7,500	Sweet-corn cannery	625–6,000
Sugar processing	500–1,500	Pea cannery	380–4,700
Fruit cannery	200–2,100	Pumpkin cannery	2,800–6,900
Tomato cannery	180–4,000	Spinach cannery	280–730
Brewery	420–1,200	Sauerkraut cannery	Up to 6,300

isms that can affect the keeping quality of the product or even its acceptability. Some ingredients, such as sweetening agents, starch, and spices, can be purchased on specification as to maximal allowable content of microorganisms or of numbers of certain kinds. The numbers of bacteria in ingredients are important in foods for which there are bacterial standards. Large numbers of spores of aerobes are undesirable in dry milk to be used in breadmaking because of the increased risk of ropiness developing; heat-resistant spores in sugar and starch may add to the difficulty in adequately heat-processing canned vegetables to which sugar or starch is added; and large numbers of bacteria in spices may favor the spoilage of summer sausage.

The microbiology of the main raw product often is important. Excessive mold mycelium in the raw fruit, which is indicative of the presence of rotten parts, may lead to condemnation of the canned or frozen product. Large numbers of thermoduric bacteria in raw milk may yield a pasteurized milk that will not meet the bacterial standards for numbers as estimated by the standard plate-count method. Large numbers of bacteria on vegetables or in fruits may indicate inferiority that will carry over into the frozen product. Laboratory examination may be employed to detect these undesirable organisms and estimate their numbers.

Often there is opportunity for microorganisms to grow in a food product during handling and processing in the plant. Examples are the buildup of thermophiles where foods are kept hot, as in forewarmers and blanchers, and increases in total numbers of bacteria in vegetables between blanching and freezing. Line samples may be tested in the laboratory to ascertain where appreciable growth of microorganisms is taking place.

Packaging Materials

Packaging materials are a possible source of contamination of foods with microorganisms, but ordinarily the penetrability of nonmetallic materials to moisture and to gases is of more significance in the preservation of foods than the microbiology of these materials, for they harbor mostly low numbers of innocuous microorganisms or no organisms. Also, as indicated previously, wrappers may be treated or impregnated with bacteriostatic or fungistatic compounds, e.g., cheese wraps with sorbic or caprylic acid.

Paper and paperboard used for milk cartons contain mostly bacilli and micrococci, and occasionally other rods, actinomycetes, and mold spores, but no organisms of public health significance. Wax paper is practically sterile as produced, as are most plastic packaging materials. All packaging materials should be protected from contamination with dust or other sources of microorganisms in handling.

According to federal regulations a food is deemed to be adulterated "if its container is composed, in whole or in part, of any poisonous or deleterious substance which render its contents injurious to health."

The Equipment

Unless the equipment that comes in contact with foods is adequately cleaned and sanitized, it may be an important source of contamination of foods with microorganisms. Not only may organisms persist on equipment, they may increase in numbers when treatment has been inadequate.

   Cleaning   From a bacteriological viewpoint, cleaning equipment is primarily to remove as much food for microorganisms as is practicable. Equipment may be disassembled for cleaning and sanitizing, although this is difficult with some pieces. To aid in the cleaning action of water, cleaning agents called **detergents** are employed. These agents may serve to soften or condition the water, improve the wetting ability of the cleaning solution, emulsify or saponify fats, solubilize minerals, deflocculate or disperse suspended materials, and dissolve as much soluble material as possible. At the same time the detergents should be noncorrosive and readily rinsed from the surfaces. Among the detergents used alone or in mixtures are the **alkaline** varieties, such as lye, soda ash, sodium metasilicate, trisodium phosphate, and the polyphosphates; **acid** detergents, usually organic acids, such as hydroxyacetic, gluconic, citric, tartaric, and levulinic acids; and **wetting agents**. These wetting agents may be anionic (NaR), such as the hydrocarbon sulfonates; nonionic, e.g., polyether alcohol; or cationic (RC1), for example, the quaternary ammonium compounds. Cleaning is often made easier by using brushes (Figure 27-1) and water under

FIGURE 27-1
General cleanup in a food processing plant. (*Klenzade Products, Beloit, Wisc.*)

pressure. High-pressure cleaning eliminates many problems associated with hand scrubbing. Commercially available systems for cleaning or sanitizing generate water sprays at 300 to 1,000 psi.

Sanitizing   The sanitizing process is an attempt to reduce the number of microorganisms on equipment surfaces. The kind of sanitizer, the concentration employed, the temperature of the sanitizer, and the method of application vary with the kind of sanitizing agent, the conditions during use, the type of equipment to be treated, and the microorganisms to be destroyed. Among the sanitizing agents in common use are hot water, flowing steam or steam under pressure, halogens (chlorine or iodine) and halogen derivatives, and the quaternary ammonium compounds.

Steam under pressure is the most effective way of applying heat as a sanitizing agent, but its use is limited to closed systems that can withstand pressure. Steam jets, flowing steam, or hot water may be used, but jets are ineffective except at very short distances, flowing steam may condense and drop in temperature as it passes through equipment, and hot water may undergo a similar drop in temperature. All microorganisms and their spores can be killed by adequate treatment with high-pressure steam. Effectively applied flowing steam and boiling water will kill all but some of the more resistant bacterial spores. The lower the temperature of hot water, the less effective it will be in killing organisms.

Chlorine, iodine, and their compounds (hypochlorites, chloramines, iodophors, etc.) are effective germicides if in proper concentrations and if given enough time to act. Usually, more sanitizer is necessary in the presence of organic matter. Bacterial spores are especially resistant to these sanitizers. Chlorine is used to destroy undesirable bacteria in water for drinking, for use in foods, for washing foods or equipment, and for cooling. Hypochlorites are more labile but more effective at acid pH values than at alkaline ones. As stated earlier, in-plant or continuous chlorination beyond the break point (where chlorine demand has been satisfied) to a residual of 5 to 7 ppm is employed for continuous application to areas where slime bacteria may be a problem, e.g., on conveyors, belts, or product washers. Chlorine (50 to 100 ppm) also is used to treat contaminated or polluted water lines.

Quaternary ammonium compounds are in general more effective against gram-positive than gram-negative bacteria. These compounds have a residual effect—i.e., they adhere to equipment surfaces and deter bacterial growth—but they rinse off onto foods coming into contact with these surfaces and, if they are present in detectable concentrations, might be considered undesirable. Many of these compounds are active under alkaline conditions. Most are affected by hardness of water.

Detergent sanitizers, which usually are a combination of an alkaline detergent and a quaternary ammonium compound, sometimes are used to clean and sanitize utensils or equipment in one operation.

Cleaned-in-Place Systems   Some industries, especially the dairy industry, leave pipelines permanently connected and clean and sanitize them in place. Apparatus is available for accomplishing this automatically. Different sequences of treatments are recommended for different cleaned-in-place (CIP) systems. Milk pipelines, for example, are rinsed first with tepid water, which is pushed or pulled through the system. Then hot (71 C) detergent solution may be passed through, followed by rinsing water and finally a sanitizing agent, such as hot water (77 C or over), chlorine solution (200 ppm), or a quaternary ammonium compound (200 ppm). Often a sanitizing treatment is given immediately before use.

References listed at the end of this chapter should be consulted for more detail on detergents and sanitizers and their selection and use.

The Preservation Process

The sanitarian usually has little to do with the processing of the foods except to check through the laboratory, if one is available, for the effectiveness of the processing. The laboratory, for example, might run keeping-quality tests on canned foods and bacterial counts on frozen foods, pasteurized milk, dry milks, etc.

Vending Machines for Foods and Beverages

With the rapid expansion of the use of vending machines to dispense perishable foods has come increased interest in the sanitation of these machines and dispensed foods. The United States Public Health Service Ordinance and Code (The Vending of Foods and Beverages) covers sanitation of foods and machines, operation of machines, and inspection. "Readily perishable foods" are defined as those consisting in whole or in part of milk, milk products, eggs, meat, fish, poultry, etc. These are foods which can support rapid growth of microorganisms and can cause food infections or intoxications. Adequately dried or canned foods are excepted. Perishable foods include sandwiches, pastries, hot coffee, tea or chocolate, malted milk, fluid milk, ice cream, frozen desserts, and hot-food plates (meat, stews, soup, baked beans, poultry, fish, etc.).

During transportation from the commissaries and in the machine, perishable foods should be kept either cold (3.3 to 4.4 C) or hot (66 C or above). Slow growth of psychrotrophs can take place at the lower temperatures and of thermophiles in the hot foods if these recommendations are barely met, and excessive heat will deteriorate many foods. All parts of vending machines in contact with readily perishable foods should be cleaned and sanitized periodically, daily if the above temperature limitations are not met. Water used in connection with the foods should be potable, and waste disposal should be adequate. Most machines dispensing perishable foods are equipped with safety devices to stop dispensing food when refrigeration or heating fails.

Food Handling on a Large Scale

Food handling on a large scale by caterers, commissaries, restaurants, institutions, airlines, camps, etc., are subject to similar considerations. General recommendations and a Food Service Sanitation Ordinance and Code are included in the Food Service Sanitation Manual published in 1962 by the Public Health Service of the U.S. Department of Health, Education, and Welfare. The ordinance defines "safe" temperatures for storage of foods as 7.2 C or below, or 60 C or above, except during necessary periods of preparation and service. It requires the washing of raw fruits and vegetables and the thorough cooking of stuffing, poultry, stuffed meats and poultry (heating to at least 74 C), and pork and pork products (all parts heated to at least 66 C) before being served. The ordinance has regulations concerning the health and cleanliness of personnel; the cleanliness, sanitization, and protection of food utensils; and the potability of water. It specifies foods that are clean, wholesome, unspoiled, free from adulteration and misbranding, safe for consumption, and capable of meeting any standards of quality or inspection. Also described is the handling of pastry fillings and of puddings.

Sandwiches

Sandwiches and other foods may be retailed without vending machines. Such foods may be a potential food-poisoning hazard, for they often are held at ambient temperatures for 18 to 24 hr before being sold. One survey (Adame et al., 1960) indicated that the wrapped sandwiches examined showed signs of contamination during preparation and of growth of bacteria before vending. All sandwiches showed high total numbers of bacteria per gram, no salmonellae or *Clostridium perfringens,* and considerable numbers of staphylococci (most of which, however, were coagulase-negative), with higher numbers in the moist sandwiches than in the dry, and appreciable numbers in those heated to 55.5 C and served hot. Similar results were obtained by McCroan et al. (1964), who concluded that spiced-ham sandwiches and cheese sandwiches were more hazardous than sandwiches containing mayonnaise, e.g., egg-salad and chicken-salad sandwiches, for contact with the acid dressing helped repress the staphylococci. A more recent survey by Christiansen and King (1971) stated that 60 percent of the sandwiches examined contained coagulase-positive staphylococci.

GOOD MANUFACTURING PRACTICES

Several recent regulations promulgated by the Department of Health, Education, and Welfare, Public Health Service, Food and Drug Administration (FDA), specify current good manufacturing practices (GMPs) in the manufacturing, processing, packing, or holding of human foods. These can be found in the Code of Federal Regulations, Title 21. Of particular interest are the "umbrella GMPs" since they cover many aspects of the food industry in a general way. The code does cover regulations that would be of interest to the food sanitarian including plant and grounds, equipment and utensils, sanitary facilities and control, sanitary operations, processes and controls, and personnel. In addition, there are specific GMPs written for fish and seafood products; cacao products and confectionery; bottled water; bakery foods; tree nuts and peanuts; pickled, fermented, acidified, and low-acid foods (proposed); and thermally processed low-acid foods packaged in hermetically sealed containers.

HAZARD ANALYSIS: CRITICAL CONTROL POINTS (HACCP)

Product processing lines in industry usually are distinct entities producing one item under constant control. In this type of operation, a careful analysis of microbiological hazards can be made and an in-house, effective monitoring system for quality assurance applied. HACCP is basically a statement of a preventive system of controls based on the hazard analysis and critical control points. **Hazard analysis** involves the identification of ingredients and products which might have a pronounced effect on food safety; might be consumed by special populations, such as infants or the elderly; or might have no history of implication as the source of pathogens. Once the sensitivity of the ingredients is known, various **critical control points** can be identified. This involves the identification and control over those processing parameters whose loss of control would result in an unacceptable risk to consumers. Microbiological critical control points have been summarized for frozen foods and canned foods. Ito (1974), Peterson and Gunnerson (1974), and Bauman (1974) should be consulted for more detail.

The HACCP concept is really a sophisticated food-control option that incorporates many of the traditional approaches that have been attempted over the years. As outlined in Table 27-3, many government agencies and other organizations have relied on various food control measures, including (1) education and training, (2) inspection of processing facilities or food handling operations, and (3) microbiological surveys and testing. The HACCP concept is a new approach, but it also utilizes some of the above principles.

How is a hazard analysis done? Knowledge that a food represent a hazard suggests that adequate epidemiological information is available (indicating that the food is potentially a health hazard) or that there is sufficient technical information on hand to indicate that the product poses a health hazard. If neither the epidemiological information nor the technical information is available or if one is concerned about a new product, information and knowledge about that product must be obtained. The report of the World Health Organization/International Commission on Microbiological Specification of Foods (Subcommittee on Microbiological Criteria, Committee on Food Protection, Food and Nutrition Board, National Council, 1985) suggests that the following questions be asked in an attempt to gather the necessary information.

1 What is the intended distribution and use?
  a Is the product to be distributed under ambient or cold storage temperatures?
  b What is the expected shelf life both during distribution and storage and in the hands of persons who will ultimately use the product?
  c How will the product be prepared for consumption?
  d Is the product likely to be cooked and then held for a period of time before consumption?
  e What handling of the product is likely to occur in the hands of the consumer or during marketing?
2 What is the product formulation?
  a What is the pH?
  b What is the a_w?
  c Are preservatives used?
  d What packaging is used, and is it critical to product stability, e.g., the vacuum packaging of fresh meats?
3 What is the intended process? Consideration should be given to steps that lead to destruction, inhibition, or growth of food-borne disease or spoilage organisms.

TABLE 27-3
PRINCIPAL FOOD CONTROL OPTIONS AVAILABLE

Approach	Components
Education and training	Develop an understanding of food hazards
	Develop an appreciation of personal hygiene, sanitation, and food hygiene
	Develop an understanding of microbial contaminants and control measures
	Introduce factors affecting microbial growth and survival
Inspection of processing facilities, food handling operations, warehouses, etc.	Monitor adherence to a recommended or required food handling practice
	Follow a recommended or required guideline such as a good manufacturing practice (GMP)
	Cite violations or make recommendations for improving performance
Microbiological surveys and testing of product	Sample and analyze ingredients, components, and finished product
	Monitor for pathogens, indicators, total numbers, etc.
	Compare to a standard, a guideline, a defect action level, etc., and advise or regulate accordingly
"New approaches"	Combinations of the above to improve upon the prevention of food-borne diseases
	HACCP concept

492 PART 6: FOOD SANITATION, CONTROL AND INSPECTION

Answers to these questions will supply information from which a food microbiologist will be able to make a preliminary assessment of the potential hazard of the process, distribution, and the product itself. Obviously, it may be necessary to actually conduct inoculated studies under the intended processing and marketing conditions to further evaluate a potential hazard.

How does one determine the critical control points? Quite frequently, after the hazard analysis has been conducted, the critical control points become obvious. If not, a further microbiological investigation at various points during the process, marketing, and distribution may be necessary to establish the critical control points.

The HACCP concept was originally proposed for the food processing industry. However, available surveillance data suggest that the incidence of foodborne disease outbreaks caused by mishandling of foods is actually higher in food service establishments and at the consumer level than in the food processing industry. Therefore, the HACCP concept has been extended to food service establishments (Bryan, 1981) and even to the home (Zottola and Wolf, 1980).

HEALTH OF EMPLOYEES

As has been pointed out, duties of the sanitarian that affect the health of employees include provision of potable drinking water, supervision of matters of personal hygiene, regulation of sanitary facilities within the plant and of sewage treatment and disposal, and supervision of sanitation in plant eating establishments and in plant-operated housing units. Most of these duties involve the sanitary aspects of plant and housing construction, selection of qualified personnel to direct operations of the facilities, and training employees in sanitary practices.

The bacteriology of drinking water and of sewage treatment and disposal has been discussed briefly. However, sanitation in eating places in the plant deserves special mention. Special places should be designated for eating carried lunches, and such places should be kept neat and sanitary. If the plant serves meals to employees in a cafeteria or restaurant, the sanitarian should be responsible for supervision of sanitation in the preparation, handling, serving, and storage of the food so as to avoid the spread of infectious microorganisms and to prevent outbreaks of food poisoning. The prevention of food intoxications and food infections has been discussed in Chapters 24 and 25. To prevent the spread of disease, food equipment and utensils should be handled, washed, and sanitized as directed in the Food Service Sanitation Manual of the U.S. Public Health Service.

BIBLIOGRAPHY

Adame, J. L., F. J. Post, and A. H. Bliss. 1960. Preliminary report on a bacteriological study of selected commercially prepared wrapped sandwiches. J. Milk Food Technol. 23:363–366.

American Public Health Association. 1985. Standard methods for the examination of water and wastewater. 16th ed. New York.

Anonymous. 1963. Sanitations: FE special report. Food Eng. 35(4):69–86.

Anonymous. 1975. Spotlight on sanitation and cleaning. Food Proc. February, pp. 18, 22, 24, 27, 29, 31, and 32.

Baldock, J. D. 1974. Microbiological monitoring of the food plant: methods to assess bacterial contamination on surfaces. J. Milk Food Technol. 37:361–367.

Bauman, H.E. 1974. The HACCP concept and microbiological hazard categories. Food Technol. 28(9):30, 32, 34, and 74.

Bobeng, B. J., and B. D. David. 1977. HACCP models for quality control of entree production in food service systems. J. Food Prot. 40:632–638.

Bryan, F. L. 1981. Hazard analysis of foodservice establishments. Food Technol. 35:78–87.

Christiansen, L. N., and N. S. King. 1971. The microbial content of some salads and sandwiches at retail outlet. J. Milk Food Technol. 34:289–292.

Clary, R. K. 1963. Evaluation of chemical sanitizers. Health Q. Bull. Wis. State Board Health, October-December, pp. 23–25.

Crisley, F. D., and M. J. Foter. 1965. The use of antimicrobial soaps and detergents for hand washing in food service establishments. J. Milk Food Technol. 28:278–284.

Davies, R. J. 1975. The national sanitation training program: Canadian restaurant association's answer to safe and sanitary foodservice. J. Milk Food Technol. 39:367–369.

Eckenfelder, W. W., and E. L. Barnhart. 1965. Treatment of food processing wastes. AVI Publishing Co., Inc., Westport. Conn.

Graham-Rack, B., and R. Binsted. 1973. Hygiene in food manufacturing and handling. 2d ed. AVI Publishing Co., Inc., Westport, Conn.

Guthrie, R. K. 1972. Food sanitation. AVI Publishing Co., Inc., Westport, Conn.

Hartley, D. E. 1963. Inspecting automatic vending operations. J. Milk Food Technol. 26:130–133.

Ito, K. 1974. Microbiological critical control points in canned foods. Food Technol. 28(9): 46, 48.

Kramer, A., and B. A. Twigg. 1973. Quality control for the food industry. Volume II. Applications. AVI Publishing Co., Inc., Westport, Conn.

Litsky, B. Y. 1973. Food service sanitation. Modern Hospital Press, Chicago.

Maxcy, R. B. 1975. Fate of bacteria exposed to washing and drying on stainless steel. J. Milk Food Technol. 38:192–194.

McCroan, J. E., T. W. McKinley, A. Brim, and W. C. Henning. 1964. Staphylococci and salmonellae in commercial wrapped sandwiches. Public Health Rep. 79:997–1004.

Microbiological and Biochemical Center, Syracuse University Research Corporation. 1964. Manual of sanitation standards for certain products of paper, paperboard, or moulded pulp. J. Milk Food Technol. 27:366–369.

Parker, M. E., and J. H. Litchfield. 1962. Food plant sanitation. Reinhold Publishing Corporation, New York.

Peterson, A. C., and R. E. Gunnerson. 1974. Microbiological critical control points in frozen foods. Food Technol. 28:(9)37–44.

Peterson, G. T., J. F. Fox, and L. E. Martin. 1959. Problems in the preparation and handling of hot vended canned foods. Food Technol. 13(4):22[of insert]. (Abstr.)

Stuart, L. S. 1962. Federal regulation of bactericidal chemicals used in building, industrial and institutional sanitation programs. J. Milk Food Technol. 25:308–312.

Subcommittee on Microbiological Criteria, Committee on Food Protection, Food and Nutrition Board, National Research Council. 1985. An evaluation of the role of microbiological criteria for foods and food ingredients. National Academy Press, Washington, D.C.

Thorner, M. E. 1973. Convenience and fast food handbook. AVI Publishing Co., Inc., Westport, Conn.

Thorner, M. E., and R. J. Herzberg. 1970. Food beverage service handbook. AVI Publishing Co., Inc., Westport, Conn.

Thorner, M. E., and P. B. Manning. 1976. Quality control in food service. AVI Publishing Co., Inc., Westport, Conn.

Troller, J. A. 1983. Sanitation in food processing. Academic Press, Inc., New York.

U.S. Department of Health, Education, and Welfare. 1953. Sanitary food service. Public Health Serv. NAVMED P-1333.

U.S. Department of Health, Education, and Welfare. 1957. The vending of foods and beverages. Public Health Serv. Publ. 546.

U.S. Department of Health, Education, and Welfare, 1962. Food service manual. Public Health Serv. Publ. 934.

U.S. Department of Health, Education, and Welfare, Public Health Service. 1958. Frozen desserts ordinance and code. [Reprinted March 1958].

U.S. Public Health Service. 1943. Ordinance and code regulating eating and drinking establishments. Bull. 280.

Zottola, E. A., and I. D. Wolf. 1980. Recipe hazard analysis—RHAS—a systematic approach to analysing potential hazards in a recipe for home food preparation (Unpublished). Cited in the subcommittee on Microbiological Criteria Committee on Food Protection Report, 1985.

FOOD CONTROL

The objectives of the control, regulation, and inspection of food are primarily to give assurance that foods received by the consumer will be pure, healthful, and of the quality claimed.

ENFORCEMENT AND CONTROL AGENCIES

Enforcement and control agencies range from international to private, as the following brief outline will illustrate.

International Agencies

Branches of the United Nations which are concerned with international food commerce include (1) the Food and Agricultural Organization (FAO), (2) the World Health Organization (WHO), and (3) the International Children's Emergency Fund (UNICEF). Although they are not major enforcement or control agencies, their common interest in adequate, healthful, and safe foods is noteworthy. FAO is primarily concerned with food production through improved methods of production, processing, preservation, and distribution of foods. WHO activities are more related to the health of the consumer and the maintenance of food wholesomeness.

Food regulation and control is the concern of all countries, and it is therefore inevitable that many of the standards or regulations developed are quite different from one country to another. The joint FAO/WHO Food Standards

Commission is a forum for the cooperation among nations to develop or agree upon various international standards for the food industry.

These finalized international standards were to be published in a food *Codex Alimentarius* as either regional or worldwide standards. Membership in the *Codex Alimentarius* Commission is voluntary and is composed of member nations of FAO and WHO. As of 1986 there were about 150 international standards adopted by the commission. Subsidiary groups of this organization have published a Code of Practice on General Principles of Food Hygiene and several Codes of Hygienic Practice for specific commodities (Olson, 1978).

Specific examples of international microbiological criteria for foods and food industries can be found in the National Research Council subcommittee report on Microbiological Criteria Committee on Food Protection, Food Nutrition Board (Food Protection Committee, 1985). Some examples are presented in Appendix B.

The International Commission on Microbiological Specifications for Foods (ICMSF) is a voluntary body which has focused primarily on establishing international sampling plans and methods of analysis. This group has been responsible for organizing collaborative studies on sampling plans and laboratory methodology with other groups, including the International Dairy Federation (IDF) and the Association of Official Analytical Chemists (AOAC). The ICMSF's first publication contains sampling plans and some methodology (ICMSF, 1974). This popular text was revised in 1985 (ICMSF, 1986).

Federal Agencies

The authority of U.S. federal enforcement agencies is confined to foods shipped interstate or foods produced in or shipped into territories. The Federal Register, published almost daily, contains news announcements of agencies of the federal government pertaining to food standards and inspection. The Code of Federal Regulations summarizes and gets such information from the Federal Register. Periodically the Agricultural Marketing Service publishes separate listings which update regulations and recommendations regarding the inspection, standards, and grades of various foods.

The Food and Drug Administration (FDA)   The Food and Drug Administration of the Department of Health, Education, and Welfare (HEW) enforces the Federal, Drug, and Cosmetic Act as amended in 1980. Basically, the functions of the FDA relate to the agency's responsibility for ensuring that all foods are safe and wholesome and that all foods are honestly and informatively labeled. Two of the main operational programs include the FDA Compliance Policy Guides (FDA, 1982*a*) and the FDA Food Defect Action Levels (FDA, 1982*b*). The Compliance Policy Guides contain specific microbiological criteria for various foods and feeds. Specifications are given for total or aerobic plate counts, coliforms, coagulase-positive staphylococci, food-borne pathogens, mycotoxins, bacterial indicators, and *Escherichia coli*. The Food Defect Actions Levels deal mostly with the level of natural defects that may be tolerated in a particular food or commodity. The natural defects are not necessarily related to any particular health hazards. Rather, they are specified levels of natural defects above which the FDA may remove products from the marketplace. The concept of defect action levels has been extrapolated to microbiological criteria. For example, a survey was conducted in several shrimp-breading processing plants in an attempt to establish good manufacturing guidelines. The data generated from this survey were used to develop a microbiological defect action level for raw breaded shrimp (FDA, 1983).

United States Department of Agriculture (USDA)   Through the Agricultural Marketing Act, the Egg Products Inspection Act, the Wholesome Meat Act (Federal Meat Inspection Act), and the Wholesome Poultry Products Act (Poultry Inspection Act), the USDA has legislative authority to promote the marketing of safe, high-quality agricultural products. Egg and egg products, meat and poultry products, and dairy products are covered by the USDA Agricultural Marketing Service (AMS) and the Food Safety and Inspection Service (FSIS).

Specific microbiological criteria have been established by the AMS under the authority of the Agricultural Marketing Act. These microbiological standards are for processed milk products and for raw milk. The AMS also has a single microbiological criterion for egg and egg products, mainly that the products be free of salmonella. The Federal Meat Inspection and the Poultry Inspection Act give the USDA the authority to carry out programs in the meat and poultry processing industries. Apparently, the Food Safety Inspection Service (FSIS) has responsibility for these products. Specific microbiological criteria have been established for many meat and poultry products, and they are listed as USDA meat and poultry advisory criteria.

National Marine Fishery Service (NMFS)   The United States Department of Commerce/National Marine Fishery Service (USDC/NMFS) is a fee-for-service fisheries products inspection program. Most of the criteria applied have to do with organoleptic evaluation of the product and examinations of the processing facility. However, USDC/NMFS is involved through several memorandums of understanding with federal agencies to establish microbiological criteria for food.

United States Army Natick Research and Development Center   Food procurement and food protection for military purposes involve problems that are not always encountered in civilian food service. Therefore, the Department of Defense, through the Defense Standardization and Specification Program, has established numerous microbiological criteria for the procurement of foods. The Natick Microbiology Branch is concerned with microbiological problems involved in military ration development and the establishment of microbiological criteria for initial procurement.

State Agencies

State food laws usually are enforced through a State Department of Public Health, Agriculture or Sanitary Engineering. Some states have microbiological standards or guidelines for food. Many states publish a state level equivalent to that of the Federal Register. For example, Maryland publishes the Maryland Register, a weekly that contains numerous announcements of the various state agencies.

Commercial Agencies

Food associations or institutes make recommendations or even attempt regulation within their own industries. Thus the National Food Processors Association has set microbiological standards for sugar and starch for canning; the American Dry Milk Institute has established bacteriological standards for dry milk; the American Bottlers of Carbonated Beverages has bacteriological standards for sweetening agents used in soft drinks, etc.

Professional Societies

The American Public Health Association has published many recommended methods for the bacteriological and microbiological examination of foods; the International Association of Milk, Food and Environmental Sanitarians has also published Recommended Procedures for the Investigation of Foodborne Illnesses. (International Association of Milk, Food, and Environmental Sanitarians, 1976).

Private Agencies

Several private agencies approve and list tested foods, e.g., the Good Housekeeping Institute.

The Processing Industry

Many specific food processing industries and/or companies have established their own in-house microbiological criteria for both finished products and raw materials and ingredients. Usually the larger the company, the more sophisticated its microbiological testing program.

Agency Cooperative Programs

The Food and Drug Administration, state agencies, and the private shellfish industry voluntarily cooperate in the National Shellfish Sanitation Program. In addition to cooperating on the standardization of regulations for shellfish sanitation, the NSFP also maintains a list of countries that participate in the program.

The FDA and USDA cooperative is a salmonella surveillance program for dry milk products. The Retail Food Protection Program (FDA) is another example of a federal-state cooperative program. Several publications, including the Vending of Food and Beverages (FDA, 1978), the Retail Food Store Sanitation Code (FDA, 1982c), and the Food Service Sanitation Manual (FDA, 1976), serve as a source of technical assistance to various state agencies.

The United States Public Health Service and the FDA have established the Grade A Pasteurized Milk Ordinance (PMO). Cooperating states use the PMO as their basic standards for certifying interstate milk shippers. Even individual milk processors use the PMO as an acceptable reference or standard for various aspects of milk sanitation.

As already mentioned, the National Marine Fishery Service (NMFS) through the United States Department of Commerce interacts and cooperates with other federal agencies, including the FDA and the Department of Defense. Additionally, the NMSF has specific agreements with numerous state agencies. Microbiological criteria for shellfish and other seafoods which have been developed between federal and state agencies are contained in the National Fisheries Institute Handbook (Martin and Pitts, 1982).

MICROBIOLOGICAL CRITERIA FOR FOODS

The stated chief purposes of microbiological criteria for foods are to give assurance (1) that the foods will be acceptable from the public health standpoint, i.e., will not be responsible for the spread of infectious disease or for food poisoning, (2) that the foods will be of satisfactory quality, i.e., will consist of good original materials that have not deteriorated or become unduly contaminated during processing, packaging, storage, handling, or marketing, (3) that the foods will be acceptable from an esthetic viewpoint in that the introduction of filth in the form of fecal material, parts of vermin, pus cells, mold mycelium, etc., has been prevented, and (4) that the foods will have keeping qualities that should be expected of the product.

Many difficulties are encountered in establishing and applying microbiological standards for foods. Sampling for tests is a problem since the lack of homogeneity in most foods makes location, size, and number of samples significant. Standards usually are based on total numbers of organisms, numbers of an indicator organism, or numbers (or total absence) of pathogens; but there has been some disagreement over what counts should be considered significant, what the indicator organism should be, and whether pathogens can be demonstrated. The correlation between the presence of an indicator and the possible presence of a pathogen is not certain in most products. Likewise, high total numbers do not necessarily imply a public health hazard.

Finally, the numbers and kinds of organisms in most foods decrease during storage in the dry or frozen condition. If an "average standard" is adopted, half of the food samples are eliminated. If legal action is involved, the level of a standard must be justified; counts or results on a sample by prosecutor, defendant, and a neutral agency may not necessarily agree.

Standards must be adapted to the types of food for which they are intended. They probably would be different for a food to be consumed raw than for the same food to be cooked or subjected to heating or other processing before being marketed. The type of spoilage organism to be feared and therefore watched for will vary with the food and the method of processing. Standards for ingredients of soft drinks, for example, include those for numbers of yeasts; for low-acid foods to be canned, numbers and kinds of heat-resistant bacterial spores are significant; and numbers of aerobic sporeformers in flour may indicate the likelihood of the development of ropiness in bread. The type of pathogen most likely to be present will be different in different foods. Tests for coliform bacteria to indicate the possible presence of intestinal pathogens are useful in setting standards for oysters but have little meaning for frozen orange juice. Salmonellae might be looked for in eggs or egg products and trichinae in raw pork.

The National Academy of Sciences, Food Protection Committee, has suggested the following definitions of microbiological criteria:

    a A *microbiological specification* is the maximum acceptable number of microorganisms or of specific types of microorganisms, as determined by prescribed methods, in a food being purchased by a firm or agency for its own use.

    b A *microbiological standard* is that part of a law or administrative regulation designating the maximum acceptable number of microorganisms or of specific types of microorganisms, as determined by prescribed methods, in a food produced, packed, or stored, or imported into the area of jurisdiction of an enforcement agency.

An additional definition was suggested by Elliott (1970):

    c A *microbiological guideline* is that level of bacteria in a final product, or in a shipped product that requires identity and correction of causative factors in current and future production, or in handling after production.

An excellent text dealing with the philosophy, establishment, and implementation of microbiology criteria is the report by the National Academy of Science, Food Protection Committee (Food Protection Committee, 1985).

It has been recommended that (1) testing procedure and standards be adapted to the particular kind of food, (2) a numerical relationship be demonstrated between the standard and the hazard, (3) tolerances be allowed for admitted inaccuracies of sampling and analysis, i.e., all samples would not be required to meet the standard and results from successive samples, taken at stated intervals, would be considered in setting and interpreting standards, and (4) any suggested criteria be tried out first on a voluntary basis.

An increasing awareness among consumers, the demand to be informed, and a confusion over the significance of a high number of bacteria have provided consumer pressure for adoption of bacterial criteria for some foods. Conversely, a general inability to correlate cell numbers or indicators with a possible health hazard and the seemingly low risks to consumer from many food products appear to lead to hesitation toward adopting standards for these food items.

BIBLIOGRAPHY

Clark, D. S. 1978. The international commission of microbiological specifications for foods. Food Technol. 31:54, 67.

Department of Defense. 1976. Defense standardization and specification program: policies, procedures and instructions. DOD Manual 4120. 3M. U.S. Naval Publ. and Forms Center, Philadelphia.

Elliott, R. P. 1970. Microbiological criteria in USDA regulatory programs for meat and poultry. J. Milk Food Technol. 33:173–177.

FDA. Good manufacturing practice regulations for bakery foods. Fed. Register, Feb. 12, 1976.

FDA. Good manufacturing practice regulations for tree nuts and peanuts. Fed. Register, June 30, 1976.

FDA. Proposed good manufacturing practices for pickled, fermented, acidified and low-acid foods. Fed. Register, July 23, 1976.

FDA. 1976. Food service sanitation manual. DHEW Publ. No. 72-2081. U. S. DHEW, Washington, D.C.

FDA. 1978. The vending of foods and beverages. DHEW Publ. No.78-2091. U.S. DHEW, Washington, D.C.

FDA. 1982*a*. Compliance policy guides manual. Publ. No.PB-271176. National Technical Information Service, Springfield, Va.

FDA. 1982*b*. The food defect action levels. DHEW Publ. No.82-2161. U.S. DHEW, Washington, D.C.

FDA. 1982*c*. Retail food store sanitation code. Recommendations of the association of food and drug officials of the U.S. DHHS, PHS, Washington, D.C.

FDA. 1983. Raw breaded shrimp, microbiological defect action levels. Fed. Register, 48(175) 405 63-40564.

Federal Food, Drug, and Cosmetic Act and general regulations for its enforcement, April 1955, U.S. Dept. Health, Education, and Welfare, FDA. SRA, Food, Drug, and Cosmetic no. 1, revised with Addenda.

Federal Food, Drug, and Cosmetic Act as amended January 1980. U.S. Dept. Health, Education, and Welfare.

Food Additives Amendment of 1958. Public Law 85-929, 85th Congr., H.R. 13254, Sept. 6, 1958.

Food Protection Committee. 1964. An evaluation of public health hazards from microbiological contamination of foods. Natl. Acad. Sci. Natl. Res. Counc. Publ. 1195.

Food Protection Committee, 1985. An evaluation of role of microbiological criteria for foods and food ingredients. Natl. Acad. Sci. Natl. Res. Counc. National Academy Press, Washington, D.C.

Foster, E. M. 1974. Interpretation of analytical results for bacterial standard enforcement. Assoc. Food Drug Off. U.S.Q. Bull.38:267–276.

Gunderson, F. L., H. W. Gunderson, and E. R. Ferguson, Jr. 1963. Food standards and definitions in the United States. Academic Press, Inc., New York.

ICMSF (International Commission on Microbiological Specifications for Foods). 1974.

Microorganisms in foods. 2. Sampling for microbiological analysis: principles and specific applications. University of Toronto Press, Canada.

ICMSF. 1986. Microorganisms in foods. Volume 2. Sampling for microbiological analysis: principles and specific applications. University of Toronoto Press, Canada.

International Association of Milk, Food, and Environmental Sanitarians. 1976. Procedures to investigate foodborne illness. Ames, Iowa.

Kimbrell, E. F. 1982. Codex almentaries food standards and their relevance to U.S. standards. Food Technol. 36:93–95.

Martin, R. E., and G. T. Pitts. 1982. Handbook of state and federal microbiological standards and guidelines. National Fisheries Institute, Washington, D.C.

Olson, J. C. Jr. 1978. Microbiological specifications for foods: international activities. Food Technol. 32:55, 57, 62.

Pivnick, H. 1978. Canadian microbiological standards for foods: international activities. Food Technol. 32:55–57, 62.

Sackett, I. D. 1982. Quality inspection activities of the National Marine Fisheries Service. Food Technol. 36:91–92.

Title 21: Food and Drugs. CFR. Thermally processed low-acid foods packaged in hermetically sealed containers. General provisions. Current good manufacturing practices. Part 113.5.

USDA. 1980. Salmonella surveillance program. FSQS/POQD, USDA, Washington, D.C.

USPHS/FDA. 1978. Grade A pasteurized milk ordinance. PHS/FDA Publ. No. 229. U.S. Government Printing Office, Washington, D.C.

NOMENCLATURE

Since the writing of the third edition of this textbook, many changes have been made in the classification and taxonomy of bacteria. The importance of codes of nomenclature is obvious, but we continue to use the names of organisms *as they appeared in the literature by the original authors*. Several of these original names have been changed or eliminated in later editions of Bergey's Manual. For one reason or another, the following are no longer "accepted" names. In all instances, lack of acceptance is based on Bergey's Manual of systematic Bacteriology, Vol. 1 (1984) and Vol. 2 (1986), unless otherwise stated. A brief statement on the current status of each organism is presented.

Acetobacter aceti subsp. *suboxydans* was not given any taxonomical status in Vol. 1.

Acetobacter aceti subsp. *xylinum*, a cellulose-synthesizing strain, is considered a synonym of *A. pasteurianus*.

Acetobacter acetigenum was an accepted species in the 6th ed. of Bergey's Manual but did not appear in the 7th or 8th eds. or in Vol. 1.

Acetobacter capsulatum was listed as a synonym of *Gluconobacter oxydans* subsp. *industrius* in the 8th ed. of Bergey's Manual. However, subsp. *industrius* was not recognized in Vol. 1.

Acetobacter oxydans was listed as a synonym of *Gluconobacter oxydans* in the 8th ed. of Bergey's Manual.

Acetobacter suboxydans was listed as a synonym of *Gluconobacter oxydans* subsp. *suboxydans*. However, the latter subsp. was not recognized in Vol. 1.

Acetobacter turbidans was listed as a synonym of *Acetobacter pasteurianus* in the 8th ed. of Bergey's Manual.

Acetobacter viscosum was listed as a synonym of *Gluconobacter oxydans* subsp. *industrius* in the 8th ed. of Bergey's Manual. However, the latter subsp. was not recognized in Vol. 1.

Acetobacter xylinum was listed as a synonym of *Acetobacter aceti* subsp. *xylinum* in the 8th ed. of Bergey's Manual; the latter was listed as a synonym of *A. pasteurianus* in Vol. 1.

Achromobacter: many of the species previously listed in this genus are now species in the genera *Alcaligenes* and *Zymomonas*.

Achromobacter anaerobium was listed as a synonym of *Zymomonas anaerobia* in the 8th ed. of Bergey's Manual. *Z. anaerobia* was listed as synonym of *Z. mobilis* in Vol. 1.

Achromobacter perolens was listed as a synonym of *Pseudomonas perolens* in the 7th ed. of Bergey's Manual. It was not listed in Vol. 1.

Aerobacillus: the species of this previously proposed genus (8th ed.) were listed as species of the genus *Bacillus*.

Aerobacter: the species previously listed in this genus were incorporated into species in the genera *Enterobacter* and *Klebsiella* in the 8th ed. of Bergey's Manual.

Aerobacter cloacae was listed as a synonym of *Entobacter cloacae* in the 8th ed. of Bergey's Manual.

Alcaligenes metalcaligenes was an accepted species in the 7th ed. but was not listed in the 8th ed. or in Vol. 1.

Alcaligenes viscolactis was an accepted species in the 7th ed. of Bergey's Manual. It was not listed in the 8th ed., and it is not listed in Vol. 1.

Bacillus betanigrificans was listed as a synonym of *B. macerans* in the 8th ed. of Bergey's Manual.

Bacillus citri was listed as a synonym of *Xanthomonas citri* in the 6th ed. of Bergey's Manual but did not appear as a synonym of *X. citri* in the 7th ed.; *X. citri* is listed in the 8th ed. as a nomenspecies of *X. campestris; Xanthomonas (Bacillus) citri* is therefore distinguishable from *X. campestris* only by plant-host reactions.

Bacillus globigii was not listed in Vol. 2. (1986).

Bacillus mesentericus was listed in the 8th ed. of Bergey's Manual but it lacked a type culture and was thought to be indistinguishable from *B. subtilis*. Vol. 2. did not list *B. mesentericus*.

Bacillus natto was listed as a synonym of *B. subtilis* in the 8th ed. of Bergey's Manual.

Bacillus nigrificans was listed as a synonym of *B. subtilis* var. *atterrimum* in the 6th ed. of Bergey's Manual. The latter var. was not recognized in Vol. 2 but was included in the species *B. subtilis*.

Bacillus subtilis var. *niger* was considered by Vol. 2. (1986) as *B. subtilis* and not given separate taxonomical status.

Bacillus vulgatus was listed in the 8th ed. as not having a type culture and being indistinguishable from *B. subtilis*. It was not listed in Vol. 2.

Brevibacterium erythrogenes was listed as a species incertae sedis in the 8th ed. of Bergey's Manual; it was not listed in Vol. 1. (1984).

Clostridium calidotolerans was not given any taxonomical status in Vol. 2 (1986).

Clostridium lentoputrescens is homologous with type strain *C. cochlearium*.

Clostridium nigrificans was listed as a synonym of *Desulfotomaculum nigrificans* in the 8th ed. of Bergey's Manual.

Clostridium putida was not listed as a species name in Vol. 2.

Enterobacter oxytocum   was not listed in Vol. 1 (1984).

Erwinia carotovora   subsp. *betavasculorum:* a new subspecies proposed.

Flavobacterium proteus   is now *Obesumbacterium proteus.*

Flavobacterium rhenanum   was listed as a synonym of *Erwinia herbicola* in the 8th ed. of Bergey's Manual.

Gluconobacter oxydans   subsp. *suboxydans* and subsp. *industrius* were not considered subsp. in Vol. 2. (1986). All are referred to as *G. oxydans.*

Halobacterium cutirubrum   is listed as a synonym of *Halobacterium salinarium.*

Lactobacillus arabinosus   was listed as a synonym of *Lactobacillus plantarum* in the 8th ed. of Bergey's Manual. It was not listed in Vol. 2.

Lactobacillus brevis   var. *rudensis* was not listed in Vol. 2. (1986).

Lactobacillus bulgaricus   is now a subspecies of *L. delbrueckii.*

Lactobacillus diastaticus   was not listed in Vol. 2.

Lactobacillus lactis   is now a subspecies of *L. delbrueckii.*

Lactobacillus leichmanii   is listed as *L. delbrueckii* subsp. *lactis.*

Lactobacillus pastorianus   was listed as a species incertae sedis in the 8th ed. of Bergey's Manual; it is not given any taxonomical status in Vol 2.

Lactobacillus plantarum   var. *rudensis* was listed as a synonym of *L. plantarum* in the 8th ed. of Bergey's Manual.

Lactobacillus salinmandus   is not given any taxonomical status in Vol. 2.

Lactobacillus thermophilus   was originally described as producing endospores. It was suggested to be similar to, if not identical to, *Bacillus coagulans* in the 8th ed. of Bergey's Manual. It was not given any taxonomical status in Vol. 2.

Lactobacillus trichodes   was listed as a junior subjective synonym of *L. fructivorans* in Vol. 2.

Lactobacillus vermiformis   was listed as *B. vermiforme* in the 6th ed. of Bergey's Manual, as a slime-forming lactobacillus, but did not appear in the 7th or 8th eds. or in Vol. 2.

Leuconostoc citrovorum   was listed as a synonym of *Leuconostoc cremoris* in the 8th ed.; however, *L. cremoris* is now listed as *L. mesenteroides* subsp. *cremoris.*

Leuconostoc cremoris   is now listed as *L. mesenteroides* subsp. *cremoris.*

Leuconostoc dextranicum   is now listed as *L. mesenteroides* subsp. *dextranicum.*

Microccoci: see the following category.

Micrococcus: this genus has been extensively altered in recent publications of Bergey's Manual. The number of species in the 8th edition had been reduced from sixteen to three; the genus *Sarcina* was retained for the anaerobic packet-forming cocci. Bergey's Manual, Vol. 2 (1986), lists nine species but suggests that the micrococci should probably be in the genus *Arthrobacter.*

Micrococcus candidus   was not listed in Vol. 2.

Micrococcus caseolyticus   was listed as an accepted species in the 7th ed. of Bergey's Manual; it was not listed in the 8th. In Vol. 2 it is mentioned in the section dealing with *Staphylococcus caseolyticus.*

Micrococcus freudenreichii   was listed as a species incertae sedis in the 8th ed. of Bergey's Manual. It is not given any taxonomical status in either Vol. 1 or Vol. 2.

Micrococcus lipolyticus   was listed in the 6th ed. of Bergey's Manual for historical interest as a fat-splitting micrococcus from salted fish.

Paracolobactrum: according to the 8th ed. this genus was proposed to include late or non-lactose-fermenting coliform bacteria; this is no longer justified. These organisms should have been placed in the genera *Escherichia, Citrobacter,* or *Klebsiella.*

Pediococcus cerevisiae as a species name has been rejected by Vol. 2, and the genus name *Pediococcus* is conserved by the species name *damnosus*. *P. damnosus* occurs in beer and the brewing industry, *P. pentosacens* is used in meat fermentations, and *P. halophilus* occurs in pickling brines.

Pediococcus soyae was listed as synonym of *Pediococcus halophilus* in the 8th ed. of Bergey's Manual.

Propionibactacerium shermanii was listed as a synonym of *Propionibacterium freudenreichii*. Vol. 1 has listed as *P. freudenreichii* subsp. *shermanii*.

Proteus melanovogenes was listed as a synonym of *Aeromonas hydrophila* in the 8th ed. of Bergey's Manual.

Pseudomonas graveolens was listed as synonym of *P. taetrolens* in the 7th ed. The 8th ed. of Bergey's Manual listed *P. taetrolens* as a species incertae sedis. Vol. 1 has given *P. taetrolens* species status.

Pseudomonas nigrifaciens is listed as a species incertae sedis and is said to be more closely related to the genus *Alteromonas*.

Pseudomonas putrefaciens was listed in the 8th ed. of Bergey's Manual as a species incertae sedis. Vol. 1 lists the organism under *Alteromonas putrefaciens*, which is currently a species incertae sedis.

Pseudomonas sapolactica was listed as a species incertae sedis in the 8th ed. of Bergey's Manual; it was not listed in Vol. 1.

Pseudomonas syncyanea was listed in the 8th ed. of Bergey's Manual as a species incertae sedis; it was not given any taxonomical significance in Vol. 1.

Pseudomonas visosa was listed in the 6th ed. of Bergey's Manual but has not appeared since.

Sarcina lutea was not listed as a valid species in Vol. 2. *S. lutea* is a packet-forming gram-positive aerobic cocci; only the anaerobic species were retained in the genus *Sarcina*. Aerobic non-spore-forming *Sarcina* were assigned to the genus *Micrococcus*.

Serratia salinaria was listed as a synonym of *Halobacterium salinarium* in the 8th ed. of Bergey's Manual.

Streptococcus cremoris is now considered a synonym of *S. lactis*. A new subsp., *S. lactis* subsp. *cremoris*, has been proposed.

Streptococcus durans was listed as a synonym of *S. faecium* in the 8th ed. of Bergey's Manual; it was not given any taxonomical status in Vol. 2.

Streptococcus faecalis subsp. *liquefaciens* is now considered a synonym of *S. faecalis*.

Streptococcus faecalis subsp. *zymogenes* is now considered a synonym of *S. faecalis*.

Streptococcus faecium subsp. *durans* is not given any taxonomical status in Vol. 2.

Streptococcus lactis was a recognized species in Vol. 2. However, a new subsp., *S. lactis* subsp. *lactis,* has been proposed.

Streptococcus lactis subsp. *cremoris* was not recognized in Vol. 2, but it is proposed as a subsp.

Streptococcus lactis subsp. *diacetylactis* was listed as a synonym of *S. lactis*. A subsp., *S. lactis* subsp. *diacetilactis* has been proposed.

Streptococcus lactis subsp. *lactis* was not recognized in Vol. 2, but it is proposed as a subsp.

Streptococcus lactis var. *maltigenes* was not a recognized name in Vol. 2 (1986).

INTERNATIONAL
MICROBIOLOGICAL
SPECIFICATIONS

The following tables are reprinted from *An Evaluation of the Role of Microbiological Criteria for Foods and Food Ingredients,* 1985, National Academy Press, Washington, D.C., with permission. The letters symbols in the tables are defined as follows:

n = number of sample units analyzed which are chosen separately and independently.

c = maximum allowable number of sample units yielding unsatisfactory test results, e.g., the presence of the organism, or a count above m.

m = a microbiological criterion that in a 2-class plan separates good quality from defective quality, or in a 3-class plan separates good quality from marginally acceptable quality.

M = a microbiological criterion that in a 3-class plan separates marginally acceptable quality from defective quality. Values at or above M are unacceptable.

case = a set of circumstances related to the nature and treatment of a food, categorized into 15 such sets which influence the anticipated hazard from the presence of specified bacterial species or groups within a food (ICMSF, 1974).

TABLE B-1
FAO/WHO EXPERT CONSULTATION ON MICROBIOLOGICAL SPECIFICATIONS
FOR FOODS: EGG PRODUCTS

Product	Test	n	c	m	M
Dried and frozen whole egg	Mesophilic aerobic bacteria	5	2	5×10^4	10^6
	Coliform	5	2	10	10^3
	Salmonella	10	0	0	—
Other egg products	*Salmonella*	10	0	0	—
Any egg product intended for special dietary purposes	*Salmonella*	30	0	0	—

Source: CAC/RCP 15, 1976.

TABLE B-2
FAO/WHO EXPERT CONSULTATION ON MICROBIOLOGICAL SPECIFICATIONS
FOR FOODS: FOODS FOR INFANTS AND CHILDREN

Product	Test	Case	n	c	m	M
Dried biscuit, plain, coated	None	—	—	—	—	—
	Coliform	5	5	2	<3	20
	Salmonella	11	10	0	0	—
Dried instant products	Mesophilic aerobic bacteria	6	5	2	10^3	10^4
	Coliform	6	5	1	<3	20
	Salmonella	12	60	0	0	—
Dried products requiring heating before consumption	Mesophilic aerobic bacteria	4	5	3	10^4	10^5
	Coliform	4	5	2	10	10^2
	Salmonella	10	5	0	0	—

Source: CAC/RCP 21, 1979.

TABLE B-3
FAO/WHO EXPERT CONSULTATION
ON MICROBIOLOGICAL SPECIFICATIONS FOR FOODS:
PRECOOKED FROZEN SHRIMP AND PRAWNS

Test	n	c	m	M
Mesophilic aerobic bacteria	5	2	10^5	10^6
Staphylococcus aureus	5	2	5×10^2	5×10^3
Salmonella	5	0	0	—

Source: CAC/RCP 17, 1978.

TABLE B-4
FAO/WHO EXPERT CONSULTATION
ON MICROBIOLOGICAL SPECIFICATIONS FOR FOODS:
ICE MIXES

Test	n	c	m	M
Mesophilic aerobic bacteria	5	2	2.5×10^4	10^5
Coliform	5	2	10	10^2
Salmonella	10	0	0	—

Source: Report of 2nd Joint FAO/WHO Expert Consultation, 1977.

TABLE B-5
FAO/WHO EXPERT CONSULTATION
ON MICROBIOLOGICAL SPECIFICATIONS FOR FOODS:
EDIBLE ICES

Test	n	c	m	M
Mesophilic aerobic bacteria	5	2	5×10^4	2.5×10^5
Coliform	5	2	10^2	10^3
Salmonella	10	0	0	—

Source: Report of 2nd Joint FAO/WHO Expert Consultation, 1977.

TABLE B-6
INTERNATIONAL DAIRY FEDERATION
PROPOSED MICROBIOLOGICAL
SPECIFICATIONS FOR DRIED MILK, 1982

Test	n	c	m	M
Mesophilic count	5	2	5×10^4	2×10^5
Coliforms	5	1	10	100
Salmonella	15	0	0	

Source: IDF: D-Doc 90, 1982.

TABLE B-7
EUROPEAN ECONOMIC COMMUNITY STANDARDS
FOR CASEINS AND CASEINATES

Organism(s)	M (maximum allowable concentration)
Total bacterial count	30,000/g
Thermophilic organisms	5,000/g
Coliforms	0(in O.1g)

Source: Regulation (EEC) No. 2940/73, O.J. No. L301/25.

TABLE B-8
EUROPEAN ECONOMIC COMMUNITY STANDARDS
FOR NATURAL MINERAL WATERS

Organism(s)	M (maximum allowable concentration)
Total count	20/ml at 37 C
	100/ml at 22 C
Parasites and pathogenic microorganisms	Absent
E. coli, coliforms and fecal streptococci	Absent in 250 ml
Sulphite-reducing anaerobes	Absent in 50 ml
Pseudomonas aeruginosa	Absent in 250 ml

Source: Council Directive 15 July 1980 (BO/7/7/EEC), O.J. No. L229/1.

TABLE B-9
EUROPEAN ECONOMIC COMMUNITY STANDARD
FOR WATER FOR HUMAN CONSUMPTION

Organism(s)	m (guide level)	M (maximum allowable concentration)
Total count	10/ml at 37 C	—
(tap water)	100/ml at 22 C	—
Total count	5/ml at 37 C	20
(bottled water)	20/ml at 22 C	100
Total coliforms	—	
Fecal coliforms	—	MPN ≤ 1
Fecal streptococci	—	
Sulphite-reducing clostridia	—	MPN ≤ 1
All pathogenic bacteria, viruses, algae, parasites	absent	

Source: Council Directive 15 July 1980 (80/778/EEC), O.J. No. L229/11.

TABLE B-10
MICROBIOLOGICAL GUIDELINES OF CODEX STANDARD
FOR NATURAL MINERAL WATERS

Organism(s)	M (maximum allowable concentration)
Aerobic mesophilic count at source	20/ml at 21 C (72 hrs)
	5/ml at 37 C (24 hrs)
Aerobic mesophilic count after bottling	100/ml at 20–22 C (72 hrs)
	20/ml at 37 C (24 hrs)
Coliforms (including E. coli)*	None in 250 ml
	(30–32 C and 44 C)
Fecal streptococci (Lancefield group D)*	None in 250 ml
Sporulated sulphite-reducing anaerobes	None in 50 ml
Pseudomonas aeruginosa, parasites and pathogenic microorganisms*	None in 250 ml

*Applies both at source and during marketing.
Source: Appendix 1 CX/FH 79/4—ADD.1, 1979.

TABLE B-11
PROPOSED GUIDELINES FOR DRINKING-WATER QUALITY

Parameter/organism	Value number per 100 ml	Remarks
I. Microbiological quality		
Piped water supplies		
Treated water entering the distribution system		
Fecal coliforms	0*	Turbidity < 1 NTU; for disinfection with chlorine, pH preferably < 8.0, free chlorine residual 0.2–0.5 mg/1 following 30 min (minimum) contact
Coliform organisms	0	
Untreated water entering the distribution system		
Fecal coliforms	0	
Coliform organisms	0	In 98% of samples examined throughout the year for large supplies with sufficient samples examined
Coliform organisms	3	In occasional sample but not in consecutive samples
Water in the distribution system		
Fecal coliforms	0	
Coliform organisms	0	In 95% of samples examined throughout the year for large supplies with sufficient samples examined
Coliform organisms	3	In occasional sample but not in consecutive samples
Unpiped water supplies		
Fecal coliforms	0	
Coliform organisms	10	Not occurring repeatedly; repeated occurrence and failure to improve sanitary protection, alternate source to be found if possible
Bottled drinking-water		
Fecal coliforms	0	
Coliform organisms	0	
Emergency water supplies		
Fecal coliforms	0	Advise public to boil water in case of failure to meet guideline values
Coliform organisms	0	
Enterovirus	—	No guideline value set
II. Biological quality		
Protozoa (pathogenic)	—	No guideline value set
Helminths (pathogenic)	—	No guideline value set
Free-living organisms (algae, others)	—	No guideline value set

*Methods employed in the United States suggest not to use zeros (0), rather to report results as less than one times the reciprocal of the lowest dilution

Source: EEP/82.39 (adapted).

INDEX

INDEX